MODERN TRIGONOMETRY

(Complete Course)

MATHEMATICS FOR
INDIVIDUALIZED INSTRUCTION

Series Editor

Eugene A. Maier

Professor
Mathematics Department
University of Oregon

MODERN TRIGONOMETRY

(Complete Course)

John P. Ashley

Chairman, Department of Mathematics
Hawthorne High School

Mathematics Instructor
El Camino College, Cerritos College

E. R. Harvey

Mathematics Instructor
Hawthorne High School

Mathematics Instructor
El Camino College

GLENCOE PRESS
A division of Benziger Bruce & Glencoe, Inc.
Beverly Hills
Collier Macmillan Publishers
London

Printed in the United States of America

GLENCOE PRESS
A division of Benziger Bruce & Glencoe, Inc.
8701 Wilshire Boulevard
Beverly Hills, California 90211
Collier-Macmillan Canada, Ltd., Toronto, Ontario

Library of Congress Catalog Card Number: 72-075146

First printing, 1974

Table of Contents

Modern Trigonometry

INTRODUCTORY REMARKS

We believe that active student participation is an essential ingredient in learning mathematics. Accordingly, this text has been designed so that the student must first read the expository material, then respond to direct questions by filling in answer blanks, and finally perform the necessary calculations. The student is reinforced in this learning process because he is able to immediately verify the validity of his response by turning to the appropriate Answer column. (You might suggest to the student that he use a piece of paper to cover answers to problems that he has not yet solved.)

In general, we have tried to present each new concept by first developing the student's intuitive grasp of the relationships involved. The idea is then presented more formally, and the concept is applied to problem-solving examples. Finally, Review Exercises are provided at the end of each chapter to allow the student to evaluate his mastery of the topics discussed.

This text also employs a "spiral approach" in its presentation of many topics; that is, a particular idea might be discussed in several different places, but each new discussion will be slightly more sophisticated in its approach than the one preceding it. For instance, functions and vectors are introduced early and then used repeatedly in the development of the properties of circular functions, trigonometry, and complex numbers.

We hope that this text will provide the student with a sound basis on which to build a strong mathematics education. We also hope that it will permit the teacher to operate at a higher level of efficiency by decreasing the need for extensive lectures, thus providing more time for work with individual students.

To the Student

This is an individualized instruction textbook. If you use it properly, it can considerably improve your comprehension of the fundamentals of mathematics.

As you thumb through the pages, you will see sentences and paragraphs interspersed with questions. Read this text with a pencil in your hand—write the answers to the questions that will complete the statements and do the required computations. Depending on your teacher's instructions, you may write your responses directly in the spaces provided in the text. If, on the other hand, this text is to be used by other students, your teacher may ask you to write your answers either on an onionskin-paper overlay or on a separate sheet of scratch paper.

To find the correct answer to each question, you must follow a simple formula.

If the question you are working on is on a *right-hand* (odd-numbered) *page*, the answer to that question can be found in the Answer column (in exactly the same position on the page) two pages *following* the question. Conversely, if the question is on a *left-hand* (even-numbered) *page*, the answer will be in the Answer column two pages *preceding* the question.

For example, the answer to a question on this page would be found on

page ______.

Ignore these answers while you are studying the material. Only after you have completed a frame, should you check your answers against those in the appropriate Answer column. If your answer is incorrect, go back and study the material again. It is very important that you find out *why* the answer in the Answer column is the correct one.

Understanding the proofs and then writing your own is also a very necessary part of this course. After studying the proof of a theorem close your book and reproduce it yourself. If you have difficulty, study the proof again and then consult your teacher.

Do not pass over any idea you do not understand!

(2,a), (2,b) and (2,c)

(3,a), (3,b), (3,c)

{(1,a), (1,b), (1,c), (2,a), (2,b), (2,c), (3,a), (3,b), (3,c)}

$S \times T$

(a,2), (a,3), (b,1), (b,2), (b,3), (c,1), (c,2), (c,3)

(a,c), (b,a), (b,b), (b,c), (c,a), (c,b) (c,c)

$\{(x,y): x \in \mathcal{R} \text{ and } y \in \mathcal{R}\}$

When $A = B$

7

(5,4)

CHAPTER 1

Functions

1.1. FUNCTIONS

The set $\{x,y\}$ and the set $\{y,x\}$ are ______ since each of the two sets is contained in the other. The order in which the elements of a set are listed is of no consequence in determining set equality. However there are situations in which the order of a pair of numbers is important, for example, to specify the coordinates of a point in an xy coordinate system.

The symbol (x,y) is used to denote a pair of elements for which order is important. Therefore (x,y) ______ (is/is not) equal to (y,x).

DEFINITION:
An **ordered pair** is a pair of objects, one of which is designated as the **first element** in the ordered pair and the other as the **second element**. The ordered pair with first element x and second element y is denoted (x,y). Two ordered pairs are equal if and only if they have the same first elements and the same second elements. Thus

$(x,y) = (u,r)$ if and only if ______________.

1

If r and s are distinct elements, that is, $r \neq s$, is it true that $(r,s) = (s,r)$?

______. Find x when $(x-2,4) = (2x-4,4)$ ______________

Given two sets, which may or may not be equal, a set of ordered pairs may be formed using one of the sets as the source of the first elements and the other set as the source of the second elements.

ANSWERS TO PAGE 4

relation

S (because there is no more than one value in the range related to a given value in the domain)

3

---

ordered pairs

$f = \{(x,f(x)):f(x) = x^2 - 2\}$ or $f = \{(x,y):y = x^2 - 2\}$

$\mathcal{R}$

Let $S = \{1,2,3\}$ be the source of the first elements and $T = \{a,b,c\}$ the second elements.

The pairs having 1 as a first element are $(1,a)$, $(1,b)$, and $(1,c)$. Those having 2 as a first element are ________________________________.

Those having 3 as a first element are ______________________. The complete set of ordered pairs is { ____ }.

Such a set is called the Cartesian product of sets S and T.

DEFINITION:
The **Cartesian product** of two sets S and T, denoted $S \times T$, is the set of ordered pairs (x,y) such that $x \epsilon S$ and $y \epsilon T$, i.e., ________ $= \{(x,y): x \epsilon S \text{ and } y \epsilon T\}$.

If $T = \{a,b,c\}$ and $S = \{1,2,3\}$, then $T \times S = \{(a,1)$, ________, ________, ________, ________, ________, ________, ________, ________}.

$T \times T = \{(a,a), (a,b)$, ________, ________, ________, ________, ________, ________, ________}.

We will devote most of our efforts to subsets of the Cartesian product $\mathcal{R} \times \mathcal{R}$. $\mathcal{R}$ denotes the set of real numbers.

The elements of $\mathcal{R} \times \mathcal{R}$ cannot be listed in a roster, however $\mathcal{R} \times \mathcal{R}$ can be described in set-builder notation as ________________________.

Answer each of the following questions for set A and set B.

(a) When is $A \times B = B \times A$? ________________________

(b) If $A \times B$ has 21 elements and A has 3 elements then how many elements has B? ___

(c) If $(4,5) \epsilon B \times A$, then name an element contained in $A \times B$ ________.

ANSWERS TO PAGE 1

If $A = \{3,4,5,6\}$ and $B = \{1,2,3,4,5\}$, then one subset of $A \times B$ is the set $S = \{(3,2),(3,3),(4,1),(6,1),(6,2),(6,5)\}$. Since $(3,2) \in S$, the element 3 in A is said to be related to the element 2 in B by the subset S of $A \times B$. Similarly S relates 3 to 3, 4 to 1, ______, ______, and ______. Every subset of $A \times B$ may be thought of as relating elements from A to elements in B. Thus the following definition.

DEFINITIONS:
A **relation** from set A to set B is a subset of $A \times B$. Consider the relation S given above. The set of all first elements, namely $\{3,4,6\}$, is called the **domain** of S.

The set of all second elements, namely ______, is called the **range** of S.

Consider the relation h that relates elements in T to elements in S as illustrated:

equal

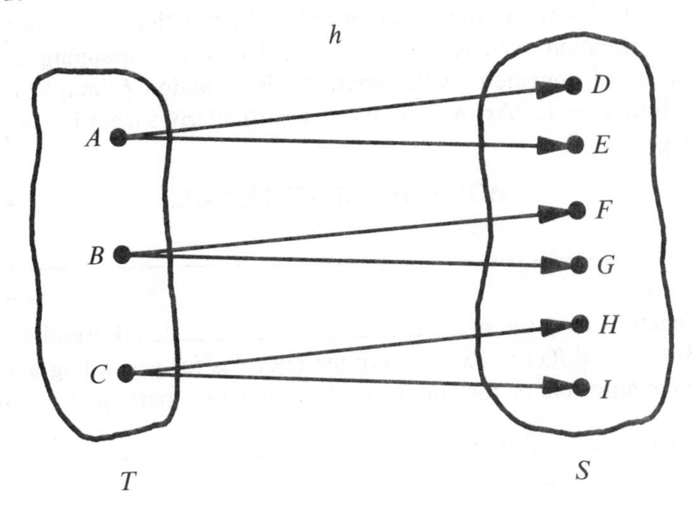

is not

The domain of h = ______. Each element in the domain is related under the relation h to two elements in the ______.

We will be particularly concerned with those relations in which every element in the domain is related to *exactly one* element in the range.

$x = u$ and $y = r$

DEFINITION:
A **function from set A to set B** is a relation from A to B in which every element in the domain is related to exactly one element in the range.

no $x = 2$

MOVE TO NEXT FRAME

Since a function is a special kind of _____________ it is a set of ordered pairs. But not all relations are functions.

Both of the sets T and S that follow are relations, but only one is a function. Which one is a function? ____

$$T = \{(2,1),(3,4),(4,7),(3,5)\}$$
$$S = \{(1,2),(2,5),(3,10),(4,17)\}$$

Which element in the domain of T is related to two different elements in the range of T? __

If f is a function and the pair (x,y) is in f, then y is called the **value** of f at x or the **image** of x in f. The symbol $f(x)$ (read "f of x") is often used to denote the value of f at x. Thus the phrases $(x,y)\epsilon f$ and $y = f(x)$ mean the same thing. In describing functions, the symbol $f(x)$ is used in place of y; thus $f = \{(x,y)\colon\ y = x^2 - 1\}$ might be written as $f = \{(x,f(x))\colon\ f(x) = x^2 - 1\}$. Other ways of describing this function are: "the function f such that $f(x) = x^2 - 1$" or notation such as $f{:}x \rightarrow x^2 - 1$. The words **mapping** and **transformation** are synonymous with **function**; the function f "maps" or "transforms" x into $x^2 - 1$. "Arrow" notation is particularly suggestive of this kind of language.

MOVE TO NEXT FRAME

A function is a set of ________________. Formulas, such as $g(t) = 3t - 1$ and $f(x) = 3x - 1$, are merely rules for generating a set. Often only the defining rule or formula is used to refer to a particular function. For example $f(x) = x^2 - 2$ refers to $f =$ ________________.

In the function $f = \{(x,y)\colon y = x^2 - 3x\}$ the domain has not been specified because it is understood, unless otherwise specified, that the domain is the set of all real numbers for which the formula or rule is defined. Also, unless otherwise noted, the range will be a subset of $\mathcal{R}$.

The domain of f above is __.

---

(1) T

(2) F

(3) T

(4) F

(5) T

(6) F

(7) T

(8) F

(9) T

(10) T

(11) F

(12) T

(13) $D = \mathcal{R}$

$R = \{$nonnegative elements in $\mathcal{R}\}$

(14) $D = \{x{:}x\epsilon\mathcal{R} \text{ and } x \geq 0\}$

$R = \{y{:}y\epsilon\mathcal{R} \text{ and } y \geq 0\}$

(15) $D = \{x{:}x\epsilon\mathcal{R} \text{ and } x \geq 0\}$

$R = \mathcal{R}$

(16) $D = \{x{:}x\epsilon\mathcal{R} \text{ and } x \neq 1\}$

$R = \{y{:}y\epsilon\mathcal{R} \text{ and } y \neq 2\}$

What is the domain of g if

$$g = \left\{ (x,y):\ y = \frac{1}{x} \right\}?$$

____

What is the domain of f if

$$f = \left\{ (x,y):\ y = \frac{3+x}{x-2} \right\}?$$

____

In the relation

$$h = \{(x,y):\ y = |x|\}$$

the domain is __ and the range is ______________________.

Let $A = \{(x,y):\ y = x^2 + 3x\}$ and $B = \{(x,y):\ y^2 = x\}$. A and B are both __________, but only __ is a function. B is not a function for if x is in the domain of B, B relates x to both $\sqrt{x}$ and $-\sqrt{x}$. For example, both $(3,\sqrt{3})$ and $(3,-\sqrt{3})$ are in B.

In the function $h = \{(x,h(x)):h(x) = |x|\}$, the image of 2 is __ and the image of -4 is __. Thus $h(2) = 2$ and $h(-4) = 4$. Find each of the following:

(a) $h(-3) =$ ______

(b) $h(-t) =$ ______

(c) $h(s-4) =$ ______

(d) $h(t)$ when $t < 0$ ______

Does the function $f = \{[x,f(x)]:f(x) = 3x - 1\}$ contain the same set of of ordered pairs as the function $g = \{[t,g(t)]:g(t) = 3t - 1\}$? ______ Is $f = g$? ______ Why? ______________________

____

____

(Remember that relations such as g or f have domains and ranges which are subsets of $\mathcal{R}$ unless otherwise specified.) We see that the letter designating the variable does not necessarily distinguish one relation from another.

ANSWERS TO PAGE 3

6 to 1 6 to 2 6 to 5

$\{1,2,3,5\}$

$\{A,B,C\}$

range

$A \times B$

function

EXERCISES. 1.1

True or False

1. $\{x,x\} = \{y,x\}$ __
2. $(a,b) = (b,a)$ __
3. If $(a,b) = (a,c)$, then $b = c$. __
4. If $m \neq n$, then $(m,n) = (n,m)$. __
5. In the function $g = \{(2,5),(3,6),(4,7)\}$, 6 is said to be the value of g at 3. __
6. The set of all relations is a subset of the set of all functions. __
7. $\{(2,4),(4,2),(2,5),(5,2),(2,7)\}$ is a relation. __
8. $\{(2,4),(4,2),(2,5),(5,2),(2,7)\}$ is a function. __
9. $\{(3,1),(5,5),(6,7)\}$ is a relation. __
10. $\{(3,1),(5,5),(6,7)\}$ is a function. __
11. The range of a function is a subset of that function. __
12. $\{(x,y):y = x^2\} = \{(t,s):s = t^2\}$. __

In Exercises 13-16, specify the domain D and range R of the relations defined by the following formulas. (D and R are subsets of $\mathcal{R}$, and x represents an element in D.)

13. $f(x) = x^2$ $\quad D =$ __________

    $R =$ __________

14. $f(x) = \sqrt{x}$ $\quad D =$ __________

    $R =$ __________

15. $y^2 = x$ (Note: $y \epsilon R$ and $x \epsilon D$.)

    $D =$ __________

    $R =$ __________

16. $y = \dfrac{2x}{x-1}$ $\quad D =$ __________

    $R =$ __________

    (*Hint:* Solve for x.)

17. If $f = \{[x,f(x)]: f(x) = 3x + 2\}$, then find the following:

(a) $f(1) =$ ___ (b) $f(2) =$ ___ (c) $f(0)$ ___

(d) $f(-2) =$ ___ (e) $f(-a) =$ ______ (f) $f(t^2) =$ ______

18. If g is the function defined by $g(x) = 2x^2 - 5x$, then find the following:

(a) $g(2) =$ ______________ (b) $g(-3) =$ ______________

(c) $g(a) =$ ______________

(d) $g(x - 2) =$ ______________

19. Some current textbooks write functions such as $\left\{[x,f(x)]: f(x) = \frac{x^2 - 4}{2}\right\}$ in the following fashion: $f:x \rightarrow \frac{x^2 - 4}{2}$. Find the respective images of x in f if the domain of f is $\{-2, -1,0,1,2\}$. ______________

____

____

20. In the function defined by $y = \sqrt{16 - x^2}$, the set of all images is called the ________ and, in this case, is the set ______________.

The domain is the set ______________.

$\{x: x \epsilon \mathcal{R} \text{ and } x \neq 0\}$

$\left(\text{since } \frac{1}{0} \text{ is not a real number}\right)$

$\{x: x \epsilon \mathcal{R} \text{ and } x \neq 2\}$

$\mathcal{R}$

$\{y: y \epsilon \mathcal{R} \text{ and } y \geq 0\}$

relations A

2

4

3 $|s - 4|$

$|t|$ $-t$

yes

yes

Functions are sets, and two sets are equal if and only if they contain the same elements

y axis

x axis

$(4, -2)$

-2 4

---

set points

---

relation

domain

range

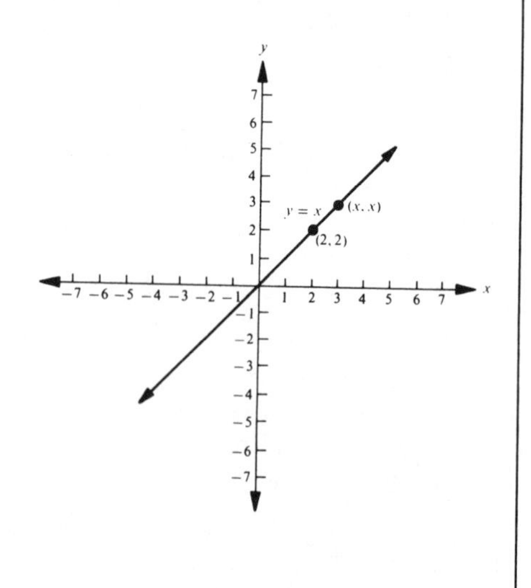

1.2. GRAPHS

In the following illustration, the elements in set A are placed in a correspondence with the elements in set B as indicated by the arrows.

$A = \{a,\quad b,\quad c,\quad d,\quad e,\quad f\}$

$B = \{1,\quad 3,\quad 5,\quad 7,\quad 9,\quad 11\}$

This is a **one-to-one correspondence**, since exactly one element in B corresponds to each element in A and exactly one element in A corresponds to each element in B.

MOVE TO NEXT FRAME

Note that the one-to-one correspondence in the preceeding frame relates elements from set A to set B and, therefore, defines a subset of __________ . Furthermore, no two elements of A are related to the same element in B so the one-to-one correspondence is a ______________.

Assume $\mathcal{R} \times \mathcal{R}$, the set of all ordered pairs of real numbers, can be placed in a one-to-one correspondence with the set of points in a plane. See the illustration.

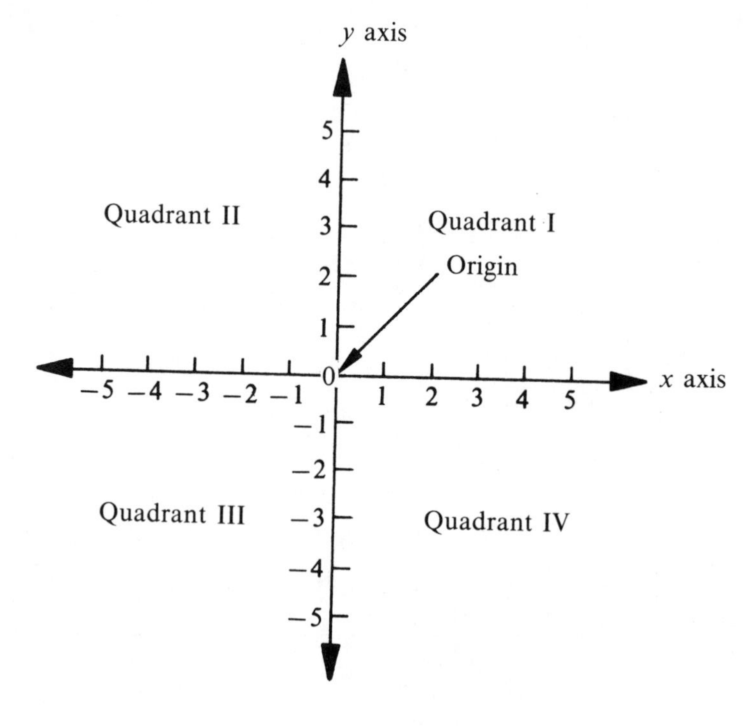

The points on each of two perpendicular lines, or axes, are placed in a one-to-one correspondence with $\mathcal{R}$. In each case the point corresponding to zero is the point of intersection of the two lines. This point of intersection is called the ______ and is designated by O.

For convenience we have drawn one of the intersecting lines parallel to the bottom of the page. Referring to the illustration in the previous frame, we see that this line is labeled the ________.

The other line, sometimes referred to as the vertical axis, is labeled the ________.

The x axis and the y axis also separate the plane into four quadrants. Again, referring to the previous illustration, we see that the quadrants are labeled I, II, III, and IV. Quadrant I is the upper right and II, III, and IV respectively are in the remaining quadrants, as we move in a ________ ________ (clockwise/counterclockwise) direction about the origin.

The positive real numbers correspond to points to the ________ of the origin on the x axis and to points ________ the origin on the y axis.

Any ordered pair $(x,y) \in \mathcal{R} \times \mathcal{R}$ may now be placed in correspondence with a single point P in the plane as shown.

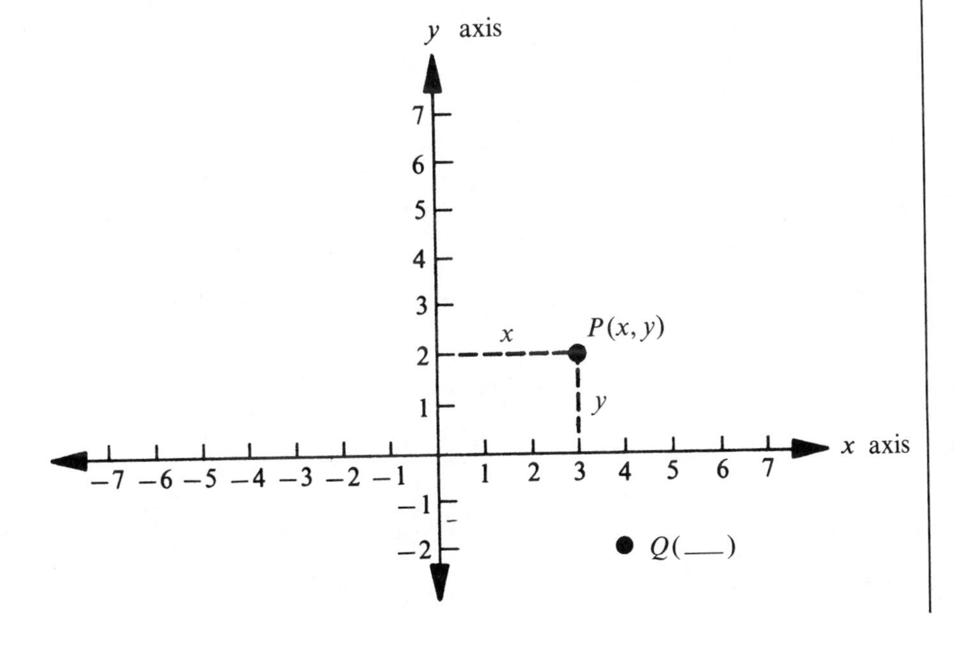

ANSWERS TO PAGE 7

(17)(a) 5 (b) 8 (c) 2

(d) −4 (e) $-3a + 2$

(f) $3t^2 + 2$

(18)(a) −2 (b) 33

(c) $2a^2 - 5a$

(d) $2(x-2)^2 - 5(x-2) = 2x^2 - 13x + 18$

(19) $f(-2) = 0,\quad f(-1) = \frac{-3}{2}.$

$f(0) = -2,\quad f(1) = \frac{-3}{2}.$

$f(2) = 0$

(20) range

$\{y: y \in \mathcal{R} \text{ and } 0 \leq y \leq 4\}$

$\{x: x \in \mathcal{R} \text{ and } -4 \leq x \leq 4\}$

ANSWERS TO PAGE 12

x coordinate

does not

function

$y = +\sqrt{9 - x^2}, \quad y = -\sqrt{9 - x^2}$

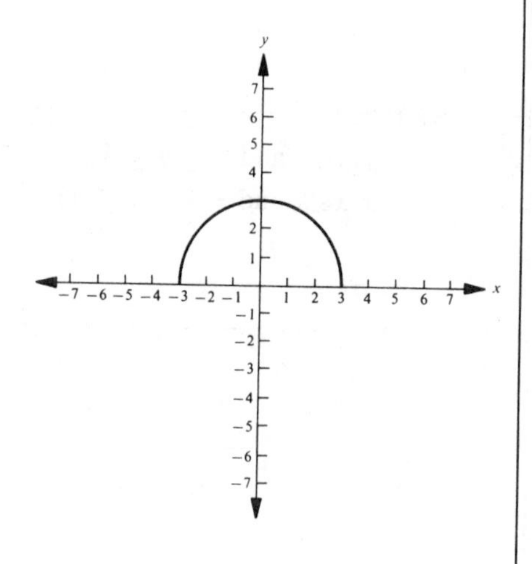

function

The first number in the ordered pair is called the abscissa or **x coordinate** and denotes the directed distance P is from the __________.

The second number in the ordered pair is called the ordinate or **y coordinate** and denotes the directed distance P is from the __________.

The ordered pair itself is called the **coordinates** of the point.

The coordinates of point Q above are __________. The ordinate of Q is ____ and the abscissa of Q is __.

A **plane coordinate system** is a one-to-one correspondence between the set of points in a plane and $\mathcal{R} \times \mathcal{R}$. The coordinate system we have described is called a **rectangular coordinate system** or **Cartesian coordinate system.**

We will refer to the points corresponding to a subset of $\mathcal{R} \times \mathcal{R}$ as the **graph** of that subset. Therefore, a graph is a ________ of ________.

$A = \{(x,y): y = x\}$ is a subset of $\mathcal{R} \times \mathcal{R}$. It is a __________ since it is a set of ordered pairs. Its domain is $\mathcal{R}$ and its range is $\mathcal{R}$. It is a function since it relates every element in its __________ to exactly one element in its range. Furthermore it is a one-to-one correspondence since no two elements in the domain are related to the same element in the __________. A is called the **identity function** because it maps every real number x into itself.

Sketch a graph of A on the given coordinate system.

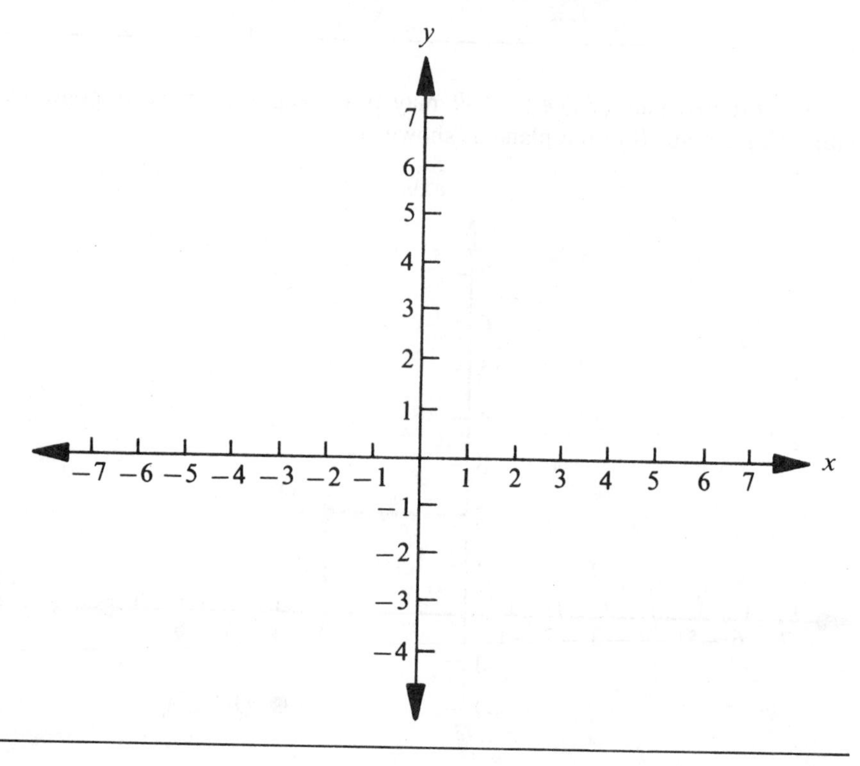

Every point of the graph of a relation has coordinates. These coordinates are ordered pairs of numbers which are contained in the __________. Conversely, if an ordered pair of numbers is in the relation, then they are the coordinates of a point in the ________.

All graphs (points corresponding to a subset of $\mathcal{R} \times \mathcal{R}$) are the graphs of relations but only certain graphs are graphs of __________. An examination of the graph of a given relation often helps determine whether or not the relation is a function.

Consider the relation defined by $x^2 + y^2 = 9$. The graph of this relation is the set of points called a _______ having a radius $r =$ __ and center at the _________.

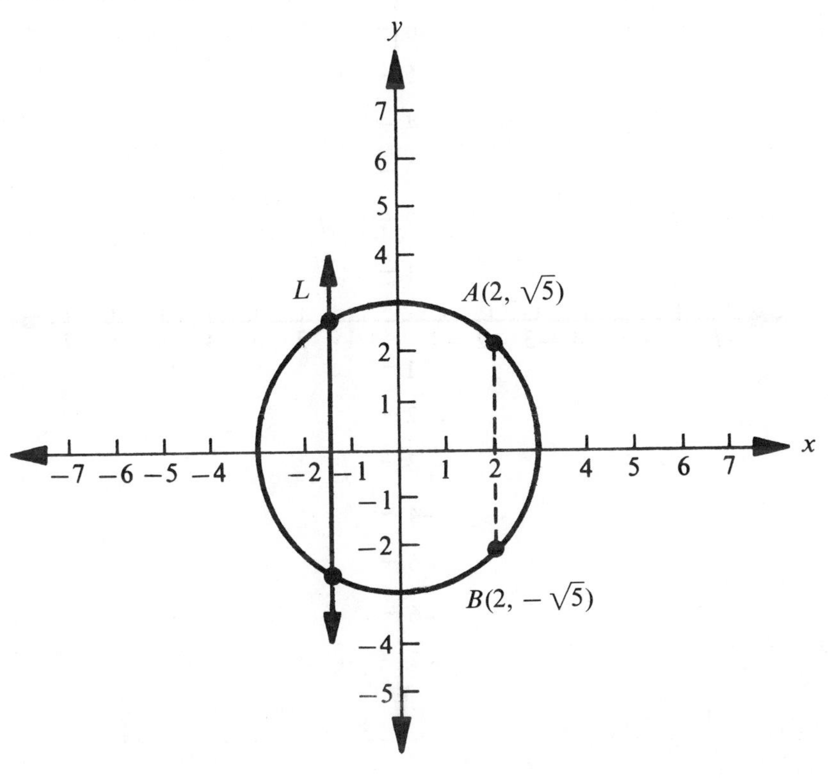

If a relation is defined by an equation, that equation is also called the **equation of the graph** of the relation. Thus the equation of this circle is ________________.

ANSWERS TO PAGE 9

origin

---

x axis

y axis

---

counterclockwise

"right"

"above"

ANSWERS TO PAGE 14

(a)

We see points A and B in the graph of the circle that we have been discussing have the same ____________. Therefore 2 is related to both $\sqrt{5}$ and $-\sqrt{5}$, and $x^2 + y^2 = 9$ ____________ (does/does not) define a function.

If any vertical line L intersects a graph of a relation in more than one point, as in the case of a circle, then the graph is not the graph of a ________.

However, we may solve $x^2 + y^2 = 9$ for the variable y and the result is

(a) $y = +$ ________________ or (b) $y = -$ ________________.
Graph (a) on the first coordinate system and (b) on the second system.

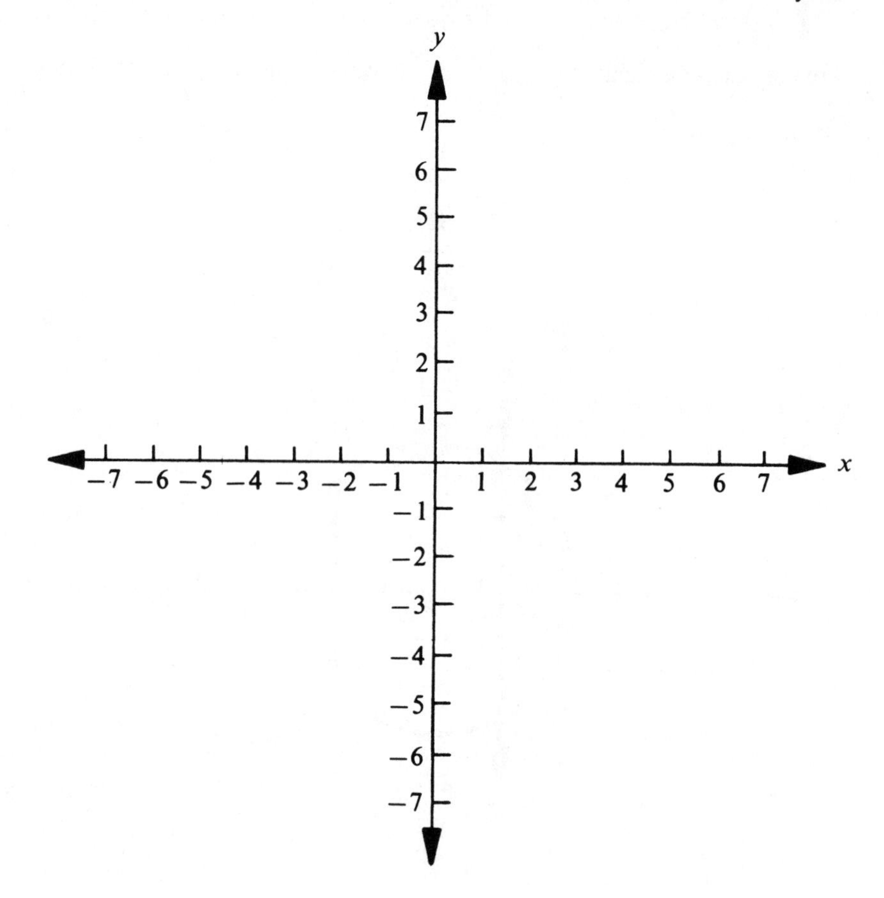

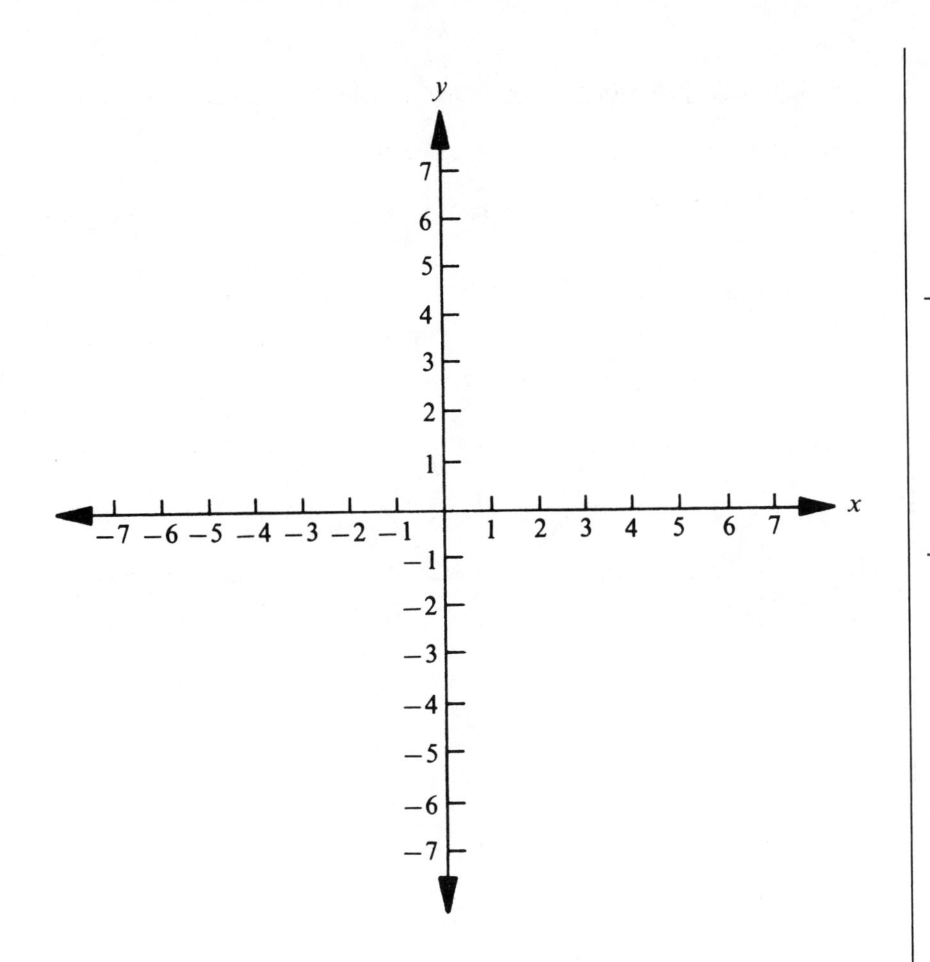

We see that each of the "semicircular" graphs represents a __________, since no two distinct points have the same x coordinate.

ANSWERS TO PAGE 11

relation

graph

functions

circle 3

origin

$x^2 + y^2 = 9$

ANSWERS TO PAGE 16

a line 2 units above the x axis and parallel to the x axis.

function

---

parallel

the x axis

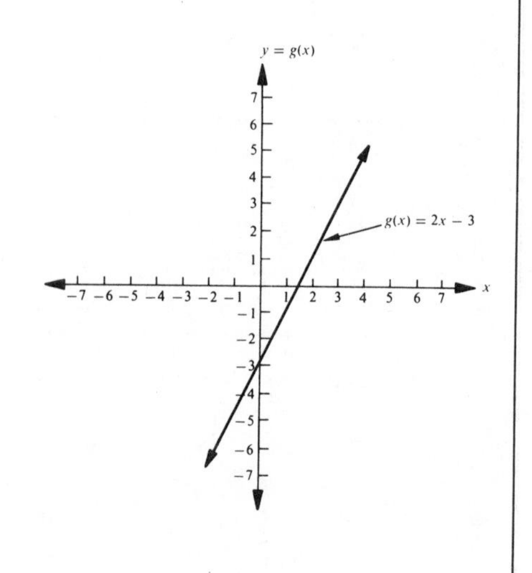

Which of the following are graphs of functions? ________

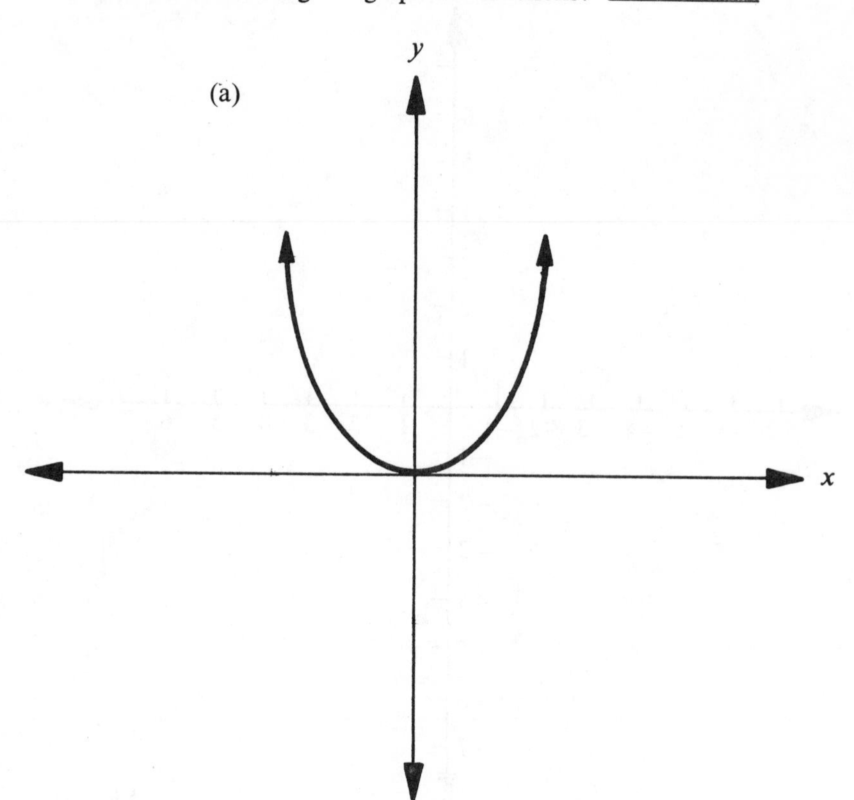

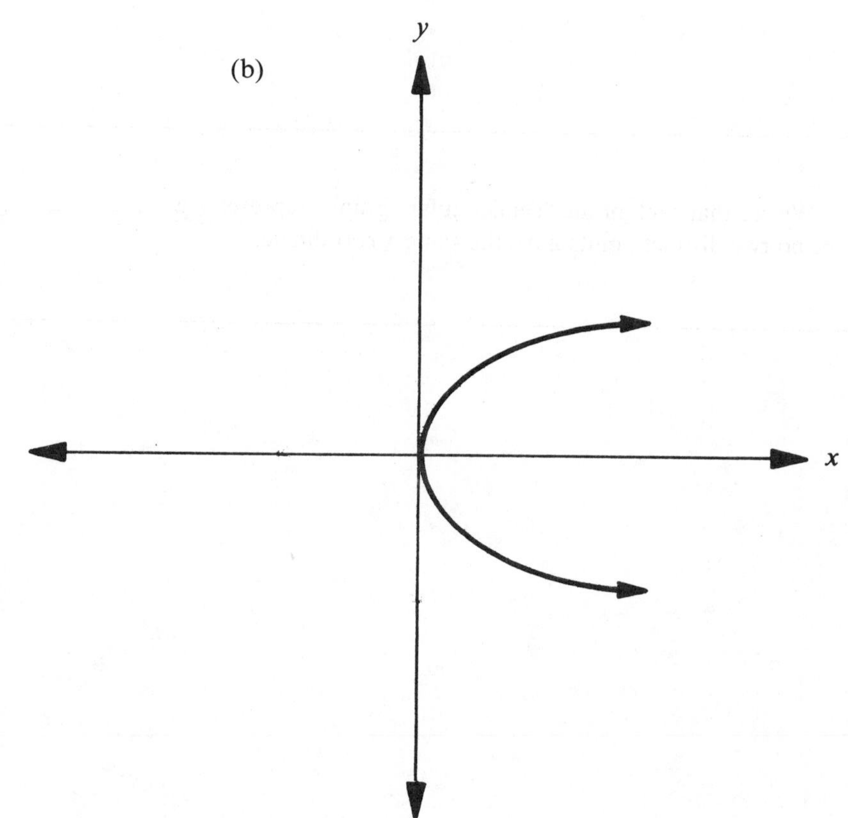

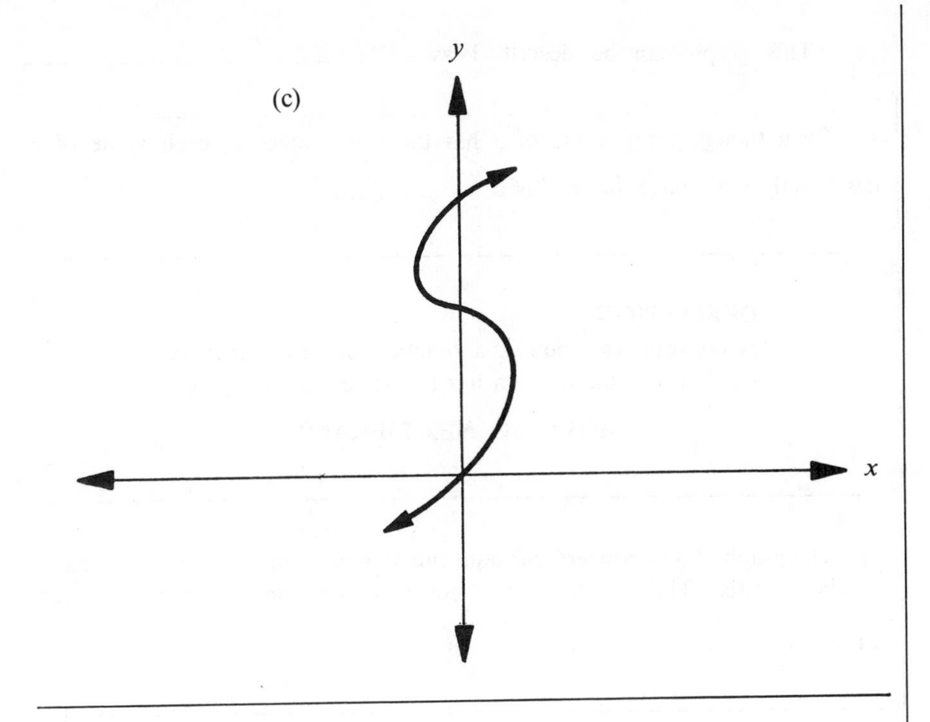

Graph the set $f = \{[x,f(x)]: f(x) = 2\}$

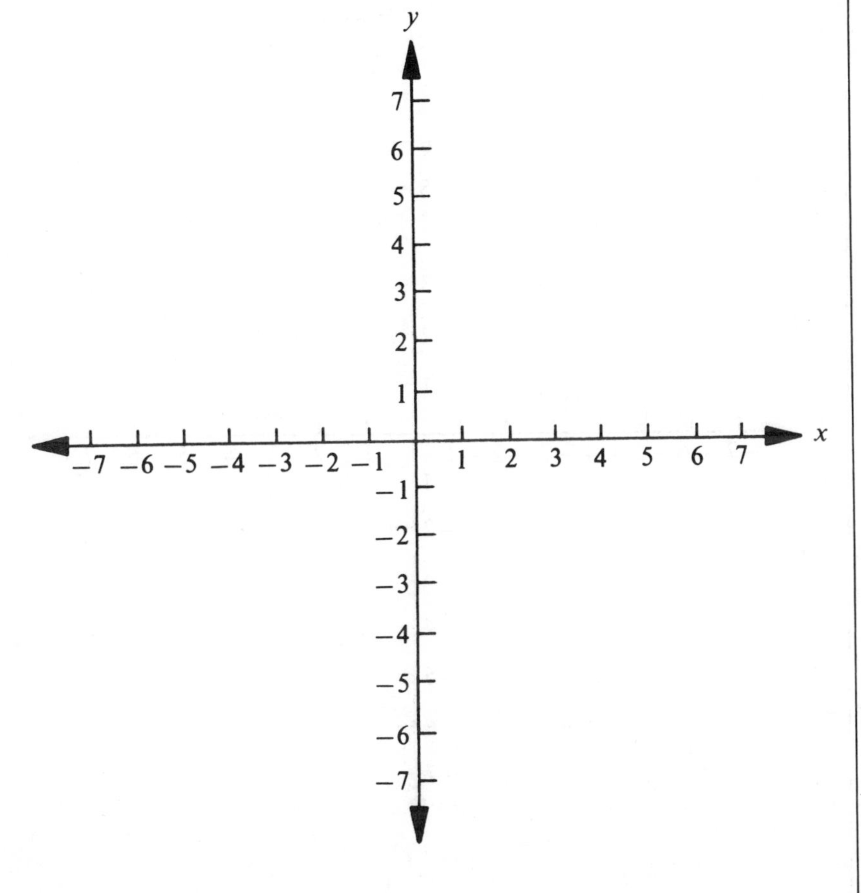

ANSWERS TO PAGE 13

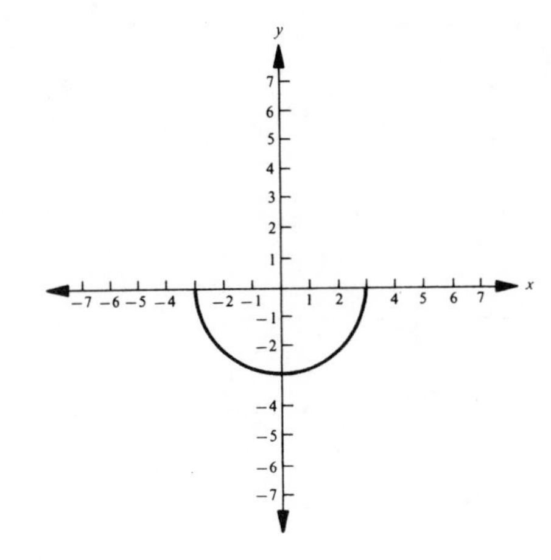

function

This graph can be described as ______________________________

______________________________.

Even though every value of x has the same image 2, each value of x has exactly one image, hence f is a ______________.

-4 (since the direction is down as we go from P to Q).

DEFINITION:
A **constant function** is a function in which each real number x in the domain has the same fixed image c.

MOVE TO NEXT FRAME

The graph of any nonzero constant function is a line ______________ to the x axis. The graph of the constant function which maps every x into 0 is ______________.

Graph $g = \{[x,g(x)]: g(x) = 2x - 3\}$

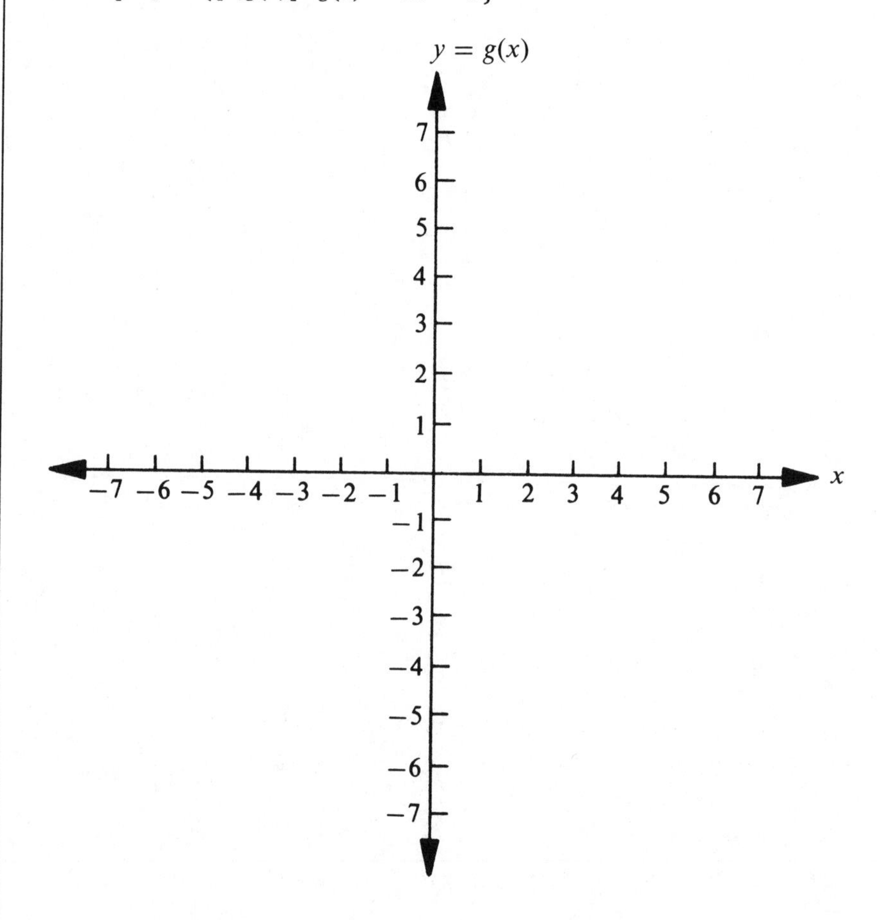

$+2$ (since the direction is to the right as we go from P to Q).

---

negative

positive

zero

$-\frac{2}{1}$

The graph of g in the preceding frame is a ________ line. The graph intersects the x axis at the point whose coordinates are ________. The value of x in (x,y) at this point is called the **x intercept**. The **y intercept** for the graph of g is ______. Since the graph of g is a straight line, g is said to be a linear function. g is called a function, since there is exactly one ________ for every value of x.

DEFINITION:
A **linear function** is a function f with domain $\mathcal{R}$ such that $f(x) = mx + b$ for some m and b in $\mathcal{R}$, with $m \neq 0$.

MOVE TO NEXT FRAME

Consider the graph of a function defined by $y = mx + b$. This graph is a line L.

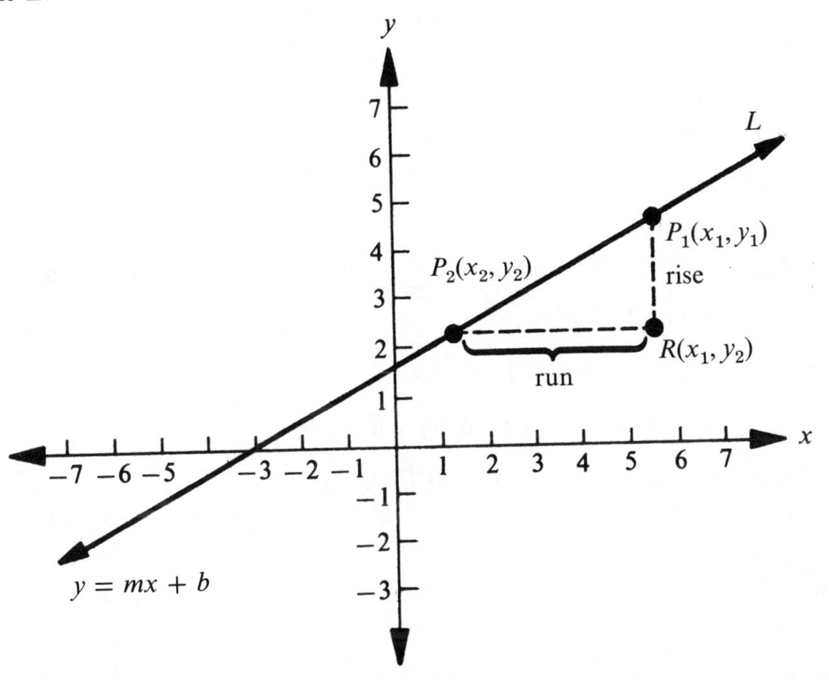

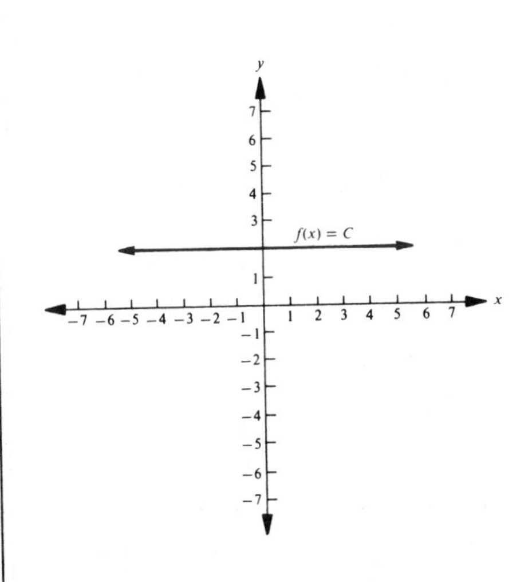

The **rise** from point $P_1(x_1, y_1)$ to the point $P_2(x_2, y_2)$ of the line L is $y_2 - y_1$ and the **run** from P_1 to P_2 is $x_2 - x_1$. (*Note:* Henceforth, the notation $P(x,y)$ will mean the point P whose coordinates are (x,y).) The rise from P_1 to P_2 is the additive inverse of the rise from P_2 to P_1. That is, $y_2 - y_1 = -(y_1 - y_2)$. Similarly, the run from P_1 to P_2 is the negative of the run from P_2 to P_1 and $x_2 - x_1 = -(x_1 - x_2)$.

MOVE TO NEXT FRAME

ANSWERS TO PAGE 20

$x \geq 0$

$x < 0$

---

(1) a

(2) d

(3) a

(4) c

$|x|$

Calculate the rise and the run from point $P(-1,5)$ to point $Q(1,1)$ on the graph of the function defined by $y = -2x + 3$.

rise = ______________

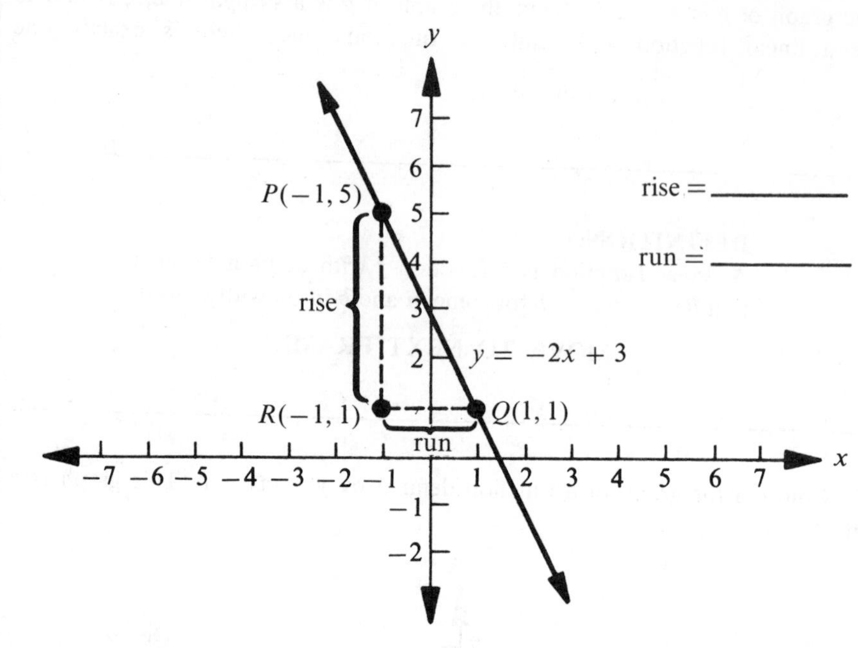

run = ______________

The ratio of the rise to the run, $\frac{\text{rise}}{\text{run}}$, between any two points on a non-vertical line is the *slope* of that line. If your eyes go "downhill" as they move from left to right on the line, the slope is ______________. If your eyes go "uphill" as they move from left to right, the slope is ______________.

The x axis or any line parallel to the x axis has a slope of ______________.

The slope of the graph of $y = -2x + 3$ in the preceding frame is $\frac{\text{rise}}{\text{run}} =$ ______________.

DEFINITION:
The **slope** of the line containing the points $P(x_1,y_1)$ and $Q(x_2,y_2)$ is the number $\frac{y_2 - y_1}{x_2 - x_1}$ whenever $x_1 \neq x_2$. If $x_1 = x_2$ the line is parallel to or coincides with the y axis and the slope is *not* defined.

MOVE TO NEXT FRAME

Pick any two points on the graph of the linear function defined by $f(x) = mx + b$. Let the coordinates of these two points be $(x_1, f(x_1))$ and $(x_2, f(x_2))$ and use them to calculate the slope of the corresponding line.

$$\text{slope} = \frac{f(x_2) - f(x_1)}{x_2 - x_1} = \frac{(\qquad) - (\qquad)}{x_2 - x_1} = m$$

Thus we see that the slope of the graph of $f(x) = mx + b$ is ______. Furthermore, the slope is independent of the choice of the two points.

The line with slope m and y intercept b is the graph of $\{(x,y): y = mx + b\}$. The equation $y = mx + b$ is called the **slope-intercept** form of the equation of the line.

MOVE TO NEXT FRAME

The defining equation for a linear function may also be written in standard form. The **standard form** of a linear equation in two variables is $ax + by = c$.

$y = \frac{2}{3}x - 5$ is the equation of a line in ______________ form

The equation equivalent to $y = \frac{2}{3}x - 5$ written in standard form is ________.

On the given coordinate system, graph the function that is defined as follows: Whenever $x \in \mathcal{R}$ and $x \geq 0$, let $f(x) = x$ and whenever $x \in \mathcal{R}$ and $x < 0$, let $f(x) = -x$.

This function is called the absolute value function.

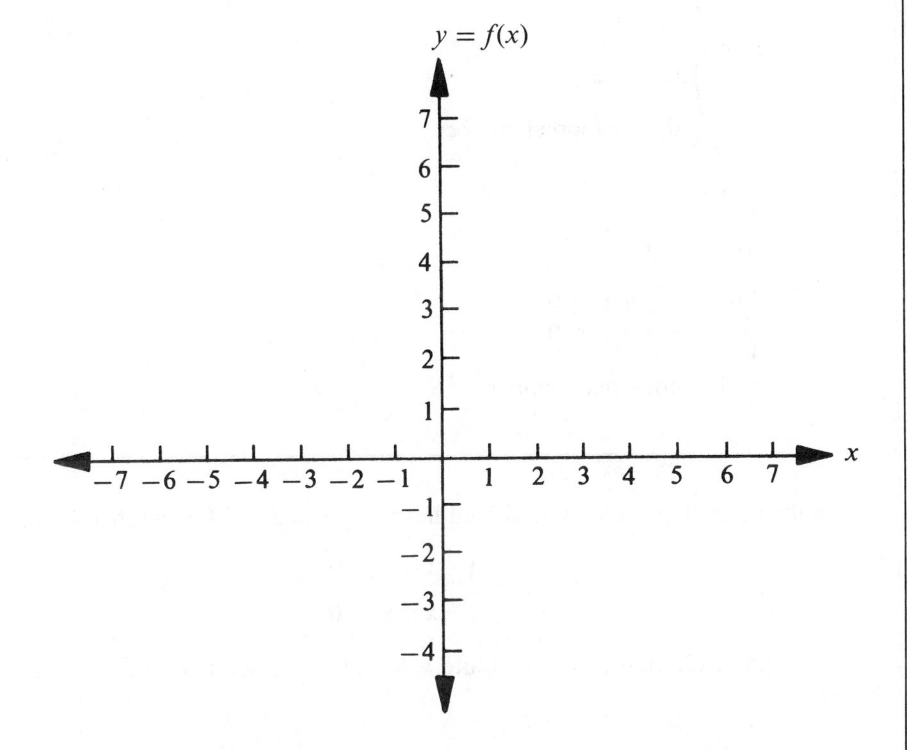

ANSWERS TO PAGE 17

straight

$\left(\frac{3}{2}, 0\right)$

-3

image

ANSWERS TO PAGE 22

no

DEFINITION:
If x is a real number, the **absolute value of** x, denoted $|x|$, is defined as follows:

$$|x| = \begin{cases} x \text{ if } \_\_\_\_\_\_\_\_\_\_, \\ -x \text{ if } \_\_\_\_\_\_\_\_\_\_. \end{cases}$$

Therefore the **absolute value function** is $\{(x,y):y = |x|\}$.

From your knowledge of the definition of the square-root symbol, $\sqrt{}$, select the correct response, a, b, c, or d, for each of the following:

1. $\sqrt{9} =$ (a) 3 (b) -3 (c) ± 3 (d) not a real number ______

2. $\sqrt{-(3^2)} =$ (a) 3 (b) -3 (c) ± 3 (d) not a real number ______

3. $\sqrt{(-3)^2} =$ (a) 3 (b) -3 (c) ± 3 (d) not a real number ______

4. $\sqrt{x^2} =$ (a) x (b) $-x$ (c) x if $x \geq 0$; $-x$ if $x < 0$ (d) not a real number ______

In the preceding frame, you should have responded "c" for number 4, *i.e.,*

$$\sqrt{x^2} = \begin{cases} x \text{ if } x \geq 0 \\ -x \text{ if } x < 0 \end{cases}$$

From the definition of the absolute value of x, we see that $\sqrt{x^2} =$ ____ for every $x \in \mathcal{R}$.

This discussion should remind you that if t is a nonnegative real number the number designated by $\sqrt{t}$ is never a ______________ (positive/negative) number.

It is true, however, that every positive number has ______ (how many?) real square roots, one of which is a ________ and the other a ________ number. The symbol $\sqrt{}$ only represents the ________ square root of 9, namely, 3. We call this positive square root the **principal** square root.

In the graph of $\left\{(x,y)\colon\ y \leq \frac{1}{2}x - 2\right\}$ the line is the graph of all those ordered pairs (x,y) where $y = \frac{1}{2}x - 2$ and the shaded portion is the graph of all those ordered pairs (x,y) where ______________.

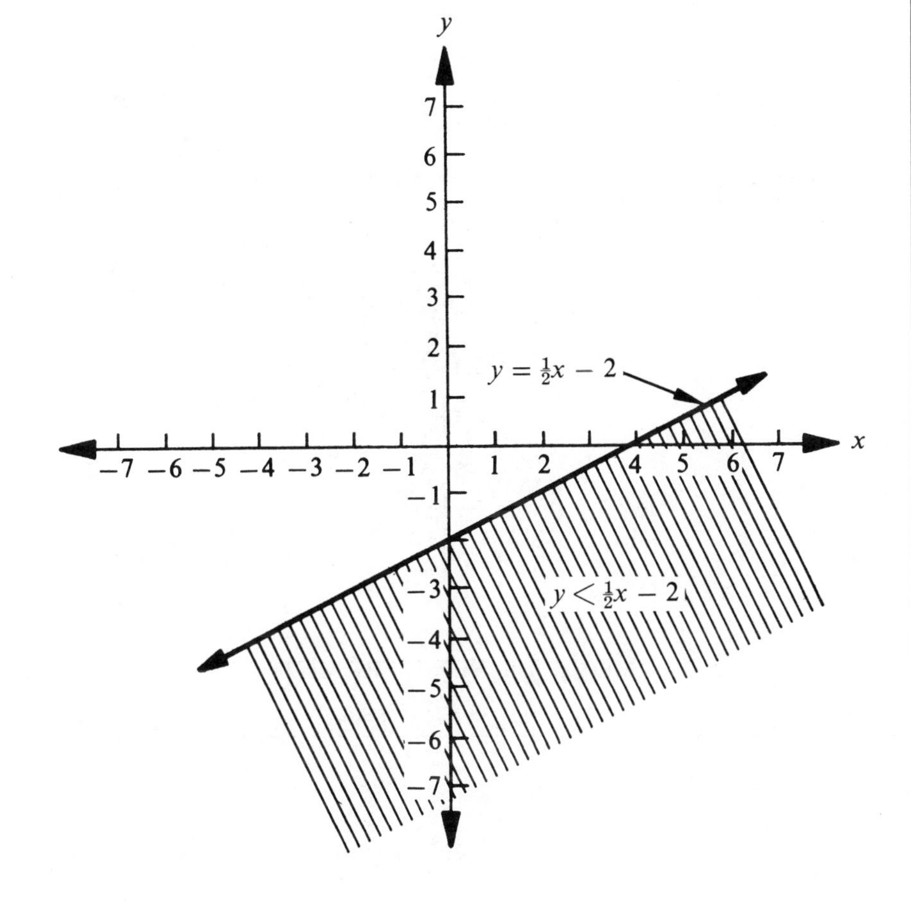

ANSWERS TO PAGE 19

$$\frac{(mx_2 + b) - (mx_1 + b)}{x_2 - x_1}$$

m

---

slope-intercept

$2x - 3y = 15$

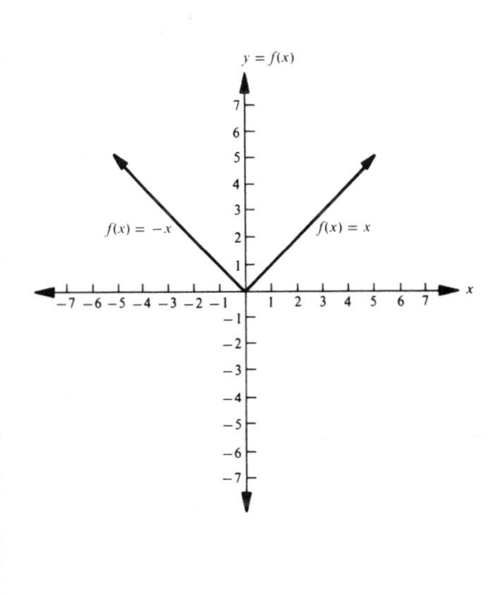

ANSWERS TO PAGE 24

(a), (b)

Is the graph of $\left\{(x,y):y \leq \frac{1}{2}x - 2\right\}$ the graph of a function? ______

If the set of ordered pairs described by $\left\{(x,y):y \leq \frac{1}{2}x - 2\right\}$ is replaced by $\left\{(x,y): y \leq \frac{1}{2}x - 2\right\}$, the line described by the equation $y = \frac{1}{2}x - 2$ would no longer be part of the graph. To indicate this property of the graph of $\left\{(x,y):y < \frac{1}{2}x - 2\right\}$, the graph corresponding to $y = \frac{1}{2}x - 2$ is represented by a dashed line (← — — — →) line. See the illustration.

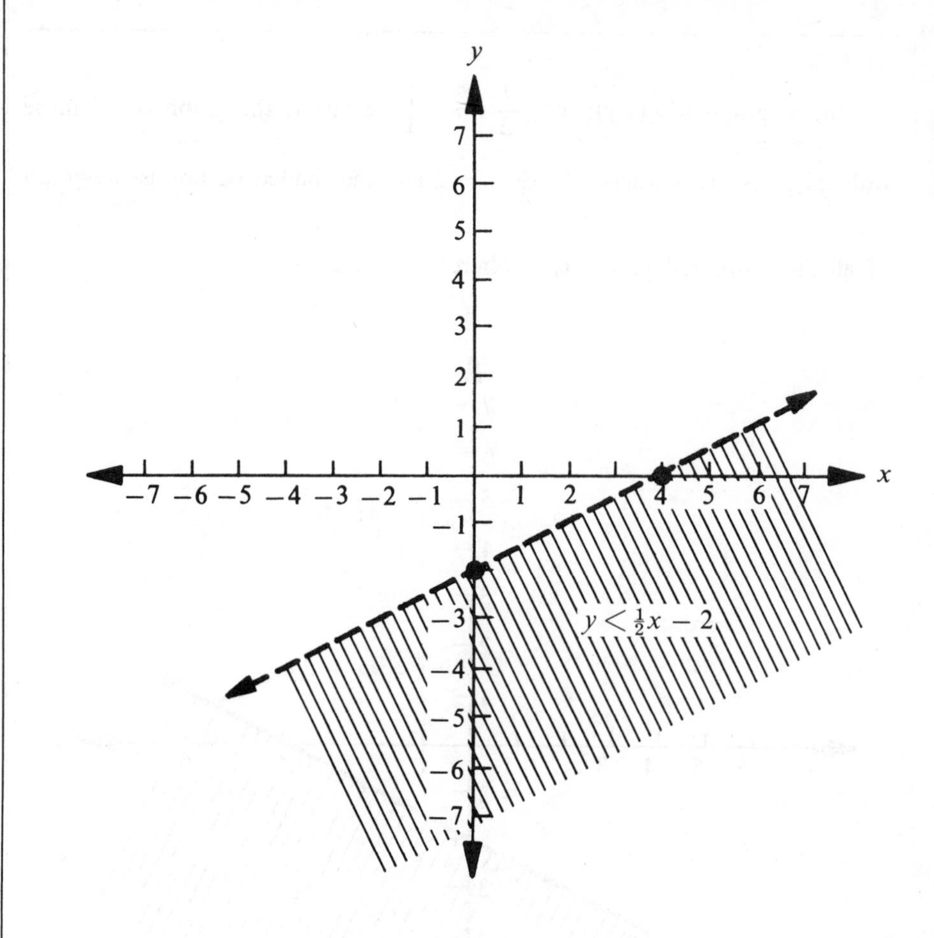

MOVE TO NEXT FRAME

The graph of a relation is shown in the following illustration. Is the relation a function? ________________.The domain of the relation is the set

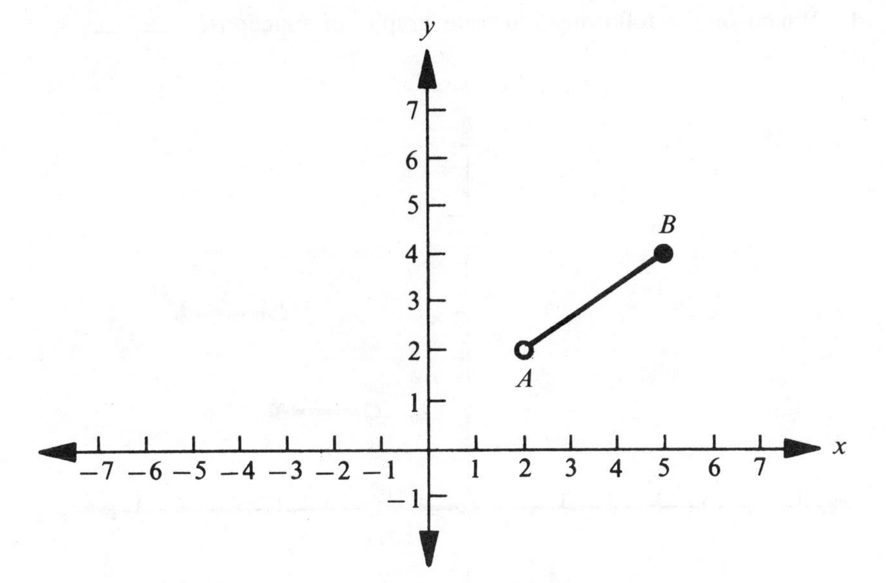

________________. The open dot means that 2 ______ (is/is not) to be included in the domain. The range of the relation is ________________. The slope of $\overline{AB}$ is ________.

ANSWERS TO PAGE 21

negative

---

two

negative positive

positive

$y < \frac{1}{2}x - 2$

ANSWERS TO PAGE 26

EXERCISES. 1.2

1. Which of the following illustrate graphs of functions? ______

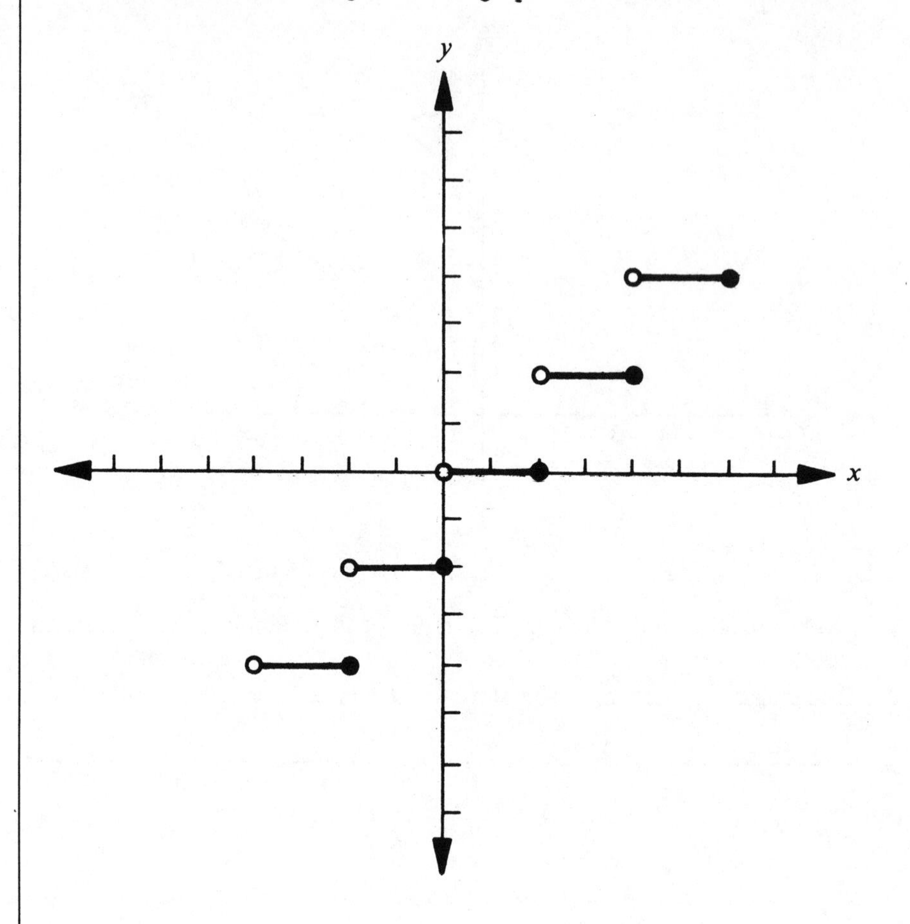

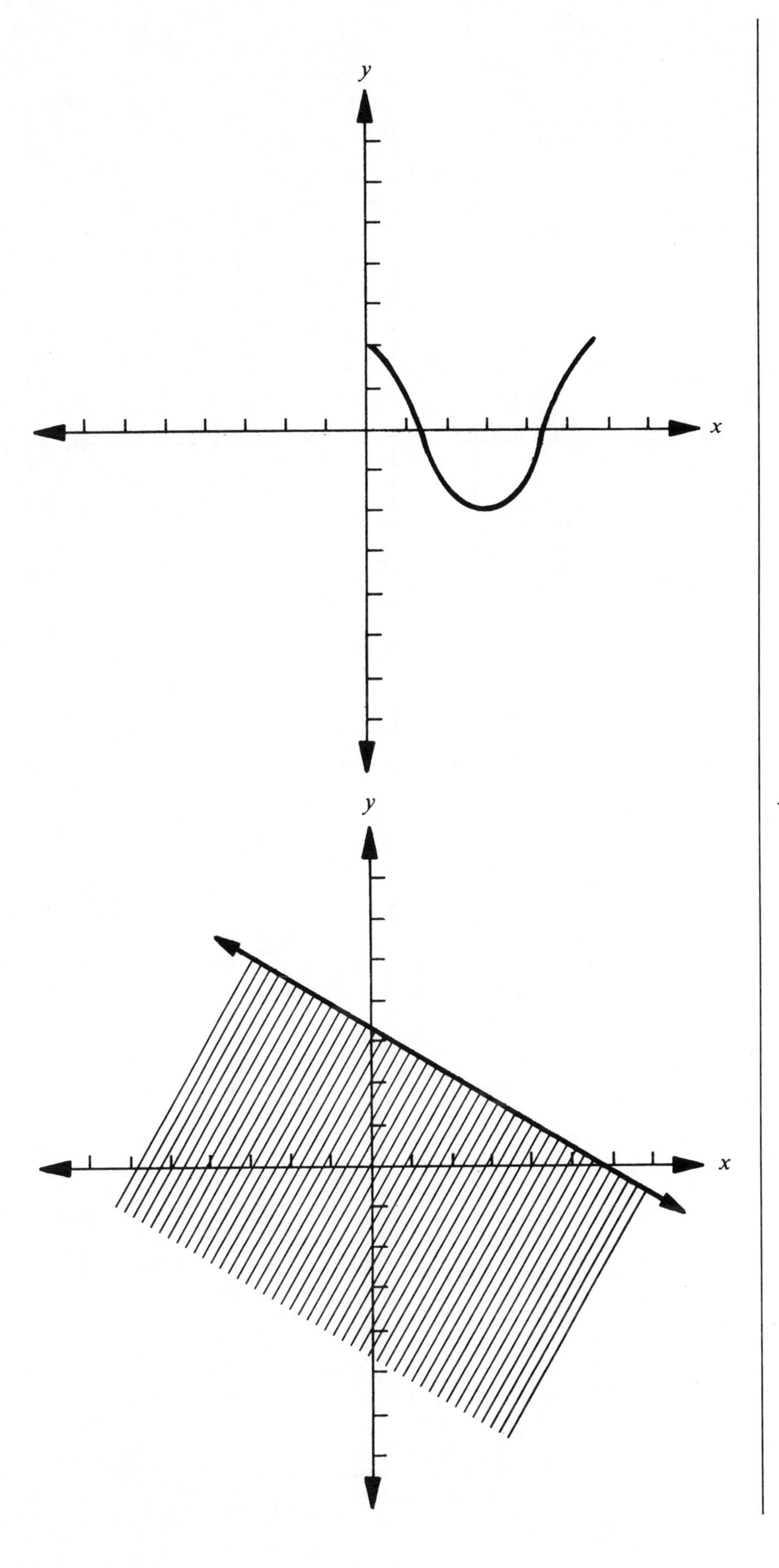

yes

$\{x : x \in \mathcal{R} \text{ and } 2 < x \leq 5\}$; is not

$\{y : y \in \mathcal{R} \text{ and } 2 < y \leq 4\}$

$\frac{2}{3}$

(b)

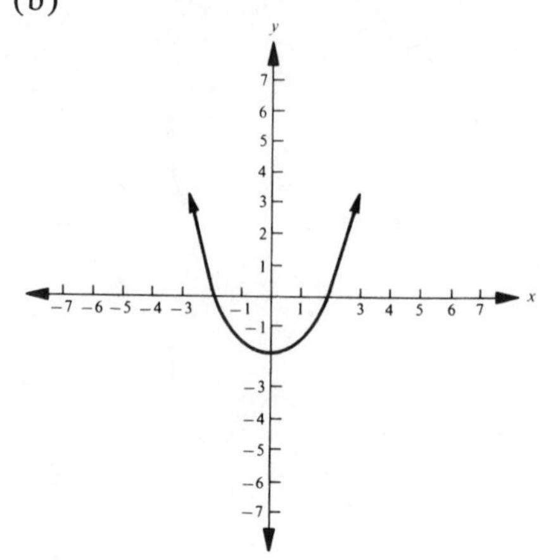
y
x
7
6
5
4
3
2
1
-1
-3
-4
-5
-6
-7
-7 -6 -5 -4 -3
-1
1
3 4 5 6 7

(c)

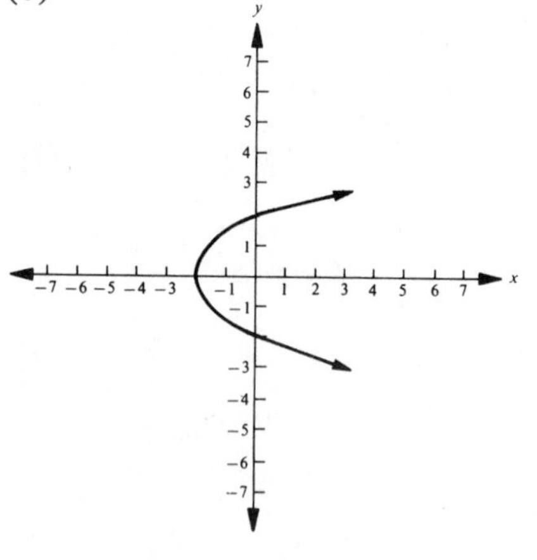
y
x
7
6
5
4
3
1
-1
-3
-4
-5
-6
-7
-7 -6 -5 -4 -3
-1
1 2 3 4 5 6 7

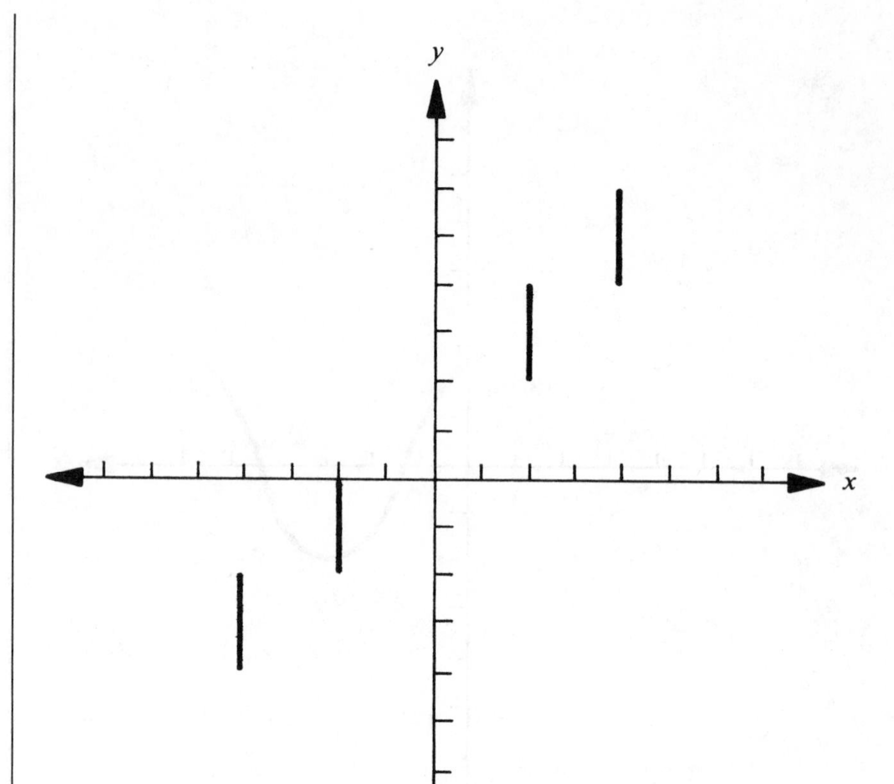
y
x

2. Graph the relations defined by each of the following. Each relation is a subset of $\mathcal{R} \times \mathcal{R}$.

   (a) $f(x) = \frac{1}{3}x - 2$

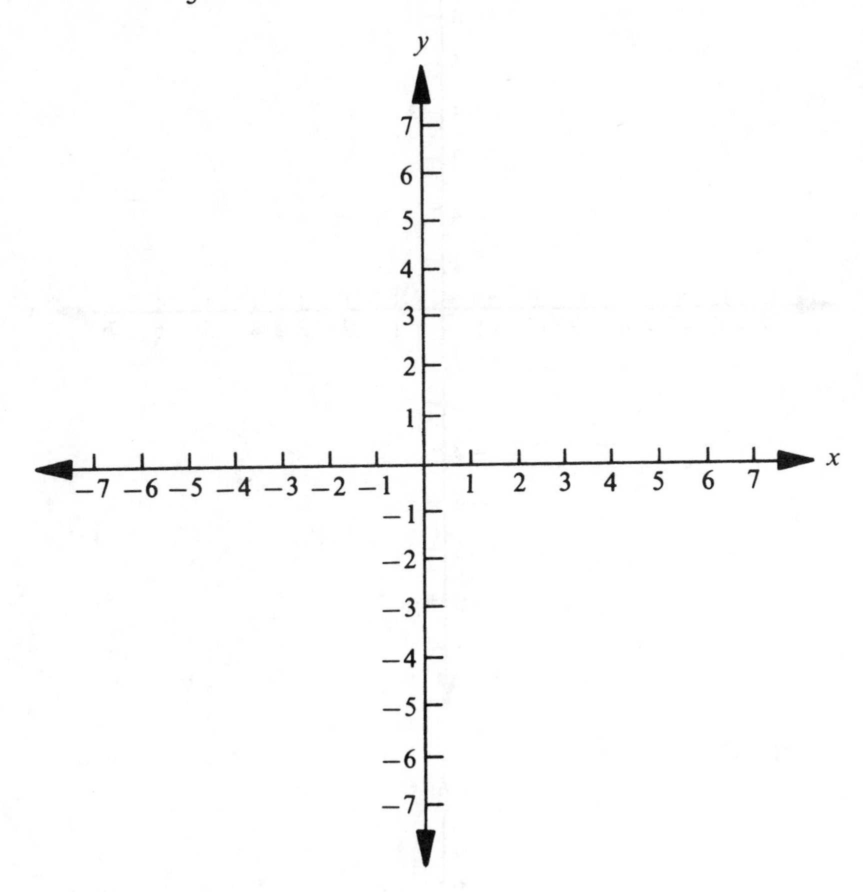

(c) $\dfrac{y+3}{x-4} = -\dfrac{5}{3}$

(d) $5x + 3y = 11$

(7) $8x + 7y = 3$

(8) (a) -3

(b) 6

(9) $\dfrac{54-40}{37-36} = \dfrac{f(36.2)-40}{36.2-36}$

$\dfrac{14}{1} = \dfrac{f(36.2)-40}{0.2}$

$f(36.2) - 40 = 0.2(14)$

$f(36.2) = 40 + 2.8$

$= 42.8$

(10) (a) 26.8

(b) 32.2

(c) 34

(11) (a) $x \geq 0$

(b) $x \leq 0$

(c) $x - 2 \geq 0$ or $x \geq 2$

(d) $x \leq 2$

(12) $x \geq 1$

(13) Proof:
$|xy| = \sqrt{(xy)^2} = \sqrt{x^2y^2} = \sqrt{x^2} \cdot \sqrt{y^2} = |x| \cdot |y|$.

(14) See Appendix.

(b) $y = \dfrac{1}{2}x^2 - 2$

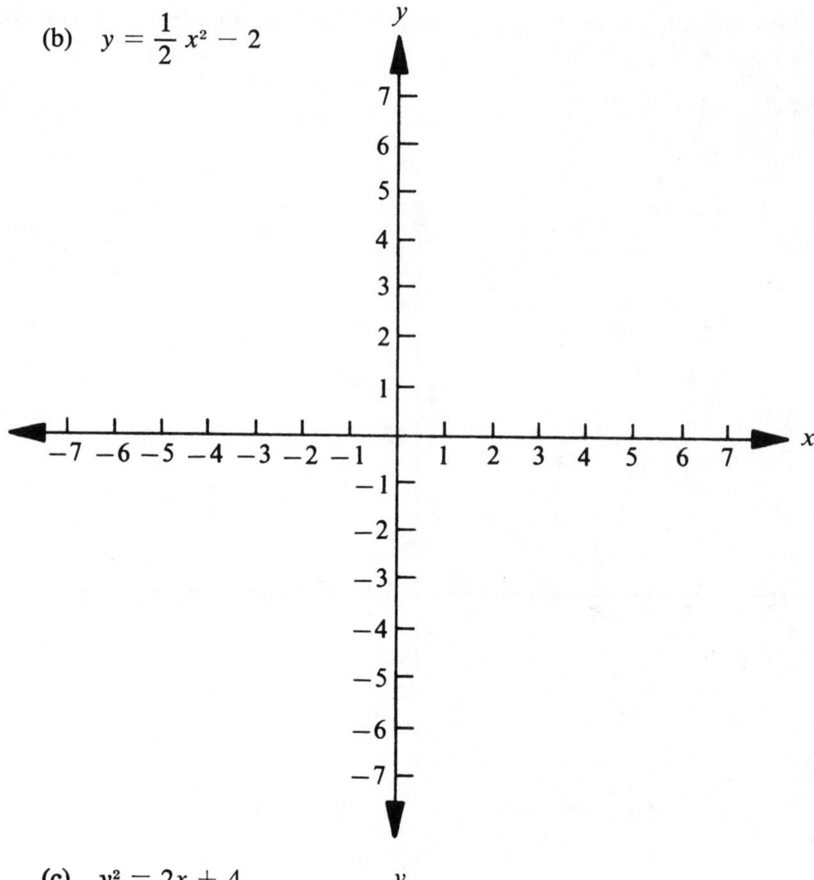

(c) $y^2 = 2x + 4$

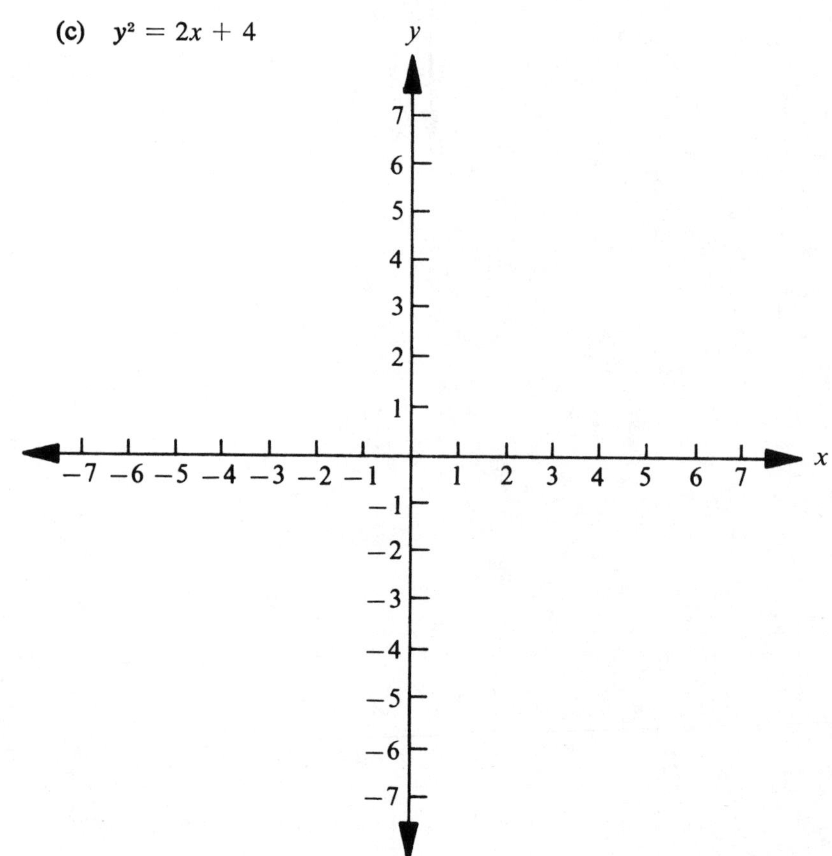

(d) $f(x) = -\sqrt{16 - x^2}$

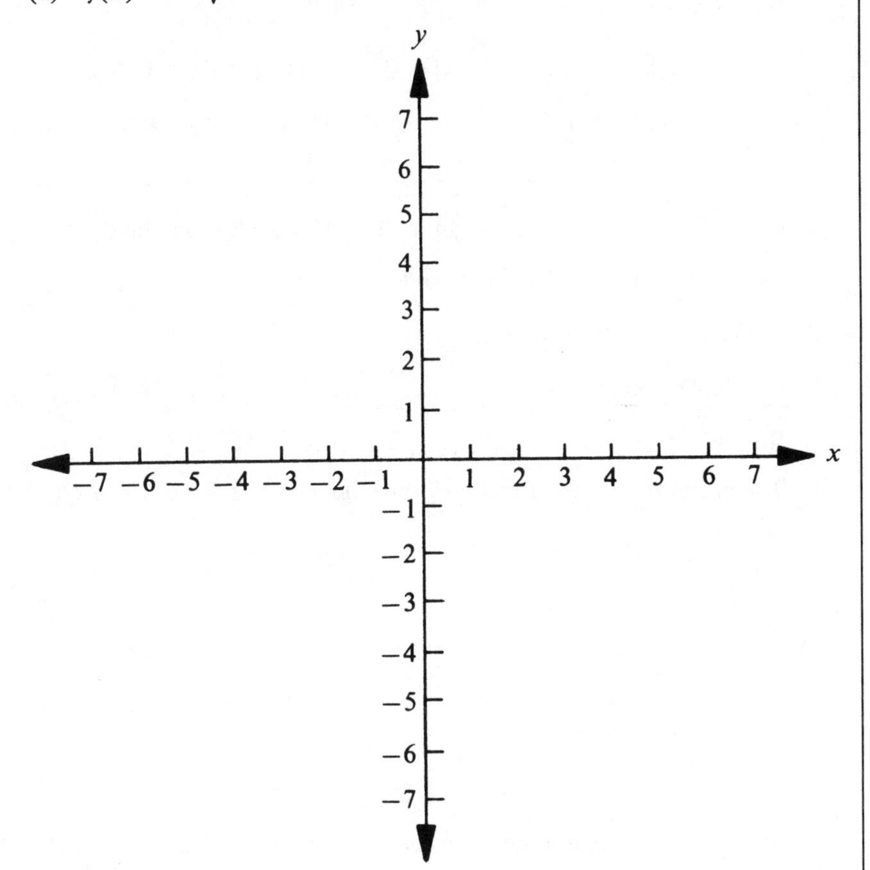

(a)

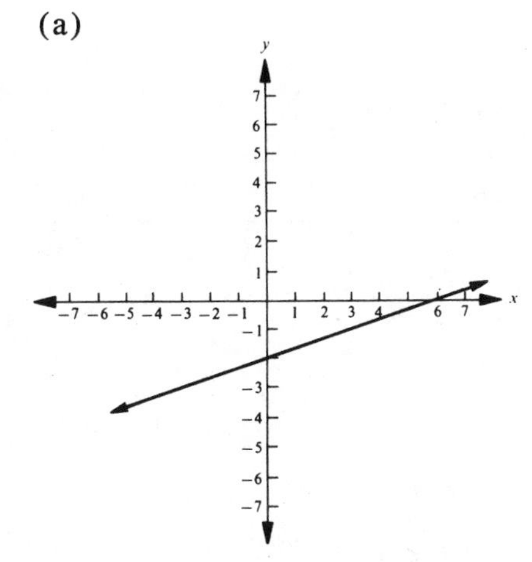

3. Which of the relations in problem number 2 are functions? ________

4. Find the slope of the graph corresponding to the functions defined by the following:

   (a) $f(x) = 3x - 5$ $m =$ ________

   (b) $f(x) = 3 - 4x$ $m =$ ________

   (c) $3[f(x)] = 4 - x$ $m =$ ________

   (d) $4y - 3x = 12$ $m =$ ________

5. Find the slope of the graph of the linear function f: if (a) $f(1) = 3$ and $f(2) = 6$ ________; (b) $f(-2) = 3$ and $f(2) = -4$ ________.

6. Calculate the slope m_1 of the line containing

   (a) $P(x,y)$ and $P_1(4, -3)$. $m_1 =$ ________.

   (b) If $P_2(1,2)$ is on the same line as P_1, then calculate the slope, m_2, using the coordinates of P_1 and P_2. $m_2 =$ ________.

ANSWERS TO PAGE 32

$\left\{(x,y): y = \frac{1}{x} + 2x \text{ and } x \neq 0\right\}$

(a) $\{(2,-5),(4,-3),(1,0), (0,2)\}$

(b) $\{(x,[-h](x)): [-h](x) = -x^2 + 3x\}$

(c) $\left\{(x,y): y = -\frac{1}{x^2-3}\right\}$

$\{(6,-2),(0,6),(-3,-9)\}$

$\{(x,y): y = 5x + 2 - x^2\}$

(c) Since P, P_1, and P_2 are on the same line $m_1 = m_2$ and $\frac{y+3}{x-4} =$ ______________. (d) This is the equation of the line containing P_1 and P_2 and when written in standard form is ____________________.

7. Using number 6 above as a guide, find the equation in standard form of the line containing $P_1(-4,5)$ and $P_2(3,-3)$. ________________.

8. If g is a constant function find

   (a) $g(4)$, if $g(1) = -3$ ________________

   (b) $g(-5)$, if $g(0) = 6$ ________________

9. The graph of a linear function f contains points $P(36,40)$ and $Q(37,54)$. Find $f(36.2)$ ____________________

10. The graph of a linear function g contains points $P(100,25)$ and $Q(101,43)$. Find

    (a) $g(100.1)$ ______

    (b) $g(100.4)$ ______

    (c) $g(100.5)$ ______

11. (a) For what $x \in \mathcal{R}$ is it true that $\sqrt{x^2} = x$? ______

    (b) For what $x \in \mathcal{R}$ is it true that $\sqrt{x^2} = -x$? ______

    (c) For what $x \in \mathcal{R}$ is it true that $|x-2| = x - 2$? ______

    (d) For what $x \in \mathcal{R}$ is it true that $|x-2| = -x + 2$? ______

12. If $f(x) = |x-1|$ and $g(x) = |x| - 1$, then for what values of x is $f(x) = g(x)$? ______

13. Recall $|x| = \sqrt{x^2}$ and use the properties of exponents and radicals to prove $|xy| = |x||y|$.

14. Prove that for $x \in \mathcal{R}$ and $y \in \mathcal{R}$, $|x+y| \leq |x| + |y|$.

1.3. ALGEBRA OF FUNCTIONS

The set of all functions is a subset of the set of all __________. Since a function is, by definition, a particular kind of relation, it is therefore a

__________________.

A function g, being a set, is equal to a function f if and only if $g \subset f$ and

______.

Since functions are sets, they are equal if and only if they contain the

______ elements. Thus if f and g are functions, $f = g$ if and only if $(x,y) \epsilon f$

implies that __________. Thus $f = g$ if and only if they have the same

domain D and for every x in D, $f(x) =$ ______.

If $f(x) = x^2$ and $g(x) = 2x$ each define functions in $\mathcal{R} \times \mathcal{R}$, then $f(x) +$

$g(x) =$ __________ defines a third function in $\mathcal{R} \times \mathcal{R}$.

Furthermore $\frac{f(x)}{g(x)} =$ ______, $x \neq 0$, $f(x) \cdot g(x) =$ ______, and $f(x) -$

$g(x) =$ __________ also define functions in $\mathcal{R} \times \mathcal{R}$.

DEFINITION:
The **sum, $f + g$, of two functions** f and g in $\mathcal{R} \times \mathcal{R}$ is the function h whose domain D is the intersection of the domains of f and g and $h(x) = f(x) + g(x)$ for every $x \epsilon D$.

MOVE TO NEXT FRAME

Examples: Add the functions g and h in $\mathcal{R} \times \mathcal{R}$ as specified in each of the following: (*Remember:* according to the definition of the sum of two functions, only the second elements of the functions are added, and this is done only when the first elements are equal.)

(a) $g = \{(1,3),(2,5),(7,0),(-3,-4)\}$

$h = \{(0,8),(2,4),(7,8),(-3,2)\}$

$g + h =$ ____________________

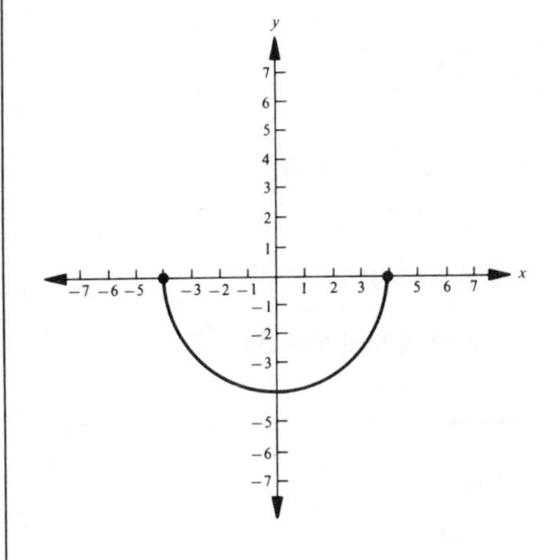

(3) (a), (b), and (d)

(4) (a) 3

(b) -4

(c) $-\frac{1}{3}$

(d) $\frac{3}{4}$

(5) (a) 3 (b) $-\frac{7}{4}$

(6) (a) $m_1 = \frac{y+3}{x-4}$

(b) $m_2 = -\frac{5}{3}$

(b) $g = \left\{(x,y): y = \dfrac{1}{x} \text{ and } x \neq 0\right\}$

$h = \{(x,y): y = 2x\}$

$g + h =$ ______________________

$x + 3, x \neq 3$

$\{x : x \in \mathcal{R} \text{ and } x \neq 3\}$

DEFINITION:
If f is a function in $\mathcal{R} \times \mathcal{R}$, then the **negative** of f is the function $-f$ whose domain D is the domain of f and $[-f](x) = -f(x)$ for every $x \in D$.

MOVE TO NEXT FRAME

Examples: Find the negative of each of the following functions in $\mathcal{R} \times \mathcal{R}$:

(a) $g = \{(2,5),(4,3),(1,0),(0,-2)\}$

$-g =$ ______________________

(b) $h = \{(h,h(x)): h(x) = x^2 - 3x\}$

$-h =$ ______________________

(c) $f = \left\{(x,y): y = \dfrac{1}{x^2 - 3}\right\}$

$-f =$ ______________________

DEFINITION:
The **difference, $f - g$, of two functions** f and g in $\mathcal{R} \times \mathcal{R}$ is the function $h = f + (-g)$. Thus, $f - g = f + (-g)$.

MOVE TO NEXT FRAME

Examples: Find the function $d = g - h$ in $\mathcal{R} \times \mathcal{R}$ for each of the following:

(a) $g = \{(4,2),(0,7),(-3,-2),(6,0)\}$

$h = \{(6,2),(0,1),(-3,7),(10,5)\}$

$d =$ ______________________

(b) $g = \{(x,y): y = 5x + 2\}$

$h = \{(x,y): y = x^2\}$

$d =$ ______________________

DEFINITION:
The **product ($f \cdot g$, or fg) of two functions** f and g in $\mathcal{R} \times \mathcal{R}$ is the function h whose domain D is the intersection of the domains of f and g and $h(x) = f(x) \cdot g(x)$ for every $x \epsilon D$.

MOVE TO NEXT FRAME

Examples: Find the function $h = fg$ in $\mathcal{R} \times \mathcal{R}$ for each of the following.

(a) $f = \{(0,5),(2,3),(-4,3),(6,2)\}$

$g = \{(2,5),(-4,0),(0,7)\}$

$h =$ ______________________

(b) $f = \{(x,f(x)): f(x) = \sqrt{x}\}$

$g = \{(x,g(x)): g(x) = 2x\}$

$h =$ ______________________ .

The domain of h is ______________________ .

DEFINITION:
The **reciprocal $\frac{1}{g}$ of a function** g in $\mathcal{R} \times \mathcal{R}$ is the function h whose domain D consists of those elements in the domain of g for which $g(x) \neq 0$ and such that $h(x) = \frac{1}{g(x)}$ for every x in D.
for every x in D.

MOVE TO NEXT FRAME

Examples: Find the function $g = \frac{1}{f}$ for the following functions:

(a) $f = \{(0,2),(-6,4),(3,7),(4,0)\}$

$g =$ ______________________

(b) $f = \{(x,y): y = x - 4\}$

$g = \{(x,y):$ ______________________ $\}$

ANSWERS TO PAGE 31

relations

set of ordered pairs

$f \subset g$

---

same

$(x,y) \epsilon g$

$g(x)$

$x^2 + 2x$

$\frac{x^2}{2x}$ $\quad$ $x^2(2x)$

$x^2 - 2x$

$\{(2,9),(7,8),(-3,-2)\}$

ANSWERS TO PAGE 36

DEFINITION:

The **quotient** $\frac{f}{g}$ **of two functions** f and g in $\mathcal{R} \times \mathcal{R}$ is the function $h = f \cdot \left(\frac{1}{g}\right)$. Thus $\frac{f}{g} = f \cdot \left(\frac{1}{g}\right)$.

Examples: Find the function $h = \frac{f}{g}$ if

$f = \{(x,f(x)): f(x) = x^2 - 9\}$ and

$g = \{(x,g(x)): g(x) = x - 3\}$.

$h = \{(x,h(x)): h(x) =$ ______________ $\}$,

and the domain of $h =$ ______________ .

The properties of the sum, difference, product, and quotient of functions can be explored further, but this short introduction will be sufficient for our purposes. In general, the properties of these operations on functions are those of the *set of numbers* (in this case $\mathcal{R}$) in which we find the ranges of the functions.

MOVE TO NEXT FRAME

$g(x)$

There is another important operation defined for two or more functions that has no counterpart in the algebra of numbers.

Consider the function f that has the range of a function g as its domain. See the following illustration of such a mapping.

$\{(0,-8),(1,8),(2,1)\}$

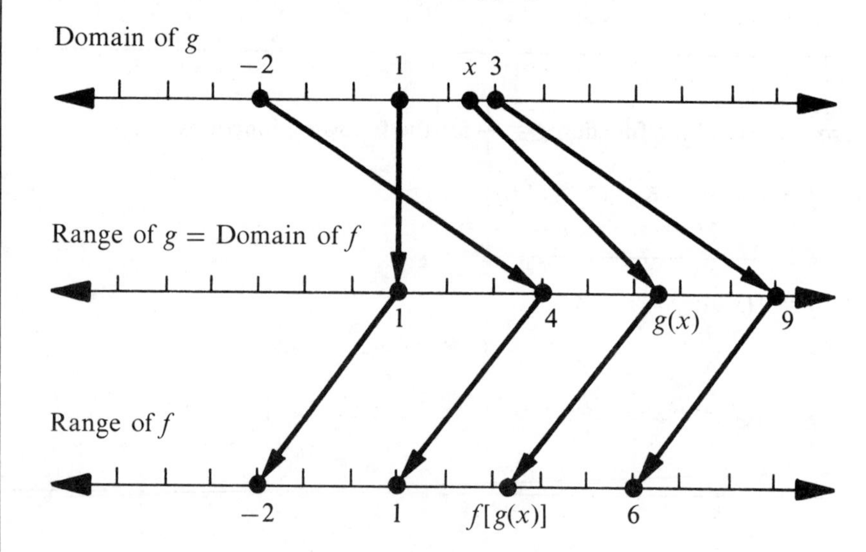

$f[g(x)] = [(2x + 3) - 2]^2 = (2x + 1)^2$

$g[f(x)] = 2(x - 2)^2 + 3$

ANSWERS TO PAGE 33

In the mapping represented by this illustration, the function g takes -2 into $g(-2) =$ ___ and the function f takes $g(-2)$ into $f[g(-2)] =$ ___. In general, the function g takes x into ___, and the function f takes ___ into ___.

Putting the functions g and f together in the order illustrated forms a third function, h, which takes x into $h(x) = f[g(x)]$. That is, h takes 3 from the domain of g into ___, which is in the range of f.

If g in the preceding frame is the function defined by $g(x) = x^2$ and f is the function defined by $(fx) = x - 3$, then $f[g(x)] = g(x) - 3 =$ ___, whereas $g[f(x)] = (f(x))^2 =$ ___. Thus, in general, $f[g(x)] \neq g[f(x)]$.

$\{(2,15),(-4,0),(0,35)\}$

$\{(x,h(x)): h(x) = (\sqrt{x})2x, x \geq 0\}$

$\{x: x \geq 0 \text{ and } x \in \mathcal{R}\}$

DEFINITION:
The **composite, $f \circ g$, of two functions** f and g is the function h where $h(x) = f[g(x)]$. The domain of h is the set of all x for which $g(x)$ is defined and $g(x)$ is in the domain of f.

The operation of forming the composite of two functions is called the **composition** of functions.

MOVE TO NEXT FRAME

One of the better descriptions of a function compares it with a machine having an input of x, which is an element of the ___ of the function, and an output $f(x)$, which is the corresponding element of the ___ of the function. See the illustration.

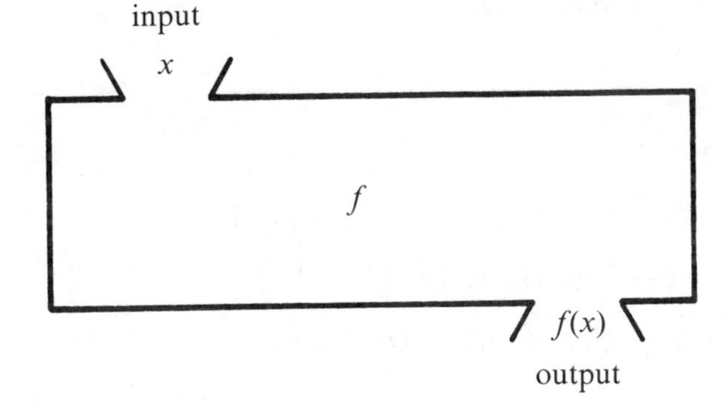

function machine for f

$\left\{\left(0,\frac{1}{2}\right), \left(-6,\frac{1}{4}\right), \left(3,\frac{1}{7}\right)\right\}$

Note that $g(4)$ does not exist since $f(4) = 0$.

$\left\{(x,y): y = \frac{1}{x-4} \text{ and } x \neq 4\right\}$

The analogy can be extended to the composition of functions by considering two "function machines" arranged in succession so that the output of the first machine feeds into the input of the second machine. See the illustration.

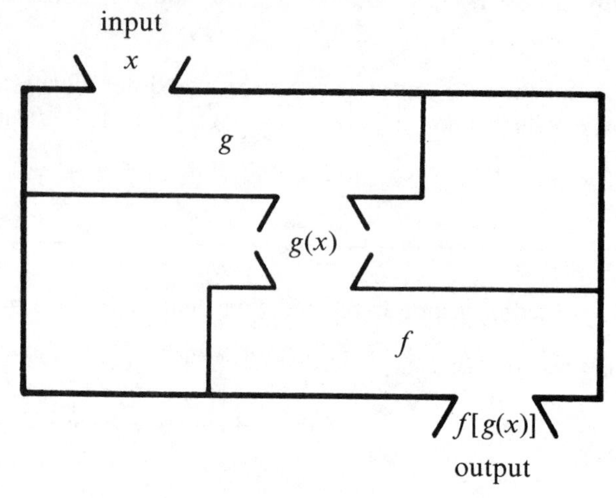

function machine for $f \circ g$

MOVE TO NEXT FRAME

To find $f \circ g(x)$, the function g is first applied to x and then the function f is applied to ______.

$\{(3,5),(4,7),(0,4)\}$

$\{(5,3),(7,4),(4,0)\}$

(b,a)

Examples: If f is the function $\{(-2,-8),(-1,3),(0,1),(1,4),(2,8)\}$, and $g = \{(-2,-7),(-1,-4),(0,-2),(1,2),(2,0),(3,8)\}$,

then $g \circ f = \{(-1,8),(0,2)\}$

and $f \circ g =$ ______________ .

Remember: the domain of $f \circ g$ is the set of elements x in the domain of g for which $g(x)$ is in the domain of f.

$2\left(\frac{x+3}{2}\right) - 3 = x$

x

Examples: If

$$f = \{(x,f(x)): f(x) = (x-2)^2\} \text{ and}$$

$$g = \{(x,g(x)): g(x) = 2x+3\},$$

and $f \circ g = \{(x,f \circ g(x)): f \circ g(x) =$ ______________ $\}$

then $g \circ f = \{(x,g \circ f(x)): g \circ f(x) =$ ______________ $\}$

Recall that a *commutative* operation is one in which the same result is achieved regardless of the order in the operation. That is, $a + b = b + a$, $ab = ba$, and in general a "operate" $b = b$ "operate" a.

In the previous frame you found $g \circ f$ and $f \circ g$. What do these results tell you about the operation "composition of functions"? ______

______

______.

Suppose you have three functions f, g, and h defined as follows:

$$f = \{(x,f(x)): f(x) = x^2 + x + 1\}$$
$$g = \{(x,g(x)): g(x) = x + 2\}$$
$$h = \{(x,h(x)): h(x) = -2x - 3\}$$

Calculate:

(a) $f \circ g = \{(x,y)$: ______$\}$

(b) $g \circ h = \{(x,y)$: ______$\}$

(c) $(f \circ g) \circ h = \{x,y)$: ______$\}$

(d) $f \circ (g \circ h) = \{(x,y)$: ______$\}$

Multiplication and addition of real numbers are both associative operations since $(ab)c = a(bc)$ and $(a + b) + c = a + (b + c)$ for any three real numbers. That is, an operation on three elements which is first performed with a and b yields the same results as the operation performed first with b and c.

It appears composition of functions is ______ from the previous frame, since $(f \circ g) \circ h = f \circ (g \circ h)$.

This is indeed the case, and the proof of the associative property, which will not be shown here, involves a direct application of the definition of composition of functions.

The composite of two functions f and g is a third function $h = g \circ f$ having a domain that is a ______ of the domain of f and a range that is a ______ of the range of __.

ANSWERS TO PAGE 35

4 1

$g(x)$ $g(x)$

$f[g(x)]$

6

$x^2 - 3$

$(x - 3)^2 = x^2 - 6x + 9$

---

domain

range

ANSWERS TO PAGE 40

$\{x : x \epsilon \mathcal{R} \text{ and } x \geq 0\}$

If f is the function that "maps" 3 into 5, 4 into 7, and 0 into 4 as illustrated, then there could very well be another function g which takes each

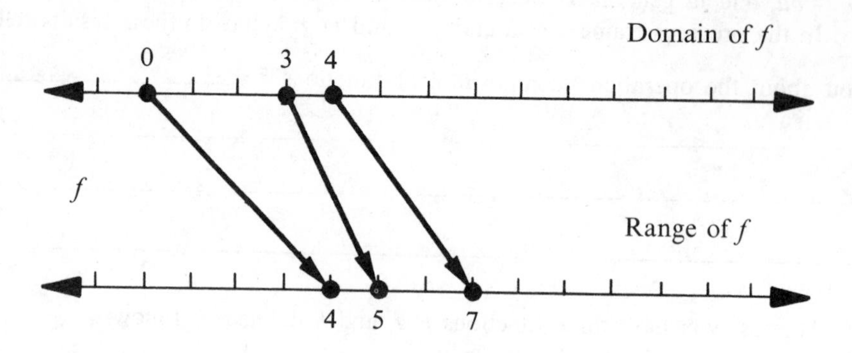

element in the range of f right back to its corresponding element in the domain. See the following illustration.

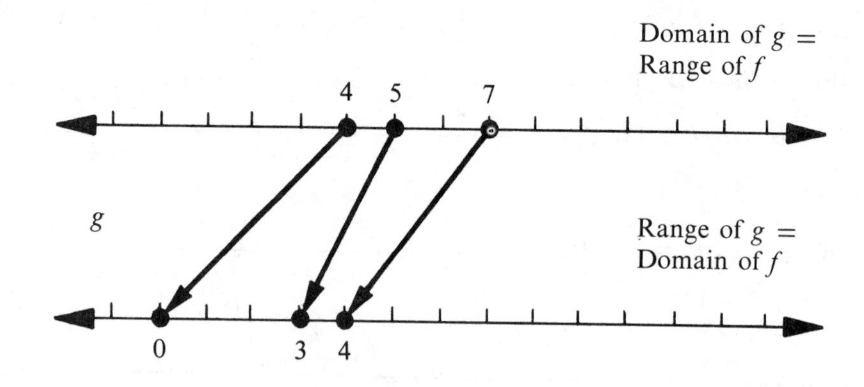

Note that the set of ordered pairs for f above is {________________}

and the set of ordered pairs for g is {________________}.

Two functions related as f and g are, *i.e.*,

$(a,b) \epsilon f$ if and only if (________________) ϵ g,

are said to be **inverses** of each other.

If f is the function defined by $f(x) = 2x - 3$ and g is defined by $g(x) = \frac{x+3}{2}$, then $f \circ g(x) = f[g(x)] =$ ________________, and $g \circ f = g[f(x)] =$ ___.

Functions such as f and g in the preceding frame are said to be **inverses** of each other. f will "undo" what g does and g will undo what f does. If f and g are inverses of each other, the image of x in the composite function $f \circ g$ is ___, and the image of y in the composite function $g \circ f$ is ___.

composition of functions is not commutative since $f \circ g \neq g \circ f$.

DEFINITION:
Two functions f and g are said to be **inverses** of each other if and only if for every x in the domain of g, x is in the domain of $f \circ g$ and $f \circ g(x) = x$ and for every y in the domain of f, y is in the domain of $g \circ f$ and $g \circ f(y) = y$.

In this case each function f and g is said to **have an inverse**, and each is said to be an **inverse** of the other.

MOVE TO NEXT FRAME

(a) $y = x^2 + 5x + 7$

(b) $y = -2x - 1$

(c) $y = (-2x - 3)^2 + 5(-2x - 3) + 7 = 4x^2 + 2x + 1$

(d) $y = (-2x - 1)^2 + (-2x - 1) + 1 = 4x^2 + 2x + 1$

In general, $f \circ g \neq g \circ f$, that is, the composition of functions is not a(n) ________________ (commutative/associative) operation. However, the composition of functions that are inverses of each other is commutative.

The inverse of a function f is often denoted by f^{-1} and read "f inverse." f^{-1} is not to be confused with $\frac{1}{f}$. Throughout this book, f^{-1} will mean the inverse of f whenever f is a function and *not* the reciprocal of f.

MOVE TO NEXT FRAME

---

associative

Not all functions have inverse functions. Suppose f and g are defined by $f(x) = x^2$ and $g(x) = \sqrt{x}$. The domain of f is the set of all $x \epsilon \mathcal{R}$ and the range of f is ________________.

The domain of g is ________________ and the range of g is ________________.

It can easily be seen that g is not the inverse of f, that is, $g \neq f^{-1}$, because for $g \circ f(x) = g(x^2) = \sqrt{x^2} = |x| \neq x$, $x < 0$. Note that all negative x are in domain of f, but *not* in the ________ of g.

subset

subset $\quad g$

If we restrict the domain of f in the preceding frame to ____________, then g will be the inverse of the **restricted** function f, since for $x \geq 0$, $g \circ f(x) = g(x^2) = \sqrt{x^2} = |x| = x$ and $f \circ g(x) = f(\sqrt{x}) = (\sqrt{x})^2 = x$. (We have really created a different function with this restriction.)

A function has an inverse function if and only if there exists a one-to-one correspondence between the elements of its domain and the elements of its range.

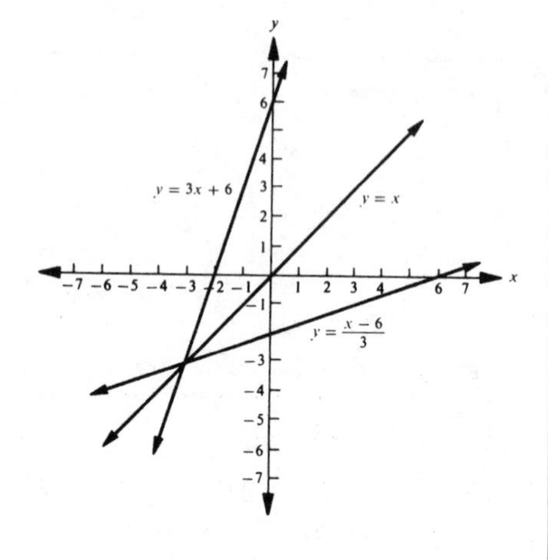

If the function f is a one-to-one correspondence, then its inverse function may be found by interchanging the first and second elements in the pairs of f, thus if $f = \{(x,y)\colon\ y = 2x\}$, then $f^{-1} = \{(y,x)\colon y = 2x\} = \left\{(y,x)\colon x = \frac{1}{2}y\right\}$.

If, in f^{-1}, one replaces x by y and y by x, one may write $f^{-1} = \left\{(x,y)\colon y = \frac{1}{2}x\right\}$.

Note further that if $f(x) = 2x$ and $f^{-1}(x) = \frac{1}{2}x$, then $f \circ f^{-1}(x) = f\left(\frac{1}{2}x\right) = 2\left(\frac{1}{2}x\right) = x$ and $f^{-1} \circ f(x) = f^{-1}(2x) = \frac{1}{2}(2x) = x$.

MOVE TO NEXT FRAME

In the future we will have occasion to restrict the domain or range of a function, as we have with f in the preceding frame, so that it may have an inverse function.

MOVE TO NEXT FRAME

$$f\left(\frac{x-6}{3}\right) = 3\left(\frac{x-6}{3}\right) + 6 = x$$

$$f^{-1}(3x+6) = \frac{(3x+6)-6}{3} = x$$

x

If $h = \{(3,6),(4,-5),(5,0)\}$, then $h^{-1} =$ ______________________.
The graph of h, and h^{-1} are shown on the following coordinate system.

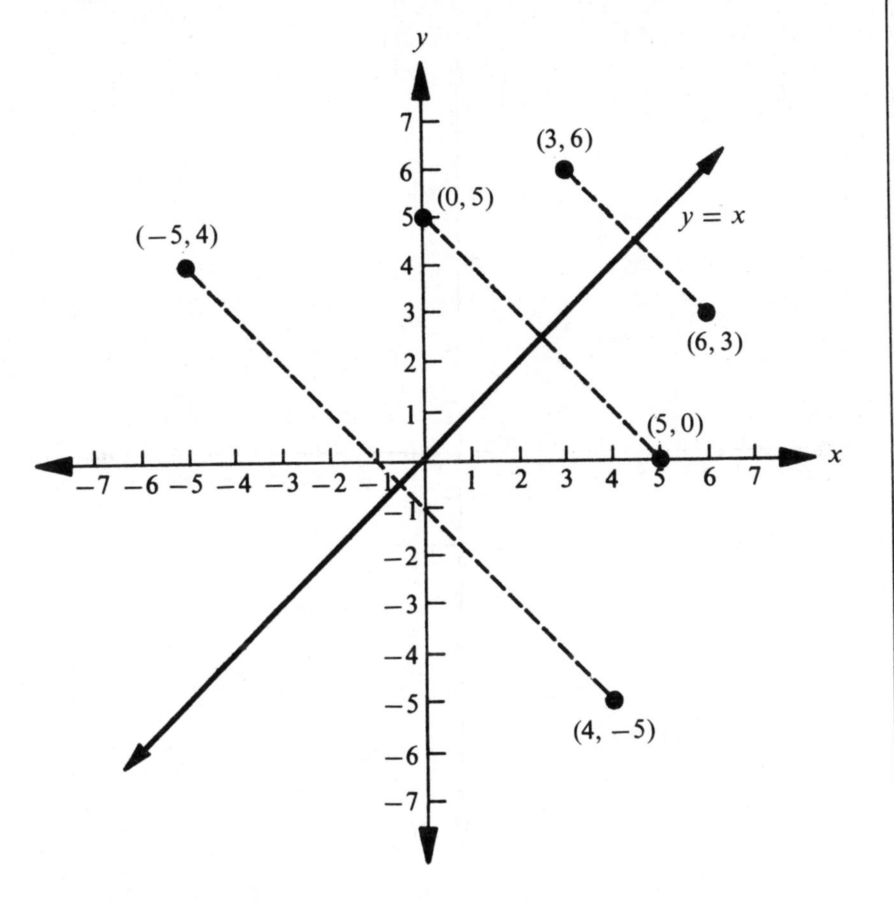

It can be seen that the graph of $y = x$ is the perpendicular __________ of the line segments joining related ordered pairs in h and h^{-1}, respectively.

Because of this property, we say the graphs of h and h^{-1} are **symmetric** with respect to the graph of $y = x$.

If $f = \{(x,y) : y = 3x + 6\}$, then f^{-1} may be defined by interchanging the roles of x and y in $y = 3x + 6$ and solving for y again as follows:

$$x = 3y + 6.$$
$$3y = x - 6.$$
$$y = \frac{x-6}{3}.$$

Therefore $f^{-1} =$ ______________________.

Thus, if $f(x) = 3x + 6$, then $f^{-1}(x) = \dfrac{x-6}{3}$.

ANSWERS TO PAGE 39

x y

---

commutative

$\{y : y \in \mathcal{R} \text{ and } y \geq 0\}$

$\{x : x \in \mathcal{R} \text{ and } x \geq 0\}$

$\{y : y \in \mathcal{R} \text{ and } y \geq 0\}$

range

ANSWERS TO PAGE 44

(c) $f^{-1}(x) = \dfrac{2x+1}{x}$,

$f^{-1}(x) \neq 2$

(d) $f^{-1}(x) = \sqrt{x} + 3$

(9) See Appendix.

(10)

Graph f and f^{-1} on the following coordinate system. Note the symmetry about $y = x$.

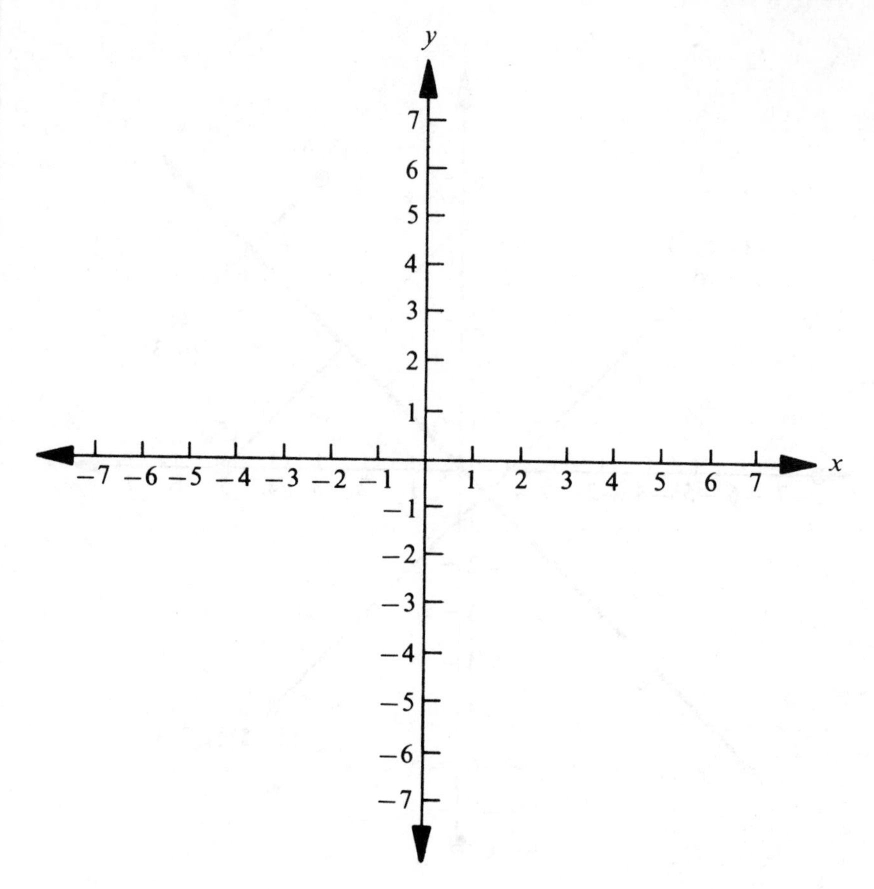

Using $f(x)$ and $f^{-1}(x)$ from the preceding frame, compute

(a) $f \circ f^{-1}(x) =$ ______________________ and

(b) $f^{-1} \circ f(x) =$ ______________________.

Thus showing that $f \circ f^{-1}(x) = f^{-1} \circ f(x) =$ ___.

ANSWERS TO PAGE 41

$\{(6,3),(-5,4),(0,5)\}$

bisector

$f^{-1} = \left\{(x,y) : y = \frac{x-6}{3}\right\}$

EXERCISES. 1.3

1. What relation exists between the function $f = \{(x,y): y = 3x - 2\}$ and the function $g = \{(u,v): v = 3u - 2\}$? ______ Why?

2. If the domain of the function $g = \{2,4,6,8,10\}$ and the domain of the function $\theta = \{x: x > 5\}$, then the domain of the function $h = g + \theta$ is ____________.

3. If $f = \{(x,y): y = 2x - 5\}$ and $g = \{(x,y): y = x^2\}$, then
   (a) $f + g =$ ____________
   (b) $-g =$ ____________
   (c) $g - f =$ ____________
   (d) $f \cdot g =$ ____________
   (e) $\frac{g}{f} =$ ____________ with the restriction that ____________.

4. If $g = \{(-4,6),(-2,3),(0,5)\}$ and $\theta = \{(-2,3),(2,4),(5,6)\}$, then the domain for the sum, difference, product, and quotient is the ______ of the domains of g and θ and
   (a) $g + \theta =$ ____________
   (b) $g - \theta =$ ____________
   (c) $g \cdot \theta =$ ____________
   (d) $\frac{g}{\theta} =$ ____________

5. If $f(x) = x^2 + 3$ and $g(x) = 2x$ define functions f and g in $\mathcal{R} \times \mathcal{R}$, find each of the following:
   (a) $f[g(2)] =$ ______ (b) $g[f(2)] =$ ______
   (c) $g[g(1)] =$ ______ (d) $f(f[g(x)]) =$ ______
   (e) $f[f(x)] =$ ____________

6. If $f(x) = x^3$ and $g(x) = 3x + 4$ define functions f and g, then $f \circ g = \{(x,y):$ ____________$\}$ and $g \circ f = \{(x,y):$ ____________$\}$.

7. Show that the composition of linear functions is associative.

8. Find $f^{-1}(x)$ if
   (a) $f(x) = x - 7$ ____________
   (b) $f(x) = 5x - 3$ ____________

(c) $f(x) = \dfrac{1}{x-2}$, $x \neq 2$, $f(x) \neq 0$ ______________________

(d) $f(x) = (x-3)^2$, $x \geq 3$ ______________________

9. If $f(x) = x^2$ and $g(x) = \sqrt{16 - x^2}$, find the domains and ranges of f, g, $f \circ g$, and $g \circ f$. ______________________

____

____

____

10. The graph illustrated is that of a function f. Sketch the graph of f^{-1} on the same coordinate system. *Hint:* "Rotate" the graph of f about the graph of $y = x$.

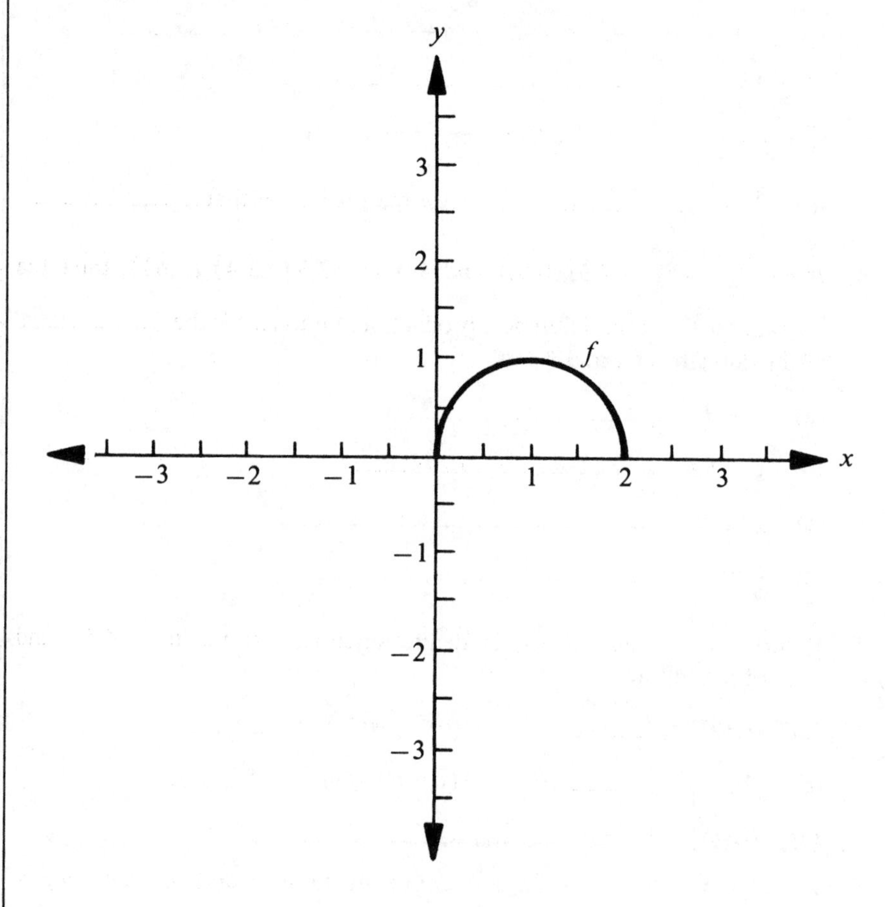

CHAPTER 1 REVIEW EXERCISES

True or False

1. In the composition of functions f, g, and h, we find that, in general, $f \circ g = g \circ f$, but $f \circ (g \circ h) \neq (f \circ g) \circ h$. ___ (1.3)

Complete the statement, answer the question, or perform the activity requested for each exercise.

2. If $T = \{x,y\}$ and $S = \{3,4\}$, then $T \times S =$ ______________ (1.1)
3. The best description of $\{(2,3),(-6,2),(2,-6)\}$ is: (a) a function; (b) a relation; (c) a set of points; (d) all of the previous descriptions. ___ (1.1)
4. The set consisting of all the first coordinates in a set of ordered pairs in a relation is called the ______________ of the relation. (1.1)
5. Specify the domain D and the range R for $f = \{(x,f(x)): f(x) = \sqrt{x}\}$. (1.1)

   $D =$ ______________ . $R =$ ______________ .
6. Which of the following formulas define a function? (a) $y = |x|$ (b) $y = 3x + 2$ (c) $y^2 = x$ (d) $x^2 + y^2 = 16$ ______ (1.1)
7. Which of the following are graphs of a function? ______ (1.2)

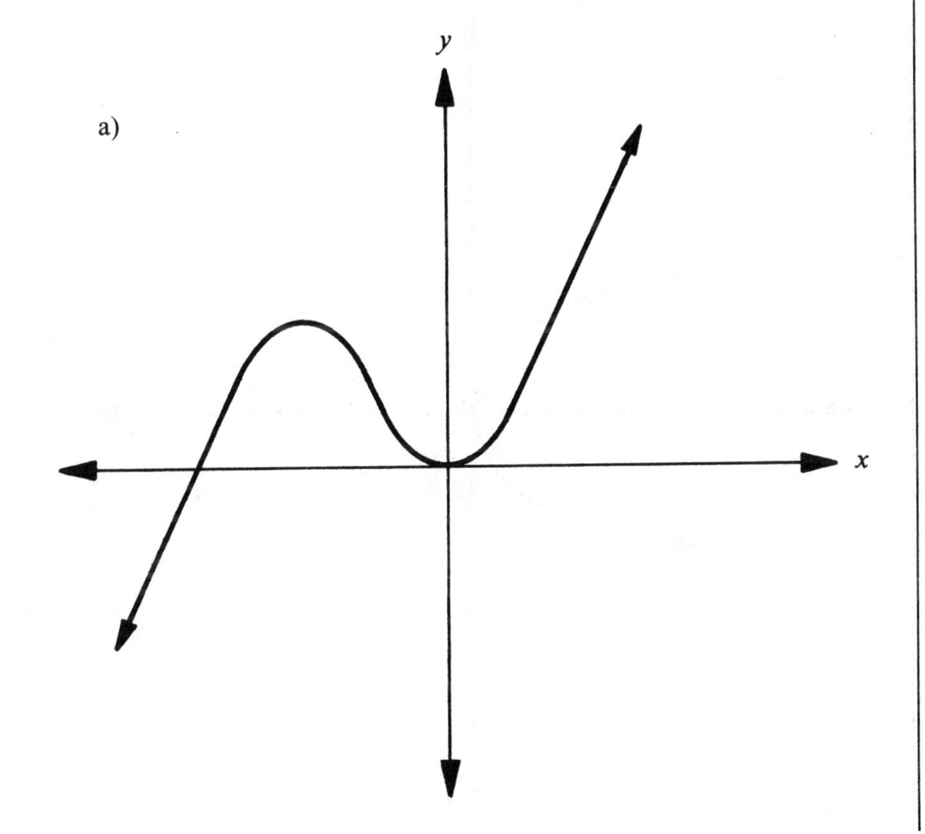

(1) $f = g$
Because f and g consist of the same set of ordered pairs.

(2) $\{6,8,10\}$

(3)(a) $\{(x,y) : y = x^2 + 2x - 5\}$

(b) $\{(x,y) : y = -x^2\}$

(c) $\{(x,y) : y = x^2 - 2x + 5\}$

(d) $\{(x,y) : y = 2x^3 - 5x^2\}$

(e) $\left\{(x,y) : y = \dfrac{x^2}{2x-5}\right\}$ $x \neq \dfrac{5}{2}$

(4) intersection

(a) $\{(-2,6)\}$

(b) $\{(-2,0)\}$

(c) $\{(-2,9)\}$

(d) $\{(-2,1)\}$

(5)(a) 19 (b) 14

(c) 4 (d) $(4x^2 + 3)^2 + 3$

(e) $(x^2 + 3)^2 + 3$

(6) $y = (3x + 4)^3$, $y = 3x^3 + 4$

(7) See Appendix.

(8)(a) $f^{-1}(x) = x + 7$

(b) $f^{-1}(x) = \dfrac{x+3}{5}$

ANSWERS TO PAGE 48

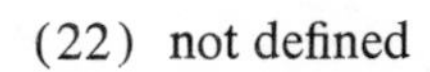

(22) not defined

$\frac{2}{3}$ $\qquad \frac{|a|}{a^2-1},\ a \neq \pm 1$

$\{x : x \geq 0,\ x \neq 1\}$

(23) image

formula

range

(24)

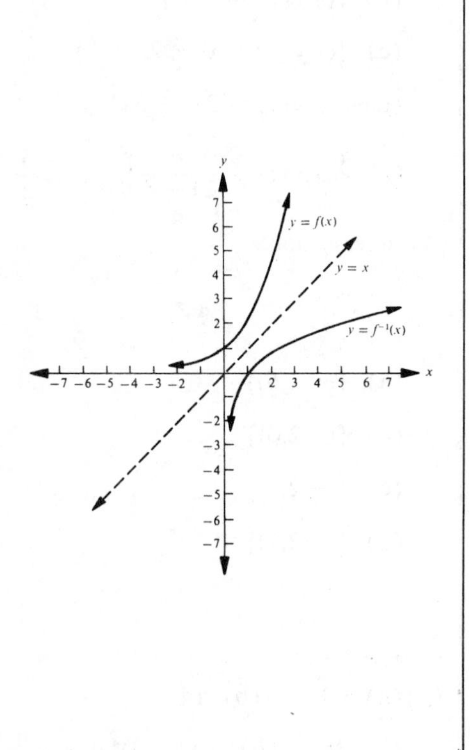

b)

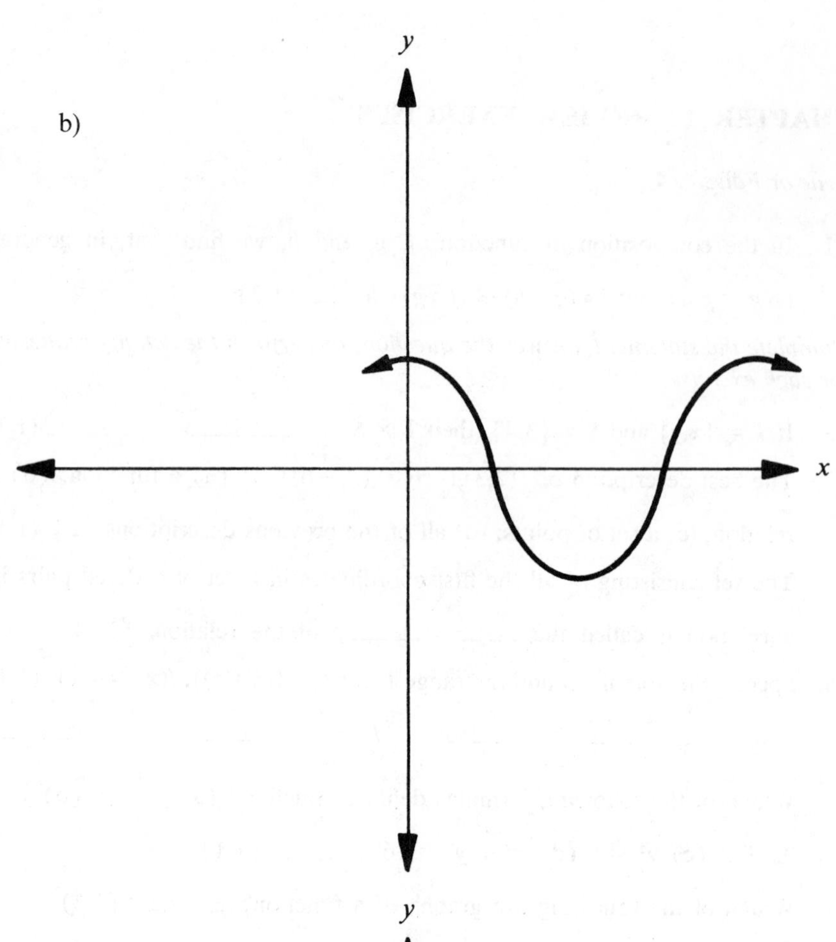

c)

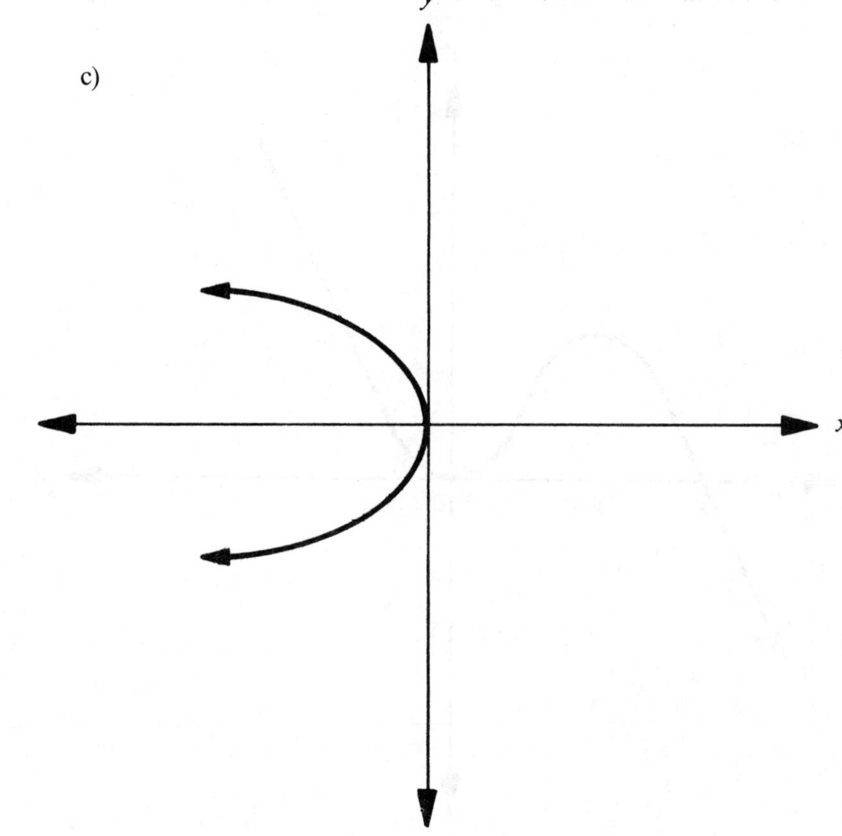

8. Find the slope of the graph of the linear function defined by $f(x) = 2x + 5$. ___ (1.2)

9. Find the slope of the graph of a linear function g, if $g(0) = 5$ and $g(-2) = 0$. ___ (1.2)

10. Find the set of real numbers in the domain of $f = \{(x, f(x)) : f(x) = \sqrt{x^2}\}$ for which $f(x) < 0$. ______________ (1.2)

11. Write the equation of the line containing the points with coordinates $(-3,1)$ and $(2,4)$. ______________. (1.2)

12. If f is a constant function and $f(-3) = 2$, then $f(2) =$ ___. (1.2)

13. If h is a linear function, $(25,30)\epsilon h$, and $(26,40)\epsilon h$, then $h(25.4) =$ ______________ (1.2)

14. If $g = \{(1,3),(2,7),(5,1),(-6,2),(0,8)\}$ and $h = \{(1,4),(3,6),(5,-4),(8,2)\}$, then the function $h + g =$ ______________, the function $-h =$ ______________, and the function $g \circ h =$ ______________. (1.3)

15. If $f = \{(2,4),(7,9)\}$, then

$f^{-1} =$ ______________ and

$\frac{1}{f} =$ ______________. (1.3)

16. If $h = \left\{(x,y) : y = \frac{1}{2}x - 3\right\}$, then $h^{-1} =$ ______________. (1.3)

17. If $f = \{(x,y) : y = x^2 + 2\}$ and $g = \{(x,y) : y = 4x - 1\}$, then

$f \circ g =$ ______________.(1.3)

18. If $f = \{(x,y) : y = 0.014x - 3.1415\}$ and $g = f^{-1}$, then $f[g(1.49)] =$ ______________. (1.3)

19. If $f = \{(u,v) : v = 3u - 4\}$, $g = \{(x,y) : y = 3x - 4\}$, and $h = \{(x,y) : y = 3x - 4\}$, and $x \geq 0$, then which of the following are true?

(a) $f = h$ (b) $f = g$ (c) $h \subset f$

(d) $f \subset h$ (e) none of the preceding are true. ______. (1.3)

20. If $(3,7)\epsilon f$ and $(3,3)\epsilon g$, then ______ $\epsilon f + g$, ______ $\epsilon f \circ g$ and ______ ϵf^{-1}. (1.3)

21. Which one of the following is a true statement? (1.2) (a) $\sqrt{-(2)^2} = 2$ (b) $\sqrt{-(2)^2} = -2$ (c) $\sqrt{-(2)^2} = \pm 2$ (d) neither a, b, nor c. ______

ANSWERS TO PAGE 45

F

(2) $\{(x,3),(x,4),(y,3),(y,4)\}$

(3) b

(4) domain

(5)
$D = \{x : x\epsilon\mathcal{R} \text{ and } x \geq 0\}$
$R = \{y : y\epsilon\mathcal{R} \text{ and } y \geq 0\}$

(6) a, b

(7) a, b

terminal

BA

22. If $f = \left\{(x,f(x)) \colon f(x) = \dfrac{\sqrt{x}}{x-1}\right\}$, then $f(-4) =$ ________________,
$f(4) =$ __, and $f(a^2) =$ ______ (note restriction), and the domain of f is ________________________. (1.2)

23. In the function $g = \{(x,g(x)) \colon g(x) = 2x\}$, $g(x)$ is called the ________ of x, $g(x) = 2x$ is called the defining ________, and $\{g(x) \colon g(x) \epsilon \mathcal{R}\}$ is called the ________ of g. (1.1)

24. The following graph corresponds to a function f. Sketch the graph of f^{-1} on the same coordinate axes. (1.3)

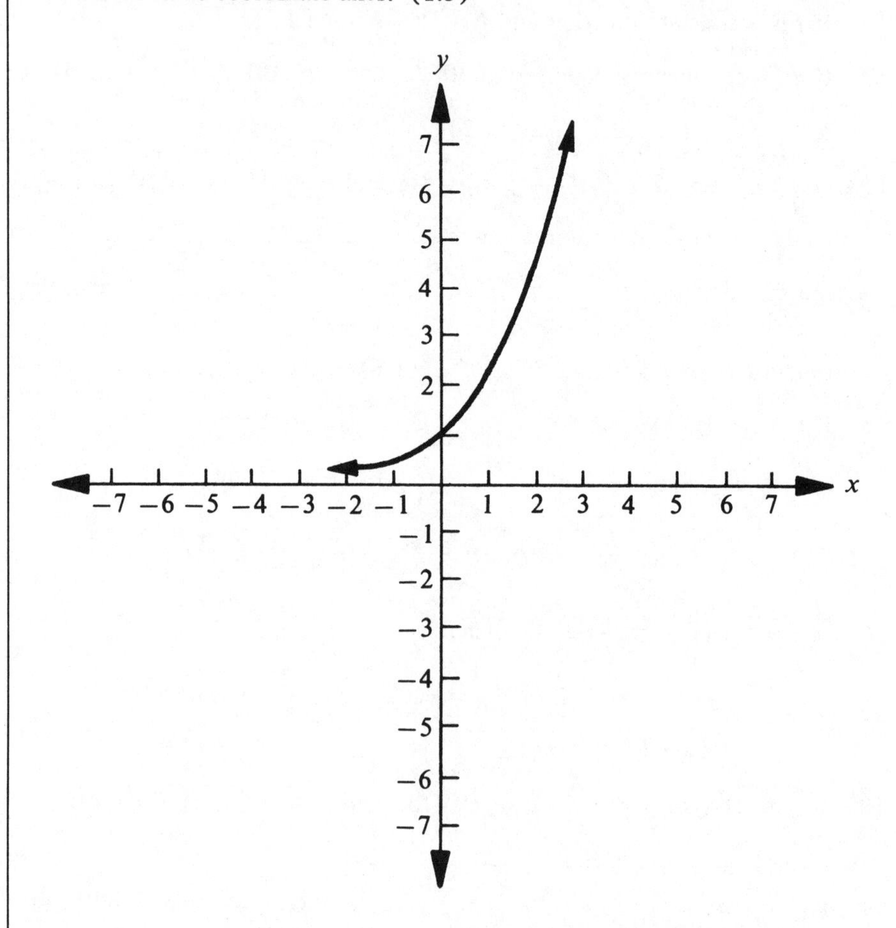

CHAPTER 2

Vectors

2.1. DISPLACEMENTS AND VECTORS

There exists a one-to-one correspondence between the set of points in a plane and the set of ordered pairs of numbers in ________. This correspondence enables us to apply algebra to the solution of geometric problems and geometry to algebraic problems. We often call an ordered pair of real numbers a ________. For instance, we can refer to the point (2,3), or the point (−6,7), and so on.

We can also make a correspondence between an ordered pair of real numbers and the "movement" from one point to another point in a plane.

DEFINITION:
The "movement" from one point to another point in a plane is called a **displacement.** The displacement *from point A to point B is denoted by* $\overrightarrow{AB}$. *A* is called the *initial point* and *B* is called the *terminal point* of $\overrightarrow{AB}$.

MOVE TO NEXT FRAME

Examples: Denote the following displacements by the appropriate symbol.

(a) From point *B* to point *A*. ______

(b) From point *P* to point *Q*. ______

(c) From point *Q* to point *P*. ______

(d) The displacement with an initial point *S* and terminal point *R*. ______

A displacement in a plane is determined by two points, one of which is designated its ________ point and the other its ________ point.

ANSWERS TO PAGE 47

(8) 2

(9) $\frac{5}{2}$

(10) ϕ

(11) $3x - 5y = -14$

(12) 2

(13) 34

(14) $\{(1,7),(5,-3)\}$

$\{(1,-4),(3,-6),(5,4),(8,-2)\}$

$\{(8,7)\}$

(15) $\{(4,2),(9,7)\}$

$\left\{\left(2,\frac{1}{4}\right)\left(7,\frac{1}{9}\right)\right\}$

(16) $\{(x,y) : y = 2x + 6\}$

(17) $\{(x,y) : y = 16x^2 - 8x + 3\}$

(18) 1.49

(19) b, c

(20) (3,10) (3,7)

(7,3)

(21) d

A displacement is illustrated with an "arrow" which describes the movement from the initial to the terminal point as in the adjacent coordinate system. The head of the arrow represents the ______________ point of the displacement. Thus the displacement illustrated is ______.

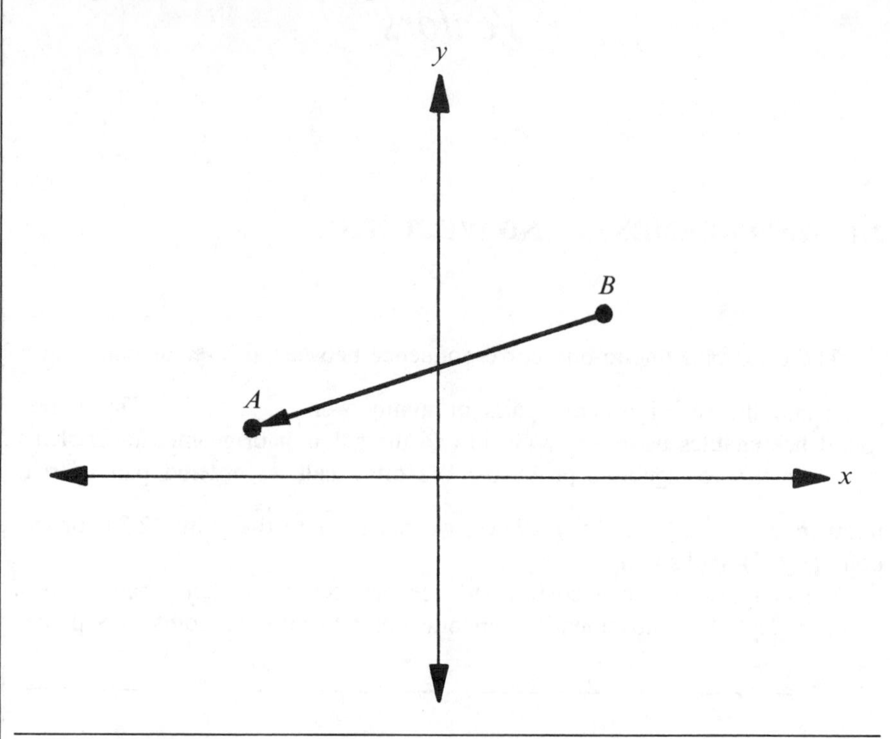

If A and B are any two points in the plane, an ordered pair of numbers may be made to correspond to the displacement AB. See the following figure.

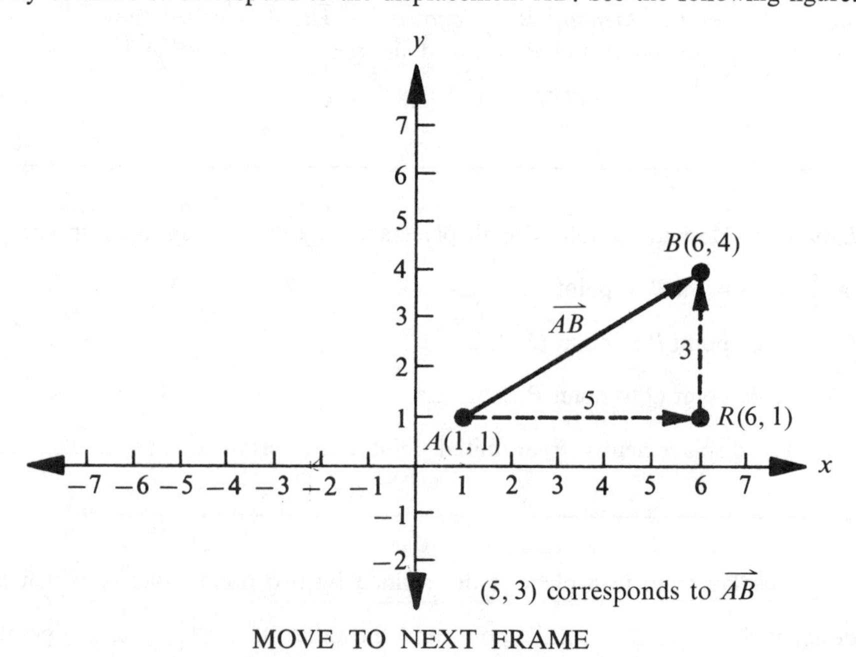

MOVE TO NEXT FRAME

ANSWERS TO PAGE 52

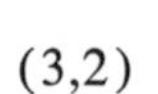

(3,2)

(0,−5)

(2,−3)

(3,2)

(−3,1)

(4,0)

(3,2)

---

equal

$a = c \quad b = d$

The displacement from A to B in the preceeding frame may be considered a displacement from A to R, thence from R to B. In this case, the displacement along the x axis $(x_R - x_A) = (6 - 1) = 5$, and the displacement along the y axis $(y_B - y_R) = (\_\_ - \_\_) = \_\_$. We use the numbers 5 and 3 to form the ordered pair ______ which corresponds to the displacement $\overrightarrow{AB}$. The first number of the ordered pair corresponds to a displacement parallel to the ________ and the second number to a displacement parallel to the ________ .

$\mathcal{R} \times \mathcal{R}$

point

DEFINITIONS:
The ordered pair (x,y) **corresponds to** the displacement $\overrightarrow{AB}$ if and only if $x = x_B - x_A$ and $y = y_B - y_A$, where x_B and x_A are the x coordinates of B and A, respectively, and y_B and y_A are the y coordinates of B and A, respectively.
An ordered pair of real numbers will be called a **vector.** Thus every displacement has a vector which corresponds to it.

MOVE TO NEXT FRAME

(a) BA

(b) PQ

(c) QP

(d) SR

Examples:

(a) If $A(3,-5)$ and $B(-7,2)$ are points in a coordinate plane, then the vector which corresponds to $\overrightarrow{AB}$ is ________________ .

(b) If $R(4,7)$ and $S(4,-3)$ are points in a coordinate plane, then the vector corresponding to $\overrightarrow{RS}$ is ________ and the vector corresponding to $\overrightarrow{SR}$ is ________ .

initial terminal

ANSWERS TO PAGE 54

ordered pair

A *B*

A

B

---

the origin

standard position

(5,2)

(−1,−6)

(−4,4)

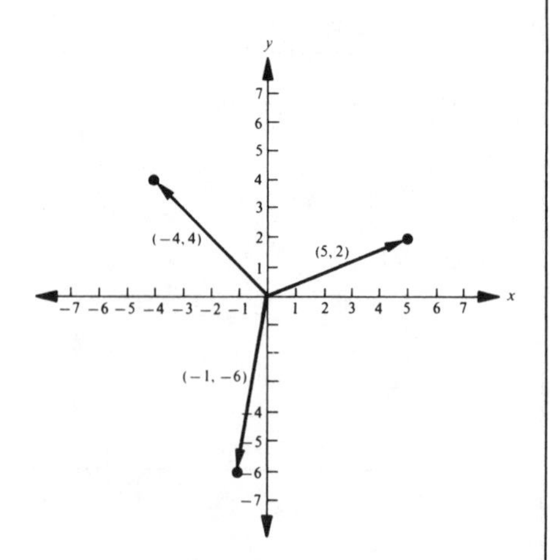

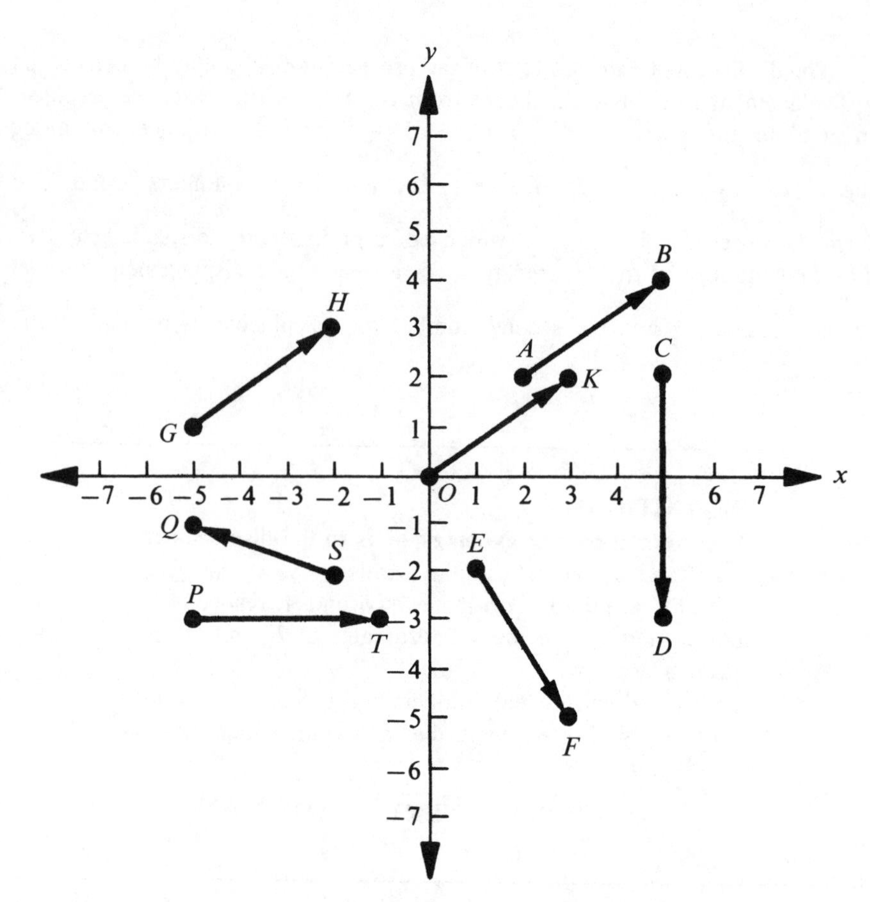

Some displacements are depicted in the preceding illustration. Find the ordered pair, or vector, corresponding to each displacement.

MOVE TO NEXT FRAME

Example: (2,−3) corresponds to $\overrightarrow{EF}$

______ corresponds to $\overrightarrow{AB}$

______ corresponds to $\overrightarrow{CD}$

______ corresponds to $\overrightarrow{EF}$

______ corresponds to $\overrightarrow{GH}$

______ corresponds to $\overrightarrow{SQ}$

______ corresponds to $\overrightarrow{PT}$

______ corresponds to $\overrightarrow{OK}$

Note that the vectors corresponding to $\overrightarrow{AB}$, $\overrightarrow{GH}$, and $\overrightarrow{OK}$ are ________. Recall that ordered pairs are equal if and only if they have the same first element and the same second element. Thus vector (a,b) equals vector (c,d) if and only if ________ and ________.

If vector $(3x - 2, y + 1)$ is equal to vector $(4,8)$, then $3x - 2 =$ __ and $y + 1 =$ __. Therefore $x =$ __ and $y =$ __.

If (x,y) is the vector which corresponds to $\overrightarrow{AB}$, we say that $\overrightarrow{AB}$ is a **representation** of vector (x,y).

There are many representations of a given vector (a,b) depending on which point is taken for the initial point. $\overrightarrow{PQ}$, $\overrightarrow{RS}$, $\overrightarrow{AB}$, $\overrightarrow{CD}$, and $\overrightarrow{OT}$ in the illustration all represent the vector ________. The representation having its initial point at the origin is ____ .

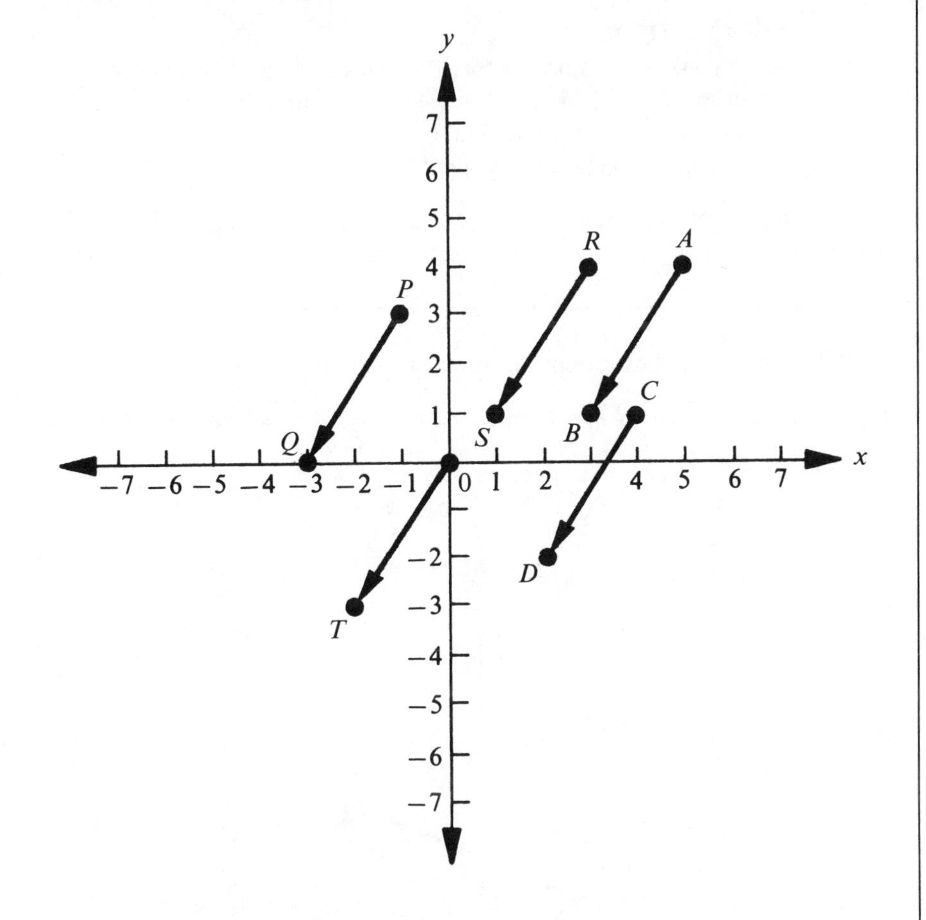

DEFINITION:
The **standard representation** of a vector is the representation having its initial point at the origin. We say that a vector representation is in **standard position** if its initial point is at the ________ .

MOVE TO NEXT FRAME

ANSWERS TO PAGE 51

$4 - 1 = 3$

$(5,3)$

x axis

y axis

(a) $(-7-3, 2-(-5)) = (-10,7)$

(b) $(0,-10)$

$(0,10)$

$y' = 3x' - 5$

$|y_B - y_A|$

A vector is a/an __________ __________ of real numbers.

Vectors will frequently be denoted by a letter having a single barbed arrow over it, such as $\vec{v}$ or $\vec{w}$.

If $\vec{v} = (x,y)$ is the vector which corresponds to $\overrightarrow{AB}$, then x is found by subtracting the x coordinate of point __ from the x coordinate of point __, and y is found by subtracting the y coordinate of point __ from the y coordinate of point __.

DEFINITION:
$\vec{0} = (0,0)$ is the **zero vector**. $\vec{0}$ corresponds to any displacement whose initial and terminal points coincide. The standard representation of $\vec{0}$ is the displacement whose initial point and terminal point is __________.

A vector representation is in ________________ if its initial point is at the origin.

Referring to the illustration, the vector represented by $\overrightarrow{DE}$ is ________, the vector represented by $\overrightarrow{EF}$ is __________, and the vector represented by $\overrightarrow{FD}$ is __________.

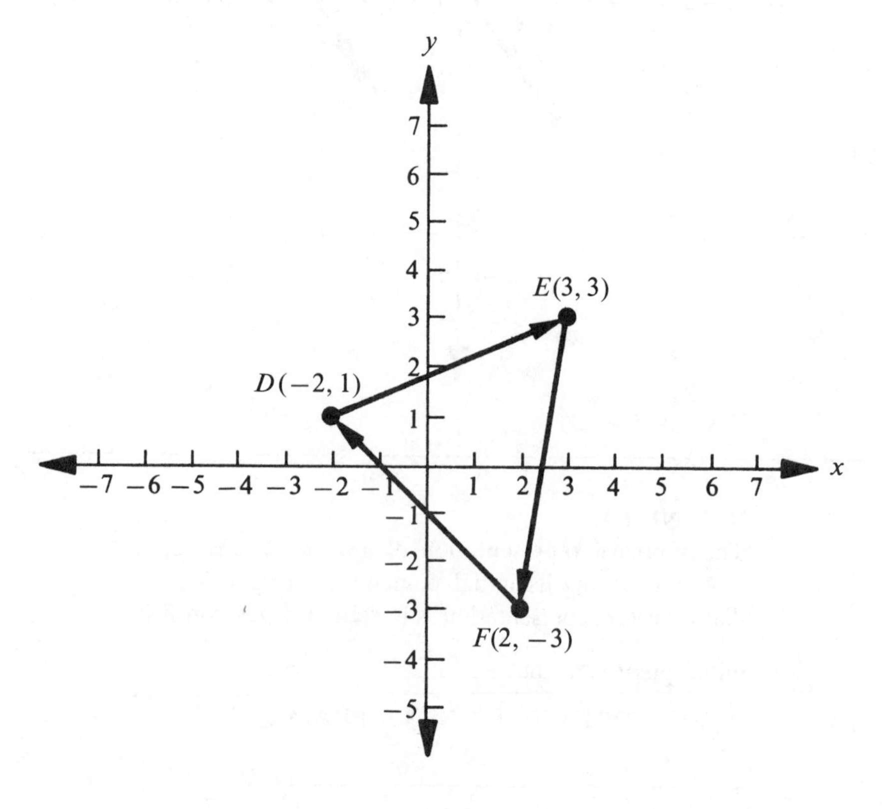

On the illustration, sketch the standard representation of the vectors corresponding to $\overrightarrow{DE}$, $\overrightarrow{EF}$, and $\overrightarrow{FD}$. Label each representation with the appropriate vector (ordered pair).

For each vector, which is an ordered pair of ______ ________,

there is/are ____________________ (how many?) representation(s) on the rectangular coordinate system, but there is ____________ standard representation.

Since there exists a one-to-one correspondence between $\mathcal{R} \times \mathcal{R}$ and the set of points in a plane, it follows there exists a one-to-one correspondence between ________ and the set of all standard representations of vectors.

The standard representation of a vector has its initial point at the ______ and its terminal point at some specified point in the plane.

If $\overrightarrow{AB}$ represents the vector $(-4,3)$, and $(1,2)$ are the coordinate of A, then the coordinates of B are ________. (*Hint:* Suppose (x,y) are the coordinates of B, then $x - 1 =$ ____ and $y - 2 =$ ___.)

Displacements are sometimes called **translations**.

What vector corresponds to the displacement which translates $P(4,3)$ into $Q(2,4)$? __________

If $T(a,b)$ is translated into S by a displacement whose vector is $(2,3)$, then the coordinates of S are ______________.

Let L be the line whose equation is $y = 3x - 2$. Suppose each point of L is translated by a displacement with corresponding vector $(2,3)$. Then the point on L whose coordinates are (x,y) is translated to the point whose coordinates are (x',y') if and only if $x' - x = 2$ and $y' - y =$ ___. Solving for x and y, we obtain $x =$ ________, and $y = y' - 3$. Since $y = 3x - 2$, it follows by substitution that $y' - 3 = 3(x' - 2) - 2$ or, simplifying, $y' =$ _____.

ANSWERS TO PAGE 53

4

8 2 7

$(-2,-3)$

$\overrightarrow{OT}$

---

origin

ANSWERS TO PAGE 58

displacement

norm

(a) 5

(b) 13

(c) 10

(d) $5a$

(a) T

(b) T

(c) T

(d) T

This is the equation of a line. Hence the line L is translated by the given displacement into the line L' whose equation is ____________.
The line L' can be described by the graph of $\{(x',y') : y' = 3x' - 5\}$ or $\{(x,y) : y = 3x - 5\}$.

Note: $\{(x',y') : y' = 3x' - 5\} = \{(x,y) : y = 3x - 5\}$ because they are the same set of ordered pairs.

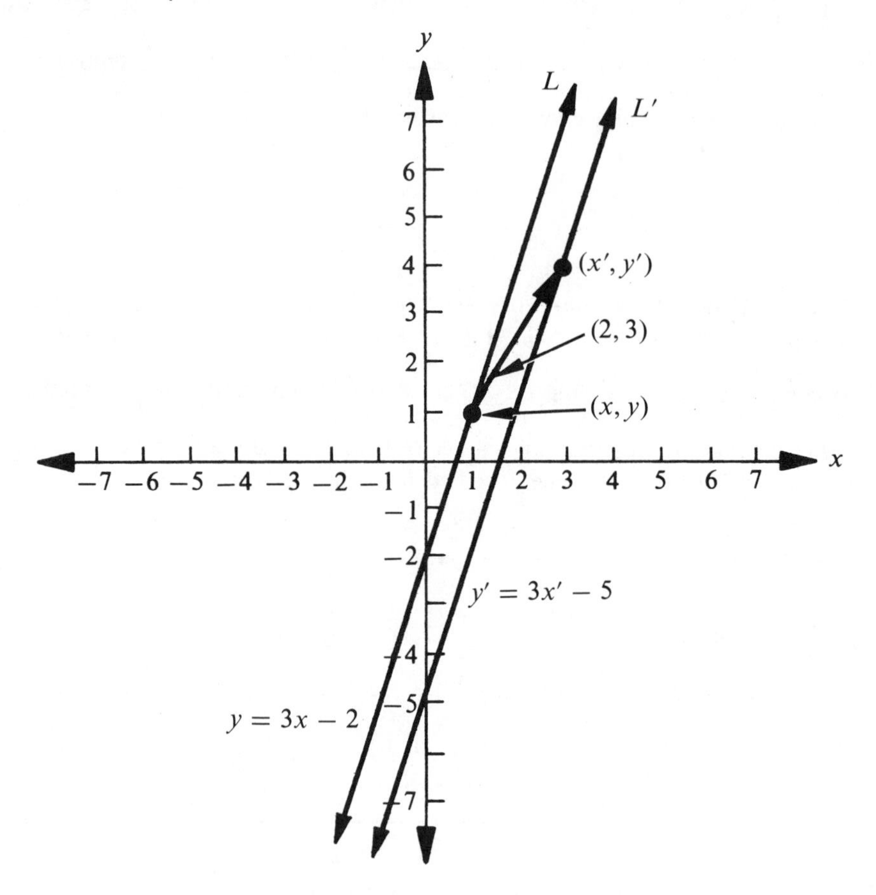

DEFINITION:
The **magnitude** of a displacement $\vec{AB}$, denoted $||\vec{AB}||$, is the distance between points A and B.

MOVE TO NEXT FRAME

If $\vec{AB}$ is a displacement parallel to the x axis, then $||\vec{AB}|| = |x_B - x_A|$.
If $\vec{AB}$ is a displacement parallel to the y axis, then $||\vec{AB}|| =$ __________.

For $T(-6,2)$, $R(-6, -3)$, and $S(3, -3)$ (see the figure), $||\overrightarrow{RS}|| = |3 - (-6)| = |9| = 9$, and $||\overrightarrow{TR}|| =$ ___. Also, by the Pythagorean Theorem, $||\overrightarrow{TS}||^2 = ||\overrightarrow{RS}||^2 + ||\overrightarrow{TR}||^2 =$ ______, and thus $||\overrightarrow{TS}|| =$ ____________.

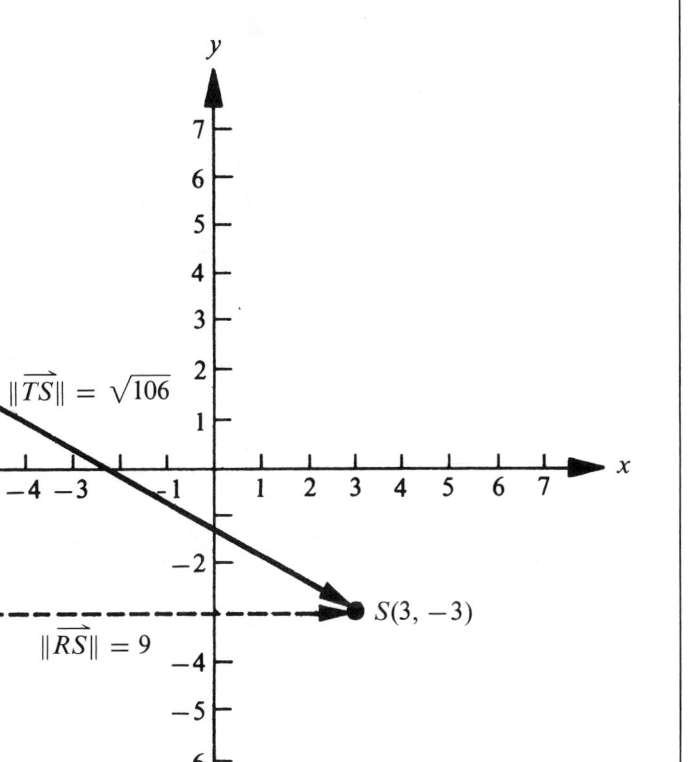

DEFINITION:
The **norm** or **length of a vector** $\vec{v} = (x,y)$, denoted $||\vec{v}||$, is $\sqrt{x^2 + y^2}$. In the preceding frame, the vector corresponding to $\overrightarrow{TS}$ is $\vec{v} =$ __________. In this case $||\vec{v}|| = \sqrt{9^2 + (-5)^2} = \sqrt{106}$. Note that $||\overrightarrow{TS}|| = ||\vec{v}||$, i.e., the magnitude of a displacement is equal to the norm, or length, of the corresponding vector.

In general, if T has coordinates (x_T,y_T) and S has coordinates (x_S,y_S), then $v = (x_S - x_T, y_S - y_T)$ is the vector corresponding to TS, and using the Pythagorean Theorem we have

$$\begin{aligned} ||\overrightarrow{TS}|| &= \sqrt{||\overrightarrow{RS}||^2 + ||\overrightarrow{TR}||^2} \\ &= \sqrt{(x_S - x_T)^2 + (y_S - y_T)^2} \\ &= ||\vec{v}||. \end{aligned}$$

ANSWERS TO PAGE 55

---

real numbers

an infinite number of

exactly one

$\mathcal{R} \times \mathcal{R}$

origin

$(-3,5)$

$-4 \quad 3$

$(-2,1)$

$(a + 2, b + 3)$

3

$x' - 2$

$3x' - 5$

Hence the magnitude of a ______________ is equal to the ________ of its corresponding vector.

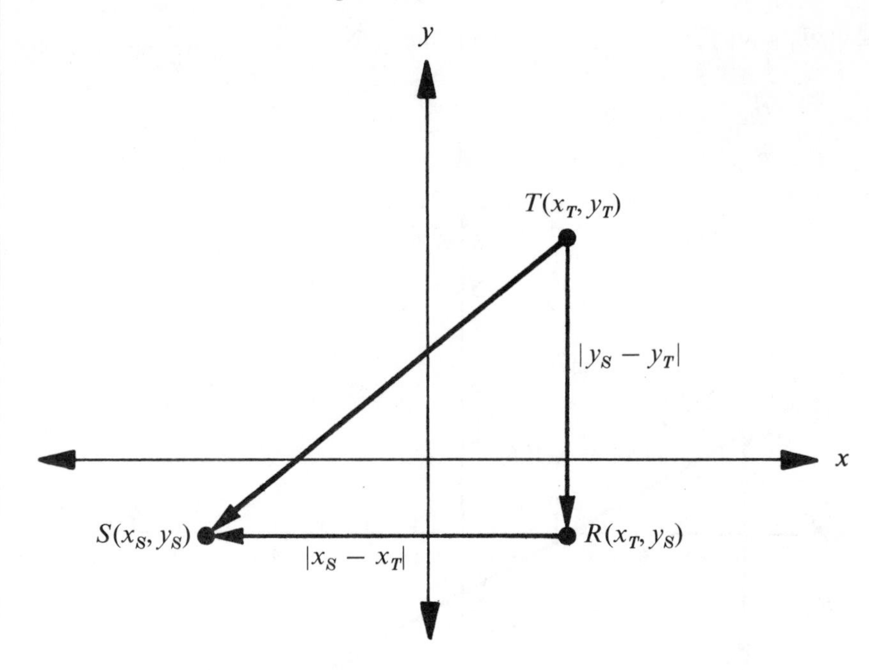

Examples: Find the norm of $\vec{w}$ for each of the following:

(a) $\vec{w} = (4,3)$; $\|\vec{w}\| =$ ______

(b) $\vec{w} = (5,-12)$; $\|\vec{w}\| =$ ______

(c) $\vec{w} = (5,5\sqrt{3})$; $\|\vec{w}\| =$ ______

(d) $\vec{w} = (3a,4a)$; $\|\vec{w}\| =$ ______

(4,1)

(2,6) (6,7)

True or False:

(a) If $\vec{v} \in \mathcal{R} \times \mathcal{R}$, then $\|\vec{v}\| \in \mathcal{R}$. __

(b) If $\vec{v} \in \mathcal{R} \times \mathcal{R}$, then $\|\vec{v}\| \geq 0$. __

(c) If $\vec{v} \in \mathcal{R} \times \mathcal{R}$ and $\|\vec{v}\| = 0$, then $\|\vec{v}\| = (0,0)$. __

(d) If $\vec{v} = (0,0)$, then $\|\vec{v}\| = 0$.

The statements in the preceding frame are theorems. They are logical consequences of the definition of the norm of a vector and the properties of $\mathcal{R}$, the set of real numbers. Their proofs are left for exercises.

MOVE TO NEXT FRAME

5

106 $\sqrt{106}$

EXERCISES. 2.1

1. In the displacement $\overrightarrow{PT}$, P is the ______ point and T is the ______ point.
2. The vector $(-3,1)$ corresponds to $\overrightarrow{RS}$. Find the coordinates of S when when the coordinates of R are:

   (a) $(2,3)$ ______ (b) $(-4,5)$ ______

   (c) $(0,0)$ ______ (d) $(3,-6)$ ______

   (e) (m,n) ______ (f) $(3,-1)$ ______
3. Find the values of x and y for which each of the following is true.

   (a) $(x-1,2y) = (3,6)$ ______

   (b) $(x^2-5,y-3) = (11,2)$ ______
4. Find the vector represented by $\overrightarrow{AB}$, if the coordinates of A and B, respectively, are as follows:

   (a) $(7,6);(2,3)$ ______ (b) $(1,1);(-3,2)$ ______

   (c) $(0,0);(4,-5)$ ______ (d) $(0,3);(0,-2)$ ______

   (e) $(x,y);(-1,-3)$ ______ (f) $(3,4);(3,4)$ ______
5. Let L be the line with equation $y = 2x + 4$. If each point $P(x,y)$ of L is translated into a corresponding point $Q(x',y')$ by a displacement whose vector is $(-1,3)$, then L is translated into the line, which is the graph of

   ______ .
6. Find the norm of each of the following vectors:

   (a) $(-6,8)$ ______ (b) $(9,-40)$ ______

   (c) $(15,-8)$ ______ (d) $(1,2)$ ______

   (e) $\left(\frac{\sqrt{2}}{2}, \frac{\sqrt{2}}{2}\right)$ ______ (f) $(-2,-2\sqrt{3})$ ______
7. Complete the following proof. If $\vec{v} \in \mathcal{R} \times \mathcal{R}$, then $\|\vec{v}\| \in \mathcal{R}$.

   Proof:
   (a) If $\vec{v} \in \mathcal{R} \times \mathcal{R}$, then $\vec{v} = (x,y)$ with $x \in \mathcal{R}$ and $y \in \mathcal{R}$ because of the definition of ______ .

   (b) By the ______ properties of $\mathcal{R}$, $x^2 + y^2 \in \mathcal{R}$.

   (c) Also $x^2 + y^2$ is a nonnegative real number, and, hence, $\|\vec{v}\| = \sqrt{x^2 + y^2} \in \mathcal{R}$ by the definition of ______.
8. Prove that if $\vec{v} \in \mathcal{R} \times \mathcal{R}$, then $\|\vec{v}\| = 0$ if and only if $\vec{v} = (0,0)$.

$(9,-5)$

$(u,v) + (x,y) = (x,y)$

---

additive

identity closure

---

yes

yes

2.2. VECTOR ADDITION

A displacement from $A(-2,3)$ to $B(2,4)$ and thence from B to $C(4,10)$ is indicated in the following illustration.

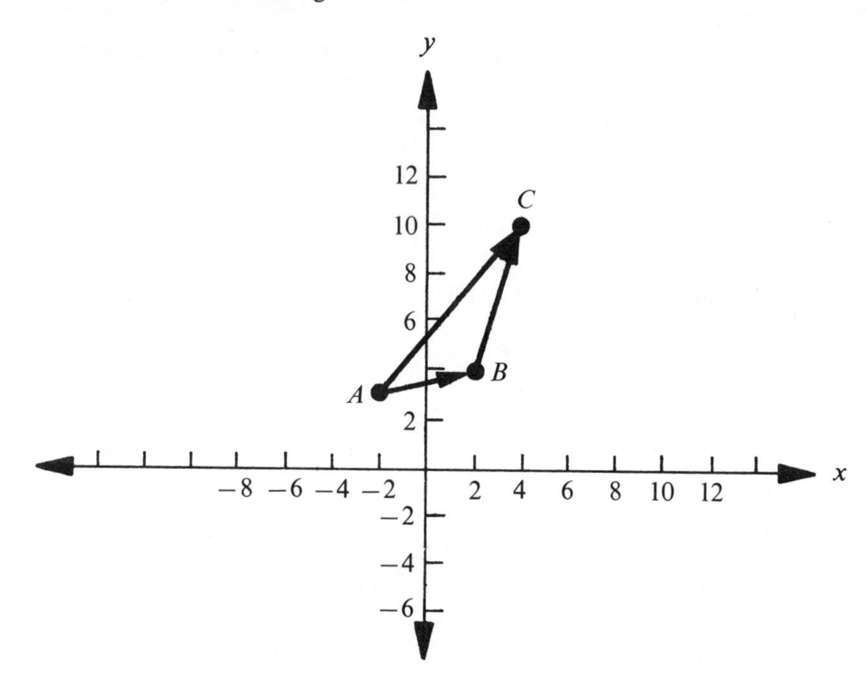

The net effect of these two displacements is the displacement from A to C. The vector corresponding to $\overrightarrow{AB}$ is ______ . The vector corresponding to $\overrightarrow{BC}$ is ______ . The vector corresponding to $\overrightarrow{AC}$ is ______ .

The vector $(6,7)$ has coordinates that are the sums of the corresponding coordinates in $(4,1)$ and $(2,6)$. This and other such examples motivate the following definition of a vector sum.

DEFINITION OF VECTOR ADDITION:
The **vector sum** or **resultant** of two vectors (x,y) and (r,s) in $\mathcal{R} \times \mathcal{R}$ is the vector $(x + r, y + s)$, i.e., $(x,y) + (r,s) = (x + r, y + s)$.

MOVE TO NEXT FRAME

The properties of vector addition in $\mathcal{R} \times \mathcal{R}$ are logical consequences of the properties of addition in $\mathcal{R}$. You may refer to the properties of the field of real numbers $\mathcal{R}$ in the appendix.

MOVE TO NEXT FRAME

A given set, such as a set of numbers or a set of vectors, is said to be *closed* under a specified operation if and only if the result of that operation is exactly one element of the given set.

If $\vec{r}$ and $\vec{s}$ are vectors in $\mathcal{R} \times \mathcal{R}$, then there is exactly one vector in $\mathcal{R} \times \mathcal{R}$ which is their sum. This is a statement of the ______ property of vector addition.

We can let $\vec{r} = (r_1,r_2)$ and $\vec{s} = (s_1,s_2)$ where r_1, r_2, s_1, and s_2 are ______ numbers since vectors are ordered pairs of real numbers.

The proof of **closure** is as follows.

(a) $\vec{r} + \vec{s} = (r_1,r_2) + (s_1,s_2) = \big((r_1 + s_1),(r_2 + s_2)\big)$ by the definition of ______ ______.

(b) $\vec{u} = (r_1 + s_1)$ and $\vec{v} = (r_2 + s_2)$ are unique real numbers. Why? ______ ______ ______.

Thus $\vec{r} + \vec{s} = (u,v) = (r_1 + s_1),(r_2 + s_2)$.

(c) If there were some other sum $\vec{r} + \vec{s} = (a,b)$, then $(a,b) = (u,v)$, $a = u$, and $b = v$ by substitution and the property of ______ of vectors.

(d) Therefore, there is exactly one sum $\big((r_1 + s_1),(r_2 + s_2)\big) = r + s \in \mathcal{R} \times \mathcal{R}$, and $\mathcal{R} \times \mathcal{R}$ is said to be ______ under vector addition.

$\mathcal{R} \times \mathcal{R}$ contains exactly one **identity element** for vector addition. This can be established as follows:

(a) Since $0 \in \mathcal{R}$, $(0,0) \in \mathcal{R} \times \mathcal{R}$ by ______

(b) Let (x,y) be any vector in $\mathcal{R} \times \mathcal{R}$ and add it to $(0,0)$.

$$(0,0) + (x,y) = (0 + x, 0 + y)$$

by ______.

(c) $(0 + x, 0 + y) = (x,y)$ because of ______ ______.

(d) It is also the case that $(x,y) + (0,0) = (x + 0, y + 0) = (x,y)$ for the same reasons as (b) and (c).

$$\therefore (0,0) + (x,y) = (x,y) + (0,0) = (x,y).$$

Thus $(0,0)$ is an identity element for vector addition.

ANSWERS TO PAGE 59

(1) initial

terminal

(2) (a) $(-1,4)$ (b) $(-7,6)$

(c) $(-3,1)$ (d) $(0,-5)$

(e) $(m-3,n+1)$ (f) $(0,0)$

(3) (a) $(x,y) = (4,3)$

(b) $(x,y) = (4,5)$ or $(-4,5)$

(4) (a) $(-5,-3)$ (b) $(-4,1)$

(c) $(4,-5)$ (d) $(0,-5)$

(e) $(-1-x, -3-y)$ (f) $(0,0)$

(5) $\{(x',y'):y' = 2x' + 9\}$ or $\{(x,y) : y = 2x + 9\}$

(6) (a) 10 (b) 41

(c) 17 (d) $\sqrt{5}$

(e) 1 (f) 4

(7) (a) Cartesian product

(b) closure

(c) $\sqrt{\ }$

(8) See Appendix.

ANSWERS TO PAGE 64

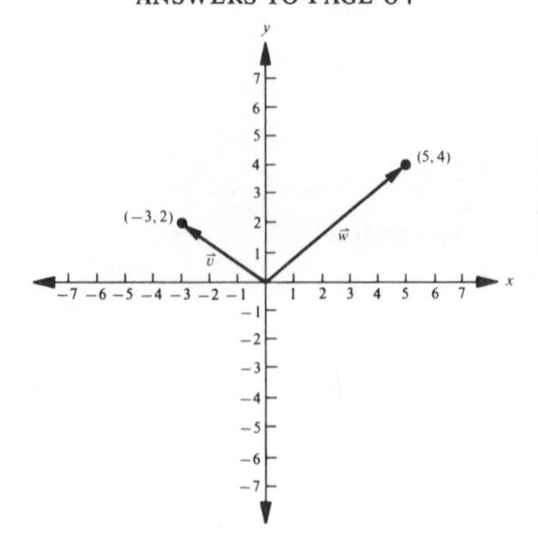

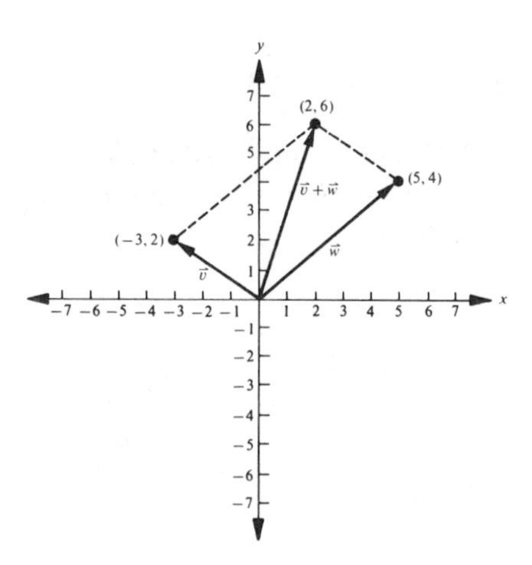

(2,6)

See the illustration.

(7,−2)

See the illustration.

(e) But is (0,0) unique?
Suppose it isn't, then there exists some other vector (u,v) such that
____________________, i.e., $u + x = x$, and $v + y = y$.
But again, the only real number u and the only real number v for which this is true is the real number $u = v = 0$. Hence, there is only one identity for vector addition, namely (0,0). We will call (0,0) the zero vector and denote it by 0.

The two preceding frames establish the existence of the __________ __________ vector in $\mathcal{R} \times \mathcal{R}$ and the property of __________ of vector addition. Vector addition in $\mathcal{R} \times \mathcal{R}$ is **associative** and **commutative**. Also every vector has an **additive inverse**. The proofs of these properties will be left as exercises.

The next frame contains a list of the properties of vector addition in $\mathcal{R} \times \mathcal{R}$.

Properties of Vector Addition:

(1) **Closure:** If $\vec{r} \epsilon \mathcal{R} \times \mathcal{R}$ and $\vec{s} \epsilon \mathcal{R} \times \mathcal{R}$ then there is *exactly one* element $\vec{r} + \vec{s}$ in $\mathcal{R} \times \mathcal{R}$.

(2) **Associative:** If $\vec{r}, \vec{s}$, and $\vec{t}$ are in $\mathcal{R} \times \mathcal{R}$, then $\vec{r} + (\vec{s} + \vec{t}) = (\vec{r} + \vec{s}) + \vec{t}$.

(3) **Identity:** There exists *exactly one* vector $\vec{0} \epsilon \mathcal{R} \times \mathcal{R}$ such that for every $\vec{r} \epsilon \mathcal{R} \times \mathcal{R}$, $\vec{0} + \vec{r} = \vec{r} + \vec{0} = \vec{r}$.

(4) **Inverse:** If $\vec{r} \epsilon \mathcal{R} \times \mathcal{R}$, then there exists *exactly one vector*, $-\vec{r}$, such that $\vec{r} + (-\vec{r}) = (-\vec{r}) + \vec{r} = \vec{0}$.

(5) **Commutative:** For every $\vec{r}$ and $\vec{s}$ in $\mathcal{R} \times \mathcal{R}$, $\vec{r} + \vec{s} = \vec{s} + \vec{r}$.

MOVE TO NEXT FRAME

DEFINITION:
A **group** is a set of elements on which an operation is defined that is **closed** and **associative**, has an **identity**, and in which all elements have **inverses**. If the operation is also **commutative**, the group is said to be a commutative or **Abelian group.**

MOVE TO NEXT FRAME

Is $\mathcal{R} \times \mathcal{R}$ a group under vector addition? ________ Is it also a commutative group? ________

A displacement is represented by sketching an arrow whose tail is the

____________ point and whose head is the ____________ point of the displacement. Since two points determine a line segment, we may associate a displacement with a "directed" line segment. One endpoint of this directed line segment is designated the initial point and the other endpoint the terminal point of the segment. Such a line segment is called a **geometric vector.**

DEFINITIONS:
A **geometric vector** is a line segment, one endpoint of which is designated its **initial point** and the other endpoint its **terminal point**. A **standard geometric vector** is a geometric vector whose initial point is the origin.

MOVE TO NEXT FRAME

Given a displacement, there is exactly one geometric vector whose initial and terminal points are, respectively, the initial and terminal points of the displacement. Conversely, given a geometric vector, there is exactly one displacement whose initial and terminal points are, respectively, the initial and terminal points of the geometric vector. Hence, there is a ______ - ____ - ______ correspondence between geometric vectors and displacements. Thus we may identify the displacement $\vec{AB}$ with the geometric vector which has initial point __ and terminal point __. This geometric vector is also designated $\vec{AB}$ and, in a sketch, is represented by an arrow originating at A and terminating at B.

The vector $\vec{v}$ *corresponds to* the geometric vector $\vec{AB}$ if and only if $\vec{v}$ corresponds to displacement $\vec{AB}$ and, similarly, the geometric vector $\vec{AB}$ represents $\vec{v}$ if and only if the displacement $\vec{AB}$ represents $\vec{v}$. The *norm* of geometric vector $\vec{AB}$, denoted $||\vec{AB}||$, is the norm of the vector corresponding to $\vec{AB}$. Thus the norm of the geometric vector $\vec{AB}$ is the same as the magnitude of the displacement $\vec{AB}$.

MOVE TO NEXT FRAME

ANSWERS TO PAGE 61

closure

---

real

vector

addition

$\mathcal{R}$ is closed under addition. (See properties of real numbers in appendix.)

equality

closed

---

definition of $\mathcal{R} \times \mathcal{R}$

definition of vector addition

additive identity property of $0 \in \mathcal{R}$

Sketch, on the following coordinate system, the standard geometric vectors which represent $\vec{v} = (-3,2)$ and $\vec{w} = (5,4)$.

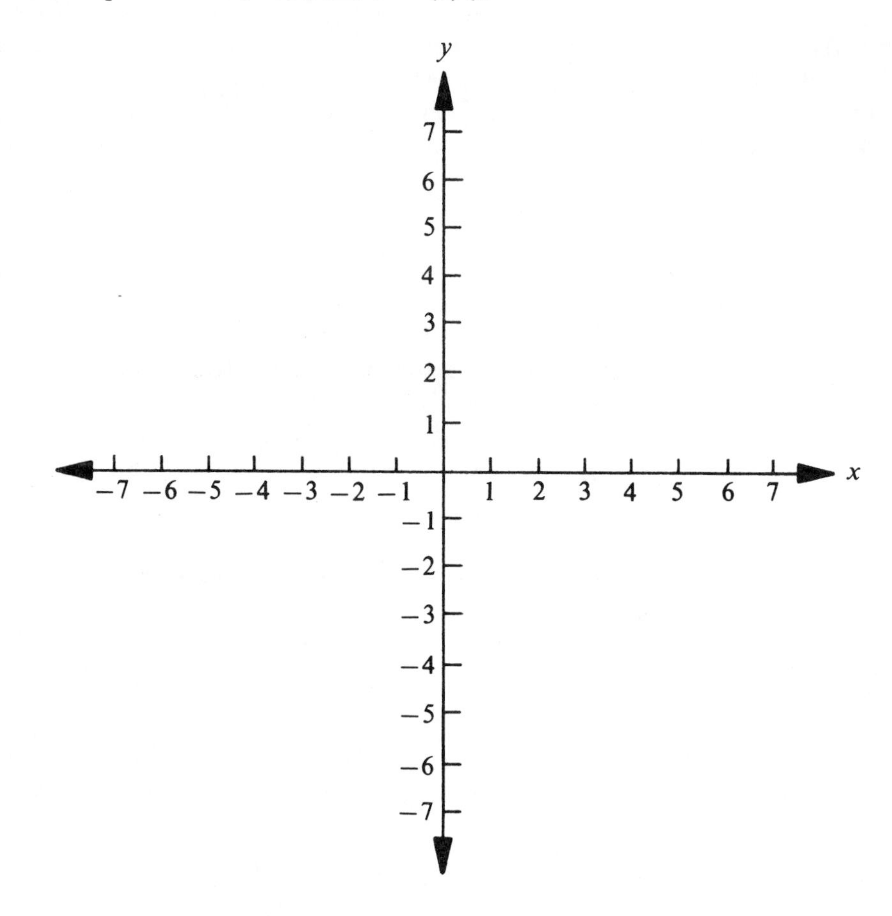

$(x_2 - x_1, y_2 - y_1)$

$||\vec{r}||$

$||\vec{s}||$ $||\vec{r}+\vec{s}||$

The sum, $\vec{v} + \vec{w}$, of the vectors in the preceeding frame is ________ .

On the same coordinate system on which you have drawn $\vec{v}$ and $\vec{w}$, sketch the standard geometric vector which represents $\vec{v} + \vec{w}$. Do you see that the standard geometric vector representing $\vec{v} + \vec{w}$ is the diagonal of the parallelogram having the standard geometric vectors representing $\vec{v}$ and $\vec{w}$ as two of its sides? This can be proved.

$(-4,-2)$ $(0,-5)$

$2\sqrt{5}$ 5

This resultant of the two vectors (3,1) and (4, −3) is their sum ________ .

To show that the sum of these two vectors is a vector corresponding to the diagonal of the parallelogram, consider the original vectors, (3,1) and (4, −3), the origin (0,0), and the resultant (7, −2), as coordinates of four points on the coordinate system. These points determine the vertices of a quadrilateral. We can then show the opposite sides of this quadrilateral have the same slope and hence are parallel. See the illustration opposite and calculate the slopes as indicated.

greater

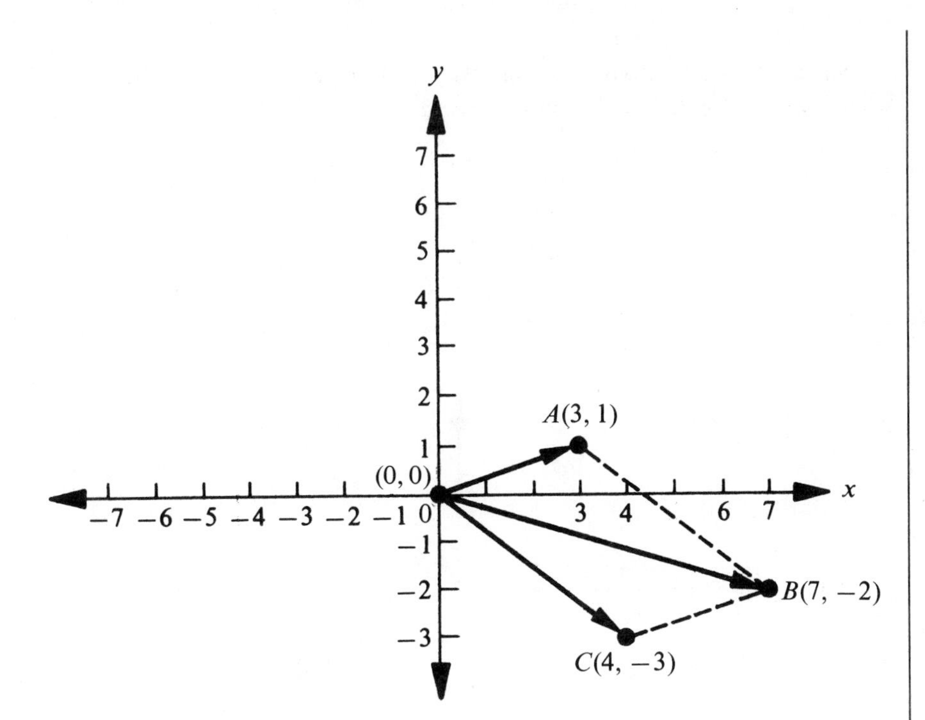

(a) Slope of $\overrightarrow{AB}$ = ______

(b) Slope of $\overrightarrow{OC}$ = ______

(c) Slop of $\overrightarrow{OA}$ = ______

(d) Slope of $\overrightarrow{CB}$ = ______

initial terminal

one-to-one

A B

The preceding frame illustrates the **parallelogram law of vectors.**

MOVE TO NEXT FRAME

THE PARALLELOGRAM LAW OF VECTORS:
If $\vec{v}_1 = (x_1,y_1)$ and $\vec{v}_2 = (x_2,y_2)$, then

$$(0,0),(x_1,y_1),(x_2,y_2),$$

and the resultant or sum

$$\vec{v}_1 + \vec{v}_2 = (x_1 + x_2, y_1 + y_2)$$

are either collinear or are vertices of a parallelogram. In the latter case, the standard geometric vector corresponding to the resultant is a diagonal of the parallelogram. (Proof is left as an exercise.)

MOVE TO NEXT FRAME

ANSWERS TO PAGE 68

$r_1^2s_2^2 - 2r_1s_2r_2s_1 + r_2^2s_1^2$

$(r_1s_2 - r_2s_1)$

---

5 13

(9,9) $9\sqrt{2}$

---

additive inverse

$(-2,4)$

$(-x,-y)$

Given three noncollinear points, $S(x_1,y_1)$, $R(x_2,y_2)$, and $T(x_3,y_3)$, let $\vec{r}$, $\vec{s}$, and $\vec{t}$ be the vectors corresponding to $\overrightarrow{ST}$, $\overrightarrow{TR}$, and $\overrightarrow{SR}$, respectively. Then

$$\vec{r} = (x_3 - x_1, y_3 - y_1)$$

$$\vec{s} = (x_2 - x_3, y_2 - y_3)$$

$$\vec{t} = (\_\_\_\_\_\_\_\_\_\_\_\_\_\_\_\_).$$

Thus, $\vec{r} + \vec{s} = (x_3 - x_1 + x_2 - x_3, y_3 - y_1 + y_2 - y_3) = \vec{t}$.

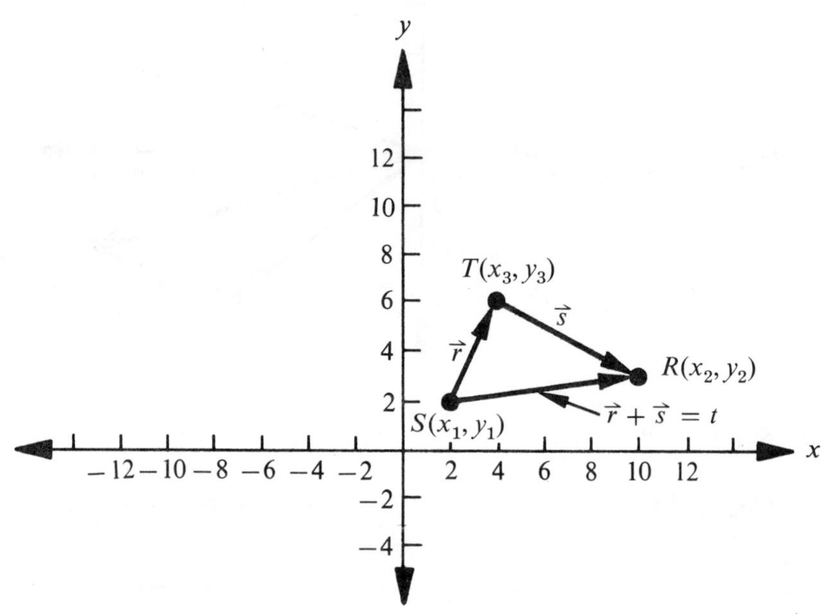

The lengths of the sides of ΔSRT in this figure are the norms of the corresponding vectors. Hence the lengths of the sides of ΔSRT are ________, ________, and ________.

Find the lengths of the sides of the triangle having the points $A(3,6)$, $B(7,3)$, and $C(3,1)$ as vertices.

Let $\vec{c}$ and $\vec{a}$ correspond to $\overrightarrow{AB}$ and $\overrightarrow{BC}$, respectively, then $\vec{c} = (4,-3)$, $\vec{a} =$ __________, and $\vec{c} + \vec{a} =$ __________. Hence the lengths of the sides of the triangle are $\|\overrightarrow{AB}\| = \|\vec{c}\| = \sqrt{4^2+(-3)^2} = 5$, $\|\overrightarrow{BC}\| = \|\vec{a}\| =$ ______ and $\|\overrightarrow{AC}\| = \|\vec{c} + \vec{a}\| =$ ___.

In geometry you proved the **triangle inequality** theorem, which states that the sum of the lengths of two sides of a triangle is __________ (greater/less) than the length of the third side. This theorem may be stated in terms of vectors.

Triangle Inequality:
If $\vec{r}$ and $\vec{s}$ are vectors in $\mathcal{R} \times \mathcal{R}$, then $\|\vec{r}\| + \|\vec{s}\| \geq \|\vec{r} + \vec{s}\|$. See illustration.

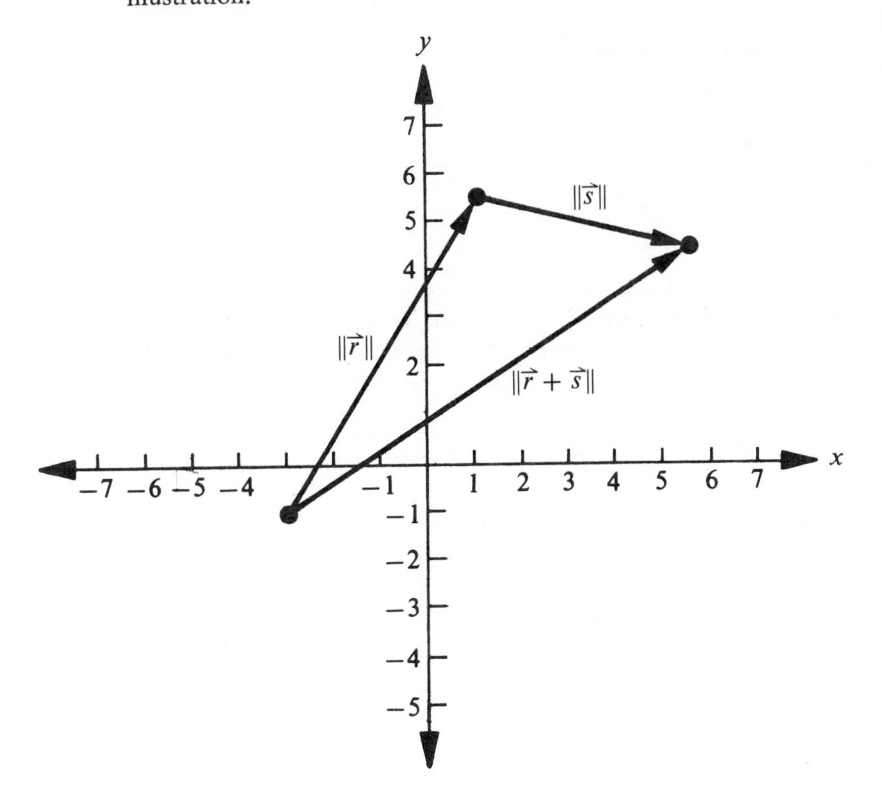

$\frac{-3}{4}$ $\frac{-3}{4}$

$\frac{1}{3}$ $\frac{1}{3}$

Proof: First, recall that if $a \geq 0$ and $b \geq 0$, then $a \geq b$ if and only if $a^2 \geq b^2$. Hence, since norms are nonnegative, we may show that $\|\vec{r}\| + \|\vec{s}\| \geq \|\vec{r} + \vec{s}\|$ by showing that

$$(\|\vec{r}\| + \|\vec{s}\|)^2 \geq (\|\vec{r} + \vec{s}\|)^2.$$

Let $\vec{r} = (r_1, r_2)$ and $\vec{s} = (s_1, s_2)$, then $\vec{r} + \vec{s} =$ ____________________ and

(a) $$\|\vec{r}\| = \sqrt{r_1^2 + r_2^2}$$

and

$$\|\vec{s}\| = \sqrt{s_1^2 + s_2^2},$$

(b) $$(\|\vec{r}\| + \|\vec{s}\|)^2 = \|\vec{r}\|^2 + 2\|\vec{r}\| \cdot \|\vec{s}\| + \|\vec{s}\|^2$$

$= $ ______________ $+ 2\sqrt{r_1^2 + r_2^2}\ \sqrt{s_1^2 + s_2^2} +$ ______________.

(c) $$\|\vec{r} + \vec{s}\|^2 = (r_1 + s_1)^2 + (r_2 + s_2)^2$$

$= $ ____________________ $+ 2r_1s_1 + 2r_2s_2$.

By comparing the right-hand member of (b) and (c), we see that the result will follow if we can show that

(d) ____________________ $\geq$ ____________________.

If the right-hand member in (d) above is negative or zero, then (d) holds, because the left-hand member is always ________. If the right-hand member

ANSWERS TO PAGE 70

(10,6) (−10,−6)

$\vec{v} = \vec{y} - \vec{x}$

---

is positive, then the inequality (d) is equivalent to the inequality obtained by squaring both of its members, namely

$$(r_1^2 + r_2^2)(s_1^2 + s_2^2) \geq (r_1 s_1 + r_2 s_2)^2,$$

which, in turn, is equivalent to

$$r_1^2 s_1^2 + r_1^2 s_2^2 + r_2^2 s_1^2 + r_2^2 s_2^2 \geq r_1^2 s_1^2 + 2 r_1 s_1 r_2 s_2 + r_2^2 s_2^2,$$

which is equivalent to

$$\underline{\qquad\qquad\qquad\qquad} \geq 0,$$

or

$$(\underline{\qquad\qquad\qquad\qquad})^2 \geq 0.$$

This last inequality is always valid since the square of a real number is always greater than or equal to zero. Thus, in all cases, statement (d) holds and therefore we have proved the triangle inequality using vectors.

Verify the triangle inequality for $\vec{r} = (4,-3)$ and $\vec{s} = (5,12)$.

$||\vec{r}|| =$ — and $||\vec{s}|| =$ ______

$\vec{r} + \vec{s} =$ ______ and $||\vec{r} + \vec{s}|| =$ ______

Therefore,

$$||\vec{r}|| + ||\vec{s}|| = 5 + 13 = 18$$

and $18 \geq 9\sqrt{2}$.

If $\vec{r} \in \mathcal{R} \times \mathcal{R}$, then there exists exactly one vector $-\vec{r}$ such that $\vec{r} + (-\vec{r}) = 0$.

This is a statement of the property of ______ ______ for vectors.

If $\vec{r} = (2,-4)$, then $-\vec{r} =$ ______ , since $(2,-4) + (-2,+4) = (0,0)$.

Note that for any vector (x,y) the additive inverse is the vector ______ .

If the displacement $\overrightarrow{AB}$ represents the vector $\vec{r}$, then the displacement ____ represents the vector $-\vec{r}$. (See the following illustration.)

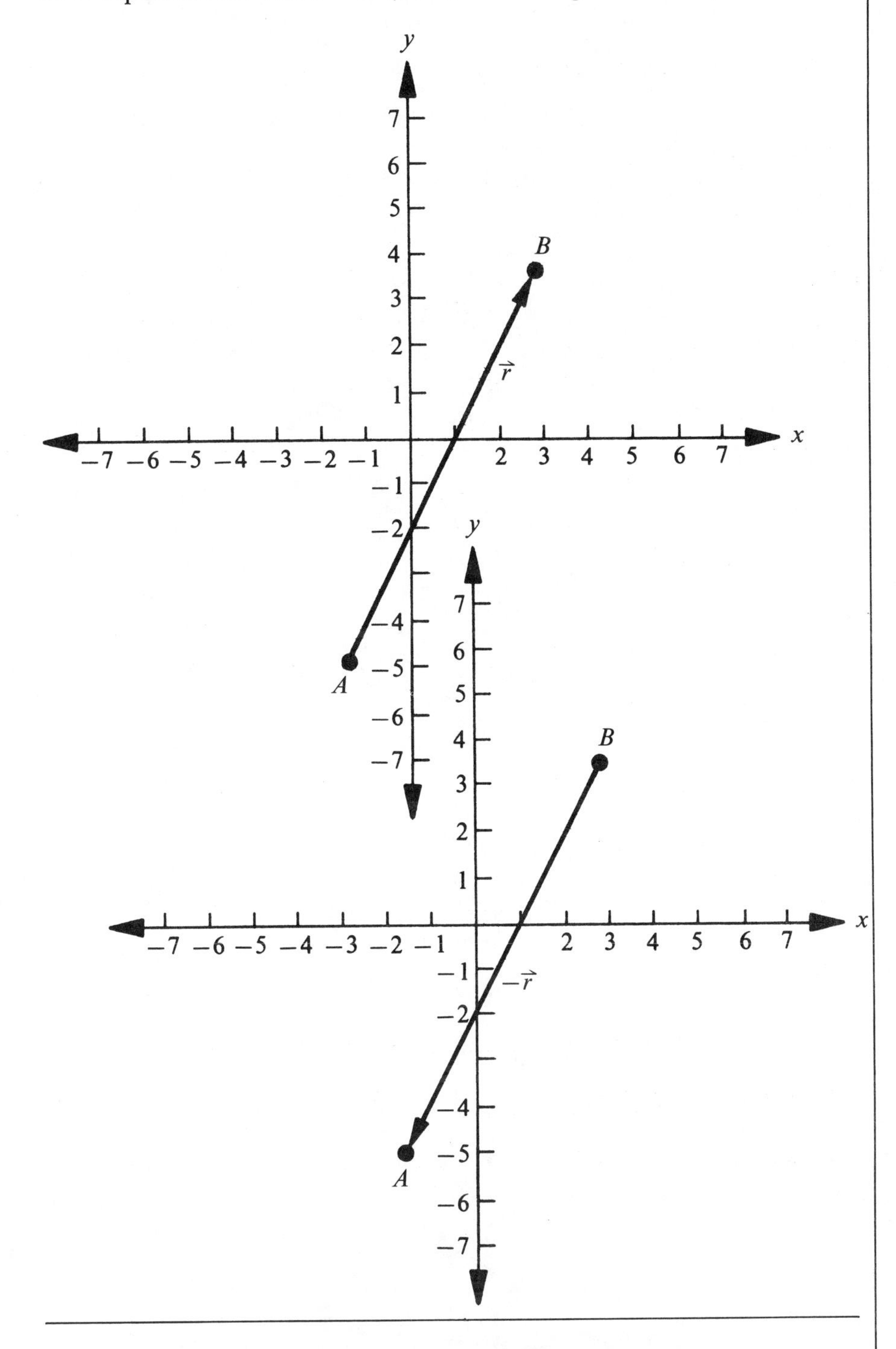

DEFINITION OF VECTOR SUBTRACTION:
The **vector difference** of vectors $\vec{r}$ and $\vec{s}$, denoted $\vec{r}-\vec{s}$, is the sum of $\vec{r}$ and the additive inverse of $\vec{s}$, i.e., $\vec{r}-\vec{s}=\vec{r}+(-\vec{s})$.

MOVE TO NEXT FRAME

ANSWERS TO PAGE 67

(r_1+s_1, r_2+s_2)

$r_1^2+r_2^2 \qquad s_1^2+s_2^2$

$r_1^2+s_1^2+r_2^2+s_2^2$

$\sqrt{(r_1^2+r_2^2)(s_1^2+s_2^2)} \geq (r_1s_1+r_2s_2)$

≥ 0

(1)

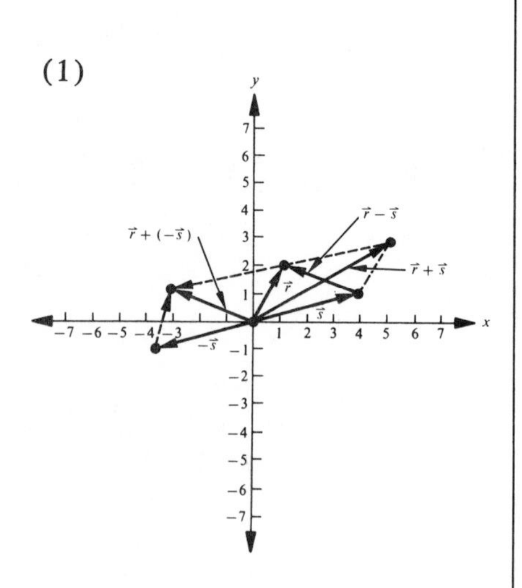

(2)(a) Any triangle constructed of vectors drawn so that the head of each points to the tail of another.

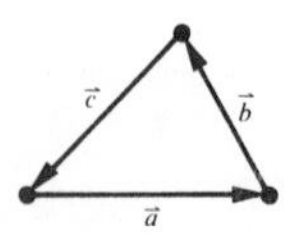

If $\vec{r} = (6,8)$ and $\vec{s} = (-4,2)$, then

$\vec{r} - \vec{s} = (\_\_\_\_\_\_)$ and $\vec{s} - \vec{r} = (\_\_\_\_\_\_)$.

If $\vec{r}$ and $\vec{s}$ are represented by geometric vectors in standard position, then, since $(\vec{r} - \vec{s}) + \vec{s} = \vec{r}$, the vector $\vec{r} - \vec{s}$ corresponds to the geometric vector from the terminal point of s to the terminal point of $\vec{r}$. (See the following illustration.)

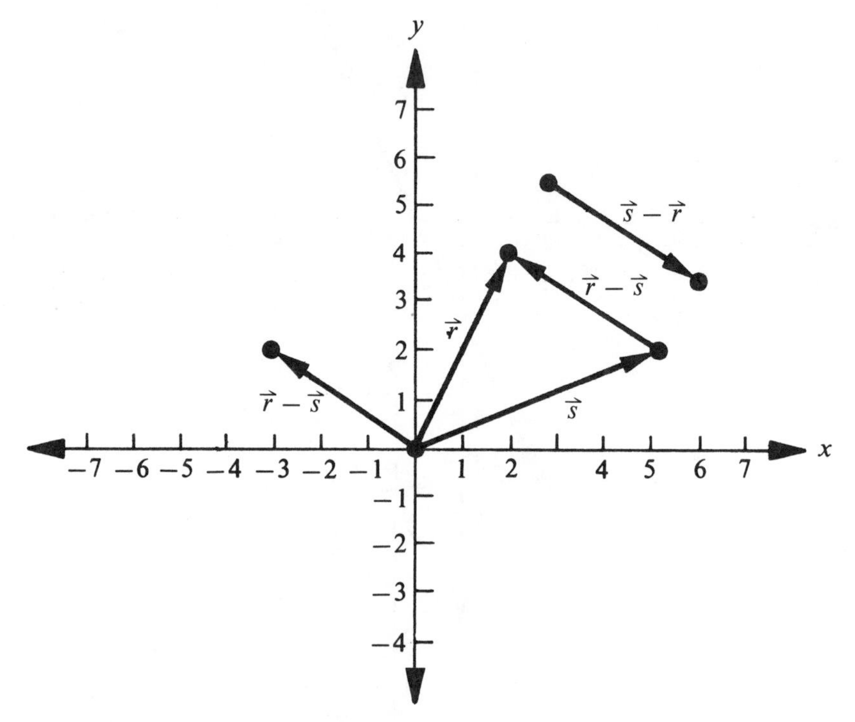

It is important to distinguish between $\vec{r} - \vec{s}$ and $\vec{s} - \vec{r}$.

MOVE TO NEXT FRAME

Suppose $\vec{v}$, $\vec{x}$, and $\vec{y}$ correspond to the geometric vectors illustrated.

Determine the vector $\vec{v}$ in terms of $\vec{x}$ and $\vec{y}$. ______

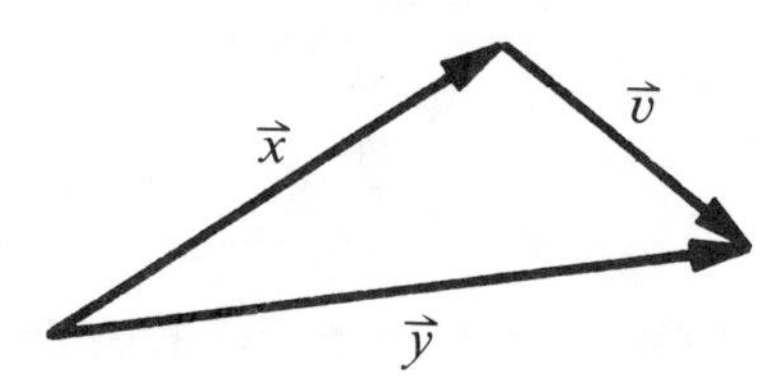

Do you see that $\vec{y} = \vec{x} + \vec{v}$?

For each of the following figures, determine $\vec{v}$ in terms of $\vec{x}$ and $\vec{y}$.

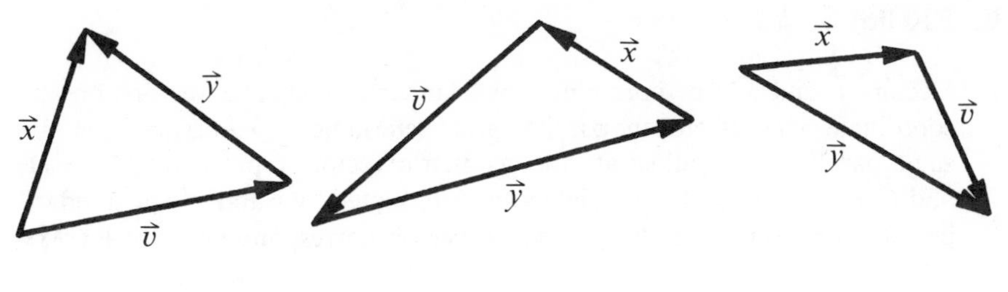

(a) ______________

(b) ______________

(c) ______________

If A, B, and C are three points on a coordinate system, the displacement from A to B plus the displacement from B to C plus the displacement from C to A results in a total displacement whose corresponding vector is $\vec{0}$. See the illustration.

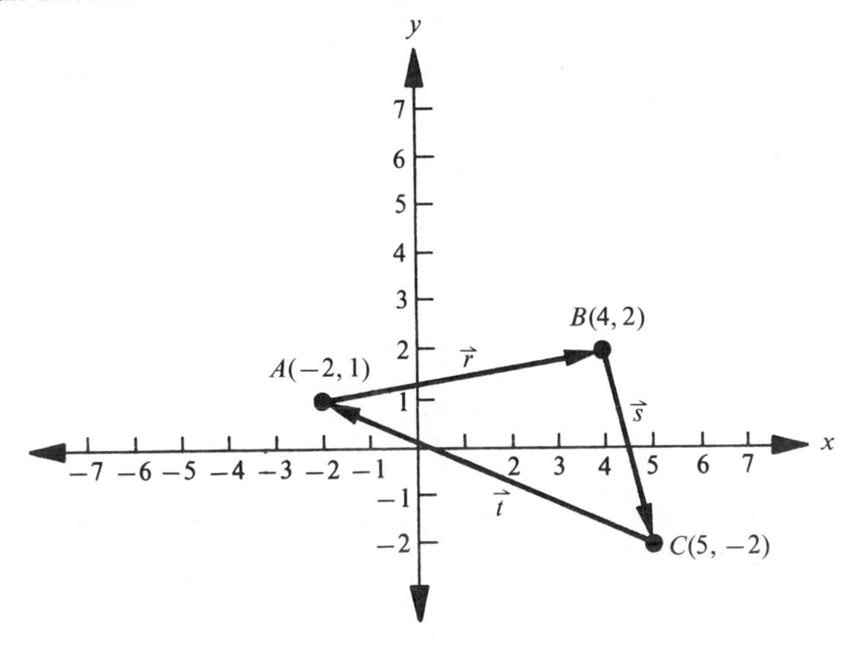

From the figure $\vec{r}=$ ______, $\vec{s}=$ ______, and $\vec{t}=$ ______.

Verify that $\vec{r}+\vec{s}+\vec{t}=\vec{0}$.

Given $A(x_1,y_1)$, $B(x_2,y_2)$, and $C(x_3,y_3)$, let $\vec{r}$, $\vec{s}$, and $\vec{t}$ be the vectors corresponding to $\overrightarrow{AB}$, $\overrightarrow{BC}$, and $\overrightarrow{CA}$ respectively. Then, $\vec{r}=(x_2-x_1,y_2-y_1)$,

$\vec{s}=($______________$)$, and $\vec{t}=($______________$)$. Therefore note $\vec{r}+\vec{s}+\vec{t}=\vec{0}$ in general.

ANSWERS TO PAGE 69

$\overrightarrow{BA}$

ANSWERS TO PAGE 74

(7) $\sqrt{17}$

(8) See Appendix.

EXERCISES. 2.2

1. Vectors $\vec{r}$ and $\vec{s}$ are represented by standard geometric vectors on the coordinate axes. Sketch the parallelogram determined by $\vec{r}$ and $\vec{s}$, and, on the same parallelogram, illustrate the geometric vectors representing $(\vec{r}+\vec{s})$, and $(\vec{r}-\vec{s})$. Sketch the parallelogram determined by $\vec{r}$ and $-\vec{s}$ in standard position and illustrate the geometric vector corresponding to $\vec{r}+(-\vec{s})$.

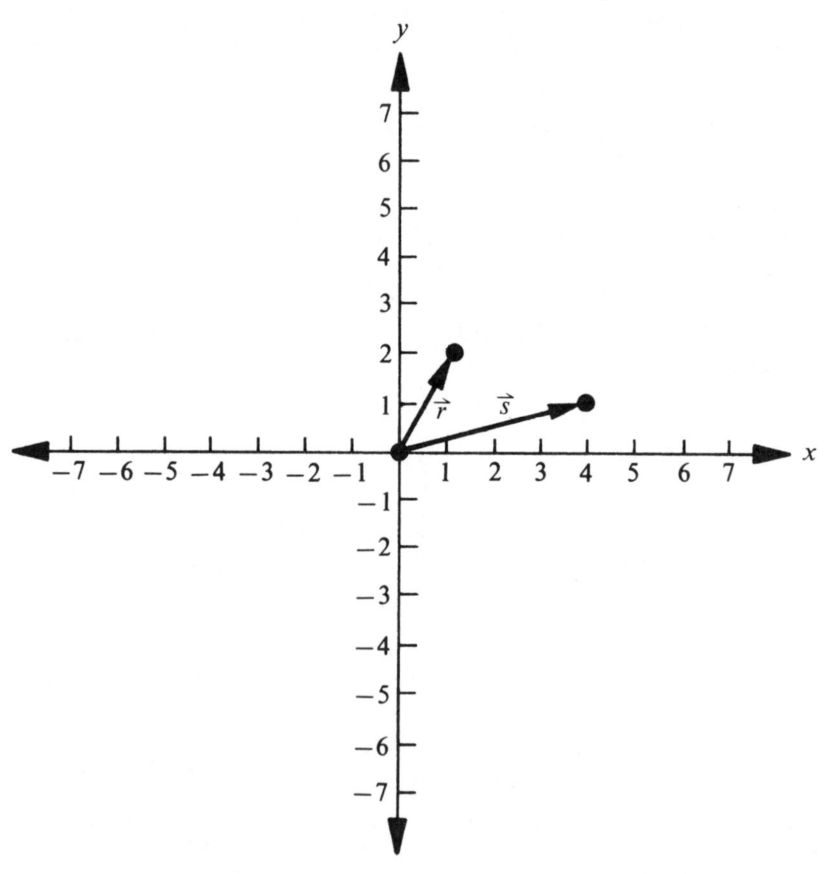

2. Sketch geometric vectors whose relative positions determine a figure which illustrates each of the following vector equations.

   (a) $\vec{a}+\vec{b}+\vec{c}=\vec{0}$

(b) $\vec{a}+\vec{b}+\vec{c}+\vec{d}=\vec{0}$

3. Using the adjacent illustration name a single vector equal to each of the following:

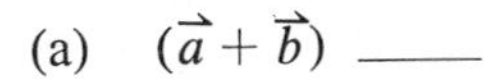

(a) $(\vec{a}+\vec{b})$ ____ (b) $(\vec{a}+\vec{b}+\vec{c})$ ____

(c) $(\vec{d}-\vec{c})$ ____ (d) $(\vec{e}-\vec{b})$ ____

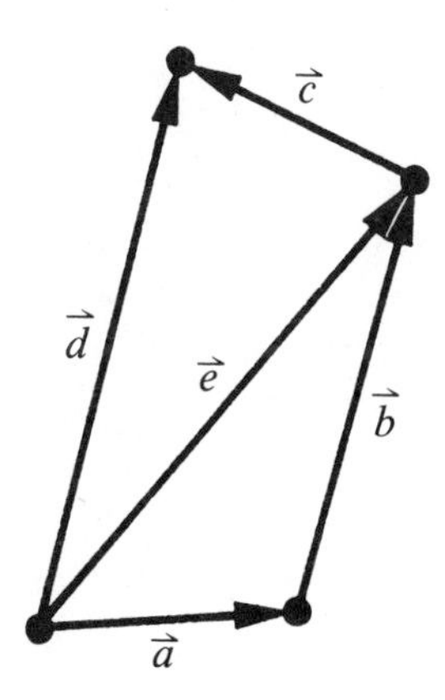

4. Prove that vector addition is commutative. (Use supplementary paper.)

5. The set of vectors in $\mathcal{R} \times \mathcal{R}$ is a commutative group under vector addition. This means ____

____

____.

6. If $A(3,1)$, $B(-4,4)$, and $C(-2,-3)$ are the vertices of $\triangle ABC$, find each of the following:

(a) Vectors corresponding to $\overrightarrow{AB}$, $\overrightarrow{BC}$, and $\overrightarrow{CA}$ are ________,

________, and ________.

(b) The sum of the vectors in (a) is ___.

(c) The norm of each vector in (a) is ____, ____, and ____.

(d) The perimeter of $\triangle ABC$ is ____________________.

ANSWERS TO PAGE 71

$\vec{v}=\vec{x}-\vec{y}$

$\vec{v}=-(\vec{x}+\vec{y})$

$\vec{v}=\vec{y}-\vec{x}$

(6,1) (1,−4) (−7,3)

$\vec{r}+\vec{s}=(7,-3)$

$(\vec{r}+\vec{s})+\vec{t}=\vec{0}$

(x_3-x_2, y_3-y_2) (x_1-x_3, y_1-y_3)

ANSWERS TO PAGE 76

$\frac{-4}{9}$

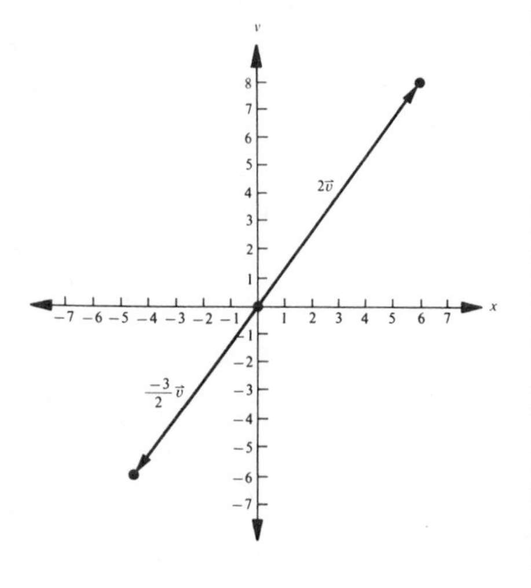

---

7. Find the length of the shorter diagonal of a parallelogram with adjacent sides which are formed by standard geometric vectors representing the vectors $(-3,1)$ and $(-4,-3)$. ______

8. Prove the parallelogram law of vectors, i.e., prove if (x_1,y_1) and (x_2,y_2) are vectors, then $(0,0),(x_1,y_1),(x_2,y_2)$, and the resultant (x_1+x_2,y_1+y_2) are the coordinates of points that, if not collinear, are vertices of a parallelogram. Then prove the geometric vector corresponding to the resultant is a diagonal of the parallelogram. (Use supplementary paper.)

2.3. SCALAR MULTIPLICATION OF VECTORS

Consider the sum of three identical vectors.

If $\vec{r} = (r_1,r_2)$, then $\vec{r} + \vec{r} + \vec{r} = (r_1 + r_1 + r_1, r_2 + r_2 + r_2)$

$= (\_\_ \ r_1, \ \_\_ \ r_2)$

$= \_\_ \ \vec{r}$. See the illustration.

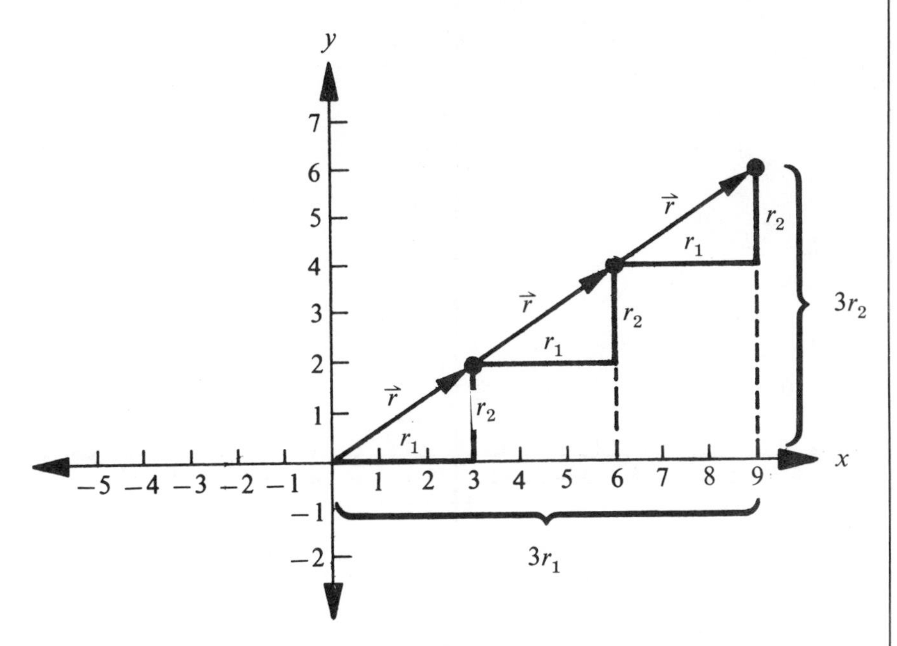

The repeated addition of vectors demonstrates the need for the definition of multiplication of a vector $\vec{r}$ by a real number k.

It is customary when dealing with vectors in $\mathcal{R} \times \mathcal{R}$ to call the real numbers **scalars.**

DEFINITION OF SCALAR MULTIPLICATION:
If $\vec{r} \epsilon \mathcal{R} \times \mathcal{R}$, $k \epsilon \mathcal{R}$, and $\vec{r} = (r_1,r_2)$, then $k\vec{r} = (kr_1,kr_2)$. $k\vec{r}$ is said to be the **scalar product** of k and $\vec{r}$. This process of operating on a vector to produce another vector is called **scalar multiplication.**

MOVE TO NEXT FRAME

Find $\vec{s} + \vec{s} + \vec{s}$ when $\vec{s} = (-4,5)$. __________

Find $3\vec{s}$ when $\vec{s} = (-4,5)$. __________

Does $3\vec{s} = \vec{s} + \vec{s} + \vec{s}$? ______

ANSWERS TO PAGE 73

(b) Any quadrilateral drawn so that the head of each vector points to the tail of another.

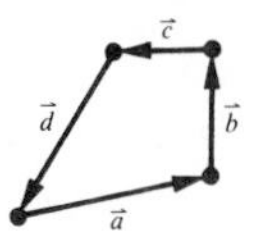

(3) (a) $\vec{e}$ (b) $\vec{d}$

(c) $\vec{e}$ (d) $\vec{a}$

(4) See Appendix.

(5) The set of vectors is closed with respect to vector addition; vector addition is associative and commutative; an identity exists for vector addition; and each vector has an additive inverse.

(6) (a) $(-7,3)$

$(2,-7)$ $(5,4)$

(b) $\vec{0}$

(c) $\sqrt{58}$, $\sqrt{53}$, and $\sqrt{41}$

(d) $\sqrt{58} + \sqrt{53} + \sqrt{41}$

ANSWERS TO PAGE 78

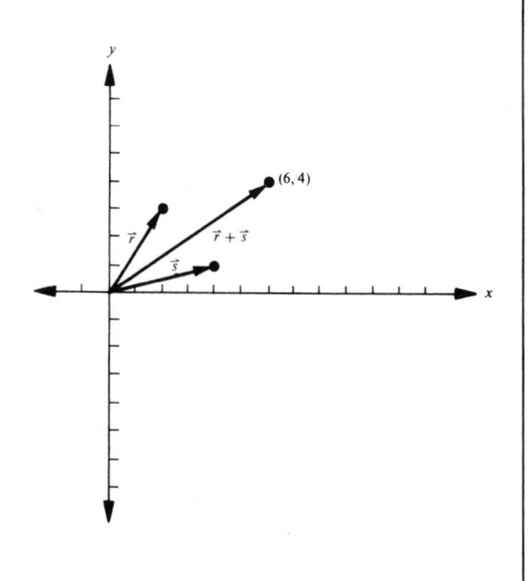

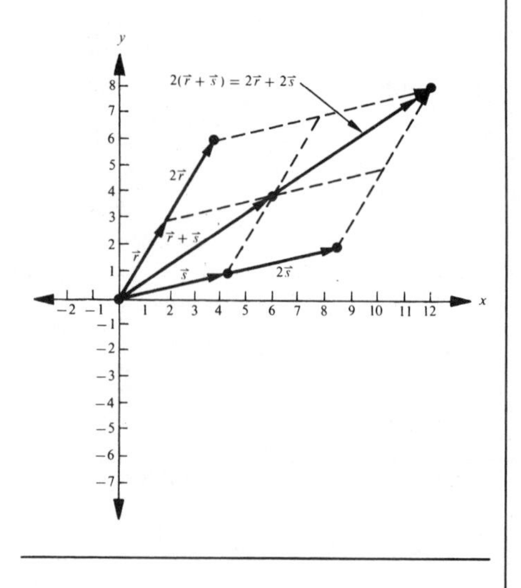

If $k(-2,3) = \left(\frac{8}{9}, \frac{-4}{3}\right)$, then $k =$ ______

If $\vec{v} = (3,4)$, sketch standard geometric vectors representing $2\vec{v}$ and $-\frac{3}{2}\vec{v}$ on the following coordinate axes.

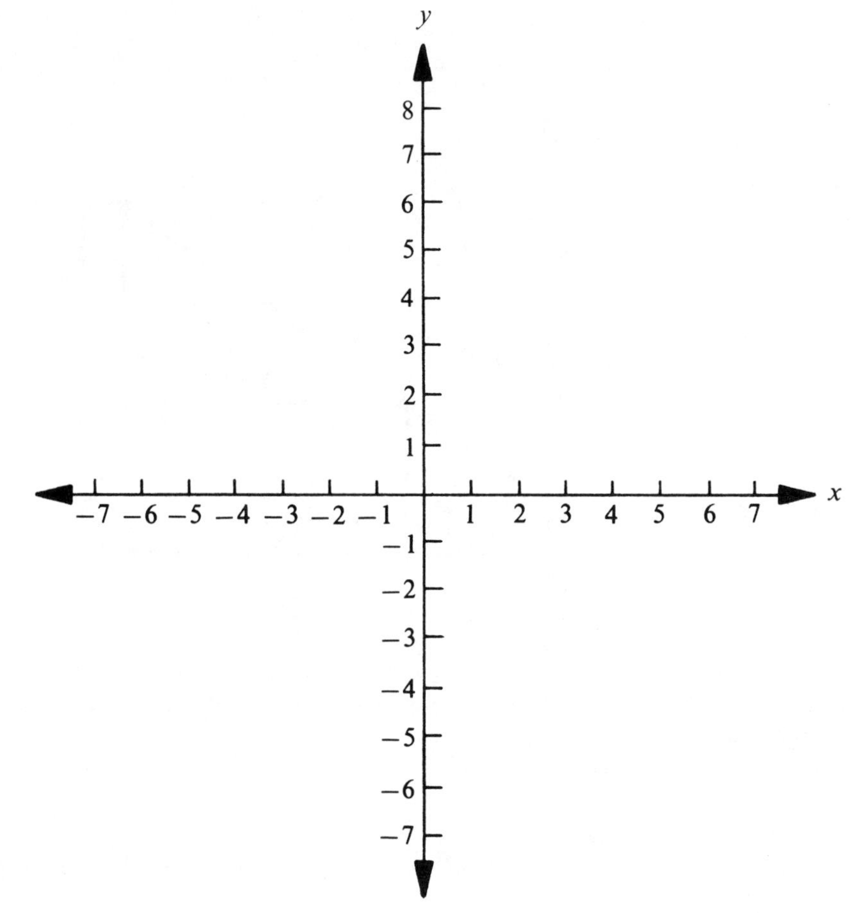

If $\vec{v} = (3,4)$, sketch standard geometric vectors representing $\frac{1}{2}\vec{v}$, $-\frac{1}{3}\vec{v}$ and $\frac{1}{\|\vec{v}\|} \cdot \vec{v}$ on the coordinate axes. (*Note:* $\frac{1}{\|\vec{v}\|}$ is a scalar because $\|\vec{v}\|$ is the length of $\vec{v}$, a positive real number.)

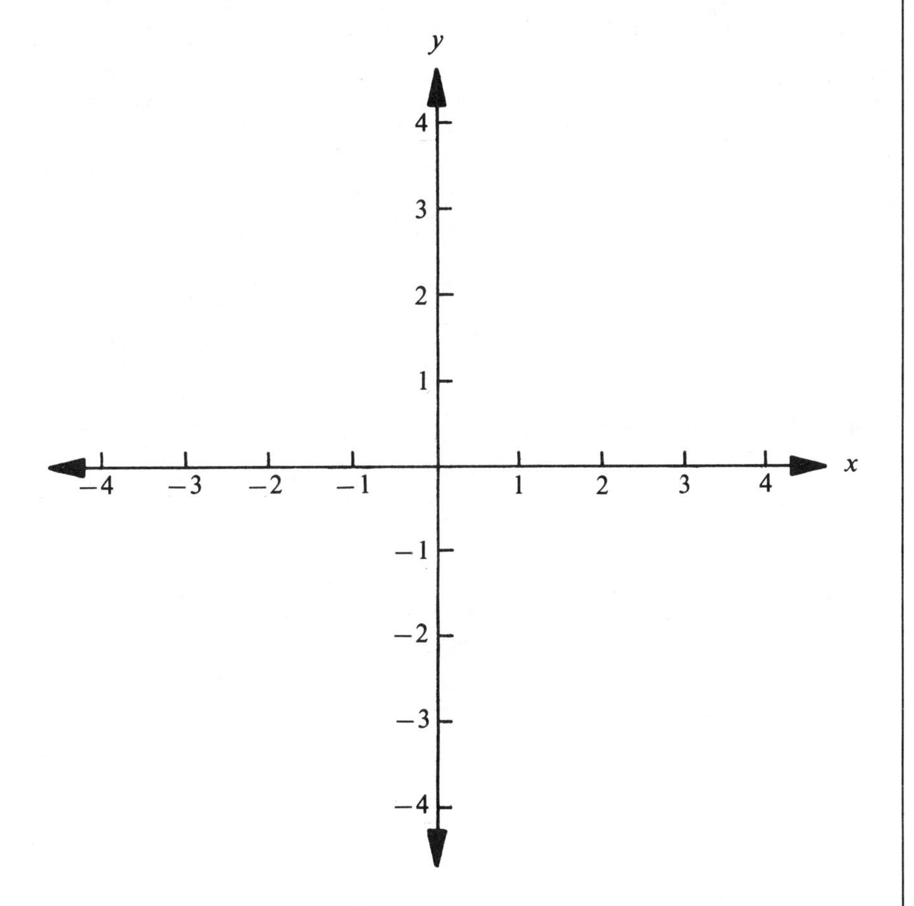

Are the standard geometric vectors representing the scalar multiples of $\vec{v}$ in the preceeding two frames collinear? ______. How long is the geometric vector representing $\vec{v}$? ___ $2\vec{v}$? ______ $\frac{1}{\|\vec{v}\|} \cdot \vec{v}$? ___

ANSWERS TO PAGE 75

3 3

3

(−12,15)

(−12,15)

yes

ANSWERS TO PAGE 80

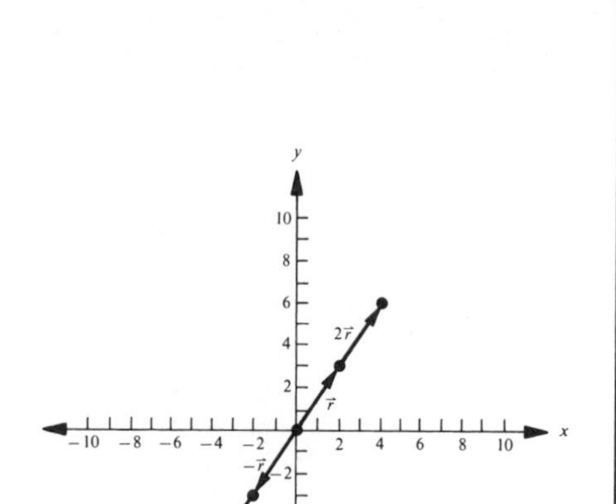

Let $\vec{r} = (2,3)$ and $\vec{s} = (4,1)$. Using the given coordinate axes, sketch standard geometric vectors representing $\vec{r}$, $\vec{s}$, and $(\vec{r} + \vec{s})$.

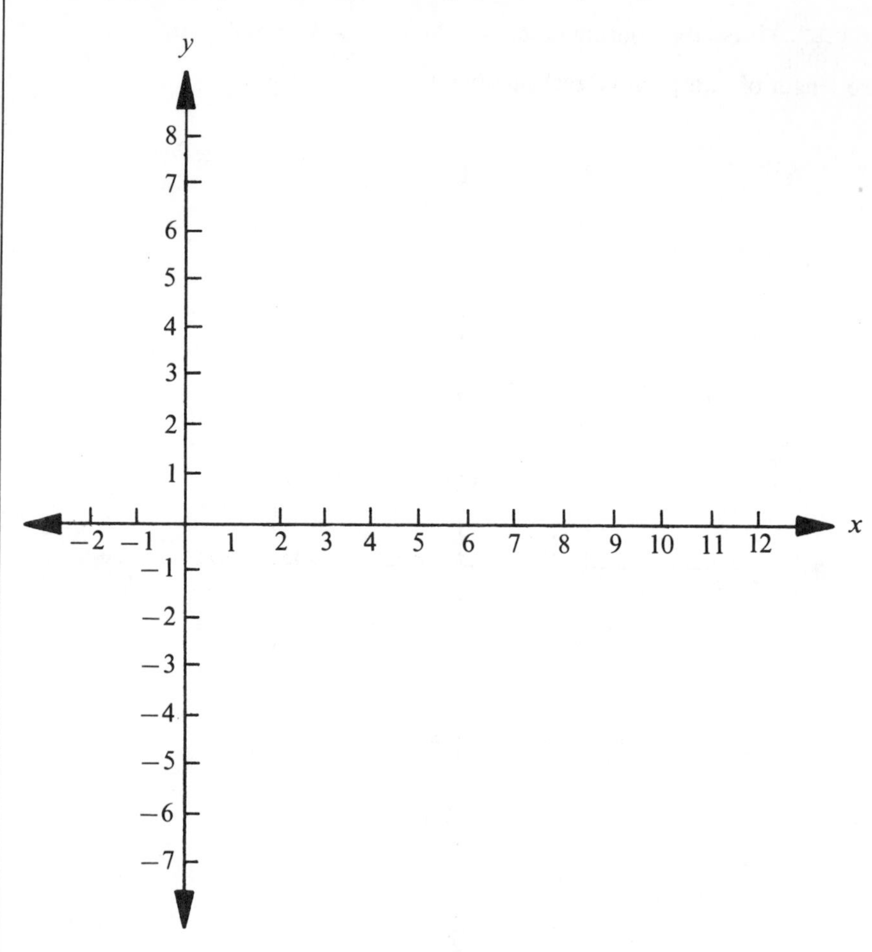

On the same axes sketch the standard geometric vectors corresponding to $2\vec{r}$, $2\vec{s}$, and their sum $(2\vec{r} + 2\vec{s})$.

Note that the geometric vector corresponding to $(2\vec{r} + 2\vec{s})$ coincides with that of $2(\vec{r} + \vec{s})$.

In general, one may prove that $k(\vec{r}+\vec{s}) = k\vec{r} + k\vec{s}$.
Proof: Let $\vec{r} = (r_1,r_2)$ and $\vec{s} = (s_1,s_2)$ be vectors in $\mathcal{R} \times \mathcal{R}$, and let k be a scalar. First, multiply the sum $\vec{r} + \vec{s}$ by k.

$$k(\vec{r}+\vec{s}) = k[(r_1,r_2) + (s_1,s_2)] = k(r_1+s_1,r_2+s_2)$$

Why? ______________________________

$$k(r_1 + s_1,r_2 + s_2) = [k(r_1 + s_1),k(r_2 + s_2)]$$

Why? ______________________________

$$[k(r_1+s_1),k(r_2+s_2)] = (kr_1+ks_1,kr_2+ks_2)$$

Why? ______________________________

$$(kr_1+ks_1,kr_2+ks_2) = (kr_1,kr_2) + (ks_1,ks_2)$$

Why? ______________________________

$$(kr_1,kr_2) + (ks_1,ks_2) = k(r_1,r_2) + k(s_1,s_2)$$

Why? ______________________________

$$k(r_1,r_2) + k(s_1,s_2) = k\vec{r} + k\vec{s}$$

Why? ______________________________

$$\therefore k(\vec{r} + \vec{s}) = k\vec{r} + k\vec{s}$$

Why? ______________________________

The following list contains the property proved in the preceding frame and other properties of scalar multiplication. Proofs of the additional properties will be reserved for exercises.

MOVE TO NEXT FRAME

PROPERTIES OF SCALAR MULTIPLICATION:
Let $k \epsilon \mathcal{R}$, $m \epsilon \mathcal{R}$, $\vec{r} \epsilon \mathcal{R} \times \mathcal{R}$, and $\vec{s} \epsilon \mathcal{R} \times \mathcal{R}$. Then

SM1: (a) $k(\vec{r}+\vec{s}) = k\vec{r} + k\vec{s}$

(b) $(k + m)\vec{r} = k\vec{r} + m\vec{r}$

SM2: $(km)\vec{r} = k(m\vec{r})$

SM3: $||k\vec{r}|| = |k| \cdot ||\vec{r}||$

SM4: (a) $(1)\vec{r} = \vec{r}$

(b) $(-1)\vec{r} = -\vec{r}$

SM5: (a) $0\vec{r} = \vec{0}$

(b) $k\vec{0} = \vec{0}$

MOVE TO NEXT FRAME

ANSWERS TO PAGE 77

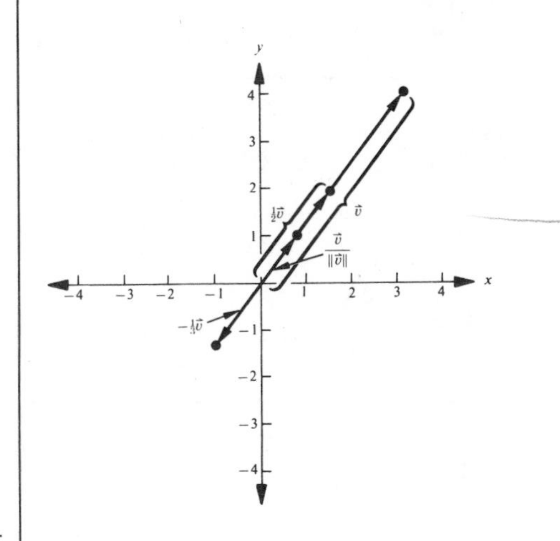

---

yes

5 10 1

ANSWERS TO PAGE 82

$|k| \cdot \|\vec{v}\|$

same

opposite

$\frac{1}{5}$

$\left(\frac{3}{5}, \frac{-4}{5}\right)$

1

$|k|$

$\left(\frac{2}{\sqrt{13}}, \frac{3}{\sqrt{13}}\right)$

$\left(\frac{20}{\sqrt{13}}, \frac{30}{\sqrt{13}}\right)$

$k(4,6)$

± 2

$2(4,6) = (8,12)$ and

$-2(4,6) = (-8,-12)$

Let $\vec{r} = (2,3)$, and sketch the standard geometric vectors representing $\vec{r}$, $-r$, $2\vec{r}$, and $-3\vec{r}$. Use the following coordinate system.

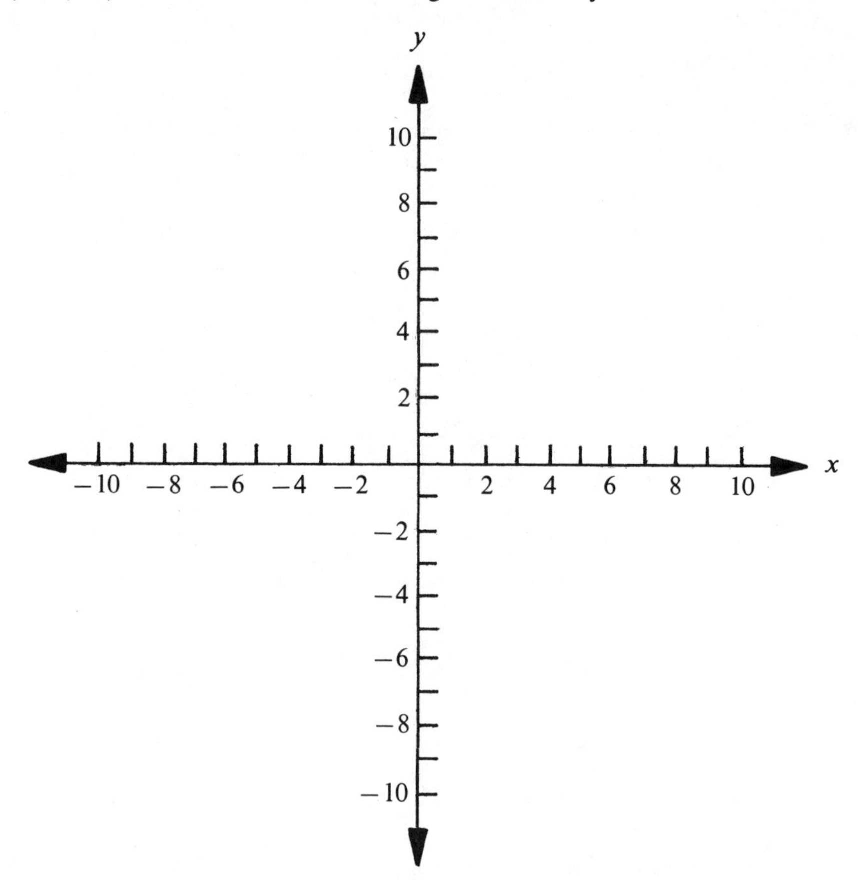

Do you see that the geometric vectors representing scalar multiples of $\vec{r}$ are collinear with the standard geometric vector representing $\vec{r}$?

DEFINITIONS:
Two vectors $\vec{r}$ and s are said to have the **same direction** if and only if $\vec{r} = k\vec{s}$ for some scalar $k \geq 0$. They are said to have **opposite directions** if and only if $\vec{r} = k\vec{s}$ for some $k < 0$.
Two geometric vectors are said to have the **same direction** if and only if the vectors they represent have the same direction, and they are said to have **opposite directions** if and only if the vectors they represent have opposite directions.

MOVE TO NEXT FRAME

If $\vec{v} = (-2,3)$, then $||\vec{v}|| =$ ________. Find each of the following.

(a) $2\vec{v} =$ ________, $||2\vec{v}|| =$ ________.

(b) $\frac{1}{2}\vec{v} =$ ________, $\left\|\frac{1}{2}\vec{v}\right\| =$ ________.

(c) $\frac{2}{3}\vec{v} =$ ________, $\left\|\frac{2}{3}\vec{v}\right\| =$ ________.

(d) $-3\vec{v} =$ ________, $||3\vec{v}|| =$ ________.

(e) $k\vec{v} =$ ________, $||k\vec{v}|| =$ ________.

Multiplying a vector $\vec{v}$ by a scalar k effects an **expansion** if $k > 1$ and a **contraction** if $0 < k < 1$.

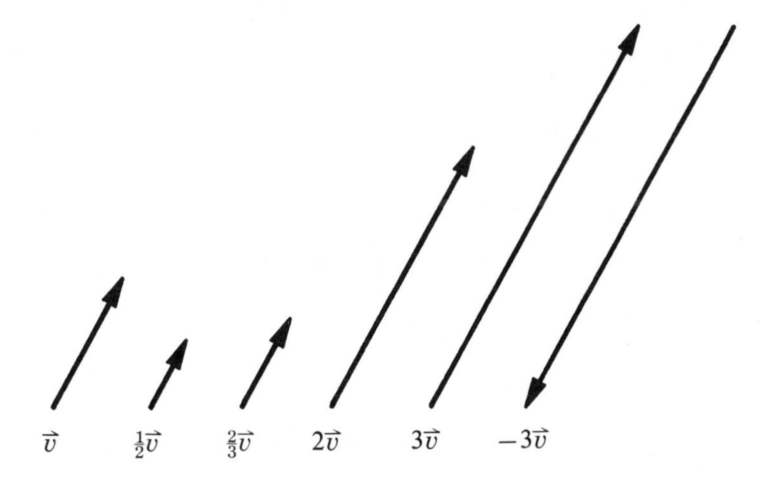

The length of the geometric vectors representing $3\vec{v}$ and $-3\vec{v}$ are ___ times as long as that representing $\vec{v}$.

The geometric vector representing $\vec{r} = (4,8)$ has the ________ (same/opposite) direction as the one representing (2,4). (2,4) corresponds to a geometric vector which is ____ as long as the one representing $\vec{r}$. ____

The geometric vector representing $(-1,2)$ has the ________ (same/opposite) direction as the geometric vector representing $(3,-6)$.

DEFINITION:
A vector $\vec{v}$ is called a **unit vector** if and only if $||\vec{v}|| = 1$.

MOVE TO NEXT FRAME

ANSWERS TO PAGE 79

definition of vector addition

definition of scalar multiplication

distributive property in $\mathcal{R}$

definition of vector addition

definition of scalar multiplication

substitution principle

transitive property of equality

(4)

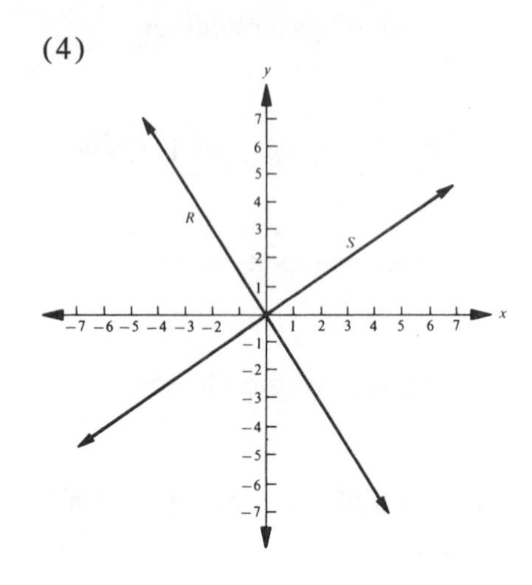

They are perpendicular lines.

(5) See Appendix.

(6) (a) $(-7,14)$ (b) $(0,-7)$

(c) $(-3,-9)$ (d) $\left(\frac{-9}{5}, \frac{8}{5}\right)$

(7) (a) $\left(\frac{5}{13}, \frac{-12}{13}\right)$

(b) $\left(\frac{-9}{41}, \frac{40}{41}\right)$

(c) $\left(\frac{\sqrt{2}}{2}, \frac{\sqrt{2}}{2}\right)$

By multiplying any nonzero vector $\vec{v}$ in $\mathcal{R} \times \mathcal{R}$ by the appropriate scalar k, we can find a unit vector in the same direction as $\vec{v}$.

Let $k\vec{v}$ be the required vector. We want to find a scalar $k > 0$ such that $||k\vec{v}|| = 1$. From **SM3** we know that $||k\vec{v}|| =$ ____________ . Thus $||k\vec{v}|| = 1$ if and only if $|k| \cdot ||\vec{v}|| = 1$. Since $\vec{v} \neq 0$, the latter equality is equivalent to $|k| = \frac{1}{||\vec{v}||}$. Since we want $k > 0$, it follows that the desired scalar is $\frac{1}{||\vec{v}||}$. Thus $\frac{1}{||\vec{v}||} \cdot \vec{v}$ is a unit vector in the ____________ direction as $\vec{v}$. Similarly, $-\frac{1}{||\vec{v}||} \cdot \vec{v}$ is a unit vector in the ____________ direction of $\vec{v}$.

Example: Find a unit vector which is in the same direction as $\vec{v} = (3,-4)$.

Solution: The required vector is equal to $\frac{1}{||\vec{v}||} \cdot \vec{v}$. $\frac{1}{||\vec{v}||} =$ ________ **and** $\frac{1}{||\vec{v}||} \cdot \vec{v} =$ ______________.

If $\vec{u}$ is a unit vector, then the length of $\vec{u}$ is __ and the length of $k\vec{u} =$ ________________ .

Example: Find a vector 10 units long and in the same direction as (2,3).

Solution: If $\vec{u}$ is the unit vector in the same direction as (2,3), then $\vec{u} =$ ________________ . The required vector is $10\,\vec{u} =$ ________________ .

Problem: Find a scalar multiple of (4,6) which is twice as long as (4,6).

Solution: Let $\vec{r}$ be such a vector. Since $\vec{r}$ is a scalar multiple of (4,6), then $r =$ ____________ for some $k \in \mathcal{R}$. Thus by **SM3**,

(1) $||\vec{r}|| = |k| \cdot ||(4,)||$

But since $\vec{r}$ is twice as long as (4,6)

(2) $||\vec{r}|| = |k| \cdot ||(4,6)||$

Comparing equations (1) and (2), we have $|k| = 2$. Thus $k =$ ______ , and there are two vectors which meet the conditions of the problem, namely ________________________ and ________________________ .

EXERCISES. 2.3

1. State which of the following are scalars and which are vectors.

(a) $3(\vec{r}+\vec{s})$ ____________ (b) $\|\vec{v}\|$ ____________

(c) $\frac{1}{\|\vec{w}\|}\cdot\vec{w}$ ____________ (d) $\|\vec{v}+\vec{w}\|$ ____________

(e) $(k+m)(\vec{r}+\vec{s})$ ____________ (f) $4(3,4)$ ____________

(g) $\|3(4,7)\|$ ____________ (h) $\frac{(3,4)}{\|(3,4)\|}$ ____________

2. Given $\vec{a}=(4,-3)$. Find each of the following scalar multiples of $\vec{a}$.

(a) $-2\vec{a}$ ____________ (b) $-\frac{1}{2}\vec{a}$ ____________

(c) $3\vec{a}$ ____________ (d) $\frac{1}{\|\vec{a}\|}\cdot\vec{a}$ ____________

(e) $\frac{3}{4}\vec{a}$ ____________

3. Find $k\in\mathcal{R}$, if possible, such that $\vec{r}=k\vec{s}$ for each of the following.

(a) $\vec{r}=(4,-6)$ and $\vec{s}=(2,-3)$. $k=$ ____________

(b) $\vec{r}=(-3,-1)$ and $\vec{s}=(6,2)$. $k=$ ____________

(c) $\vec{r}=\left(2,\frac{-\sqrt{2}}{2}\right)$ and $\vec{s}=\left(-\sqrt{2},\frac{1}{2}\right)$. $k=$ ____________

(d) $\vec{r}=(4,5)$ and $\vec{s}=(8,12)$. $k=$ ____________

4. Let S be the set of terminal points of all standard geometric vectors which represent scalar multiples of $\vec{s}=(3,2)$. Sketch the graph of S on the following coordinate system. Do the same for the set R of terminal points of all standard geometric vectors which represent scalar multiples of $\vec{r}=(-2,3)$.

ANSWERS TO PAGE 81

$(\sqrt{13})$

$(-4,6)$ $2\sqrt{13}$

$\left(-1,\frac{3}{2}\right)$ $\frac{1}{2}\sqrt{13}$

$\left(\frac{-4}{3},2\right)$ $\frac{2}{3}\sqrt{13}$

$(+6,-9)$ $3\sqrt{13}$

$(-2k,3k)$ $\sqrt{13k^2}=|k|\sqrt{13}$

3

---

same

$\frac{1}{2}$

opposite

---

norm, or magnitude

$||\vec{r}-\vec{s}||^2$

$(\sqrt{(r_1-s_1)^2+(r_2-s_2)^2})^2$

$r_1^2 - 2r_1s_1 + s_1^2 + r_2^2 - 2r_2s_2 + s_2^2$

Pythagorean

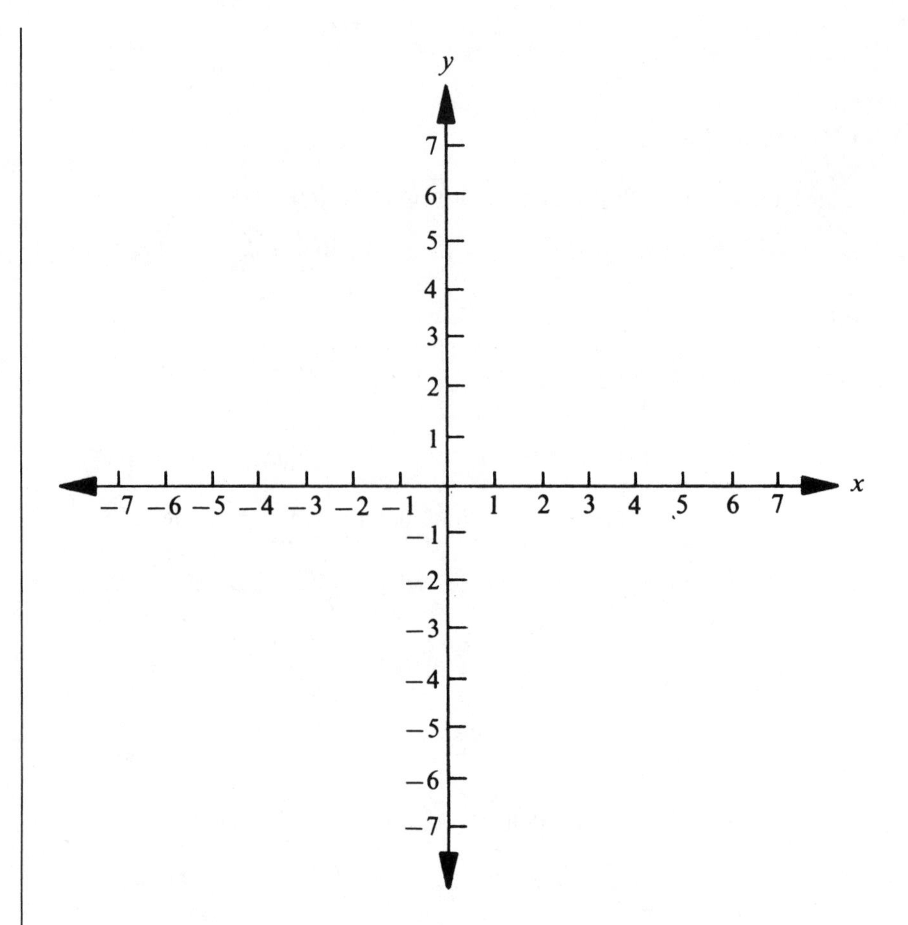

What does the geometric relationship between S and R seem to be?

______________________________.

5. Prove property **SM3**, i.e., prove that $||k\vec{r}|| = |k| \cdot ||\vec{r}||$, wherever $k \in \mathcal{R}$ and $\vec{r} \in \mathcal{R} \times \mathcal{R}$. Let $\vec{r} = (r_1, r_2)$. (Use supplementary paper.)

6. If $\vec{a} = (-2,1)$ and $\vec{b} = (-1,4)$, then determine each of the following vectors.

   (a) $2\vec{a} + 3\vec{b}$ ______________ (b) $\vec{a} - 2\vec{b}$ ______________

   (c) $3(\vec{a} - \vec{b})$ ______________ (d) $\frac{4}{5}\vec{a} + \frac{1}{5}\vec{b}$ ______________

7. Find unit vectors in the same direction as each of the following.

   (a) $(5,-12)$ ______________

   (b) $(-9,40)$ ______________

   (c) $(1,1)$ ______________

(d) $(-3,-3)$ ____________

(e) $(1,-\sqrt{3})$ ____________

(f) $(5,5\sqrt{3})$ ____________

8. Prove that if $\vec{a} = (x,y)$, then $\left\| \frac{\vec{a}}{\|\vec{a}\|} \right\| = 1$. (Use supplementary paper.)

(1) (a) vector (b) scalar

(c) vector (d) scalar

(e) vector (f) vector

(g) scalar (h) vector

(2) (a) $(-8,6)$ (b) $\left(-2, \frac{3}{2}\right)$

(c) $(12,-9)$ (d) $\left(\frac{4}{5}, \frac{-3}{5}\right)$

(e) $\left(3, \frac{-9}{4}\right)$

(3) (a) 2

(b) $-\frac{1}{2}$

(c) $-\sqrt{2}$

(d) Not possible

2.4. INNER PRODUCT

The sides of a right triangle may be thought of as geometric vectors.

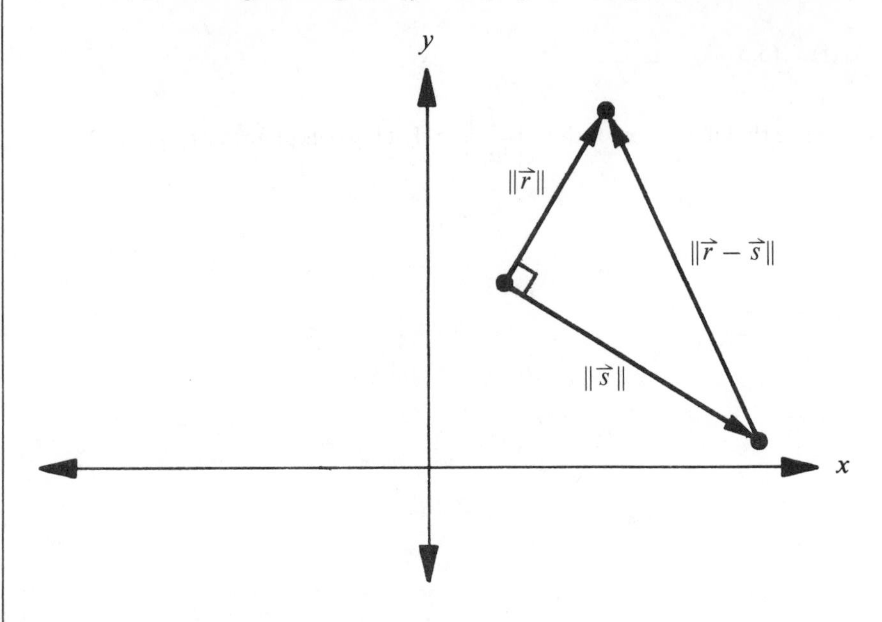

The length of each side will therefore be the ______________ of the corresponding vector. (See the illustration.) Since the triangle is a right triangle, the Pythagorean Theorem applies, and, therefore, $\|\vec{r}\|^2 + \|\vec{s}\|^2$ $=$ __________. Setting $\vec{r} = (r_1,r_2)$ and $\vec{s} = (s_1,s_2)$ we have:

$$\|(r_1,r_2)\|^2 + \|(s_1,s_2)\|^2 = \|(r_1 - s_1,r_2 - s_2)\|^2,$$

$$(\sqrt{r_1^2 + r_2^2})^2 + (\sqrt{s_1^2 + s_2^2})^2 = \text{______________},$$

$$(r_1^2 + r_2^2) + (s_1^2 + s_2^2) = (r_1 - s_1)^2 + (r_2 - s_2)^2,$$

$$r_1^2 + r_2^2 + s_1^2 + s_2^2 = \text{______________}.$$

This is equivalent to:

$$0 = -2r_1s_1 - 2r_2s_2$$

or

$$0 = r_1s_1 + r_2s_2.$$

Hence, we see that if r and s correspond to the legs of a right triangle, then $r_1s_1 + r_2s_2 = 0$.

Conversely, suppose $\vec{r} = (r_1,r_2)$, $\vec{s} = (s_1,s_2)$, and $r_1s_1 + r_2s_2 = 0$. Let $\overrightarrow{AB}$ and $\overrightarrow{AC}$ be geometric vectors representing $\vec{r}$ and $\vec{s}$, respectively. Then, reversing the steps in the above argument, we have

$$\|\vec{r}\|^2 + \|\vec{s}\|^2 = \|\vec{r} - \vec{s}\|^2.$$

Thus if $\vec{r}$ and $\vec{s}$ are nonzero vectors, and $r_1s_1 + r_2s_2 = 0$, then the points A, B, and C are noncollinear and, by the theorem which is the converse of the ______________ Theorem, $\triangle ABC$ is a right triangle.

perpendicular

geometric

$\vec{r} \cdot \vec{s} = 0$

(6,3)

(6,3) 0

The usefulness of the sum $r_1s_1 + r_2s_2$, encountered in the previous frame, motivates the following definition of the "inner product" of vectors.

MOVE TO NEXT FRAME

DEFINITION:
The **inner product** of two vectors $\vec{r} = (r_1,r_2)$ and $\vec{s} = (s_1,s_2)$, denoted $\vec{r} \cdot \vec{s}$, equal to $r_1s_1 + r_2s_2$, i.e., $(r_1,r_2) \cdot (s_1,s_2) = r_1s_1 + r_2s_2$.

MOVE TO NEXT FRAME

The inner product of two vectors is *not* a vector, it is a ____________.

The inner product is sometimes called the **dot product** or **scalar product** of two vectors.

MOVE TO NEXT FRAME

Examples: Find the inner product for each of the following:

(a) $(1,3) \cdot (-4,6) = -4 + 18 =$ ______

(b) $(2,8) \cdot (-3,4) =$ ______

(c) $(-3,6) \cdot (6,3) =$ ______

We have previously shown that if $\vec{r}$ and $\vec{s}$ are nonzero vectors which correspond to geometric vectors $\overrightarrow{AB}$ and $\overrightarrow{AC}$, then $\triangle ABC$ is a right triangle if and only if ____________.

In general, if $\vec{r}$ and $\vec{s}$ are nonzero vectors which correspond to geometric vectors $\overrightarrow{AB}$ and $\overrightarrow{CD}$, then the line L_1, which contains A and B, is perpendicular to the line L_2, which contains C and D, if and only if $\vec{r} \cdot \vec{s} = 0$. To see this, let P be a point such that $\overrightarrow{AP}$ and $\overrightarrow{CD}$ have the same length and direction.

ANSWERS TO PAGE 85

(d) $\left(\frac{-\sqrt{2}}{2}, \frac{-\sqrt{2}}{2}\right)$

(e) $\left(\frac{1}{2}, \frac{-\sqrt{3}}{2}\right)$

(f) $\left(\frac{1}{2}, \frac{\sqrt{3}}{2}\right)$

(8) See Appendix.

(See the illustration.) Then, if $\vec{t}$ is the vector corresponding to $\overrightarrow{AP}$, $\vec{t} = \vec{s}$. Now if $L_1 \perp L_2$, then $\triangle BAP$ is a right triangle and therefore $\vec{r} \cdot \vec{s} = \vec{r} \cdot \vec{t} = 0$. Conversely, if $\vec{r} \cdot \vec{s} = 0$, then $\vec{r} \cdot \vec{t} = 0$ and hence $\triangle ABP$ is a right triangle; it follows that $L_1 \perp L_2$.

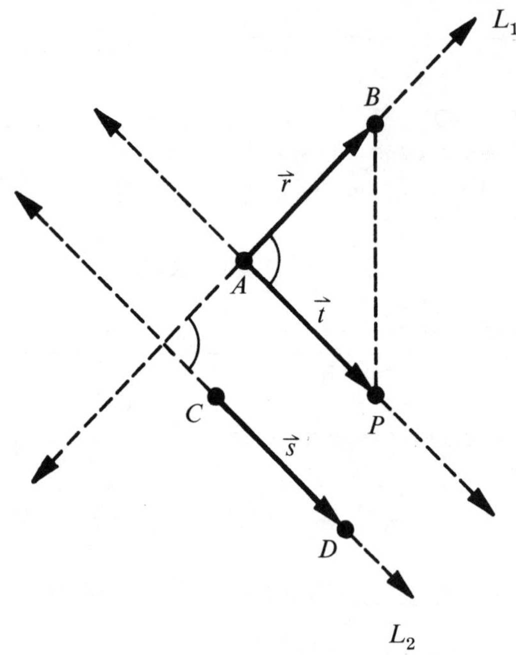

MOVE TO NEXT FRAME

---

right

perpendicular

We say that two geometric vectors are perpendicular if and only if they are contained in ____________ lines. Also, we say that two vectors are perpendicular if and only if they correspond to perpendicular ____________ vectors. We have just shown that two nonzero vectors $\vec{r}$ and $\vec{s}$ are perpendicular if and only if ____________. If we agree that the zero vector is perpendicular to every vector, then this result holds without restriction.

Problem: Show that if line L_1 contains points $A(2,8)$ and $B(5,2)$ and line L_2 contains $C(1,5)$ and $D(7,8)$, then $L_1 \perp L_2$.

$$\overrightarrow{AB} = (3,-6) \quad \text{and} \quad \overrightarrow{CD} = \_\_\_\_\_\_\_\_ .$$

The inner product of the vectors corresponding to $\overrightarrow{AB}$ and $\overrightarrow{CD}$ is $(3,-6) \cdot$ ________ = ___. Therefore $L_1 \perp L_2$.

The problem of finding a vector $\vec{v}$ perpendicular to a given vector $\vec{w} = (x,y)$, is easily solved. Simply interchange the coordinates of $\vec{w}$ and replace one of them by its negative, *e.g.*, $\vec{v} = (-y,x)$ is perpendicular to $\vec{w} = (x,y)$. This is the case since $\vec{v} \cdot \vec{w} = (-y,x) \cdot (x,y) =$ __.

Examples: Find a vector perpendicular to each of the following:

(a) $(-6,2)$ ______ (b) $(3,3)$ ______

(c) $(-4,-5)$ ______ (d) (a,b) ______

Examples: Find unit vectors perpendicular to each of the following:

(a) $(3,4)$ __________

(b) $(-5,12)$ __________

(c) $\left(-2\frac{1}{2},-6\right)$ __________

(d) (a,b) __________

Compute the inner product $\vec{a} \cdot \vec{b}$ given that $\vec{a} = (a_1,a_2)$ and $\vec{b} = (b_1,b_2)$

____

Now compute the inner product $\vec{b} \cdot \vec{a}$. __________

We see that $\vec{a} \cdot \vec{b} = \vec{b} \cdot \vec{a}$ by the ________ property of multiplication in $\mathcal{R}$.

The following is a list of certain fundamental properties of the inner product of vectors. We proved the first of these in the preceding frame. Proof of the others will be left as exercises.

PROPERTIES OF THE INNER PRODUCT OF VECTORS:
Let $\vec{x}$, $\vec{y}$, and $\vec{v}$ be elements in $\mathcal{R} \times \mathcal{R}$, and let k be any scalar.

IP1: $\vec{x} \cdot \vec{y} = \vec{y} \cdot \vec{x}$.

ANSWERS TO PAGE 87

scalar

(a) 14

(b) 26

(c) 0

$\vec{r} \cdot \vec{s} = 0$

(1) (a) vector (b) vector

(c) scalar (d) scalar

(e) scalar (f) scalar

(g) vector (h) scalar

(i) vector (j) vector

(2) (a) perpendicular

(b) neither

(c) parallel

(d) parallel

(e) perpendicular

(3) (a) 18 (b) $\frac{20}{3}$

(c) -4 (d) $\frac{-y^2}{x}$

(4) See Appendix.

(5) See Appendix.

(6) See Appendix.

(7) See Appendix.

IP2: $k(\vec{x} \cdot \vec{y}) = (k\vec{x}) \cdot \vec{y}.$

IP3: (a) $\vec{v} \cdot (\vec{x} + \vec{y}) = \vec{v} \cdot \vec{x} + \vec{v} \cdot \vec{y},$

(b) $(\vec{x} + \vec{y}) \cdot \vec{v} = \vec{x} \cdot \vec{v} + \vec{y} \cdot \vec{v}.$

IP4: $\vec{v} \cdot \vec{v} + ||\vec{v}||^2.$

IP5: $\vec{0} \cdot \vec{x} = \vec{x} \cdot \vec{0} = \vec{0}.$

MOVE TO NEXT FRAME

Inner products are useful in proving certain theorems in geometry. The following theorem may be familiar to you.

MOVE TO NEXT FRAME

THEOREM:

The angle inscribed in a semicircle is a __________ angle.

Proof: Let D be the center of the semicircle, and let vectors $\vec{r}$ and $\vec{s}$ correspond to the geometric vectors $\overrightarrow{DA}$ and $\overrightarrow{BD}$ respectively, as indicated in the illustration. We want to prove the vectors corresponding to $\overrightarrow{BA}$ and $\overrightarrow{BC}$ have an inner product of 0 and hence are __________________.

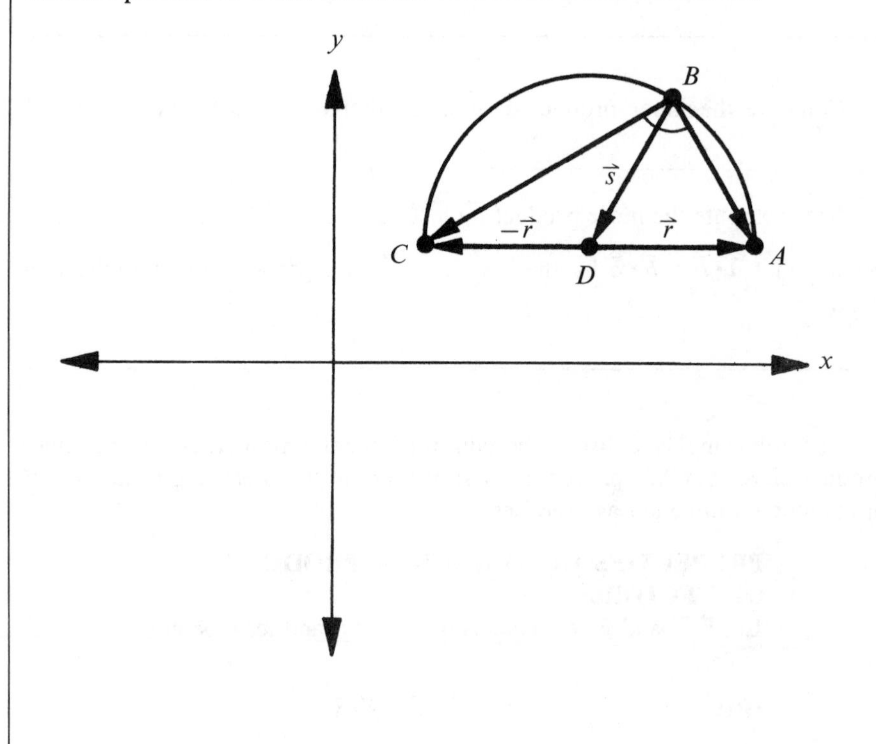

To do this, we note the vector corresponding to $\overrightarrow{BA}$ is ____________

and the vector corresponding to $\overrightarrow{BC}$ is ____________. Supply the reasons for the following steps by referring to the appropriate property of inner product.

$$(\vec{s}+(-\vec{r}))\cdot(\vec{s}+\vec{r}) = (\vec{s}+(-\vec{r}))\vec{s}+(\vec{s}+(-\vec{r}))\vec{r} \text{ by } \_\_\_\_\_\_.$$

$$= \vec{s}\cdot\vec{s}+(-\vec{r})\cdot\vec{s}+\vec{s}\cdot\vec{r}+(-\vec{r})\cdot\vec{r} \text{ by } \_\_\_\_\_\_.$$

$$= \vec{s}\cdot\vec{s}+\vec{s}\cdot(-\vec{r})+\vec{s}\cdot\vec{r}+(-\vec{r})\cdot\vec{r} \text{ by } \_\_\_\_\_\_.$$

$$= \vec{s}\cdot\vec{s}+\vec{s}\cdot[(-\vec{r})+\vec{r}]+(-\vec{r})\cdot\vec{r} \text{ by } \_\_\_\_\_\_.$$

$$= \vec{s}\cdot\vec{s}+\vec{s}\cdot 0+(-\vec{r})\cdot\vec{r}.$$

By ______, $\vec{s}\cdot\vec{0} = 0$ and by ______, $(-\vec{r})\cdot\vec{r} = -(\vec{r}\cdot\vec{r})$.

$$\therefore (\vec{s}+(-\vec{r}))\cdot(\vec{s}+\vec{r}) = \vec{s}\cdot\vec{s}-\vec{r}\cdot\vec{r}.$$

$$= \|\vec{s}\|^2 - \|\vec{r}\|^2 \text{ by } \_\_\_\_\_\_.$$

But $\|\vec{s}\|$ and $\|\vec{r}\|$ are both equal to the radius of the circle. Hence $\|\vec{s}\|^2 - \|\vec{r}\|^2 =$ ___, $[\vec{s}+(-\vec{r})]\cdot(\vec{s}+\vec{r}) = 0$, $\overrightarrow{BC} \perp \overrightarrow{BA}$, and $\angle ABC$ is a ____________

____________.

ANSWERS TO PAGE 89

0

Any scalar multiple of each of the following:

(a) (2,6) (b) (3, −3)

(c) (5, −4) (d) $(-b, a)$

Each of the following or their product with −1.

(a) $\left(\frac{-4}{5}, \frac{3}{5}\right)$

(b) $\left(\frac{12}{13}, \frac{5}{13}\right)$

(c) $\left(\frac{-12}{13}, \frac{5}{13}\right)$

(d) $\left(\frac{-b}{\sqrt{a^2+b^2}}, \frac{a}{\sqrt{a^2+b^2}}\right)$

$\vec{a}\cdot\vec{b} = a_1b_1+a_2b_2$

$\vec{b}\cdot\vec{a} = b_1a_1+b_2a_2$

commutative

(1) T

(2) F; $\frac{1}{2}(\vec{v}) \epsilon \mathcal{R} \times \mathcal{R}$ whereas $\frac{1}{2}$ the length of $\vec{v}$ is a scalar. However, the length of $\frac{1}{2}\vec{v}$ is $\frac{1}{2}$ the length of $\vec{v}$.

(3) F; $(-1,2)$ has a direction opposite to that of $(3,-6)$.

(4) T

(5) F; only standard geometric vectors have their initial point at the origin.

(6) F; the commutative property is not a group requirement.

(7) F; the length of $\vec{AC}$ is $||\vec{r}+\vec{s}||$.

(8) F; it is true when $a^2 \geq b^2$, and a and b are positive.

EXERCISES. 2.4

1. If $\vec{x}$ and $\vec{y}$ are vectors and k and m are scalars, then which of the following are vectors and which are scalars?

   (a) $\vec{x}+\vec{y}$ ______ (b) $k(\vec{x}+\vec{y})$ ______

   (c) $\vec{x}\cdot\vec{y}$ ______ (d) $||\vec{x}+\vec{y}||$ ______

   (e) $\vec{x}\cdot(\vec{x}+\vec{y})$ ______ (f) $-||\vec{x}||$ ______

   (g) $\vec{x}(k+m)$ ______ (h) $k(m\vec{x}\cdot\vec{y})$ ______

   (i) $(\vec{x}\cdot\vec{y})\vec{x}$ ______ (j) $\frac{1}{||\vec{x}||}\cdot\vec{x}$ ______

2. Determine whether the vectors in each of the following pairs are parallel, perpendicular, or neither parallel nor perpendicular.

   (a) $(-3,-3); (2,-2)$ ______

   (b) $(4,3); (6,-2)$ ______

   (c) $(0,-8); \left(-4\frac{1}{2},4\right)$ ______

   (d) $(2,-\sqrt{3}); (4,-2\sqrt{3})$ ______

   (e) $(\vec{x},\vec{y}); (k\vec{y},-k\vec{x})$ ______

3. Find the value of k for which each of the following pairs of vectors are perpendicular.

   (a) $(-6,1); (3,k)$ ______ (b) $(-3,-5); (-k,4)$ ______

   (c) $(2,4); (k,2)$ ______ (d) $(\vec{x},\vec{y}); (k,\vec{y})$ ______

4. Prove **IP2**, i.e., prove that if $\vec{x}$ and $\vec{y}$ are vectors and k is a scalar, then $k(\vec{x}\cdot\vec{y}) = (k\vec{x})\cdot\vec{y}$. (Use supplementary paper.)

5. Prove that $(\vec{r}+\vec{s})\cdot(\vec{r}+\vec{s}) = ||\vec{r}||^2 + 2\vec{r}\cdot\vec{s} + ||\vec{s}||^2$. (Use supplementary paper.)

6. Prove that the statement "if $\vec{a}\cdot\vec{c} = \vec{b}\cdot\vec{c}$, then $\vec{a}=\vec{b}$" is not true in general. (Use supplementary paper.)

7. Let $\vec{r}$ and $\vec{s}$ determine a rhombus and prove that the diagonals of a rhombus are perpendicular to each other. (Use supplementary paper.)

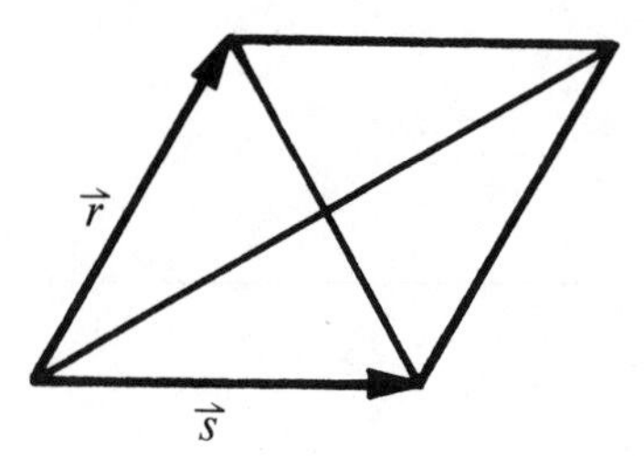

8. Prove that if $\vec{x}$ is perpendicular to $\vec{y}$, then $\vec{x}$ is perpendicular to $-\vec{y}$. (Use supplementary paper.)

9. Prove **IP4**, *i.e.*, if $\vec{v}$ is a vector, then $\vec{v} \cdot \vec{v} = ||\vec{v}||^2$.

ANSWERS TO PAGE 91

$(\vec{s} + \vec{r})$

$\vec{s} + (-\vec{r})$

IP3

IP3

IP1

IP3

IP5 **IP2**

IP4

0 right

angle

ANSWERS TO PAGE 96

(17) $2|r|$

(18) vector addition

(19) $\vec{0}$

(20) $\vec{r}\cdot\vec{s}$

(21) $|k|$

(22) $(X_P - X_Q, 0)$

(23) $(12, -8)$

(24) $(14, 16)$

(25) $\{k(-1,2), k \epsilon \mathcal{R}\}$

(26) $\vec{t} - \vec{s}$

CHAPTER 2 REVIEW EXERCISES

1-8 *True or False:*

1. The vector $3\vec{s} = \vec{s} + \vec{s} + \vec{s}$. ___ (2.3)
2. $\frac{1}{2}(\vec{v})$ is equal to $\frac{1}{2}$ the length of $\vec{v}$. ___ (2.3)
3. The geometric vector corresponding to $(-1,2)$ has the same direction as the geometric vector corresponding to $(3,-6)$. ___ (2.3)
4. For vectors $\vec{r}$ and $\vec{s}$ in $\mathcal{R} \times \mathcal{R}$, $\|\vec{r}\| + \|\vec{s}\| \geq \|\vec{r} + \vec{s}\|$. ___ (2.2)
5. The initial point of a geometric vector is always at the origin. ___ (2.1)
6. If vector addition were not a commutative operation in $\mathcal{R} \times \mathcal{R}$, then $\mathcal{R} \times \mathcal{R}$ would not be a group under vector addition. (2.2)
7. In the illustration, the length of side $\vec{AC}$ is $\|\vec{r} - \vec{s}\|$. (2.2)

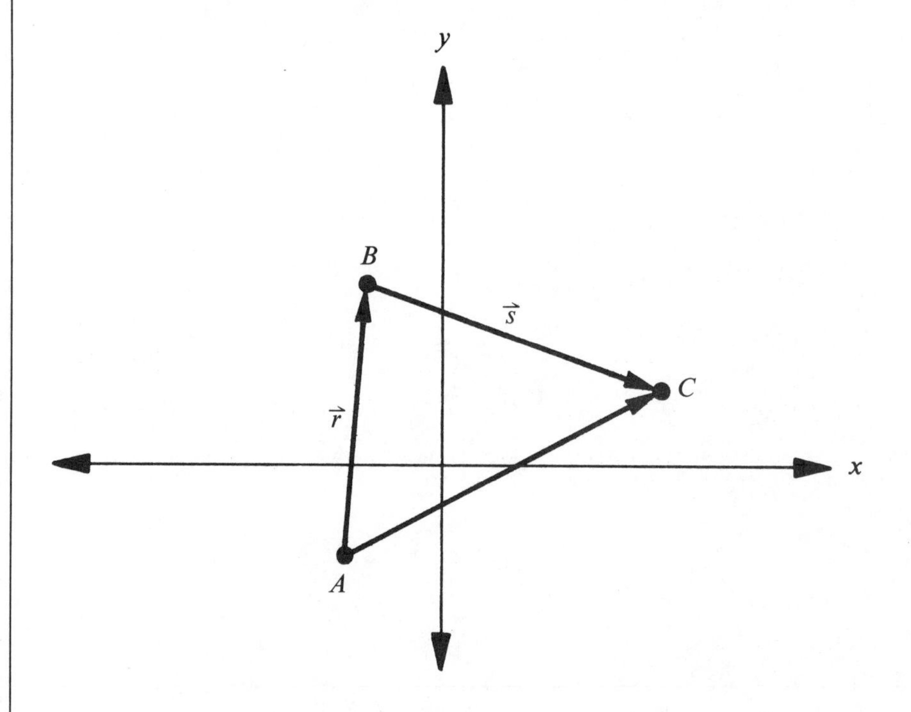

8. If $a^2 \geq b^2$, then it is always the case that $a \geq b$. ___ (2.2)

9. If the coordinates of point R are (x,y) and the coordinates of point S are (a,b), then the ordered pair corresponding to the displacement $\overrightarrow{RS}$ is ____________. (2.1)

10. If $\vec{r}$ is a vector, then which of the following is/are true? (2.1)

    (a) $\vec{r} \in \mathcal{R} \times \mathcal{R}$

    (b) $\vec{r} = (x,y)$ for some $x \in \mathcal{R}$ and $y \in \mathcal{R}$

    (c) $\vec{r}$ is a displacement

    (d) None of the preceding

11. If vector $\left(4x-3, \frac{1}{2}y-1\right) = (7,2)$, then $\vec{x} =$ __ and $\vec{y} =$ __. (2.1)

12. The ____________ representation of a vector has its initial point at the origin. (2.2)

13. A set of points in a plane corresponds to $A = \{(x,y): y = x-3\}$. Each of these points is mapped into another point by the vector $(4,-5)$, thus describing a second set of points. This second set of points corresponds to $\{(x,y):$ ________$\}$. (2.1)

14. If $\vec{a}$ and $\vec{b}$ correspond to the sides of the triangle as illustrated, then the third side corresponds to the vector ________. (2.2)

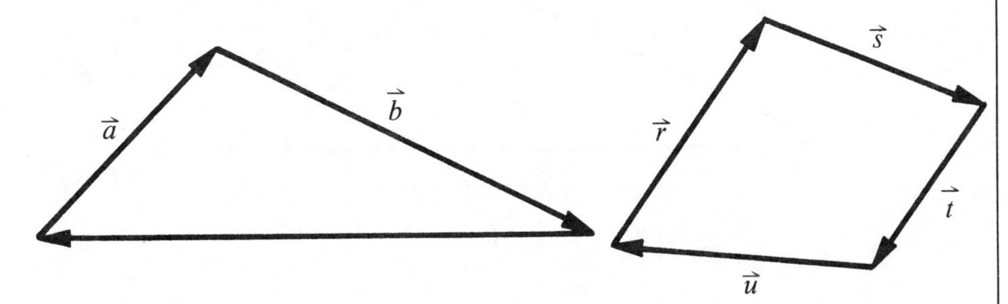

15. The sum of the vectors corresponding to the sides of the quadrilateral illustrated above is $\vec{r}+\vec{s}+\vec{t}+\vec{u} =$ __. (2.2)

16. To prove the diagonals of a rhombus are perpendicular to each other, let $\vec{r}$ and $\vec{s}$ correspond to two adjacent sides, as shown in the illustration. The diagonals, therefore, correspond to the vectors ______ and ______. We can show that the diagonals are perpendicular, because __________ $= 0$. (2.4)

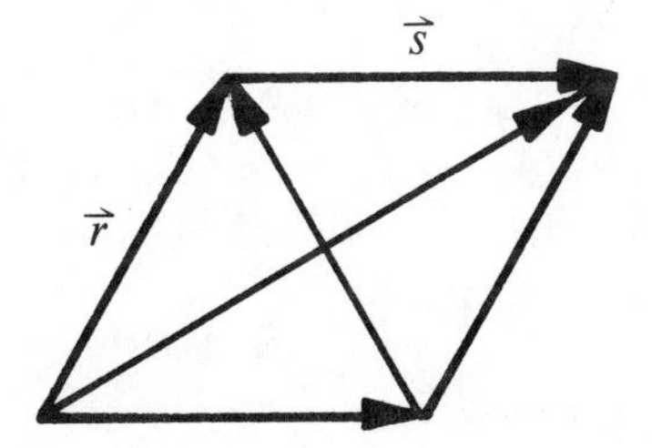

ANSWERS TO PAGE 93

(8) See Appendix.

(9) See Appendix.

ANSWERS TO PAGE 98

$u^2 + v^2 = r^2$

$u^2 + v^2 = 1$

---

u v

1

2π

π

---

17. If $\vec{w} = (r, r\sqrt{3})$, then $||\vec{w}|| =$ ______. (2.1)
18. Let (x,y) be any vector in $\mathcal{R} \times \mathcal{R}$. Then $(0,0) + (x,y) = (0 + x, 0 + y)$ because of the definition of ______ ______. (2.2)
19. For any two points A and B, the vector corresponding to the displacement from A to B plus the vector corresponding to the displacement from B to A is __. (2.1)
20. If $\vec{r}$ and $\vec{s}$ correspond to the legs of a right triangle, then ______ $= 0$. (2.4)
21. If $\vec{v} \epsilon \mathcal{R} \times \mathcal{R}$ and $k \epsilon \mathcal{R}$, then $||k\vec{v}|| =$ ______ $\cdot ||\vec{v}||$. (2.3)
22. If X_P and X_Q are the x coordinates of points P and Q on the x axis, then the vector corresponding to the displacement $\overrightarrow{QP}$ is ______. (2.1)
23. If $\vec{s} = (3, -2)$, then $4\vec{s} = ($______$)$. (2.3)
24. If $\vec{r} = (3,2)$ and $\vec{s} = (4,6)$ then $(2\vec{r} + 2\vec{s}) =$ ______. (2.3)
25. Find the set of all vectors perpendicular to $(2,1)$. ______. (2.4)
26. From the following diagram, determine the vector $\vec{r}$ in terms of $\vec{s}$ and $\vec{t}$. (2.2)

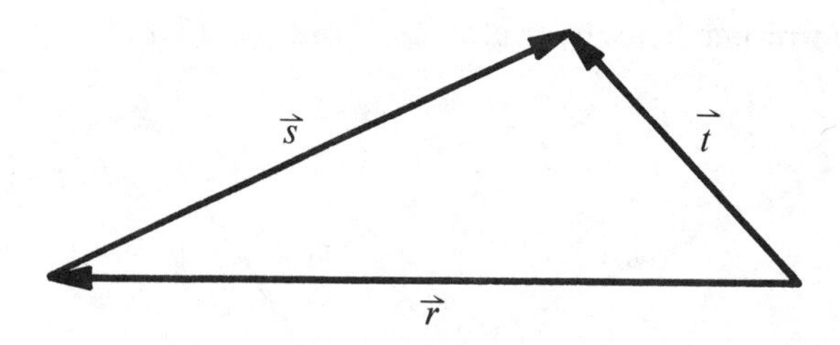

CHAPTER 3

Circular Functions

3.1. PERIODIC FUNCTIONS AND THE UNIT CIRCLE

Many processes in nature change in a cyclic or periodic fashion; they repeat in identical form time after time. The seasons of the year, the tides, the propagation of sound, and the circulation of blood are some examples of periodic events. Many processes in engineering and science are also periodic. The firing of the spark plug in your automobile, the electrical output of a generator, and the flutter of a control surface of an airplane are examples of periodic events in man-made devices. The simplest periodic motion of all is that of a point on a wheel: it returns to a given initial position with respect to its axle once every rotation.

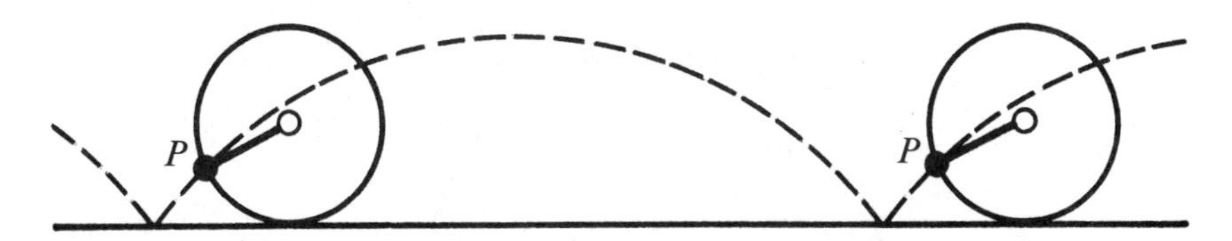

MOVE TO NEXT FRAME

Which of the following appear to be periodic processes? __________

(a) The occurrence of your birthday.

(b) The path of a falling leaf in a breeze.

(c) The movement of the minute hand of a clock.

The mathematical analysis of periodic phenomena very often occurs in terms of the simple periodicity of the path of a point describing a circle. A set of points in a plane, each of which is a given distance from a given point, is a __________.

ANSWERS TO PAGE 95

(9) $(a-x, b-y)$

(10) a,b. (Recall that $\vec{r}$ is an ordered pair of numbers, whereas a displacement is a "movement.")

(11) $\frac{5}{2}$ 6

(12) standard

(13) $y = x - 12$

(14) $-\vec{a} - \vec{b}$

(15) 0

(16) $\vec{r} - \vec{s}$ $\vec{r} + \vec{s}$

$(\vec{r} - \vec{s}) \cdot (\vec{r} + \vec{s})$

P(1,0)

P(0,−1)

(1,0)

The subset of $\mathcal{R} \times \mathcal{R}$ whose graph is a circle with center at the origin and radius r is

$$\{(u,v): \underline{\qquad\qquad}\}.$$

If we let (u,v) be the coordinates of a point on the circle whose center is $(0,0)$ and radius is 1, then u and v are related by the equation __________ .

The circle described in the preceding frame with a radius 1 is called the **unit circle.** (See the illustration.) We have labeled the horizontal and vertical axes the __ and __ axes instead of the x and y axes, in order to reserve the symbol x for a future use. From the definition of the unit circle, the radius

$$||\overrightarrow{OP}|| = \_\_.$$

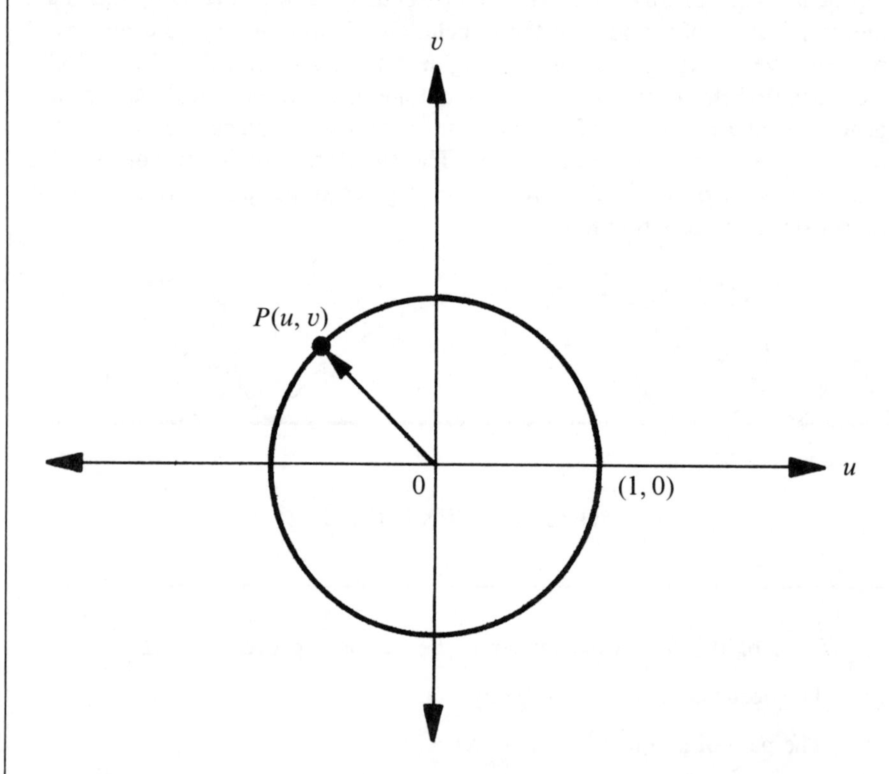

The circumference of the unit circle is _______, and the length of the arc of any of its semicircles is __, since a semicircle is half a circle.

ANSWERS TO PAGE 97

Let x be a real number. Start at the point (1,0) of the unit circle and move along the circle a distance $|x|$, in a counterclockwise direction if $x \geq 0$ and in a clockwise direction if $x < 0$. Let $P(u,v)$ be the point of the circle at which you arrive by this movement.

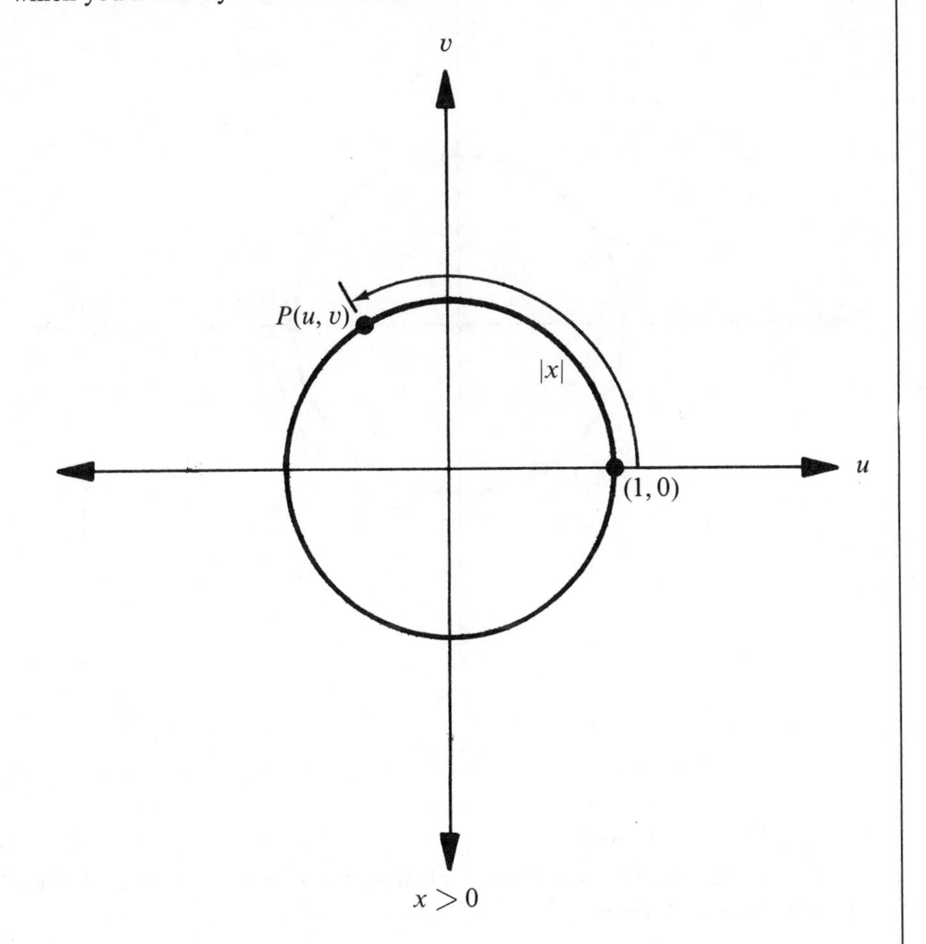

(a) (c)

circle

ANSWERS TO PAGE 102

0 1

$(-1,0)$

$(0,-1)$ 0 -1

---

u v

1

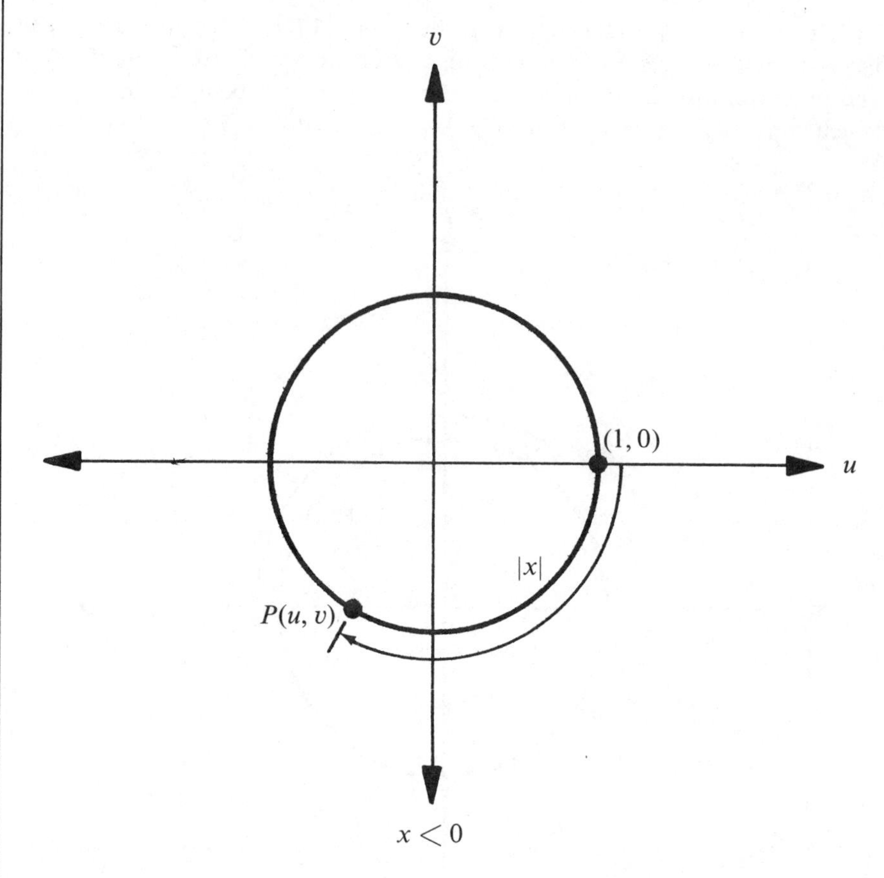

If $x = \pi$, then $P(u,v) = P(-1,0)$. If $x = 2\pi$, $P(u,v) =$ ________. If $x = \frac{-\pi}{2}$, $P(u,v) =$ ________.

If you had trouble with these problems, try sketching figures of these functions on scratch paper.

To every real number x, one can assign the coordinates of the point P on a unit circle as described in the previous frame. This establishes a correspondence between the set of real numbers and the set of coordinates of points on the unit circle. Since the point P is unique for a given x, this correspondence is a function. This function will be denoted by p.

If $x = \frac{\pi}{2}$, then $p(x) = (0,1)$; if $x = 0$, $p(x) =$ ______.

Find each of the following, where p is the function described in the last frame.

(a) $p\left(\frac{\pi}{2}\right) =$ __________ (b) $p(\pi) =$ __________

(c) $p\left(\frac{3\pi}{2}\right) =$ __________ (d) $p(3\pi) =$ __________

The __________ of the function p is the set of real numbers and the ________ of p is the subset of $\mathcal{R} \times \mathcal{R}$ whose graph is the ________.

The function p assigns the coordinates (u,v) of a point on the unit circle to each real number x. Using this function, two other functions are defined: one assigns x to the first coordinate of $p(x) = (u,v)$ and the other assigns x to the second coordinate. The first of these is called the **cosine function** and the second the **sine function.**

MOVE TO NEXT FRAME

DEFINITIONS:

cosine $= \{(x,u): u$ is the first coordinate of $p(x)\}$.

sine $= \{(x,v): v$ is the second coordinate of $p(x)\}$.

cos x is the abbreviation for the **value** or **image** of the cosine function at x and **sin x** is the abbreviation for the **value** of the sine function at x. The domain of each of these functions is $\mathcal{R}$ and the the range of each is

$\{t:$ __________ $\}$.

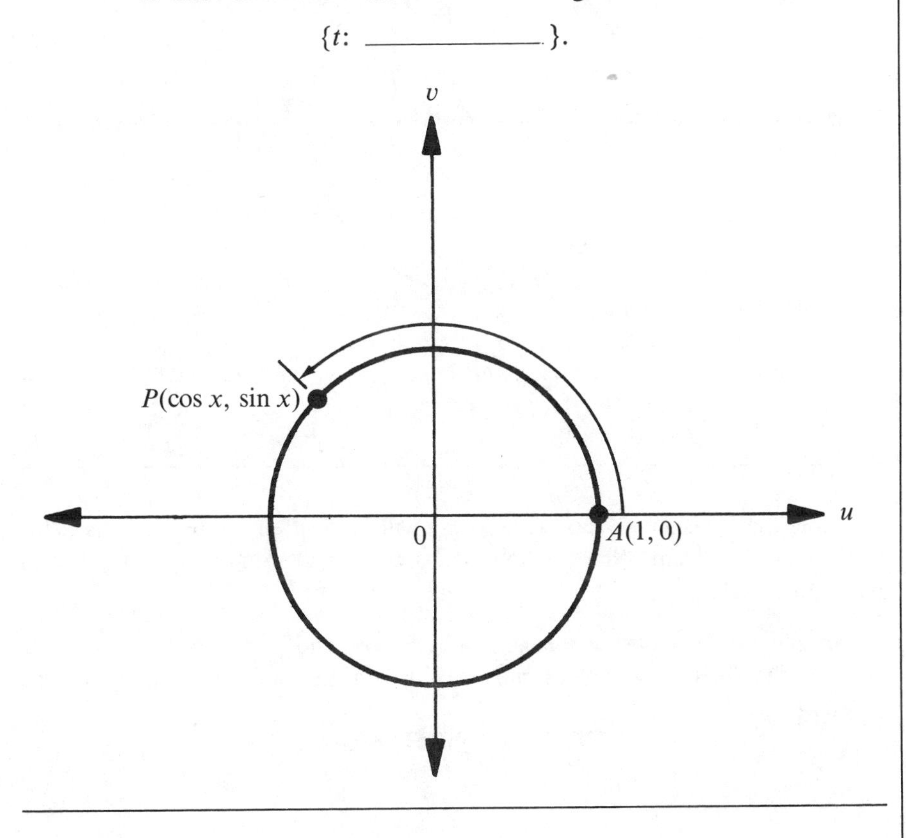

Examples: $p(0) = (1,0)$: $\cos 0 = 1$, $\sin 0 = 0$.

$$p\left(\frac{\pi}{2}\right) = (0,1); \quad \cos\frac{\pi}{2} = \_\_, \quad \sin\frac{\pi}{2} = \_\_.$$

$$p(\pi) = \_\_\_\_\_; \quad \cos \pi = -1, \quad \sin \pi = 0.$$

$$p\left(\frac{3\pi}{2}\right) = \_\_\_\_\_; \quad \cos\frac{3\pi}{2} = \_\_, \quad \sin\frac{3\pi}{2} = \_\_\_\_.$$

0 0 0

−1 −1 −1

Because their definitions are based upon the unit circle, the sine and cosine functions are called **circular functions.**

If $|x|$ is the length of an arc on the unit circle, measured from the point $(1,0)$ to the point (u,v), then $\cos x = \_\_$ and $\sin x = \_\_$. Since $u^2 + v^2 = 1$ it follows by substitution that $(\cos x)^2 + (\sin x)^2 = \_\_$.

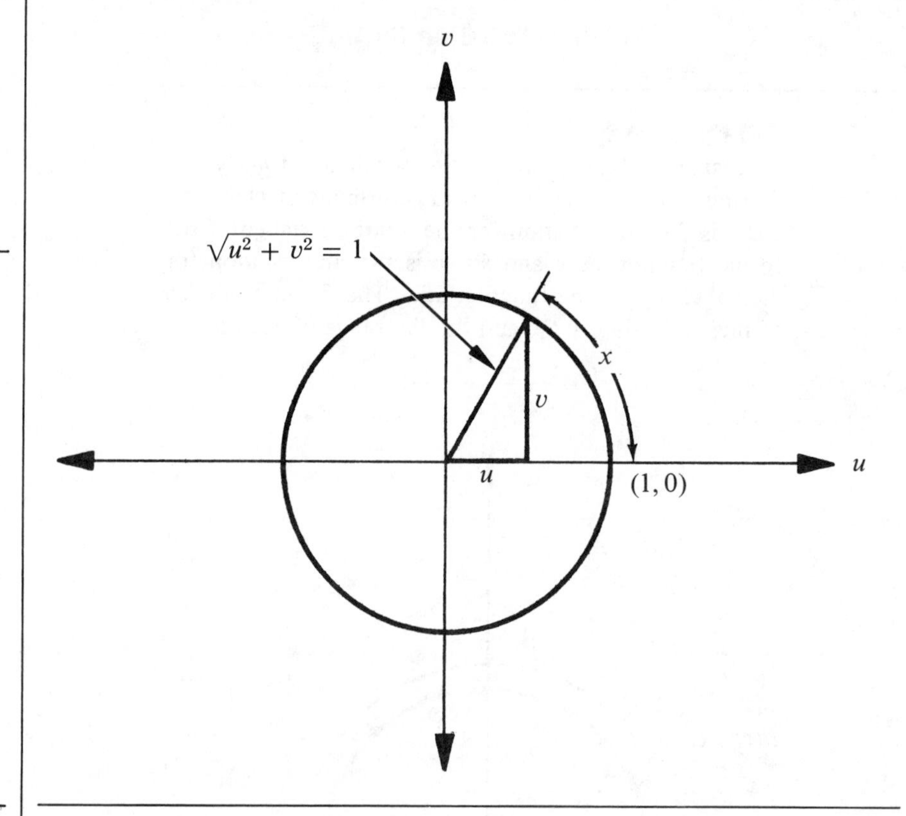

2π

Note that $(\cos x)^2 = (\cos x) \cdot (\cos x)$ will be written as $\cos^2 x$. This helps to distinguish it from $\cos x^2$, which means $\cos(x \cdot x)$. Similarly, $(\sin x)^2$ will be written $\sin^2 x$.

In general, $y = \cos^n x$ means $y = (\cos x)^n$, and $y = \cos x^n$ means $y = \cos(x^n)$. Similarly, $y = \sin^n x$ means $y = (\sin x)^n$, and $y = \sin x^n$ means $y = \sin(x^n)$.

MOVE TO NEXT FRAME

$f(x + a)$

Yes, because $f(x + 2a) = f[(x + a) + a] = f(x + a) = f(x)$.

If point P on the unit circle starts at $(1,0)$ and travels a distance $x = 2\pi$, it has returned to its starting point $(1,0)$. Thus $p(2\pi) = p(0)$, and, hence,

$\cos 0 = \cos 2\pi =$ ___ and $\sin 0 = \sin 2\pi =$ ___.

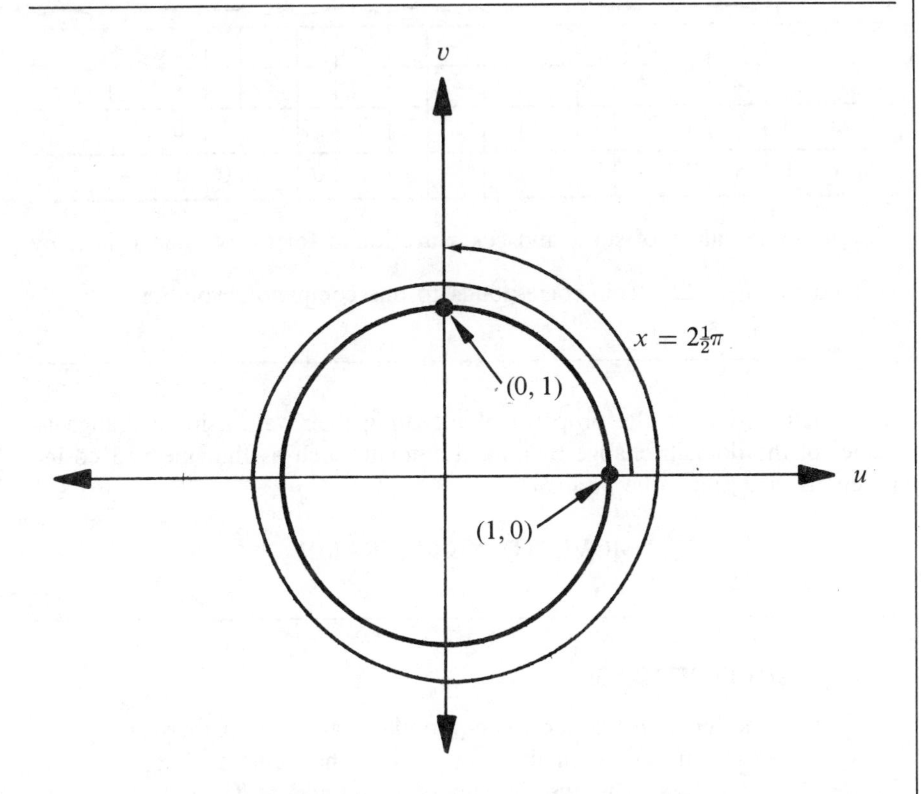

$x = 2\frac{1}{2}\pi$ corresponds to the coordinates of the point arrived at by making 1 complete revolution plus an additional $\frac{1}{4}$ of a revolution in a counter-clockwise direction.

MOVE TO NEXT FRAME

If P travels a distance $x = 2\frac{1}{2}\pi$, it has passed its starting point and continued an additional distance $\frac{1}{2}\pi$. It follows that

$$\cos 2\tfrac{1}{2}\pi = \cos \frac{\pi}{2} = \_\_,$$

and

$$\sin 2\tfrac{1}{2}\pi = \sin \_\_ = \_\_.$$

In general, as a consequence of the definitions of the sine and cosine functions,

$$\sin x = \sin(x + 2\pi) \quad \text{and} \quad \cos x = \cos(x + 2\pi).$$

ANSWERS TO PAGE 101

(a) (0,1) (b) (−1,0)

(c) (0,−1) (d) (−1,0)

domain

range unit circle

$-1 \leq t \leq 1$

2π

$0 \leq x < 2\pi$

(b) 0 (c) 0

(d) -1 (e) 1

(a) $\frac{\pi}{2}$, since $\sin 4x =$

$\sin(4x + 2\pi) = \sin 4\left(x + \frac{\pi}{2}\right)$.

(b) 4π, since $\cos \frac{1}{2} x =$

$\cos\left(\frac{1}{2}x + 2\pi\right) = \cos \frac{1}{2}(x + 4\pi)$.

In the following table, the values of x are increasing and hence one, two, three, or more revolutions around the unit circle may be necessary to find the corresponding point.

Insert the values for cos x and sin x that are missing in the table.

	1st revolution				2nd				3rd				4th...	
x	0	$\frac{\pi}{2}$	π	$\frac{3\pi}{2}$	2π	$\frac{5\pi}{2}$	3π	$\frac{7\pi}{2}$	4π	$\frac{9\pi}{2}$	5π	$\frac{11\pi}{2}$	6π	$\frac{13\pi}{2}$
$\cos x$	1	0	-1		1	0	-1		1	0	-1		1	0
$\sin x$	0	1	0		0	1	0		0	1	0		0	1

The same values of sin x and cos x are found for every change in x by an amount of ____. This corresponds to one complete revolution.

Functions having the property of repeating their values in the range as values of the domain change by a fixed amount, such as the sine and cosine functions, are said to be *periodic*.

MOVE TO NEXT FRAME

DEFINITIONS:

The function f is said to be **periodic** if and only if there exists an $a \epsilon \mathcal{R}$ such that, for all x in the domain of f, $x + a$ is also in the domain of f and $f(x) = f(x + a)$. The number a is called a **period** of $f(x)$.

The period of a function is the smallest positive value of a, if it exists, for which the equation $f(x) = f(x + a)$ is true for all x. This smallest value is sometimes called the **fundamental period** of f. The phrase **f is a function with period a** shall mean f is a periodic function whose fundamental period is a.

MOVE TO NEXT FRAME

If f is a periodic function with period a, then

$f(x) =$ ____________ for all $x \epsilon \mathcal{R}$.

If f is periodic with period a, is $f(x) = f(x + 2a)$?

Why or why not? ____________

If f is periodic with period a, show that

$$f(x - a) = f(x).$$

If f is periodic with period a, then $f(x) =$ ______________ for all x in the domain of f. Substitute $x - a$ for x in $f(x) = f(x + a)$ and you have

____.

1 0

In general, we have the following theorem:

THEOREM:
If f is periodic, with period $a > 0$, then

$$f(x + na) = f(x)$$

for all $n \epsilon J$.

The proof of the theorem is omitted. It may be proved by mathematical induction.

MOVE TO NEXT FRAME

Suppose that f is periodic with period $a = 2$, so that for all x in the domain of f, $f(x + 2) = f(x)$. Using the above theorem, we can express every value of f in the form $f(x)$ where $0 \leq x < 2$. For example, express $f(7.3)$ in this form.

$$f(7.3) = f[1.3 + 3(2)] = f(1.3).$$

To find $f(-7.3)$,

$$f(-7.3) = f[0.7 - 4(2)] = f(0.7).$$

You should see that

$$f(7.3) = f(5.3) = f(3.3) = f(1.3)$$

and similarly

$$f(-7.3) = f(-5.3) = \text{\_\_\_\_\_\_} = \text{\_\_\_\_\_\_} = f(0.7).$$

0

Let f be periodic with period 2. Write each of the following in the form $f(x)$ where $0 \leq x < 2$.

(a) $f(3.5) =$ ____________ (b) $f(-3.5) =$ ____________

(c) $f(341) =$ ____________ (d) $f(10) =$ ____________

$\frac{\pi}{2}$ 1

ANSWERS TO PAGE 108

(a) $\frac{2\pi}{3}$ (b) 8π

(c) $\frac{2\pi}{|a|}$ (d) $\frac{2\pi}{|a|}$

The sine and cosine functions are periodic with period ______. From any point P on the unit circle, a further movement of 2π units around the circle will result in a return to P again. Thus the following theorem.

THEOREM:

$$\cos (x + 2n\pi) = \cos x,$$

and

$$\sin (x + 2n\pi) = \sin x.$$

for any $n \epsilon J$.

Since the period of the cosine and sine functions is 2π, one only need determine their values for x in the interval __________ to determine their values for all real x.

Examples: Find the following.

(a) $\sin \frac{7}{2}\pi = \sin \left(\frac{7}{2}\pi - 2\pi\right) = \sin \frac{3}{2}\pi = -1$

(b) $\cos \frac{7}{2}\pi =$ __ (c) $\sin 4\pi =$ __

(d) $\cos 9\pi =$ ______ (e) $\sin 6\frac{1}{2}\pi =$ __

Since the sine function has period 2π, $\sin 2x = \sin (2x + 2\pi) = \sin 2(x + \pi)$; hence the function f is defined by $f(x) = \sin 2x$ and is periodic with period π.

Find the periods of the functions g and h where

(a) $g(x) = \sin 4x$ ____________

(b) $h(x) = \cos \frac{1}{2} x$ ____________

THEOREM:

Let k be a positive real number. If f is a periodic function with period $a > 0$ and the function g is defined $g(x) = f(kx)$, then g is periodic with period $\frac{a}{k}$.

Proof: We wish to show

$$g\left(x + \frac{a}{k}\right) = \underline{\qquad}$$

for all x in the domain of f and $\frac{a}{k}$ is the smallest positive number which has this property.

$$g\left(x + \left(\frac{a}{k}\right)\right) = f\left[k\left(x + \frac{a}{k}\right)\right]$$

by the definition of g.

$$f\left[k\left(x + \frac{a}{k}\right)\right] = f(kx + a),$$

by the ____________ property.

$$f(kx + a) = f(kx)$$

since ________________.

$$f(kx) = g(x),$$

by ________________.

$$\therefore g\left(x + \frac{a}{k}\right) = g(x)$$

for all x in the domain of g.

Hence, g is periodic. To show its period is $\frac{a}{k}$, we must show that if $t > 0$ such that $g(x + t) = g(x)$, then $t \geq \frac{a}{k}$. To do this, suppose $t > 0$ and $g(x + t) = g(x)$ for every x. Then, since g is defined by $g(x) = f(kx)$ for any real number x, and for any real number x,

$\frac{x}{k}$ is a real number, we have $g\left(\frac{x}{k}\right) = f\left[k\left(\frac{x}{k}\right)\right] = f(x)$. Hence

$$f(x) = g\left(\frac{x}{k}\right) = g\left(\frac{x}{k} + t\right) = f(x + kt)$$

for all x. Thus, since f has period a, $kt \geq a$. Therefore $t \geq \frac{a}{k}$, and $\frac{a}{k}$ is the period of g.

If f is taken to be the cosine function and g is a function of the form $g(x) = f(kx)$, which is defined by $g(x) = \cos\left(\frac{1}{2}x\right)$, then $a =$ ______ and $k =$ ____. Hence by the theorem proved in the preceding frame, g is periodic with period $\frac{2\pi}{1/2} = 4\pi$.

$f(x + a)$

$f(x - a) = f[(x - a) + a] = f(x)$

$f(-3.3)$ $\quad$ $f(-1.3)$

(a) $f(1.5)$ $\quad$ (b) $f(0.5)$

(c) $f(1)$ $\quad$ (d) $f(0)$

ANSWERS TO PAGE 110

(8) (b) $p\left(\frac{3\pi}{2}\right)$ (c) $p\left(\frac{\pi}{2}\right)$

(d) $p(\pi)$ (e) $p(0)$

(f) $p\left(\frac{\pi}{2}\right)$

(9) (a) $\frac{3\pi}{2}$; $\frac{7\pi}{2}$

(b) π; 3π

(c) 0; 2π

(d) π; 3π

(10) (a) $\frac{\pi}{4}$; $\frac{5\pi}{4}$

(b) $\frac{3\pi}{4}$; $\frac{7\pi}{4}$

(11) (a) π (b) 4π

(c) $\frac{\pi}{2}$ (d) 4π

(12) $g(x + 2)$ or $g(x + 2n)$

(13) 0 -1

(14) 8π

(15) $\frac{-7\pi}{6}$ or $\frac{-11\pi}{6}$

(16) $\frac{c}{k}$

Use the above theorem to find the periods of the functions defined by the following equations.

(a) $u = \cos 3x$ ______ (b) $v = \sin \frac{1}{4}x$ ______

(c) $u = \cos ax$ ______ (d) $v = \sin ax$ ______

$g(x)$

distributive

f has period a

definition of g

2π

$\frac{1}{2}$

EXERCISES. 3.1

1. Describe the set of ordered pairs of numbers which constitutes the set of coordinates of the points of the unit circle. ______________
2. The length of the circumference of the unit circle is ______.
3. What fraction of the circumference of a unit circle is an arc whose length is:

   (a) π — (b) $\frac{\pi}{4}$ —

   (c) $\frac{3\pi}{2}$ — (d) $\frac{\pi}{2}$ —
4. Find $p(x)$ for each of the following values of x:

   (a) $\frac{\pi}{2}$ ______ (b) $\frac{3\pi}{2}$ ______

   (c) $-\frac{\pi}{2}$ ______ (d) $\frac{\pi}{4}$ ______

   (e) 4π ______ (f) $-\frac{\pi}{4}$ ______________
5. Find each of the following numbers:

   (a) $\cos\frac{\pi}{2}$ = ______ (b) $\sin\frac{\pi}{2}$ = ______

   (c) $\sin\frac{3\pi}{2}$ = ______ (d) $\sin\frac{\pi}{4}$ = ______

   (e) $\cos 3\pi$ = ______ (f) $\sin\frac{-3\pi}{4}$ = ______
6. Specify the domain D and the range R for the sine and cosine functions.

   (a) sine: $D =$ —

   $R =$ ______________________________

   (b) cosine: $D =$ —

   $R =$ ______________________________
7. In $\{(x,v)\colon v = \sin x\}$, the number x may be interpreted as the distance from the point ______ measured counterclockwise around the ______ circle if $x > 0$ and measured ______________ around the unit circle if ______.
8. If $p(x + 2n\pi) = p(x)$, express each of the following as $p(b)$, where $0 \leq b2\pi$.

ANSWERS TO PAGE 112

x	0	$\frac{\pi}{2}$	π	$\frac{3\pi}{2}$	2π
$\cos x$	1	0	-1	0	1
$\sin x$	0	1	0	-1	0

(a) $p\left(\frac{5\pi}{2}\right) = p\left(\frac{\pi}{2} + 2\pi\right) = p\left(\frac{\pi}{2}\right)$

(b) $p\left(\frac{-\pi}{2}\right) =$ ________ (c) $p\left(\frac{-3\pi}{2}\right) =$ ________

(d) $p(3\pi) =$ ________ (e) $p(4076\pi) =$ ________

(f) $p\left(4\frac{1}{2}\pi\right) =$ ________

9. If p has the period 2π, find two values of x such that $0 \leq x < 4\pi$ and

(a) $p\left(\frac{-\pi}{2}\right) = p(x)$ ____________

(b) $p(13\pi) = p(x)$ ____________

(c) $p(12\pi) = p(x)$ ____________

(d) $p(-\pi) = p(x)$ ____________

10. For what values of x, where $0 \leq x < 2\pi$, do the following relations hold?

(a) $\cos x = \sin x$ ____________

(b) $\cos x = -\sin x$ ____________

11. Find the period of the function g if $g(x) =$

(a) $\sin 2x$ ________ (b) $\sin \frac{1}{2} x$ ________

(c) $\cos 4x$ ________ (d) $\cos \frac{1}{2} x$ ________

12. If g is periodic with period 2, then $g(x) =$ ____________________ for all x.

13. If $x = \frac{11\pi}{2}$, then $\cos x =$ ___, and $\sin x =$ _____.

14. The period of the function

$\left\{(x,f(x)) \colon f(x) = \sin \frac{1}{4} x\right\}$ is ______.

15. If $\sin x = \frac{1}{2}$ and $-2\pi \leq x < 0$, then $x =$ ______________________.

16. If the period of f is c, then the period of the function g where $g(x) = f(kx)$ is ______.

3.2. GRAPHS OF SINE AND COSINE

A graph consists of points in a plane corresponding to a subset of ______ . Sine and cosine are subsets of $\mathcal{R} \times \mathcal{R}$, because they are functions and thus sets of ______________________ .

(1) $\{(u,v): u^2 + v^2 = 1\}$

Since the sine and cosine functions are periodic with period 2π, we may determine their graphs by examining the function over an interval of length 2π. Hence we can limit our concern with x to the interval $0 \leq x <$ ______ .

(2) 2π

The unit circle is separated into four equal arcs by the axes; each of these arcs has a length ___. Beginning at the point corresponding to (1,0) and proceeding in a counterclockwise direction as in the illustration, the separation point corresponding to the arc whose length is $\frac{\pi}{2}$ has coordinates (0,1). Beginning at the point (1,0) again, the point corresponding to the arc having length π is ________ . Similarly the point corresponding to the arc having length $\frac{3\pi}{2}$ is ________ .

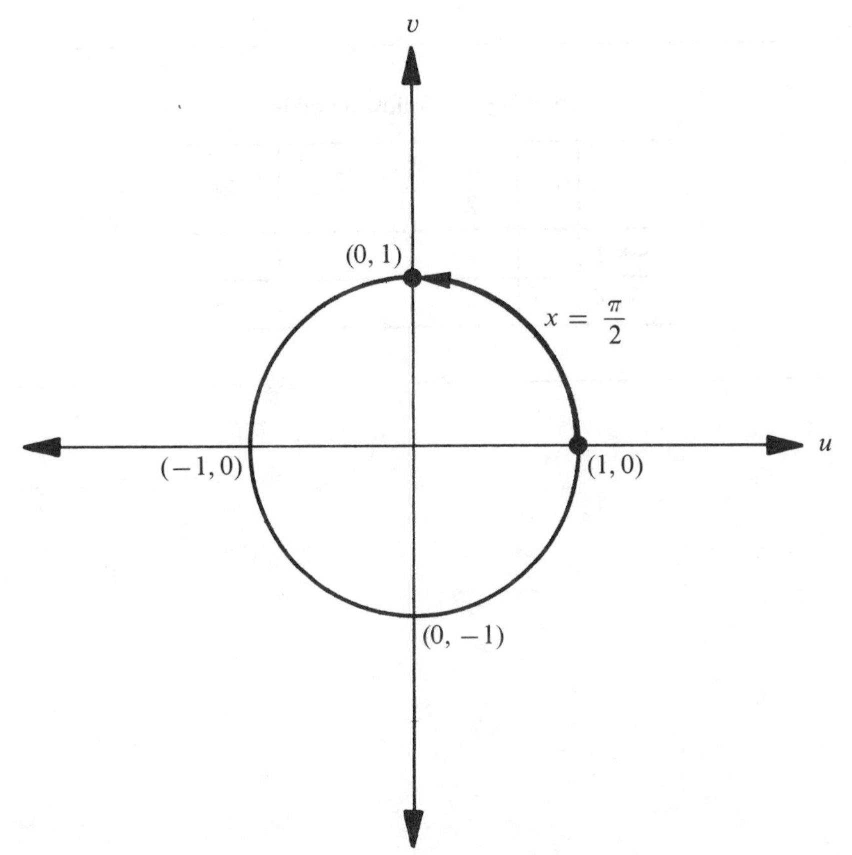

(3) (a) $\frac{1}{2}$ (b) $\frac{1}{8}$

(c) $\frac{3}{4}$ (d) $\frac{1}{4}$

(4) (a) (0,1) (b) (0, −1)

(c) (0, −1) (d) $\left(\frac{\sqrt{2}}{2}, \frac{\sqrt{2}}{2}\right)$

(e) (1,0) (f) $\left(\frac{\sqrt{2}}{2}, \frac{-\sqrt{2}}{2}\right)$

(5) (a) 0 (b) 1

(c) −1 (d) $\frac{\sqrt{2}}{2}$

(e) −1 (f) $\frac{-\sqrt{2}}{2}$

(6) (a) $\mathcal{R}$

$\{y: y \in \mathcal{R} \text{ and } -1 \leq y \leq 1\}$

(b) $\mathcal{R}$

$\{y: y \in \mathcal{R} \text{ and } -1 \leq y \leq 1\}$

(7) (1,0) unit

clockwise

$x < 0$

one

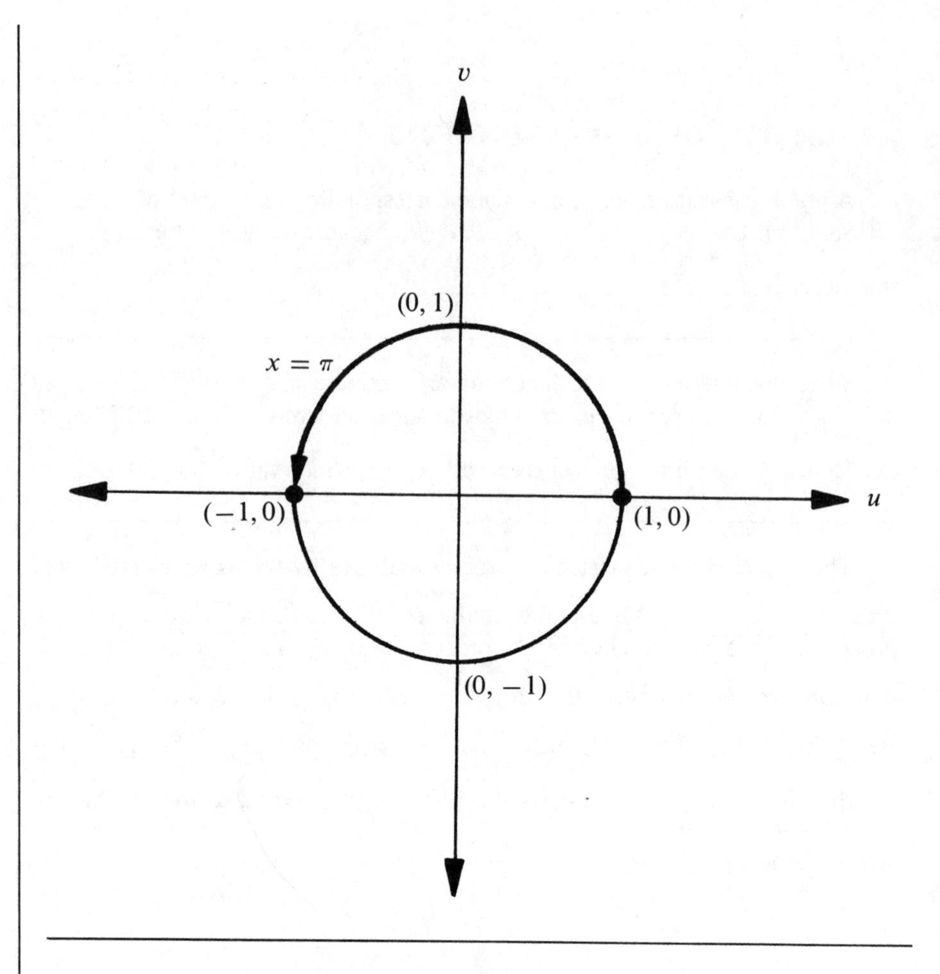

$\frac{\sqrt{2}}{2}$

$\left(\frac{\sqrt{2}}{2}, \frac{\sqrt{2}}{2}\right), \left(\frac{-\sqrt{2}}{2}, \frac{\sqrt{2}}{2}\right)$

$\left(\frac{-\sqrt{2}}{2}, \frac{-\sqrt{2}}{2}\right), \left(\frac{\sqrt{2}}{2}, \frac{-\sqrt{2}}{2}\right)$

Complete the following table:

x	0	$\frac{\pi}{2}$	$\frac{3\pi}{2}$	2π
$\cos x$				
$\sin x$				

Now consider the midpoint of each of the quarter circles formed by the axes and the unit circle. Beginning at (1,0), these points correspond to arc lengths of ______, ______, ______, and ______ . (See the illustration.)

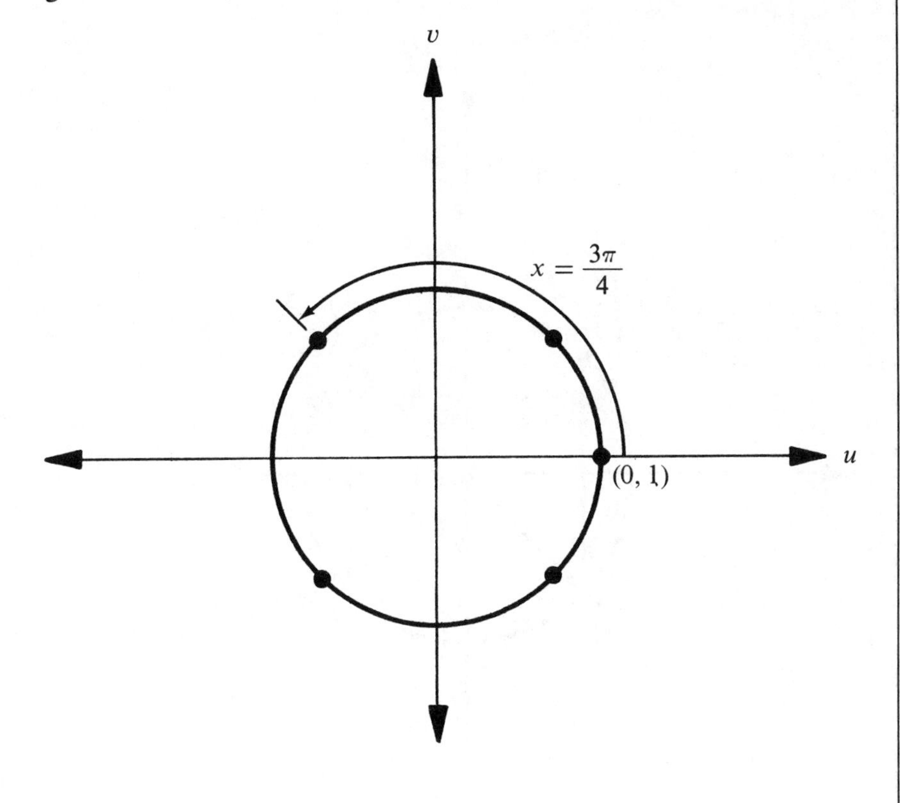

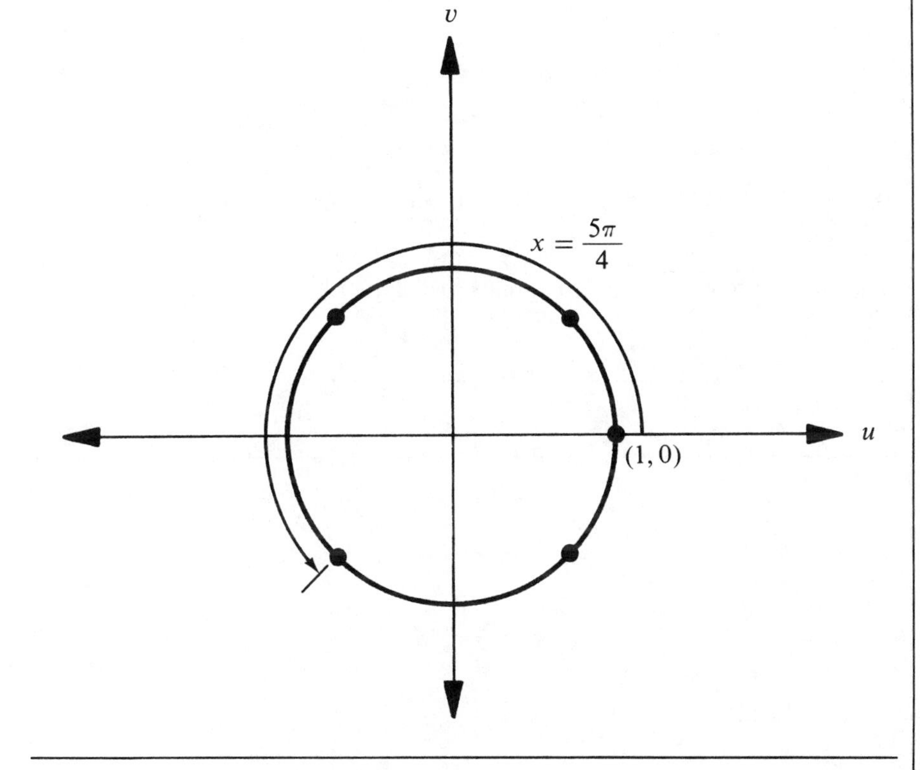

ANSWERS TO PAGE 111

$\mathcal{R} \times \mathcal{R}$

ordered pairs of numbers

2π

$\frac{\pi}{2}$

$(-1,0)$

$(0,-1)$

ANSWERS TO PAGE 116

$\frac{1}{2}$

$\frac{\sqrt{3}}{2}$

$\left(\frac{1}{2}, -\frac{\sqrt{3}}{2}\right)$

$\left(-\frac{1}{2}, \frac{-\sqrt{3}}{2}\right)$

$\left(\frac{1}{2}, \frac{-\sqrt{3}}{2}\right)$

Perpendiculars from the midpoints of the arcs of the quarter circles to the u-axis form four isosceles right triangles. Each right triangle has a hypotenuse whose length is _____. (See the illustration.)

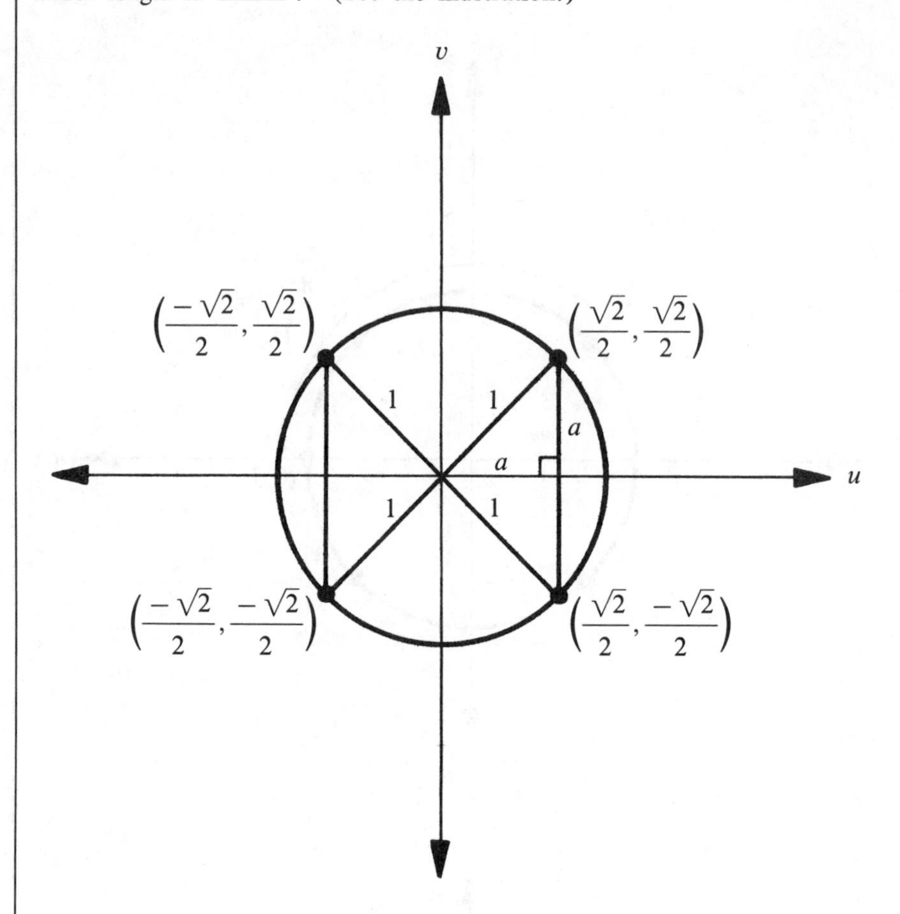

If we let a be the length of the sides of the isosceles right triangles, then by the Pythagorean Theorem, $a^2 + a^2 = 1^2$ and the length of a side is _____.

Thus the coordinates of the midpoints of the quarter circles are _________, _________, _________, and _________.

Complete the following table:

x	$\frac{\pi}{4}$	$\frac{3\pi}{4}$	$\frac{5\pi}{4}$	$\frac{7\pi}{4}$
$\cos x$				
$\sin x$				

The coordinates of points on the unit circle corresponding to arc lengths $\frac{\pi}{3}$, $\frac{2\pi}{3}$, $\frac{4\pi}{3}$, and $\frac{5\pi}{3}$ may be found also.

Beginning at $P_1(1,0)$ on the unit circle, mark a point P_2 corresponding to a chord of unit length and then from P_2 another chord of unit length, and so on. (See the illustration.)

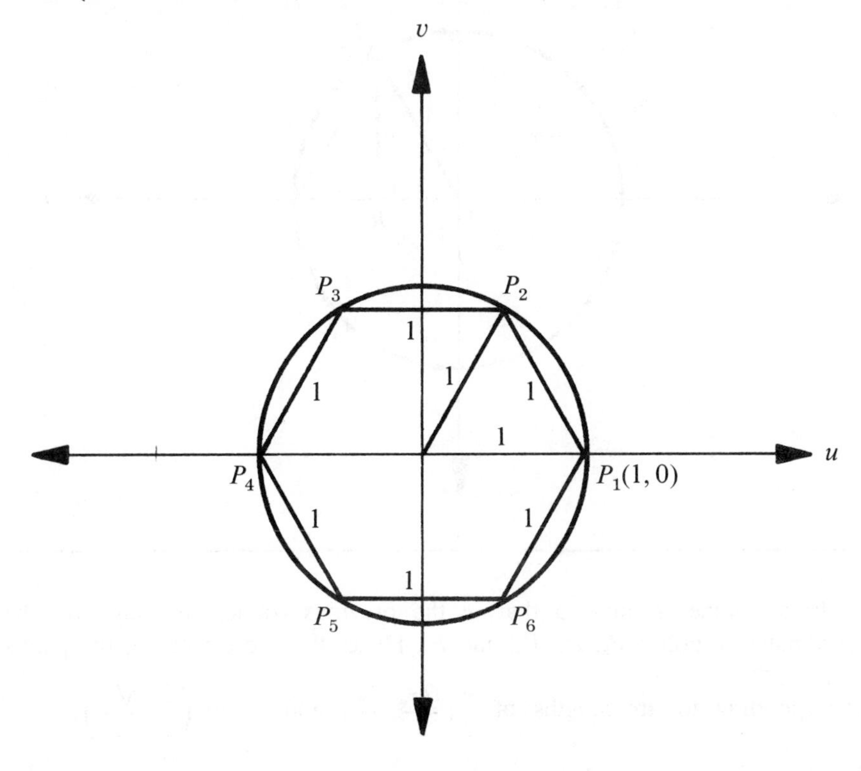

There are exactly six such chords. The circumference of the unit circle is ______ ; therefore the length of the arc corresponding to unit chord $\overline{P_1P_2}$ is ______. Beginning at (1,0) again, P_3 corresponds to an arc of length ______. P_5 corresponds to an arc length ______, and P_6 to an arc of length ______.

ANSWERS TO PAGE 113

$\frac{\pi}{4}$, $\frac{3\pi}{4}$, $\frac{5\pi}{4}$, and $\frac{7\pi}{4}$

ANSWERS TO PAGE 118

$\frac{1}{2}$ $\quad \frac{\sqrt{3}}{2}$

$\left(\frac{\sqrt{3}}{2}, \frac{1}{2}\right)$

$\frac{7\pi}{6}$

$\frac{11\pi}{6}$

$\left(\frac{\sqrt{3}}{2}, \frac{1}{2}\right)$, $\left(\frac{-\sqrt{3}}{2}, \frac{1}{2}\right)$, $\left(\frac{-\sqrt{3}}{2}, -\frac{1}{2}\right)$

$\triangle OP_1P_2$ is an equilateral triangle, with the perpendicular $\overline{P_2R}$ from P_2 to the u-axis forming two congruent right triangles. Then the first coordinate of P_2 is ___. (See the illustration.) Using the Pythagorean Theorem to find the secondary coordinate (v) of P_2, we have $v^2 + \left(\frac{1}{2}\right)^2 = 1^2$, or $v =$ ____.

Thus the coordinates of P_2 are ______.

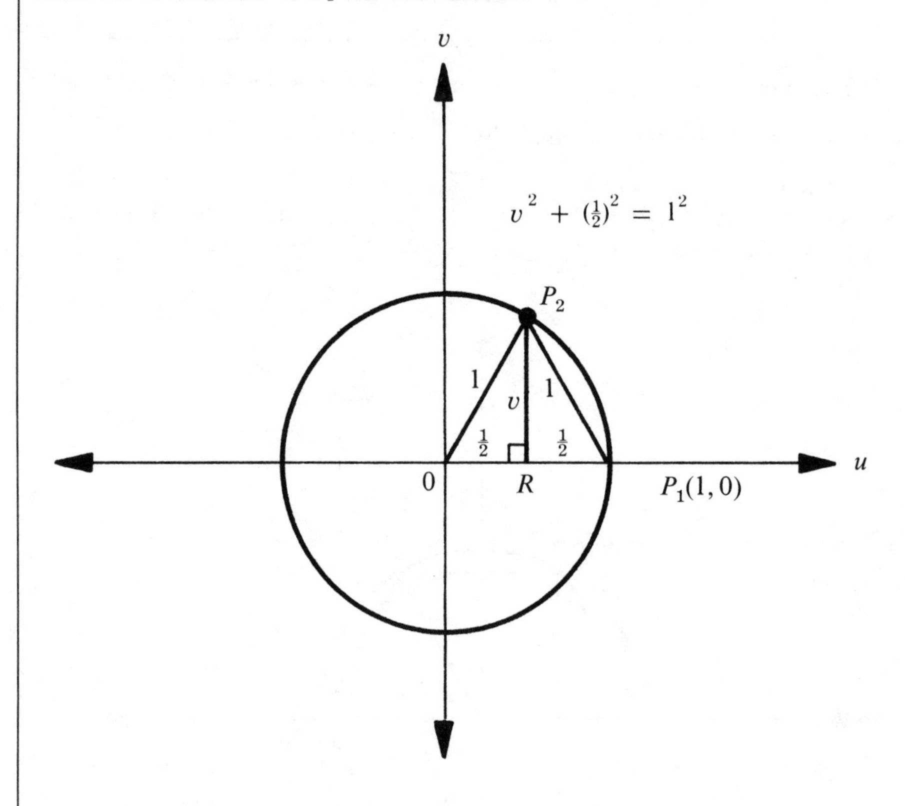

In a manner similar to that in the previous frame, we may find the coordinates of points P_3, P_4, P_5, and P_6. Hence the coordinates of the points corresponding to arc lengths of $\frac{\pi}{3}$, $\frac{2\pi}{3}$, $\frac{4\pi}{3}$, and $\frac{5\pi}{3}$ are $\left(\frac{1}{2}, \frac{\sqrt{3}}{2}\right)$, $\left(-\frac{1}{2}, \frac{\sqrt{3}}{2}\right)$, ________, and ________, respectively.

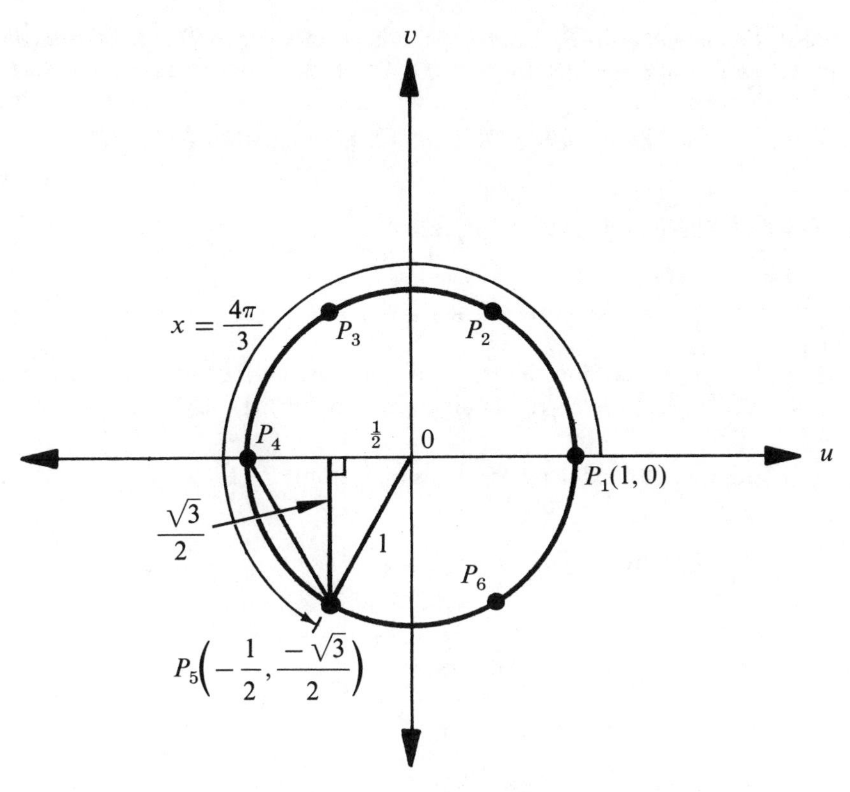

The perpendicular bisector of unit chord $\overline{P_1P_2}$ contains the center O and bisects arc $\widehat{P_1P_2}$ at M_1. Since $\widehat{P_1P_2}$ has a length of $\frac{\pi}{3}$, the length of arc $\widehat{P_1M_1}$ is ___. (See the illustration.)

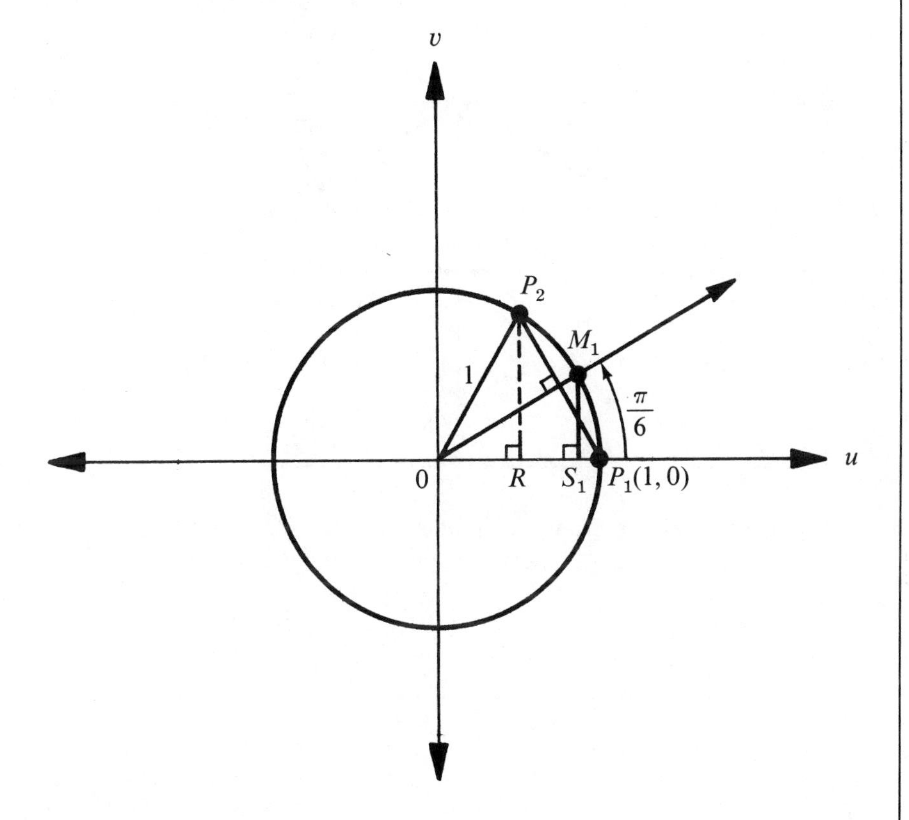

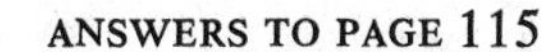
ANSWERS TO PAGE 115

x	$\frac{\pi}{4}$	$\frac{3\pi}{4}$	$\frac{5\pi}{4}$	$\frac{7\pi}{4}$
$\cos x$	$\frac{\sqrt{2}}{2}$	$\frac{-\sqrt{2}}{2}$	$\frac{-\sqrt{2}}{2}$	$\frac{\sqrt{2}}{2}$
$\sin x$	$\frac{\sqrt{2}}{2}$	$\frac{\sqrt{2}}{2}$	$\frac{-\sqrt{2}}{2}$	$\frac{-\sqrt{2}}{2}$

2π

$\frac{2\pi}{3}$

$\frac{\pi}{3}$ $\frac{4\pi}{3}$

$\frac{5\pi}{3}$

The perpendicular $\overline{M_1S_1}$ from M_1 to the u-axis forms the right triangle $\triangle OS_1M_1$, which is congruent to $\triangle P_2RO$. The hypotenuse $\overline{OM_1}$ of $\triangle\ OS_1M_1$ has a length of 1, and the legs $\overline{M_1S_1}$ and $\overline{OS_1}$ have lengths of ___ and _____, respectively. The coordinates of M_1 are __________.

In an analogous fashion the perpendicular bisectors of unit chords $\overline{P_3P_4}$, $\overline{P_4P_5}$, and $\overline{P_6P_1}$ bisect the corresponding arc at points M_2, M_3, and M_4. These points correspond to arc lengths, measured from $P_1(1,0)$, of $\frac{5\pi}{6}$, _____, and _____, respectively.

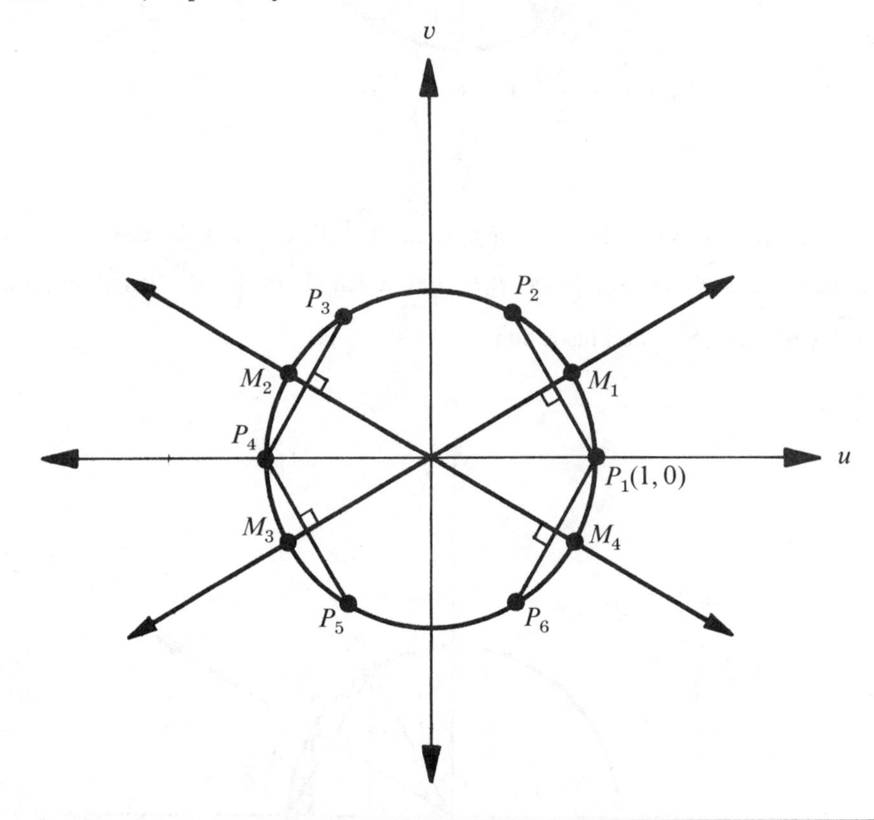

$|y| \leq 1$

0	$\frac{\pi}{6}$	$\frac{\pi}{3}$	$\frac{\pi}{2}$	π	$\frac{3\pi}{2}$	2π
2	$\sqrt{3}$	1	0	-2	0	2

The perpendiculars from the points M_1, M_2, M_3, and M_4 form four congruent right triangles. Therefore the coordinates of these points are _______, _______, _______, and $\left(\frac{\sqrt{3}}{2}, -\frac{1}{2}\right)$, respectively.

Complete the following table:

x	$\frac{\pi}{6}$	$\frac{5\pi}{6}$	$\frac{7\pi}{6}$	$\frac{11\pi}{6}$
$\cos x$				
$\sin x$				

Our first concern will be the cosine function. From the table in the preceding frame, we may obtain a set of ordered pairs of numbers, $(x, \cos x)$, with which to make a correspondence between the cosine and the points in the xy plane.

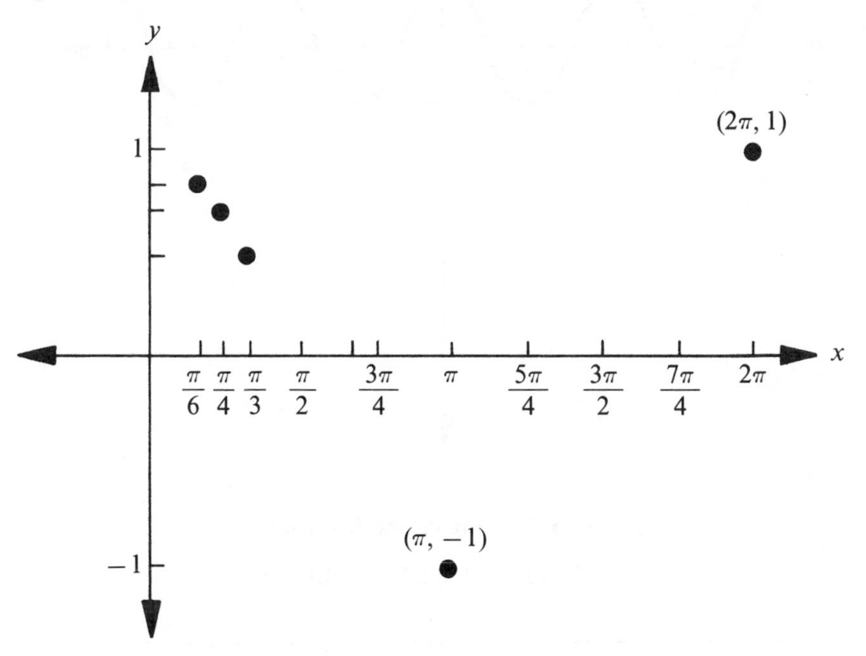

Graph of one period of the cosine function.

Plot the remaining points on the incomplete graph. Use the ordered pairs $(x, \cos x)$ that were determined at intervals of $x = \frac{\pi}{6}$ and $x = \frac{\pi}{4}$ in previous frames. Draw a smooth curve through the points. Use the approximations $\frac{\sqrt{3}}{2} = 0.87$ and $\frac{\sqrt{2}}{2} = 0.71$ as a convenience in graphing.

$\frac{\pi}{6}$

ANSWERS TO PAGE 122

$\{y: y \leq |k|\}$ or $\{y: -|k| \leq y \leq |k|\}$

1

-1

1

1

The curve you have graphed is one period of the cosine function. To extend our graph to the right and left, we can use the periodicity property to obtain the following graph.

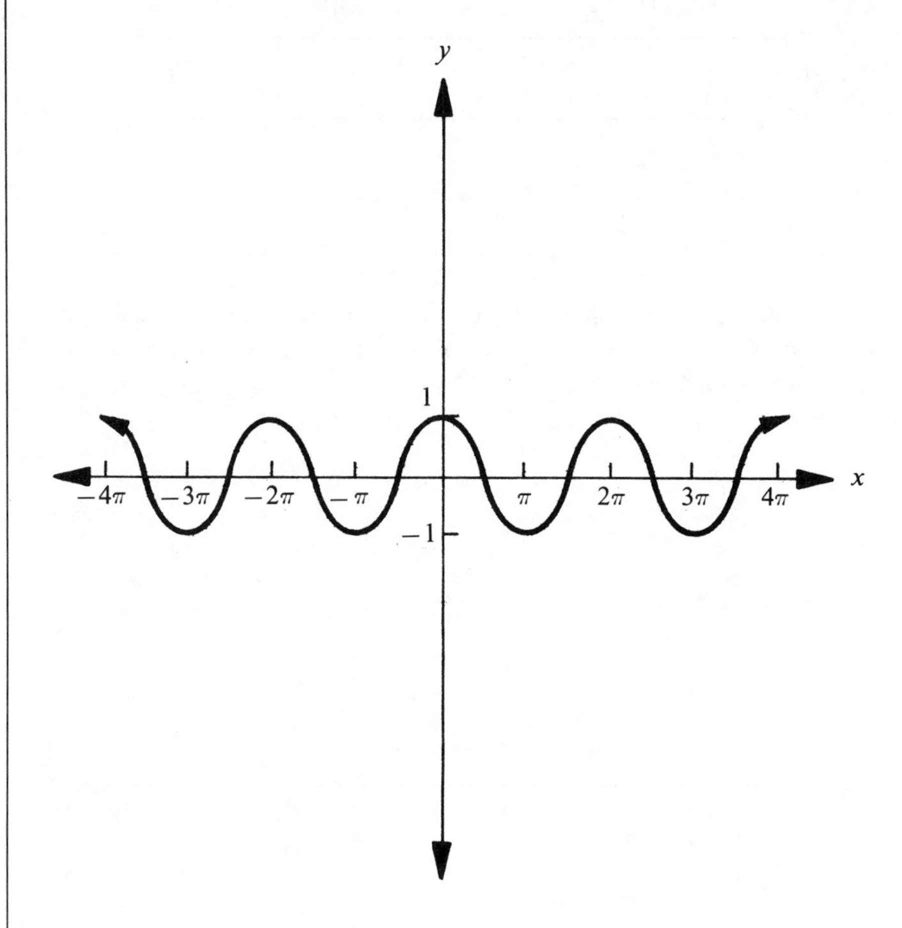

Graph of the cosine function.

MOVE TO NEXT FRAME

The range of the function defined by $y = \cos x$ is $\{y:$ ________$\}$. This means statements such as $\cos x = 4$, $\cos x = -3$, and $\cos x = \frac{3}{2}$ are impossible.

Given $y = 2 \cos x$, complete the following table:

x	0	$\frac{\pi}{6}$	$\frac{\pi}{3}$	$\frac{\pi}{2}$	π	$\frac{3\pi}{2}$	2π
$y = 2 \cos x$							

ANSWERS TO PAGE 119

x	$\frac{\pi}{6}$	$\frac{5\pi}{6}$	$\frac{7\pi}{6}$	$\frac{11\pi}{6}$
$\cos x$	$\frac{\sqrt{3}}{2}$	$\frac{-\sqrt{3}}{2}$	$\frac{-\sqrt{3}}{2}$	$\frac{\sqrt{3}}{2}$
$\sin x$	$\frac{1}{2}$	$\frac{1}{2}$	$-\frac{1}{2}$	$-\frac{1}{2}$

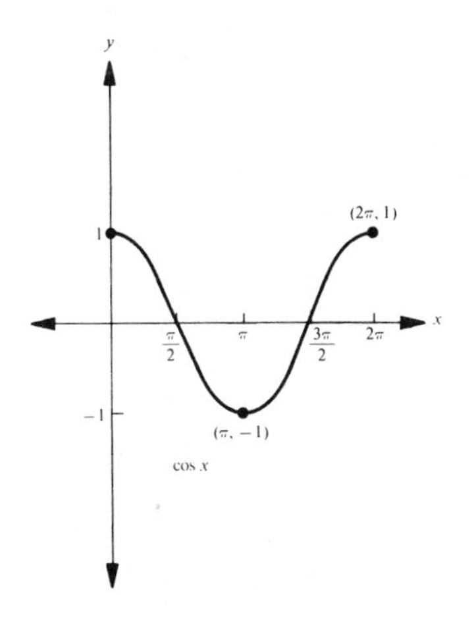

By now you should be becoming familiar with the shape of the graph of the cosine function. The following is the graph of one period or **cycle** of the function defined by $y =$ ________.

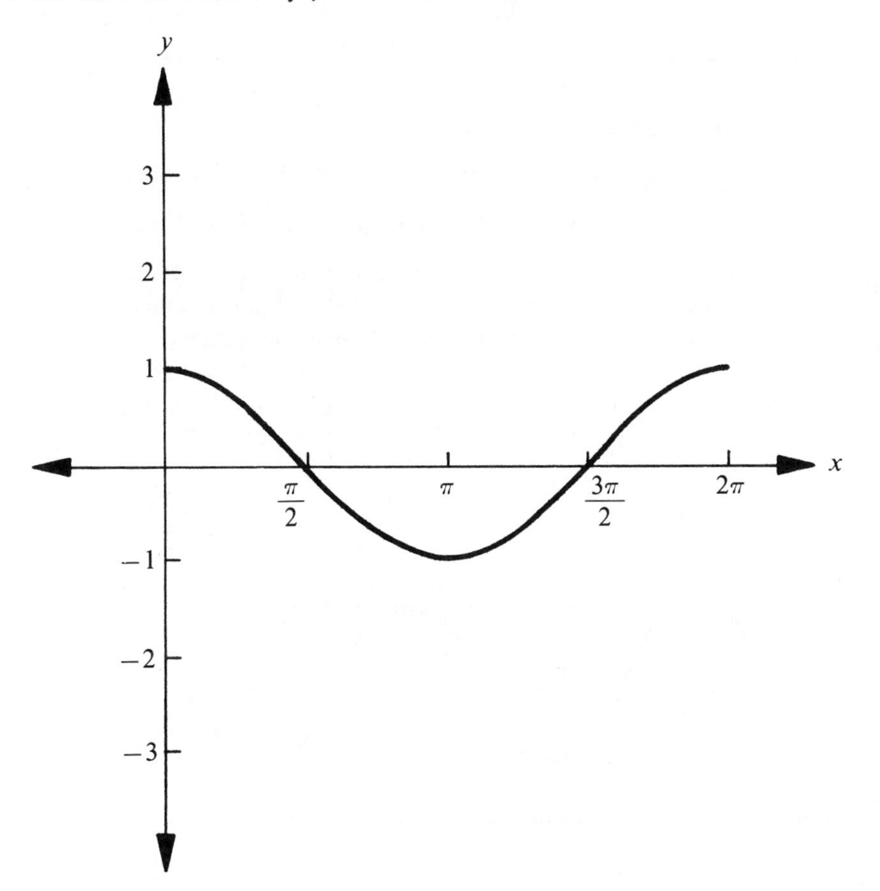

Superimpose the graph of $y = 2 \cos x$ on the graph of $y = \cos x$, using the ordered pairs calculated for the preceding frame as a guide.

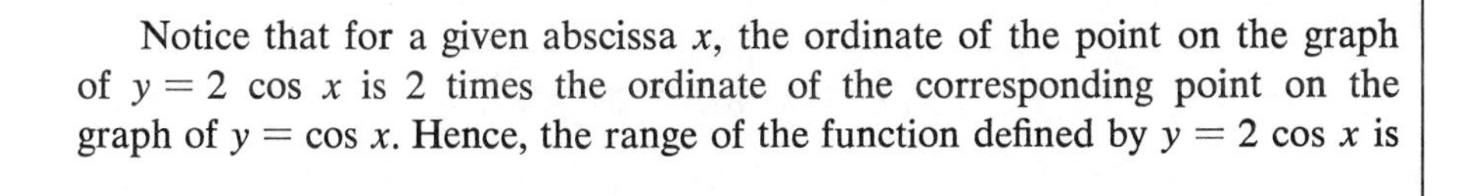

Notice that for a given abscissa x, the ordinate of the point on the graph of $y = 2 \cos x$ is 2 times the ordinate of the corresponding point on the graph of $y = \cos x$. Hence, the range of the function defined by $y = 2 \cos x$ is

________.

Similarly, for a given abscissa x, the ordinate of a point on the graph of $y = -3 \cos x$ is ____ times the ordinate of a point on the graph of $y = \cos x$. Thus the range of the function defined by $y = -3 \cos x$ may be found by multiplying each element in the range of $y = \cos x$ by ____. Therefore, the range of the function defined by $y = -3 \cos x$ is $\{y$: ____ $\leq y \leq$ ___$\}$.

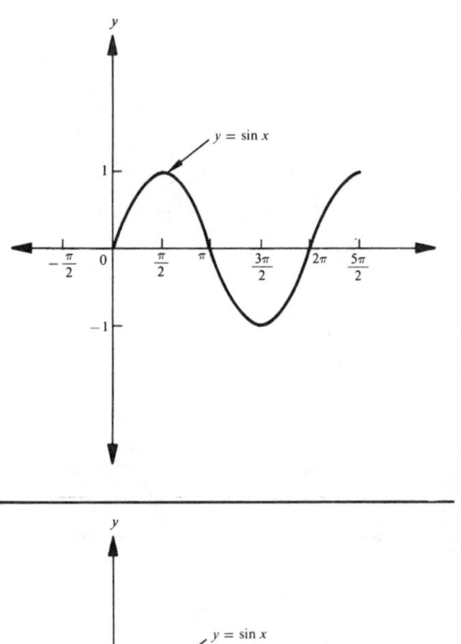

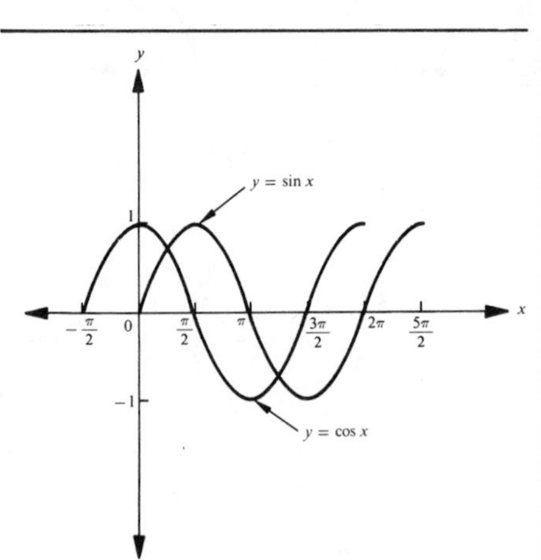

In general, the function defined by $y = k \cos x$ has a range equal to

____.

DEFINITION:

The **amplitude** of a periodic function is the number $\frac{M - m}{2}$, where M is the maximum value of the range of the function and m is the minimum value of the range of the function, provided both of these values exist. If neither exists, the amplitude is not defined.

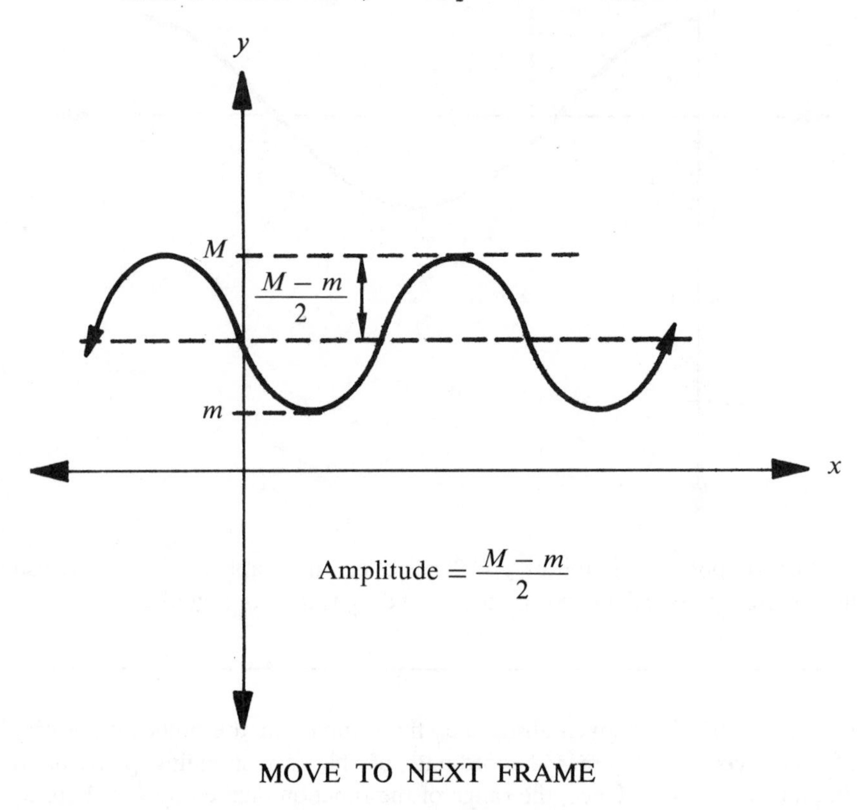

MOVE TO NEXT FRAME

The maximum value of the cosine function ($y = \cos x$) is ___ and the minimum value is ______. Thus the amplitude of the cosine function is $\frac{1-(-1)}{2} =$ ___.

The amplitude of the sine function ($y = \sin x$) is also ___.

The amplitude of the function defined by $y = k \sin x$ is ____.

The equation of the function of the form $\{(x,y): y = k \cos bx\}$, having a period equal to $\frac{2}{3}\pi$, and an amplitude equal to 2, is ________________.

Graph the function described in the preceding frame for $0 \leq x \leq 2\pi$.

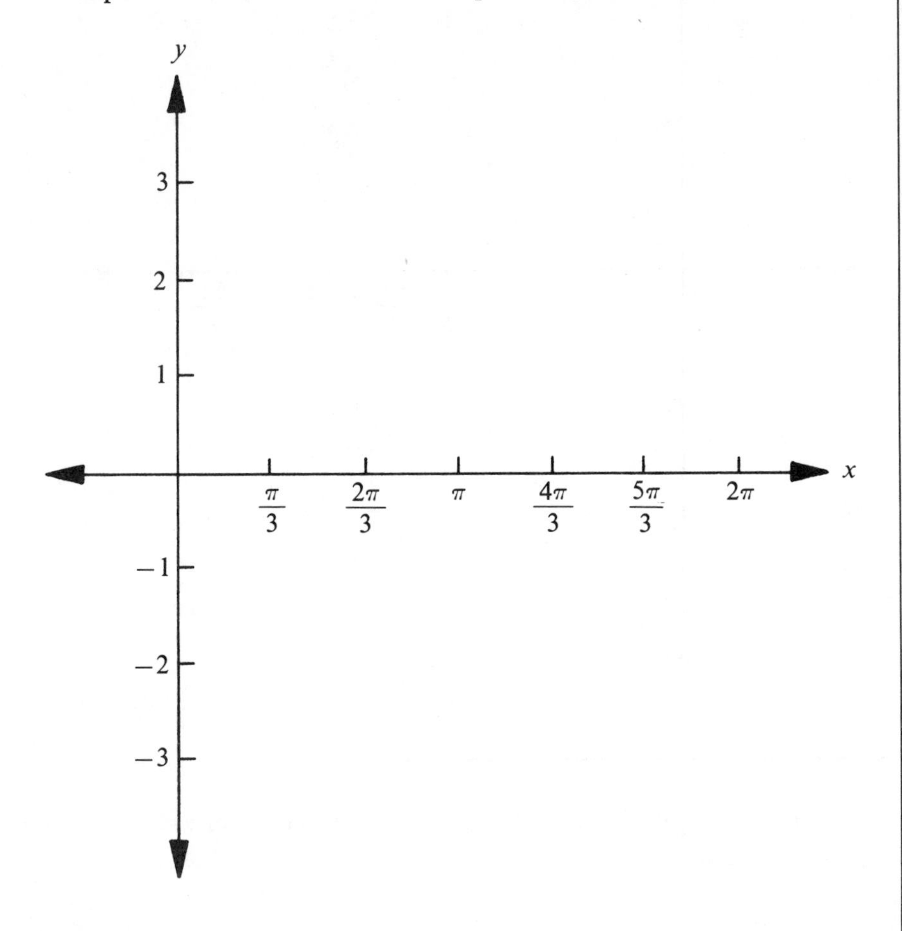

$y = \cos x$

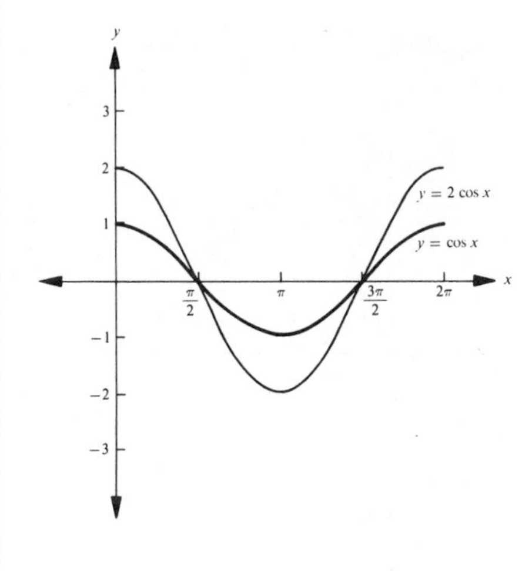

$\{y: |y| \leq 2\}$

−3

−3

−3 3

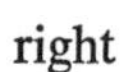

right

Using the values previously determined for the sine function, graph the function $y = \sin x$ for $0 \leq x \leq 2\pi$ on the following coordinate system. Then, using the periodic nature of the sine function, extend the graph to cover the interval $0 \leq x \leq \frac{5}{2}\pi$.

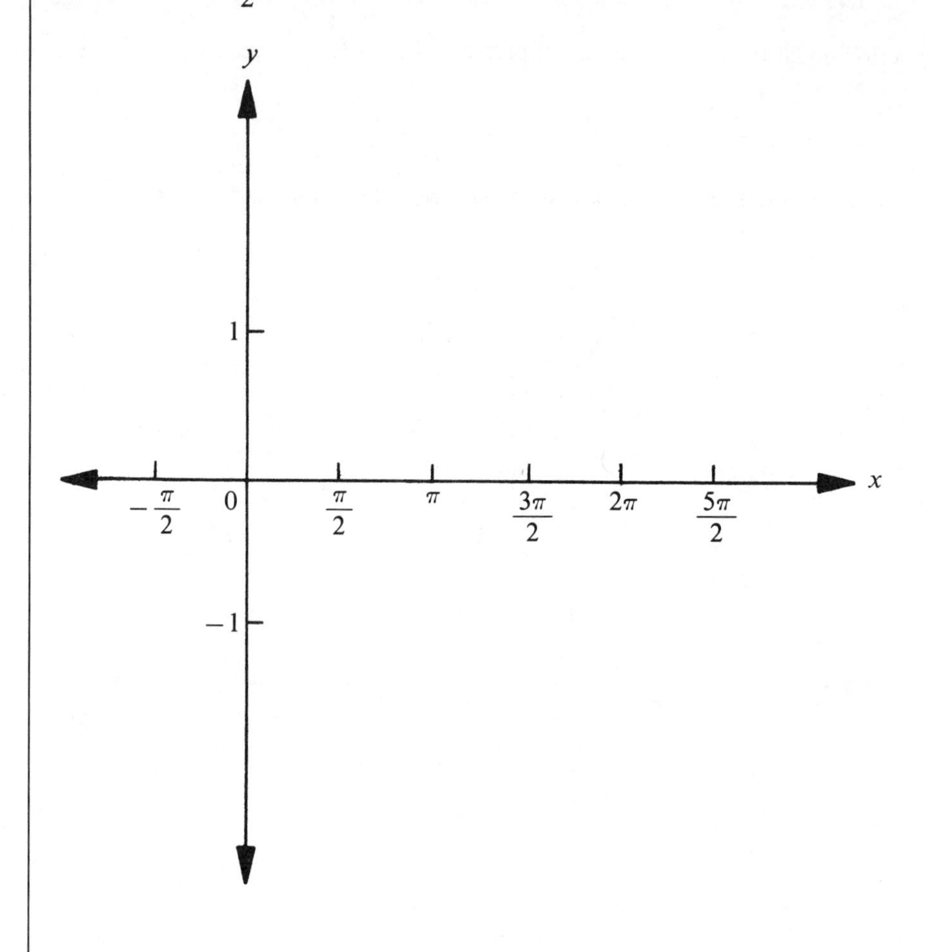

On the same coordinate system, graph the function defined by $y = \cos x$ for $-\frac{\pi}{2} \leq x \leq 2\pi$.

Do you see that the graph of $y = \cos x$, when translated $\frac{\pi}{2}$ units to the right, coincides with the graph of $y = \sin x$?

Note: In general, no attempt is made to make the scale on the x axis the same as that of the y axis. This generally accepted procedure is followed throughout this text for convenience in presentation and should not detract from your understanding.

MOVE TO NEXT FRAME

In section 2.1 a translation was described in terms of a vector, *i.e.,* if an ordered pair of numbers, (x,y), is translated into another ordered pair of numbers, (x',y'), by the vector (a,b), then $x' - x =$ ___ and $y' - y =$ ___. Thus the translation is effected by replacing x in the definition of the original function by ______ and replacing y by ______.

To translate the function $\{(x,y): y = \cos x\}$ into a function whose graph is displaced by the vector $(\pi,2)$, simply replace y in the defining equation by __________ and replace x by __________. The resulting function is ____. The prime notation may be dropped since it is merely a convenience for distinguishing the coordinates of the point being translated from the one into which it is translated.

$$\{(x',y'):y' - 2 = \cos (x' - \pi)\} = \{(x,y):y - 2 = \cos (x - \pi)\}.$$

(See the illustration.)

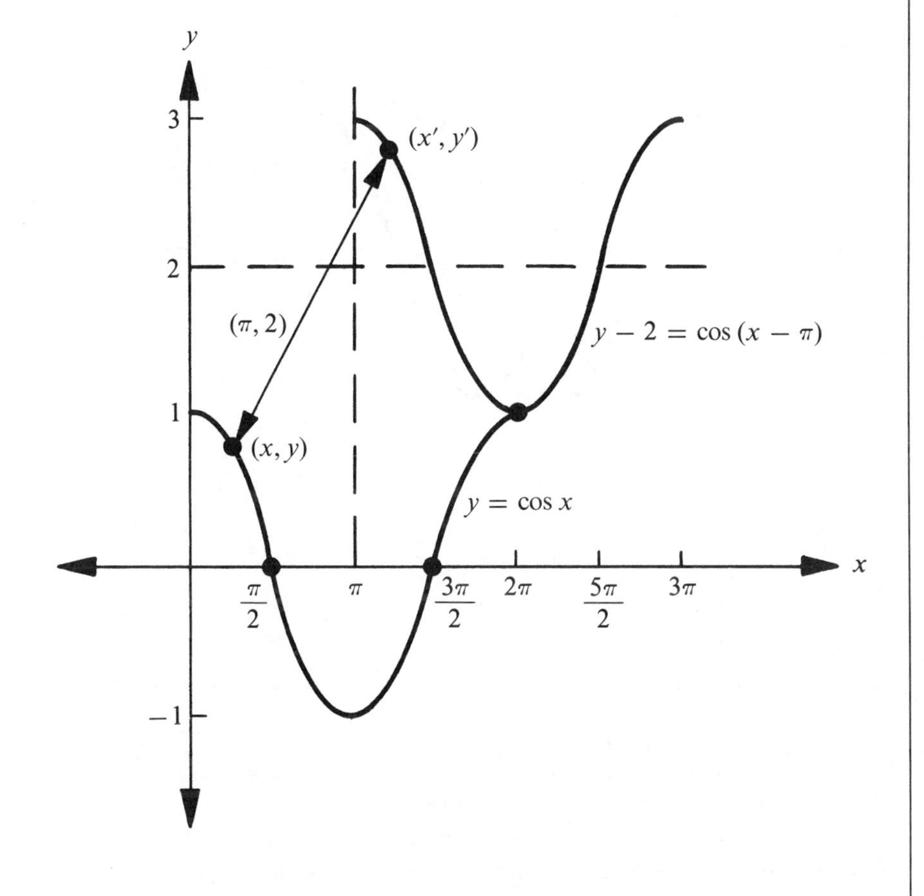

ANSWERS TO PAGE 123

$|k|$

$y = 2 \cos 3x$

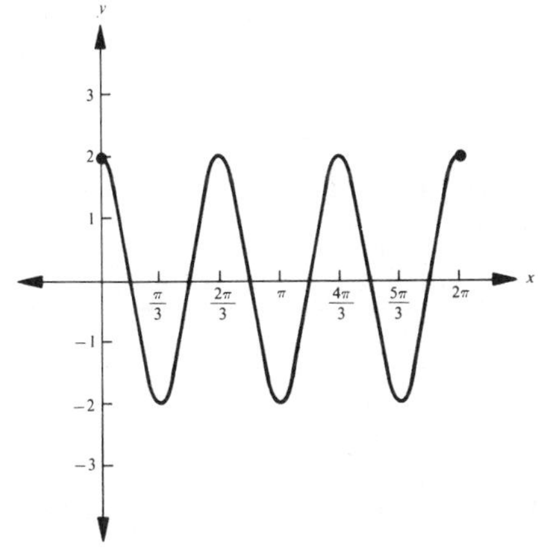

3

(0,3)

up

-1

down

$\left(\frac{\pi}{4}, -2\right)$

$-2 \quad \frac{\pi}{4}$

$\frac{1}{3} \sin x$

$\frac{1}{3}$

-3

$\frac{1}{2}$

We can use the idea of translation to simplify the sketching of the graph of a given function as in the following example.

Sketch the graph of the function

$$f = \left\{ (x,y) \colon y = \cos\left(x - \frac{\pi}{2}\right) \right\}.$$

This function is a translation of the function $y = \{(x,y)\colon y = \cos x\}$ by the vector $\left(\frac{\pi}{2}, 0\right)$. This means the graph of the function $f = \left\{(x,y)\colon y = \cos\left(x - \frac{\pi}{2}\right)\right\}$ may be obtained by shifting the graph of the well-known function $y = \cos x$ $\frac{\pi}{2}$ units to the ________ (right/left). This is illustrated in the following figure.

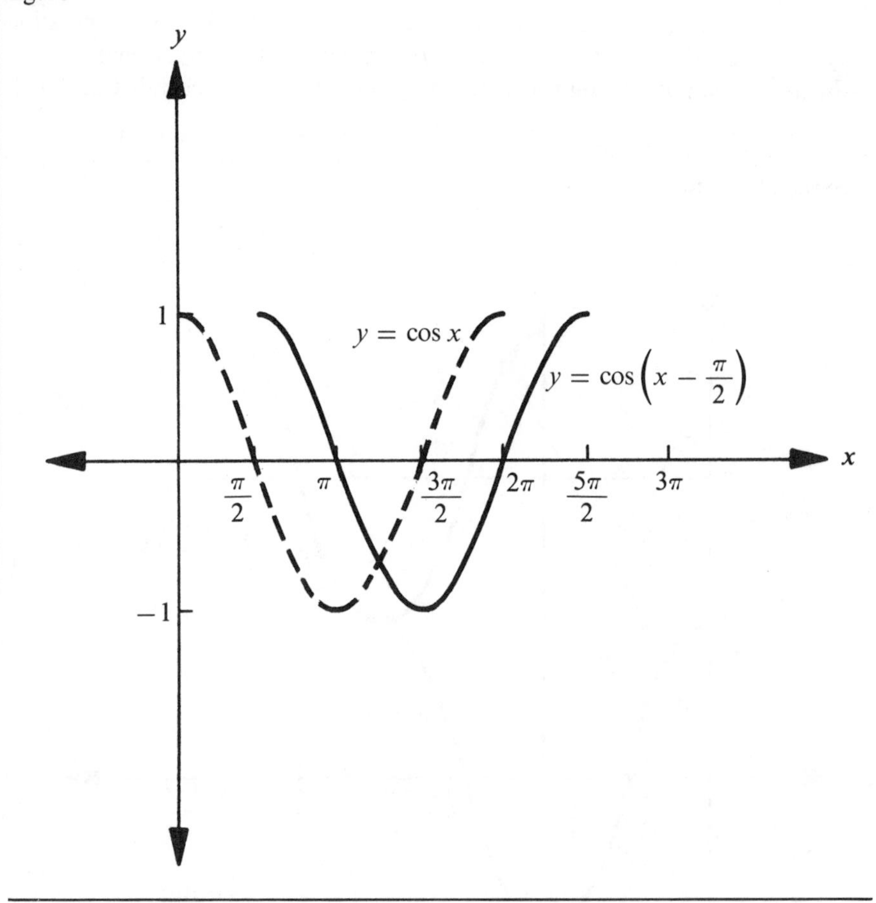

DEFINITION:
In the equations $y = \sin(x + c)$ and $y = \cos(x + c)$ the number $-c$ is called the **phase shift** of the corresponding graph. If $c < 0$, the graph of the standard $y = \cos x$ or $y = \sin x$ is translated or "shifted" to the right $|c|$ units. If $c > 0$, the graph of the standard is translated to the left $|c|$ units. If $c = 0$, the graph is said to be "in phase" with the standard $y = \cos x$ or $y = \sin x$.

MOVE TO NEXT FRAME

The function defined by $y = \cos\left(x + \frac{\pi}{3}\right)$ has a phase shift of ______ .
This function is a translation of the cosine function by the vector $\left(\frac{-\pi}{3}, 0\right)$. Its graph is obtained by shifting the graph of the cosine function $\frac{\pi}{3}$ units to the ________ (left/right).

The function defined by $y = \sin(x - \pi)$ has a phase shift of __. Its graph is obtained by shifting the graph of the sine function π units to the ________ (left/right).

Sketch the graph of $g = \{(x,y): y - 2 = \sin x\}$ on the coordinate system below.

This function is a translation of the function $g = \{(x,y): y = \sin x\}$ by the vector (0,2). This means that the graph of the function g may be obtained by shifting the graph of $y = \sin x$ two units ______ (up/down).

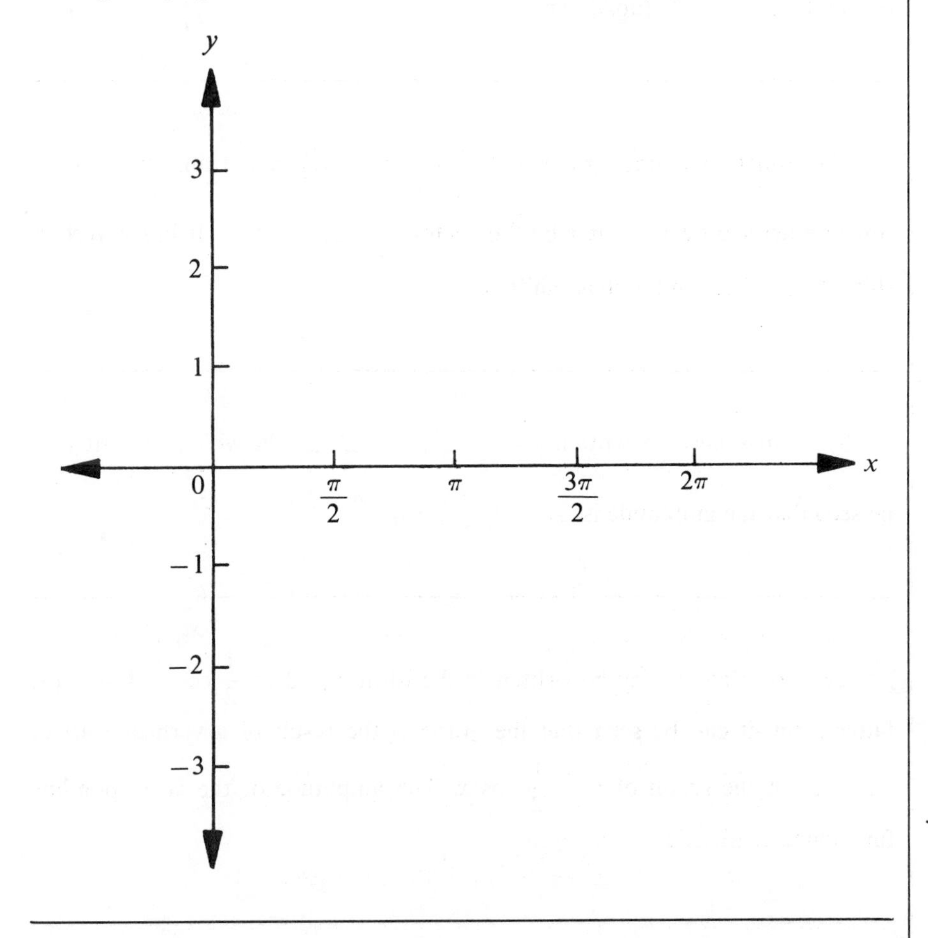

ANSWERS TO PAGE 125

$a \quad b$

$x' - a \quad y' - b$

$y' - 2 \quad x' - \pi$

$\{(x',y'): y' - 2 = \cos(x' - \pi)\}$ or

$\{(x,y): y - 2 = \cos(x - \pi)\}$

ANSWERS TO PAGE 130

DEFINITION:

In the equations $y + a = \sin x$ and $y + a = \cos x$, the number $-a$ is called the **vertical shift** of the corresponding graph. If $a < 0$, the graph of the standard $y = \cos x$ or $y = \sin x$ is "shifted" or translated up $|a|$ units. If $a > 0$, the graph of the standard $y = \cos x$ or $y = \sin x$ is translated down $|a|$ units.

MOVE TO NEXT FRAME

The function defined by $y - 3 = \cos x$ has a vertical shift of __. This function is a translation of the cosine function by the vector ______. Its graph is obtained by shifting the graph of the function defined by $y = \cos x$ three units ______ (up/down).

The function defined by $y + 1 = \sin x$ has a vertical shift of ______. Its graph is obtained by shifting the graph of the function defined by $y = \sin x$ one unit _______ (up/down).

The function defined by $y + 2 = \cos\left(x - \frac{\pi}{4}\right)$ is a translation of the function defined by $y = \cos x$ by the vector __________. It has a vertical shift of ______ and a phase shift of ______.

$3y = \sin x$ may be written $y =$ __________, in which form it may be seen that the amplitude is __.

$2y + 6 = \cos x$ may be written in the form $y + 3 = \frac{1}{2}\cos x$. Using the latter form, it can be seen that the graph is the result of a vertical shift of ______ of the graph of $y = \frac{1}{2}\cos x$. The amplitude of the corresponding function is ______.

$y = \sin x$ defines a function with a period of ______. The function defined by $y = \sin 3x$ has a period of ______.

The function defined by $y = \sin\left(x - \frac{\pi}{3}\right)$ has a phase shift of ___ and a period of ______.

$y = \sin(3x - \pi)$ may be written in the form $y = \sin 3\left(x - \frac{\pi}{3}\right)$. In the latter form, it is possible to determine that the function has a phase shift of ___ and a period of ______.

Graph one period of the functions defined by $y = 2\cos x$ and $y = -2\cos x$ on the given coordinate system.

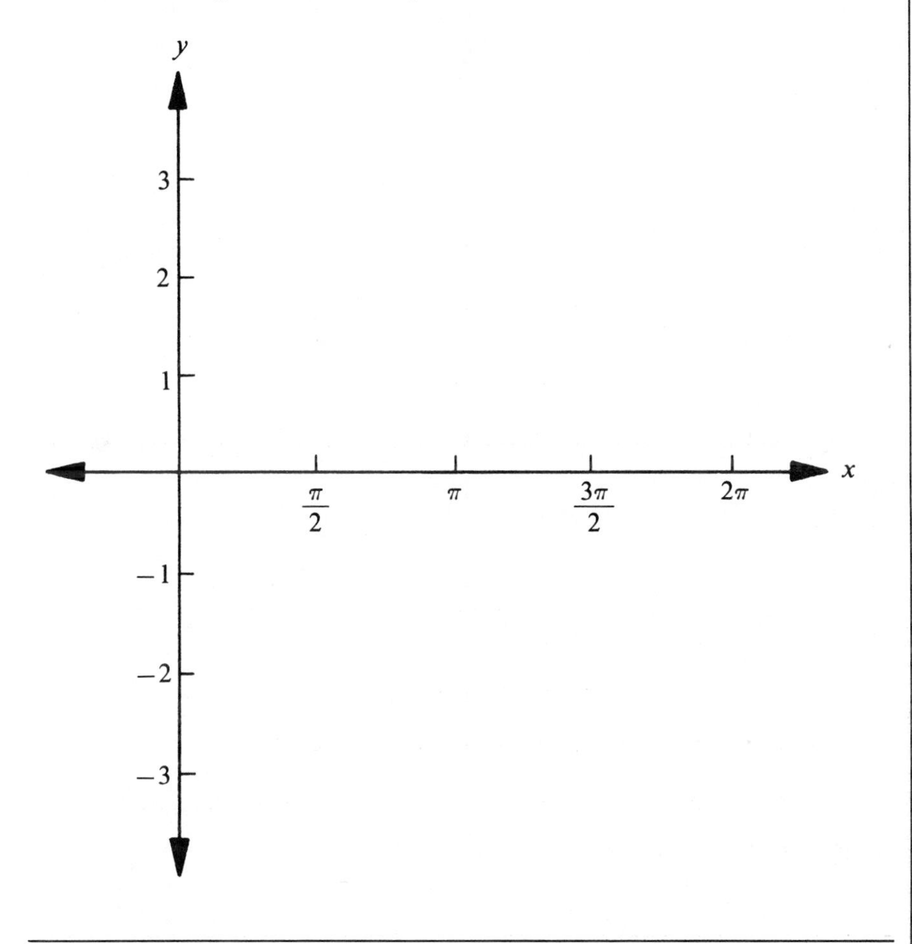

ANSWERS TO PAGE 127

$\frac{-\pi}{3}$

left

π

right

---

up

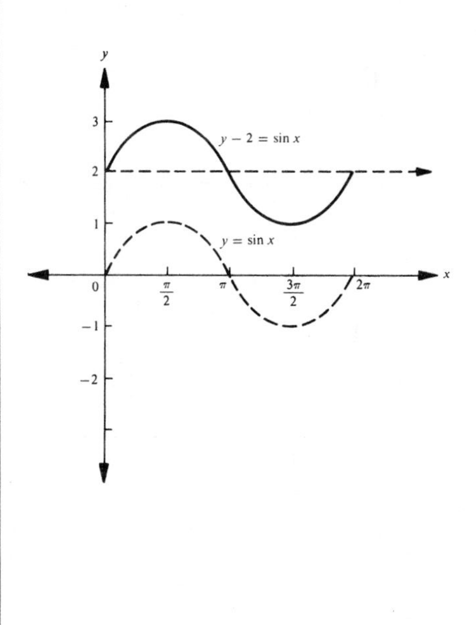

ANSWERS TO PAGE 132

$\{(x,y): -y = \cos x\}$ or

$\{(x,y): y = -\cos x\}$

(1,0)

counterclockwise clockwise

$(u, -v)$

$\cos x$ $-\sin x$

$\cos x$

$-\sin x$

reflection

Observe that for every (x,y) contained in the function defined by $y = 2\cos x$, $(x,-y)$ is contained in the function defined by $y = -2\cos x$. Notice, the converse is also true.

MOVE TO NEXT FRAME

DEFINITIONS:

The **reflection in the x axis** of a point whose coordinates are (x,y) is the point whose coordinates are $(x,-y)$. The **reflection in the y axis** of a point whose coordinates are (x,y) is the point whose coordinates are $(-x,y)$. The **reflection of a set S of points** is the set obtained by taking the reflection of each point in S. The **reflection of a function f** is the function corresponding to the reflection of the graph of f.

MOVE TO NEXT FRAME

The reflection of a point in the x axis.

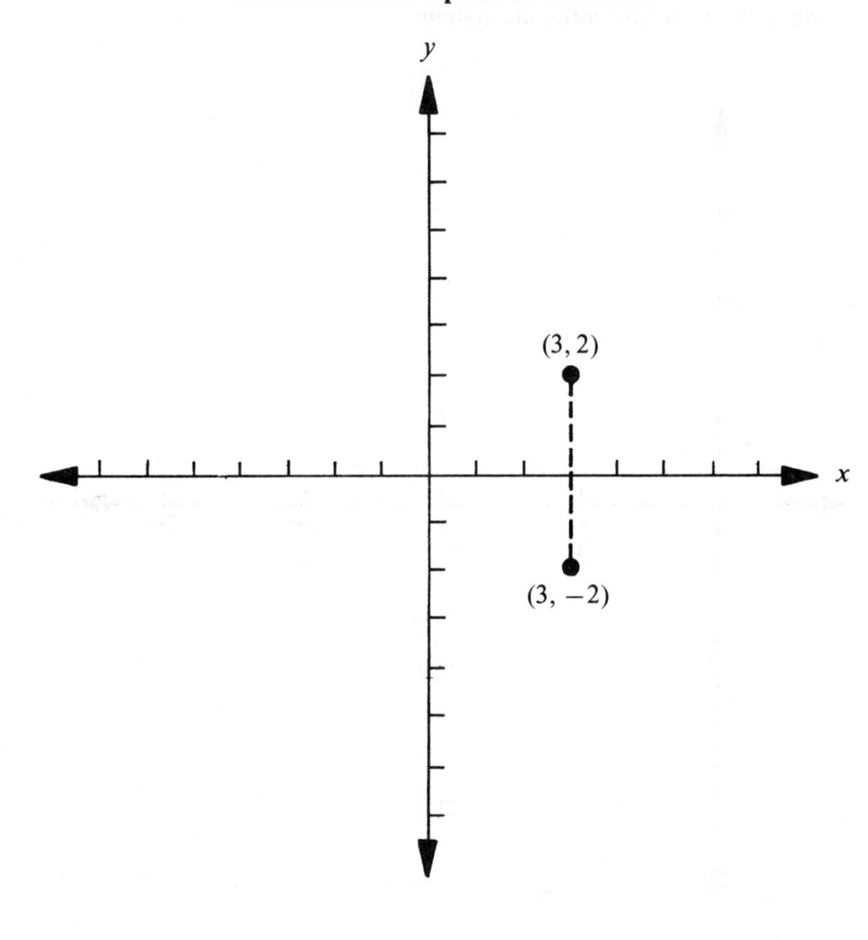

The reflection of a point in the y axis.

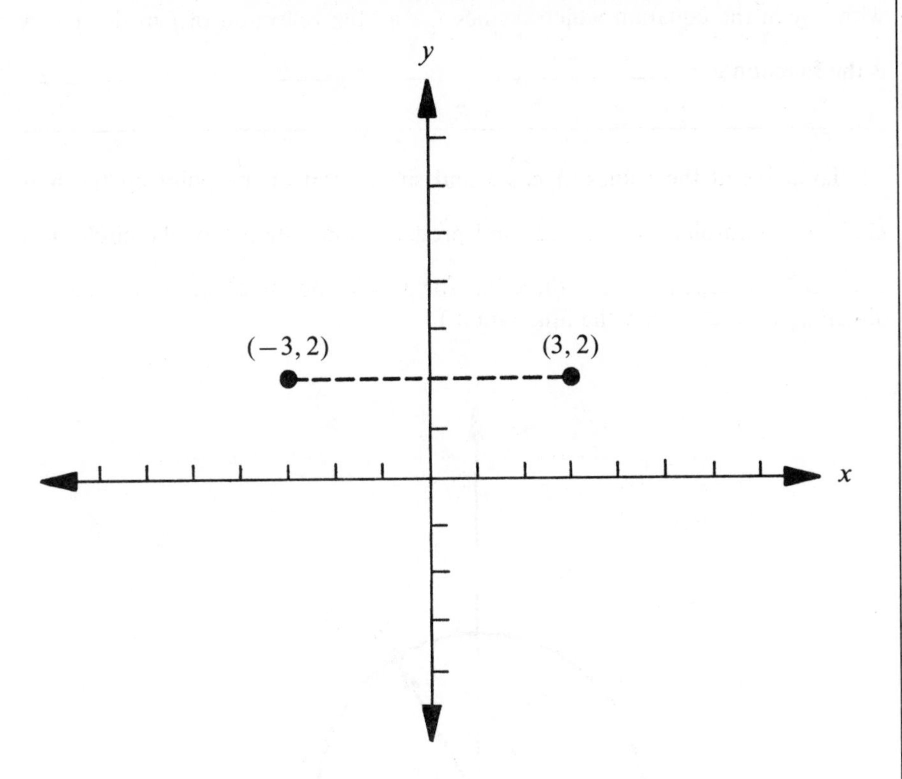

The reflection of a set of points S in the y axis.

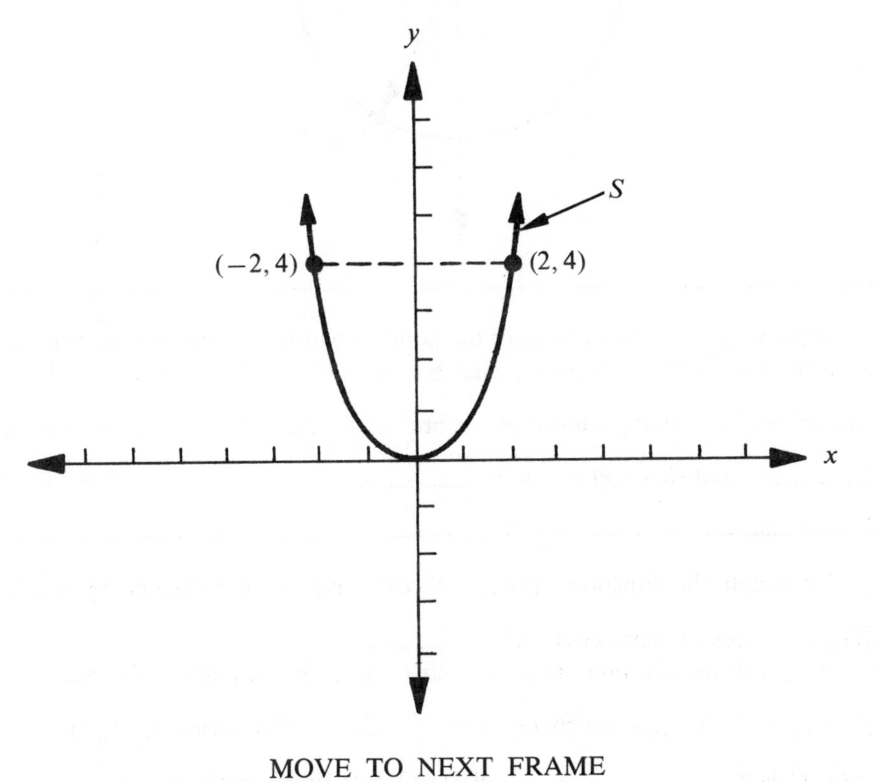

MOVE TO NEXT FRAME

ANSWERS TO PAGE 129

2π

$\frac{2\pi}{3}$

$\frac{\pi}{3}$

2π

$\frac{\pi}{3}$ $\frac{2\pi}{3}$

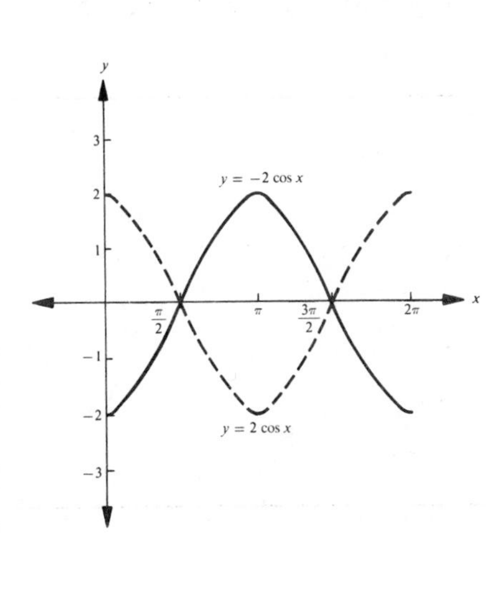

ANSWERS TO PAGE 134

To find the reflection of $f = \{(x,y): y = \cos x\}$ in the x axis, replace y with $-y$ in the equation which defines f, *e.g.*, the reflection of f in the x axis is the function $g =$ ______________________.

$-y = \sin 3x$ or $y = -\sin 3x$

To arrive at the values of $\cos x$ and $\sin x$, start at the point on the unit circle with coordinates ________ and proceed along the arc of the circle in a ________________ direction for $x > 0$ and in a ____________ direction for $x < 0$. (See the illustration.)

$y = \sin 3(-x)$, or $y = \sin(-3x)$ or $y = \sin 3x$

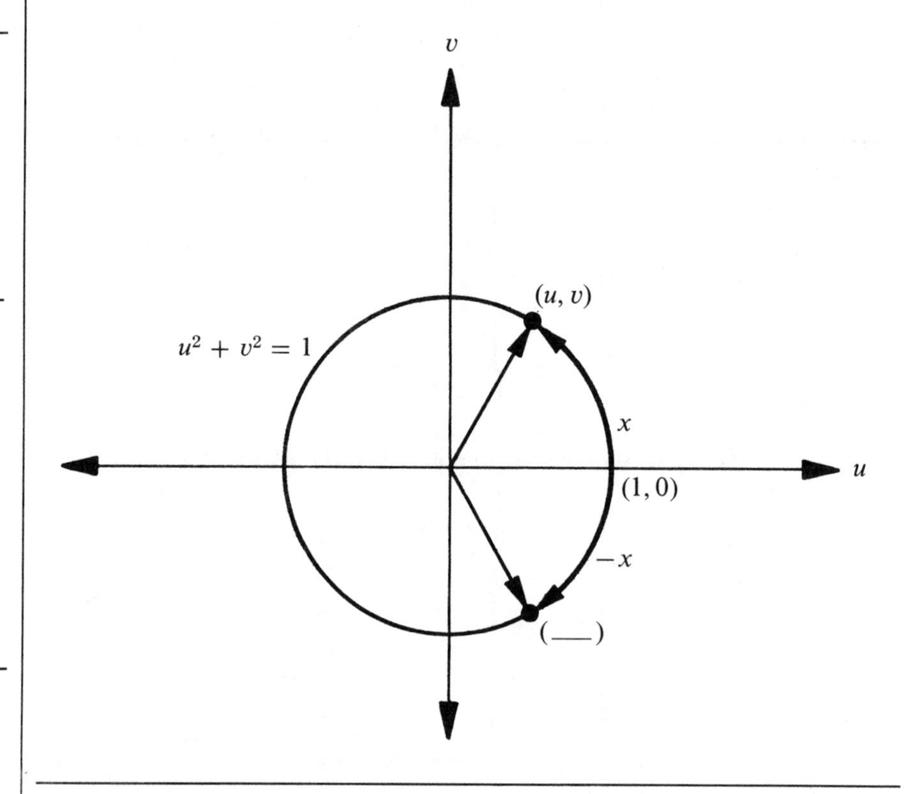

---

no

yes

If (u,v) are the coordinates of the point at which you arrive after moving a distance x on the unit circle, then the coordinates of the point at which you arrive after moving a distance $-x$ are __________. Thus $\cos(-x) = u =$ __________, and $\sin(-x) = -v =$ __________.

$y = -3x - 5$

$-y = 3x - 5$ or $y = -3x + 5$

To graph the function $\{(x,y): y = \cos(-x)\}$, it is sufficient to graph $\{(x,y): y = \cos x\}$, since $\cos(-x) =$ __________.

To graph the function $\{(x,y): y = \sin(-x)\}$, one may graph the function $\{(x,y): y = -\sin x\}$, since $\sin(-x) =$ __________. Furthermore, $\{(x,y): y = -\sin x\}$ is a ________________ of $\{(x,y): y = \sin x\}$ in the x axis.

x

Example:

Sketch the graph of $\{(x,y): y = \sin(\pi - 2x)\}$ for $0 \leq x < 2\pi$.

Solution:

The equation $y = \sin(\pi - 2x)$ may be rewritten as

$$y = \sin\left[-2\left(x - \frac{\pi}{2}\right)\right].$$

Since $\sin(-t) = -\sin t$, this is equivalent to

$$y = -\sin 2\left(x - \frac{\pi}{2}\right).$$

This is a ________________ in the x axis of the sine curve which has a ________________ of $\frac{\pi}{2}$, a ________________ of π, an amplitude of 1, and a vertical shift of 0. Complete the graph of $y = \sin(\pi - 2x)$ on the following coordinate system.

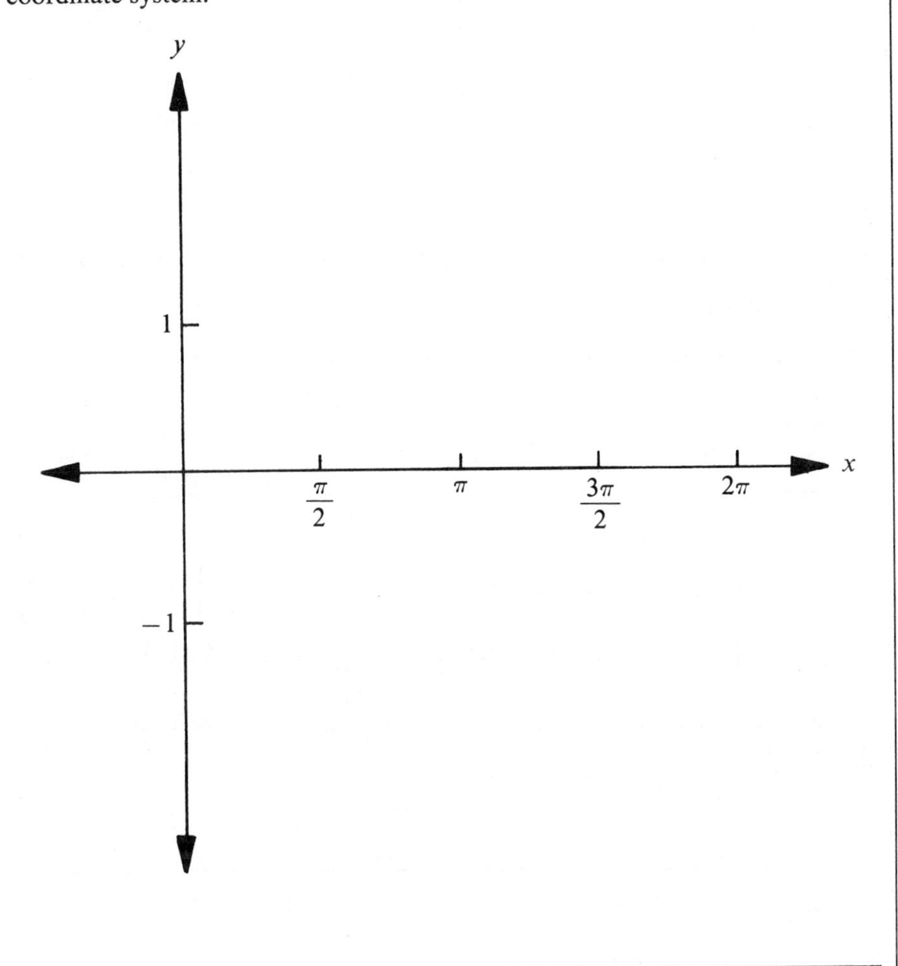

Example:

(a) Write the equation that defines the reflection of $f = \{(x,y) : y = \sin 3x\}$ in the x axis. ____________

(b) Write the equation that defines the reflection of f defined in (a), in the y axis.

____

Notice that in this case, the reflection of f in the x axis is equal to the reflection of f in the y axis. This is not true in general.

Is the reflection of $g = \{(x,y) : y = \cos 2x\}$ in the x axis equal to the reflection of g in the y axis? ______. Is the reflection of g in the y axis equal to g? ______

Example:

(a) Write the equation that defines the reflection of $f = \{(x,y) : y = 3x - 5\}$ in the y axis. ____________

(b) Write the equation that defines the reflection of f in the x axis.

____

$y = \sin\left(-2x + \frac{\pi}{3}\right)$ may be written in the form $y = \sin\left[-2\left(x - \frac{\pi}{6}\right)\right]$, $y = -\sin 2\left(x - \frac{\pi}{6}\right)$, or $-y = \sin 2\left(x - \frac{\pi}{6}\right)$. The latter form shows that the corresponding function is a reflection in the __ axis of the function defined by $y = \sin 2\left(x - \frac{\pi}{6}\right)$.

$2y - 5 = \sin(-3x + \pi)$ may be written as $y - \frac{5}{2} = -\frac{1}{2}\sin 3\left(x - \frac{\pi}{3}\right)$.
In this form it may be seen that the equation defines a translation of the function defined by $y = -\frac{1}{2}\sin 3x$ by the vector ______.

The function defined by $y = -\frac{1}{2}\sin 3x$ is a reflection in the __ axis of the function defined by ______. The function has an amplitude of __, a period of ____, a phase shift of ____, and a vertical shift of __.

reflection

phase shift period

In general:

If $k \neq 0$ and $b \neq 0$, the graph of the function $\{(x,y): y + a = k \cos(bx + c)\}$ is called a **cosine curve**, and the function $\{(x,y): y + a = k \sin(bx + c)\}$ is called a **sine curve**. These functions have a **vertical shift** of $-a$, an **amplitude** of $|k|$, a **period** of $\frac{2\pi}{|b|}$, and a **phase shift** of $\frac{-c}{b}$. If $k < 0$, the functions are **reflections** in the line $y = -a$ of the corresponding functions with $k > 0$.

MOVE TO NEXT FRAME

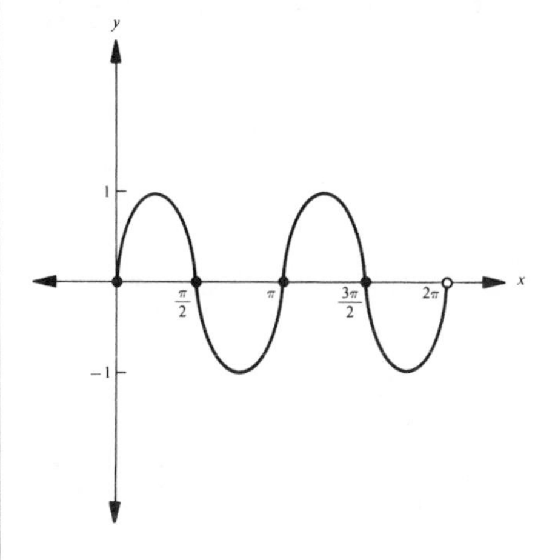

Examples:

Determine the amplitude, period, vertical shift, and phase shift of the function defined by each of the following equations.

(a) $y = \sin\left(x + \frac{\pi}{3}\right)$; period = ____; amplitude = __; phase shift = ____; vertical shift = __.

(b) $y = 2\cos\left(\frac{x}{2} + \pi\right)$; period = ____; amplitude = __; phase shift = ____; vertical shift = __.

(c) $\frac{y}{3} + \frac{1}{2} = \sin\left(-\frac{1}{2}x + \frac{\pi}{4}\right)$; period = ____, amplitude = ____, phase shift = ____, vertical shift = __.

---

(1) $\frac{-\sqrt{3}}{2}$ $\quad -\frac{1}{2}$

(2) $-\frac{1}{2}$ $\quad \frac{\sqrt{3}}{2}$

(3) $\frac{\pi}{3}$ or $\frac{5\pi}{3}$

(4) $\frac{4\pi}{3}$ or $\frac{5\pi}{3}$

(5) $\frac{5\pi}{6}$ or $\frac{7\pi}{6}$

(6) $\left\{(x,y): y = 3\sin\left(5x - \frac{5\pi}{4}\right)\right\}$

(7) $\left\{(x,y): y = \frac{1}{3}\sin(2x + \pi)\right\}$

(8) $\left\{(x,y): y = -3\sin\frac{1}{3}x\right\}$

(9) $\left\{(x,y): y = \frac{1}{5}\cos(3x + \pi)\right\}$

(10) $\left\{(x,y): y = \frac{-7}{2}\cos\left(\frac{2}{3}x - \frac{\pi}{6}\right)\right\}$

(11) 1 $\quad 2\pi$

$\left(\frac{\pi}{3}, 0\right)$

The function defined by $y = \cos x + \sin x$ is the sum of the functions defined by $y = \cos x$ and $y = \sin x$. As a consequence, it may be graphed by a direct addition of the ordinates of the graphs of $y = \cos x$ and $y = \sin x$. (See the illustration.)

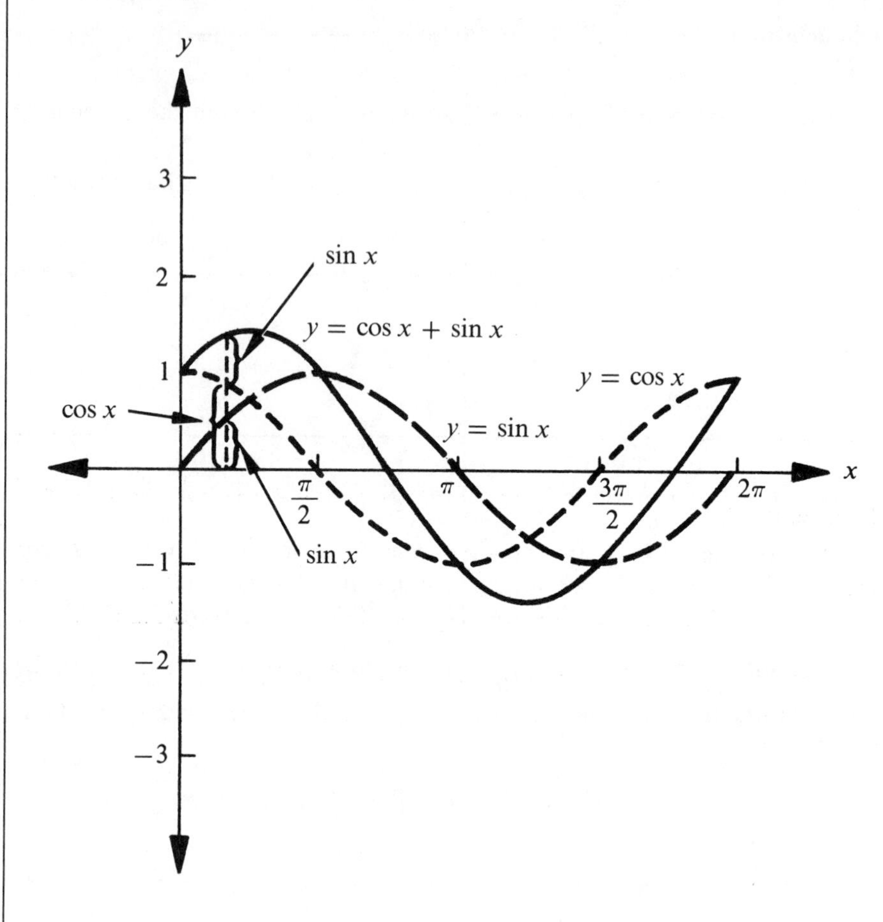

Graphing by addition of ordinates.

MOVE TO NEXT FRAME

To sketch the graph of the function defined by $y = 2 \sin x - \cos x$, first sketch the graph of the function $y = 2 \sin x$, then that of the function $y = -\cos x$, and finally add ordinates.

Use the following coordinate system to graph $y = 2 \sin x - \cos x$ for $-\pi \leq x \leq \pi$.

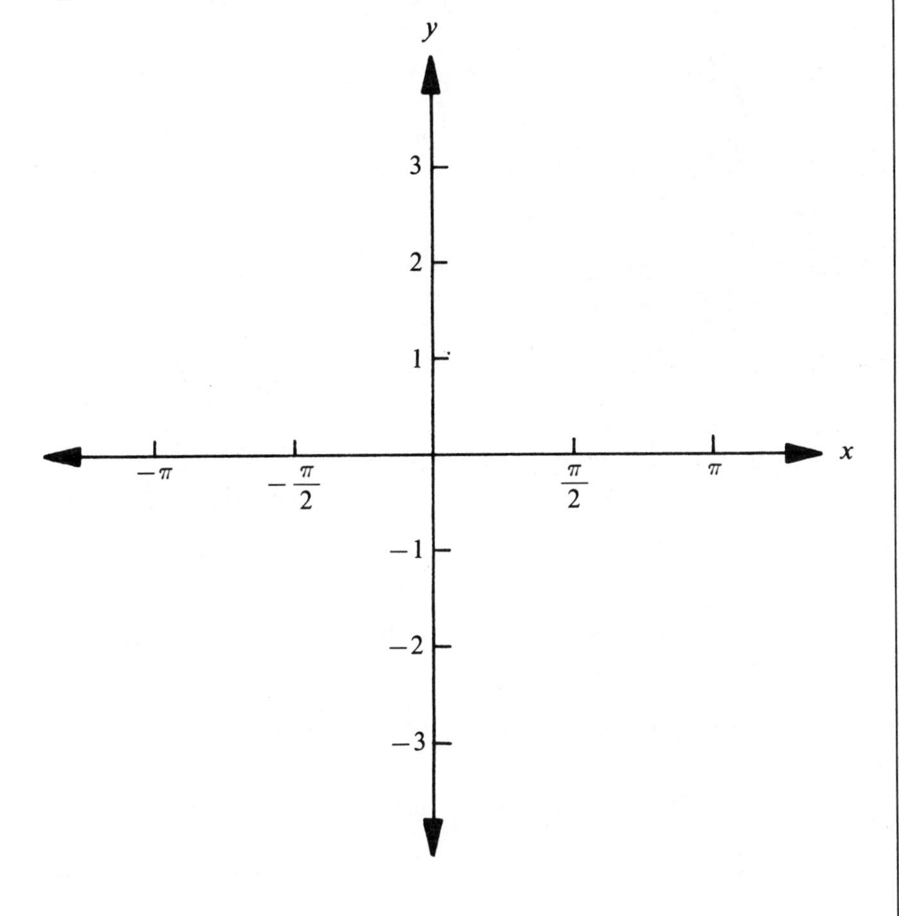

ANSWERS TO PAGE 135

$\left(\frac{\pi}{3}, \frac{5}{2}\right)$

x

$y = \frac{1}{2} \sin 3x$

$\frac{1}{2}$ $\frac{2\pi}{3}$ $\frac{\pi}{3}$

$\frac{5}{2}$

2π 1

$\frac{-\pi}{3}$ 0

4π 2

-2π 0

4π 3

$\frac{\pi}{2}$ $\frac{-3}{2}$

ANSWERS TO PAGE 140

(13) $\frac{1}{2}$ π

$\left(\frac{\pi}{6}, -2\right)$

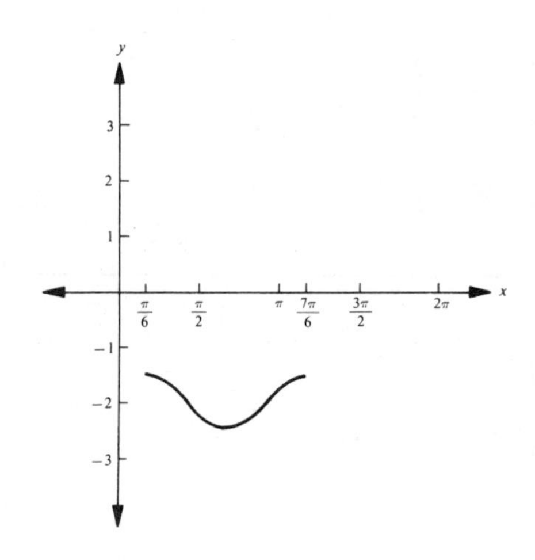

(14) 2 $\frac{2}{3}\pi$

$\left(\frac{\pi}{3}, 0\right)$

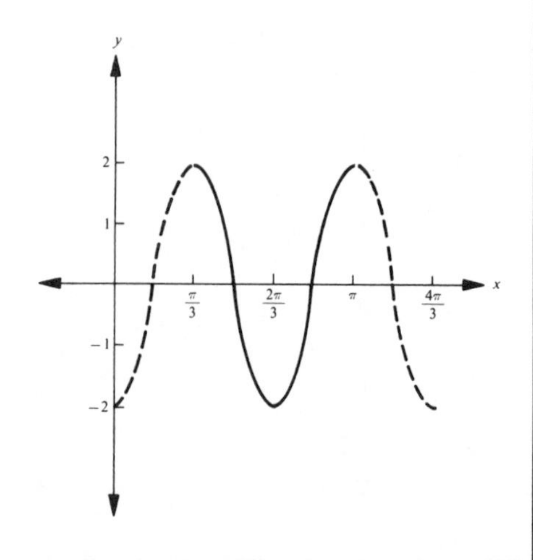

EXERCISES. 3.2

Complete:

1. If $x = \frac{7\pi}{6}$, $\cos x =$ ____ and $\sin x =$ ____.

2. If $x = \frac{20\pi}{3}$, $\cos x =$ ____ and $\sin x =$ ____.

3. If $\cos x = \frac{1}{2}$, and $0 \leq x < 2\pi$, then $x =$ ____ or ____.

4. If $\sin x = \frac{-\sqrt{3}}{2}$ and $0 \leq x < 2\pi$, then $x =$ ____ or ____.

5. If $\cos x = \frac{-\sqrt{3}}{2}$ and $0 \leq x < 2\pi$, then $x =$ ____ or ____.

Write a function which has a sine curve with the following characteristics.

6. Period $= \frac{2\pi}{5}$; amplitude $= 3$; phase shift $= \frac{\pi}{4}$. ____________

7. Period $= \pi$; amplitude $= \frac{1}{3}$; phase shift $= \frac{-\pi}{2}$. ____________

8. A reflection in the x axis of the sine curve with period $= 6\pi$; amplitude $= 3$; phase shift $= 0$. ____________

Write a function which has a cosine curve with the following characteristics.

9. Period $= \frac{2\pi}{3}$; amplitude $= \frac{1}{5}$; phase shift $= \frac{-\pi}{3}$. ____________

10. A reflection in the x axis of the cosine curve with period $= 3\pi$; amplitude $= \frac{7}{2}$; phase shift $= \frac{\pi}{4}$. ____________

Each of the problems 11-14 is the equation of a function which is the translation of a function with equation $y = a \sin bx$ or $y = a \cos bx$. In each case find the amplitude, the period, and the translating vector of the function. Then sketch one period of the graph.

11. $y = \sin\left(x - \frac{\pi}{3}\right)$; amplitude = __; period = __; translating vector = ______.

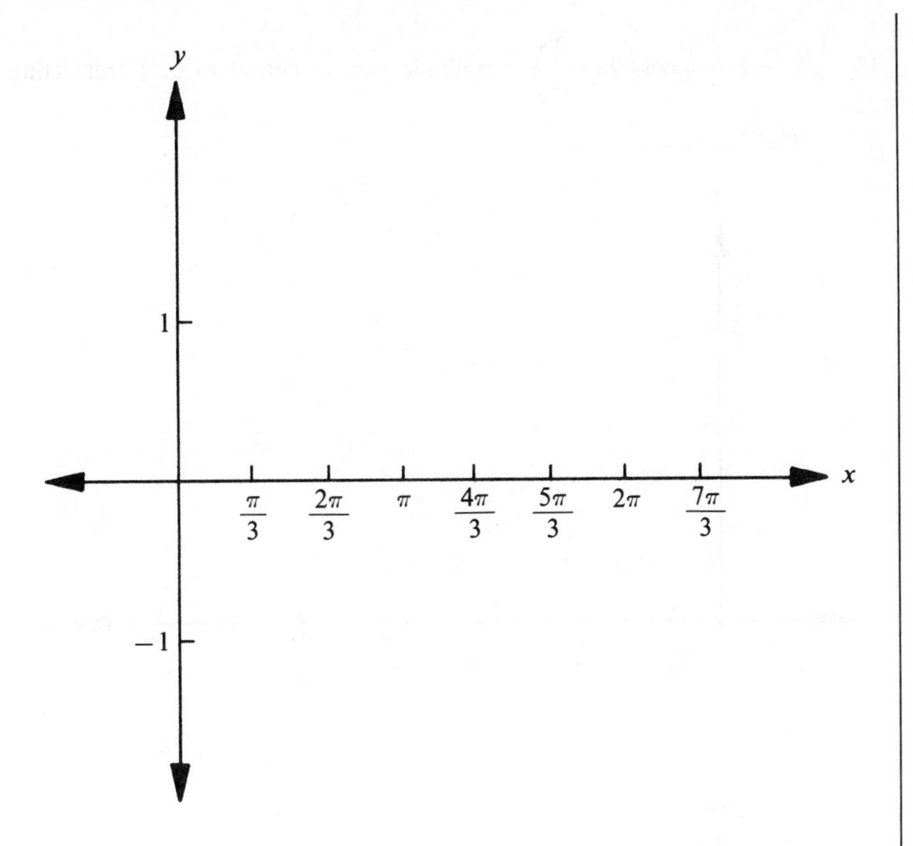

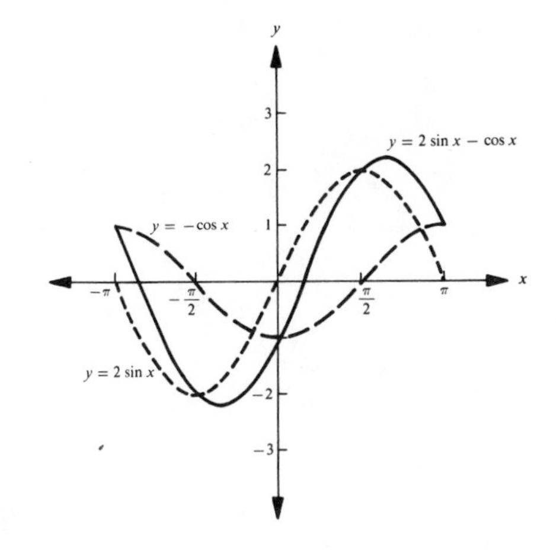

12. $y + 1 = 2\cos\left(x + \frac{\pi}{6}\right)$; amplitude = __; period = __; translating vector = __________.

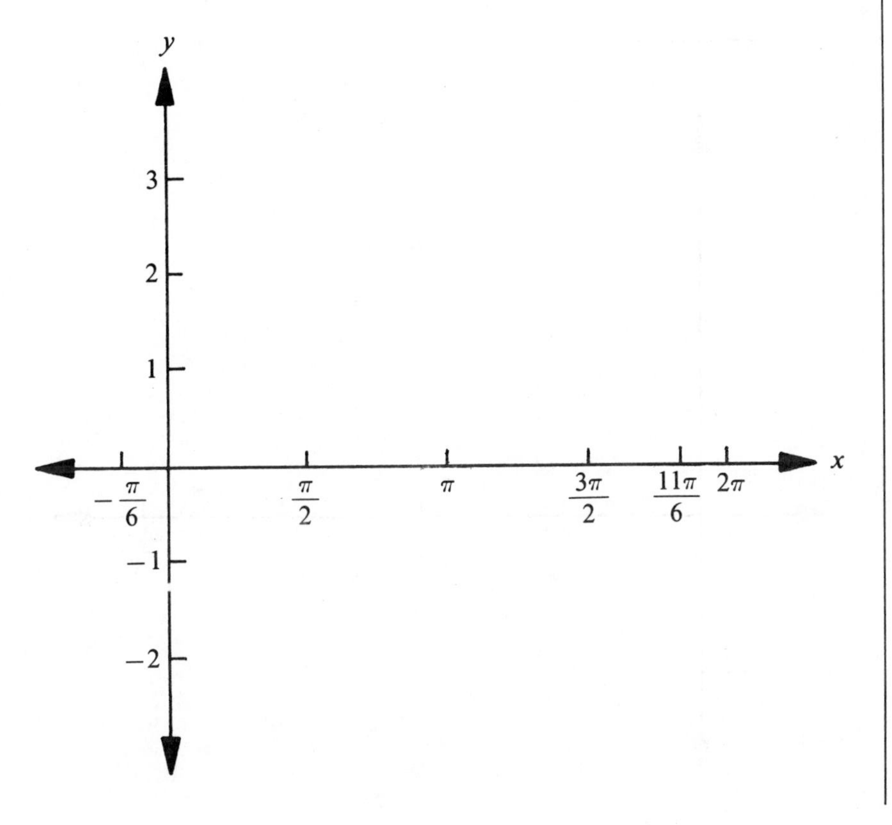

ANSWERS TO PAGE 142

$\frac{\pi}{2}, \frac{3\pi}{2}$

$\left\{\pm\frac{\pi}{2}, \pm\frac{3\pi}{2}, \pm\frac{5\pi}{2}, \pm\frac{7\pi}{2}, \cdots\right\}$
$= \left\{\text{all odd multiples of } \frac{\pi}{2}\right\}$
$= \left\{x : x = (2k + 1)\,\frac{\pi}{2}, \text{ where } k \epsilon J\right\}$

$\left\{x : x \epsilon \mathscr{R} \text{ and } x \neq (2k + 1)\frac{\pi}{2} \text{ for all } k \epsilon J\right\}$

13. $y = -2 + \frac{1}{2}\cos\left(2x - \frac{\pi}{3}\right)$; amplitude = __; period = __; translating vector = __________.

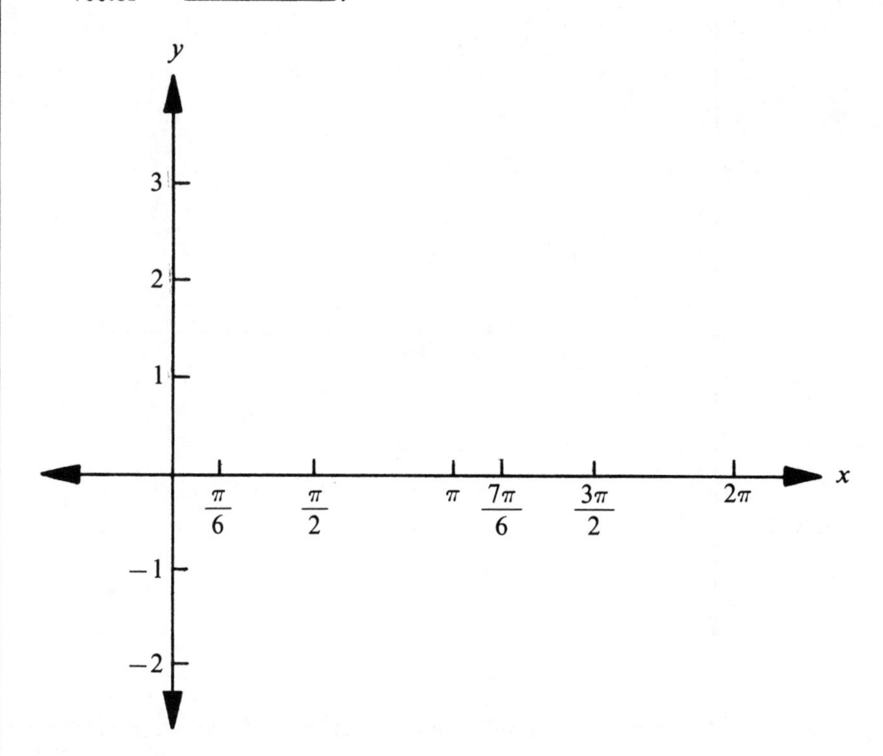

14. $y = 2\cos(\pi - 3x)$; amplitude = __; period = ____; translating vector = __________.

y
2
1
−1
x
$\frac{\pi}{3}$ $\frac{2\pi}{3}$ π $\frac{4\pi}{3}$

15. Graph the function defined by $y = 2 \sin x + \sin\left(x - \frac{\pi}{4}\right)$ over the interval $0 \leq x \leq 3\pi$ by the method of addition of ordinates. Show the graph of $y = 2 \sin x$, $y = \sin\left(x - \frac{\pi}{4}\right)$, and $y = 2 \sin x + \sin\left(x - \frac{\pi}{4}\right)$.

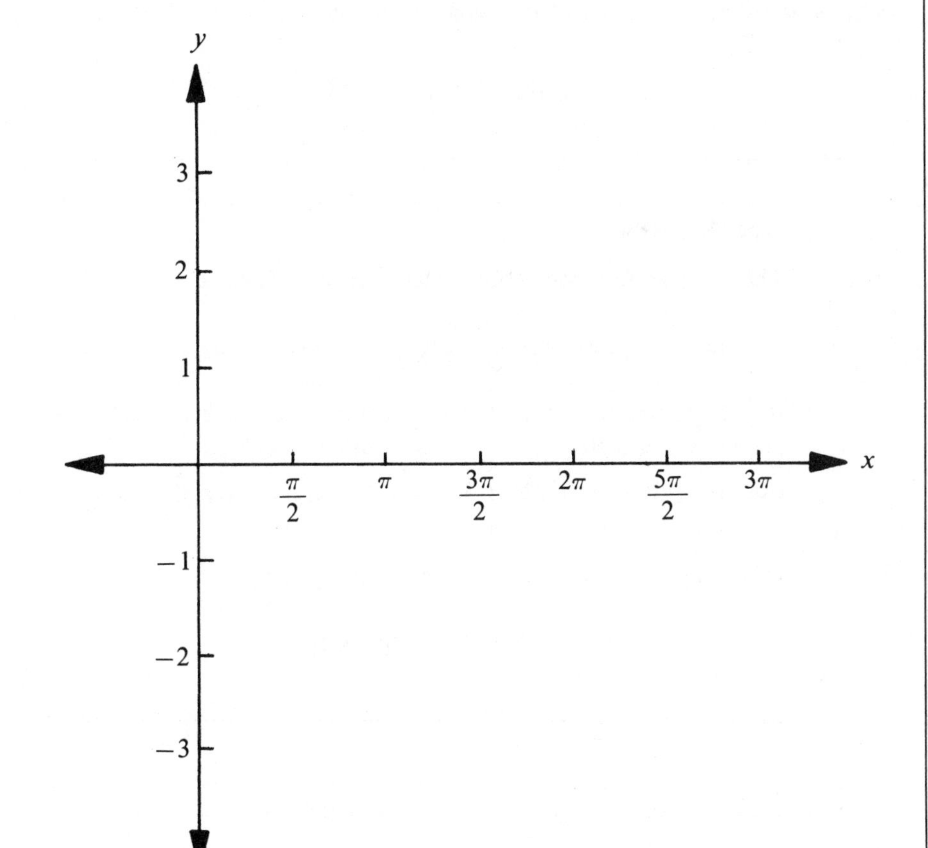

ANSWERS TO PAGE 139

(11)

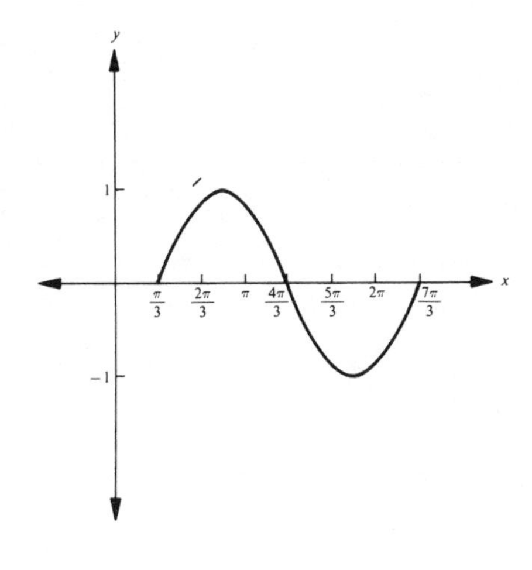

(12) 2 $\quad 2\pi$

$\left(\frac{-\pi}{6}, -1\right)$

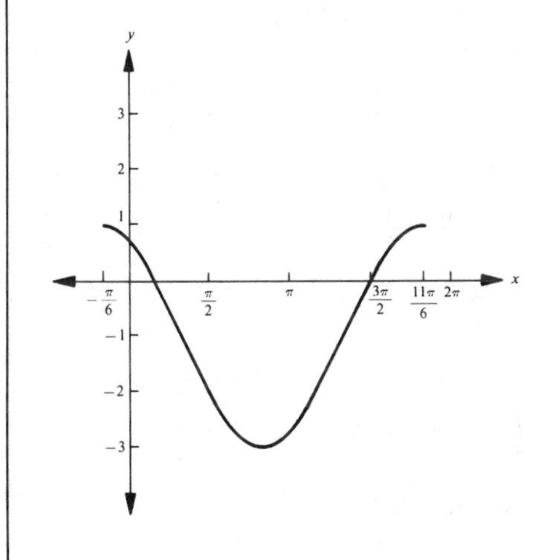

3.3. TANGENT, COTANGENT, SECANT AND COSECANT

Operations on the sine and cosine functions form many other functions. Some of these functions are given their own names due to their special usefulness.

MOVE TO NEXT FRAME

DEFINITION:

The **tangent** function, abbreviated **tan**, is defined as

$$\tan = \left\{ (x,y) : y = \frac{\sin x}{\cos x}, \cos x \neq 0 \right\} \text{ for } x \in \mathcal{R}.$$

It is customary to write **tan** x to denote the value of the tangent function at x. Thus, from the definition, $y = \tan x$ if and only if $y = \dfrac{\sin x}{\cos x}$ and $\cos x \neq 0$.

Hence whenever $\cos x \neq 0$, we have $\tan x = \dfrac{\sin x}{\cos x}$.

MOVE TO NEXT FRAME

---

negative

For what values of x, $0 \leq x < 2\pi$, is tan undefined? __________

---

zero

For what values of x, $x \in \mathcal{R}$, is tan undefined? __________

---

zero

infinity

zero

From the previous frames we can conclude that the domain of the tangent function is ____________________.

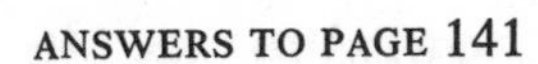

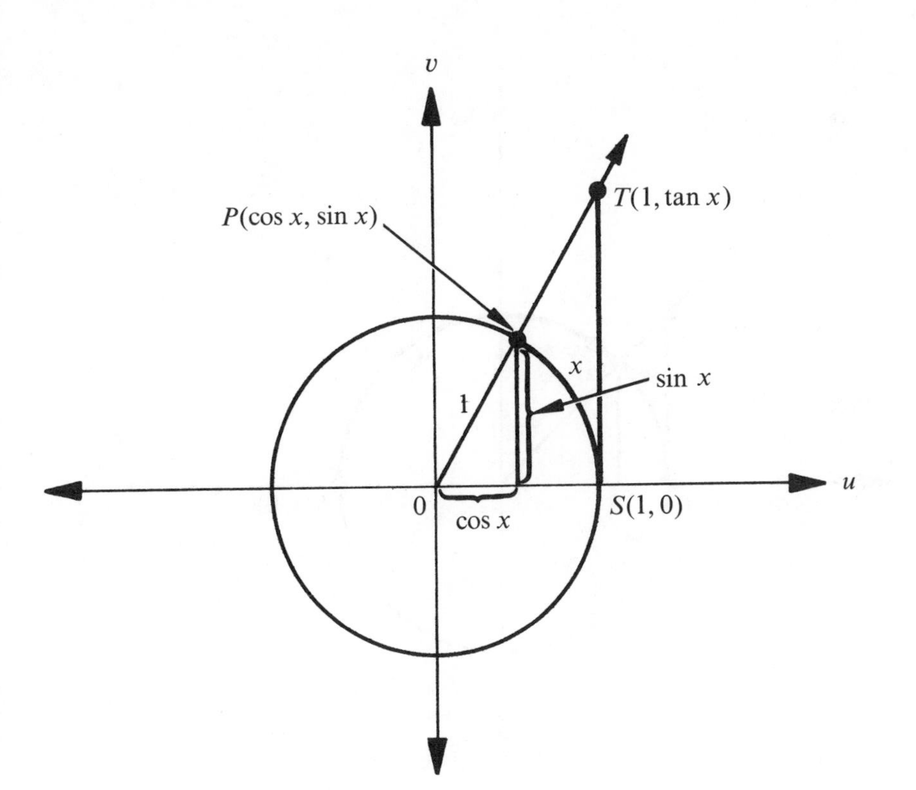

The value of tan x changes as x changes. This may be visualized by returning to the unit circle. (See the illustration.) For any point P in the first quadrant that is a distance x from $(1,0)$, the coordinates of P are ________. Using proportional parts of similar triangles we have $\frac{\sin x}{\cos x} = \frac{\overline{TS}}{\overline{OS}} = \tan x$. Thus the length of $\overline{TS}$ represents the value of tan x for $0 \le x < \frac{\pi}{2}$.

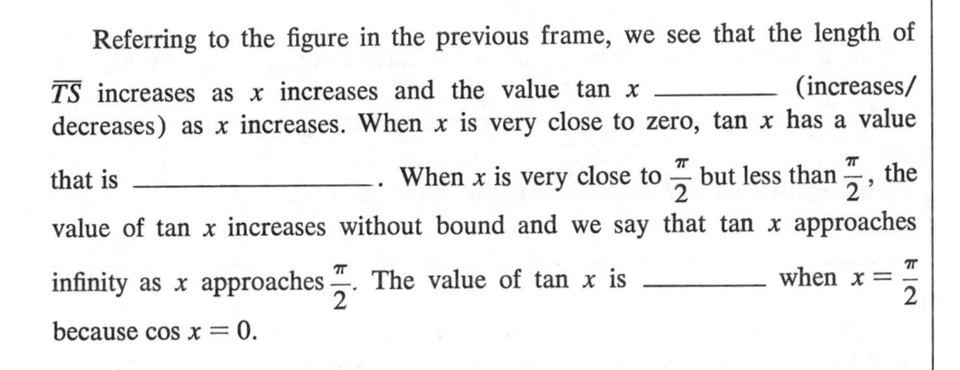

Referring to the figure in the previous frame, we see that the length of $\overline{TS}$ increases as x increases and the value tan x ________ (increases/decreases) as x increases. When x is very close to zero, tan x has a value that is ________________. When x is very close to $\frac{\pi}{2}$ but less than $\frac{\pi}{2}$, the value of tan x increases without bound and we say that tan x approaches infinity as x approaches $\frac{\pi}{2}$. The value of tan x is ________ when $x = \frac{\pi}{2}$ because $\cos x = 0$.

---

(15)

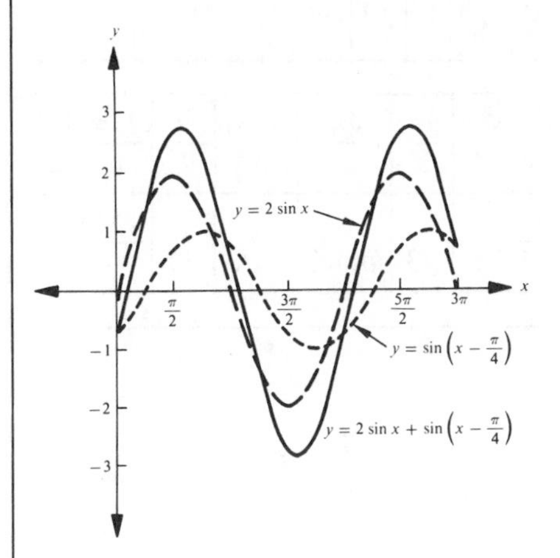

0	$\frac{\pi}{6}$	$\frac{\pi}{4}$	$\frac{\pi}{3}$	$\frac{\pi}{2}$	$\frac{2\pi}{3}$	$\frac{3\pi}{4}$	$\frac{5\pi}{6}$	π
0	$\frac{\sqrt{3}}{3}$	1	$\sqrt{3}$	undef	$-\sqrt{3}$	-1	$\frac{-\sqrt{3}}{3}$	0

$\frac{7\pi}{6}$	$\frac{5\pi}{4}$	$\frac{4\pi}{3}$	$\frac{3\pi}{2}$	$\frac{5\pi}{3}$	$\frac{7\pi}{4}$	$\frac{11\pi}{6}$	2π
$\frac{\sqrt{3}}{3}$	1	$\sqrt{3}$	undef	$-\sqrt{3}$	-1	$\frac{-\sqrt{3}}{3}$	0

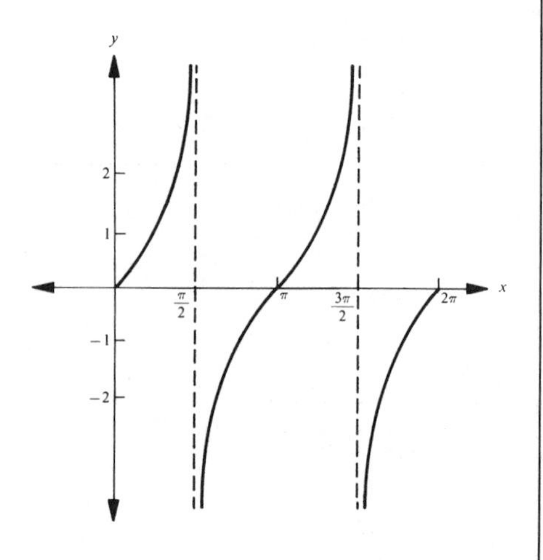

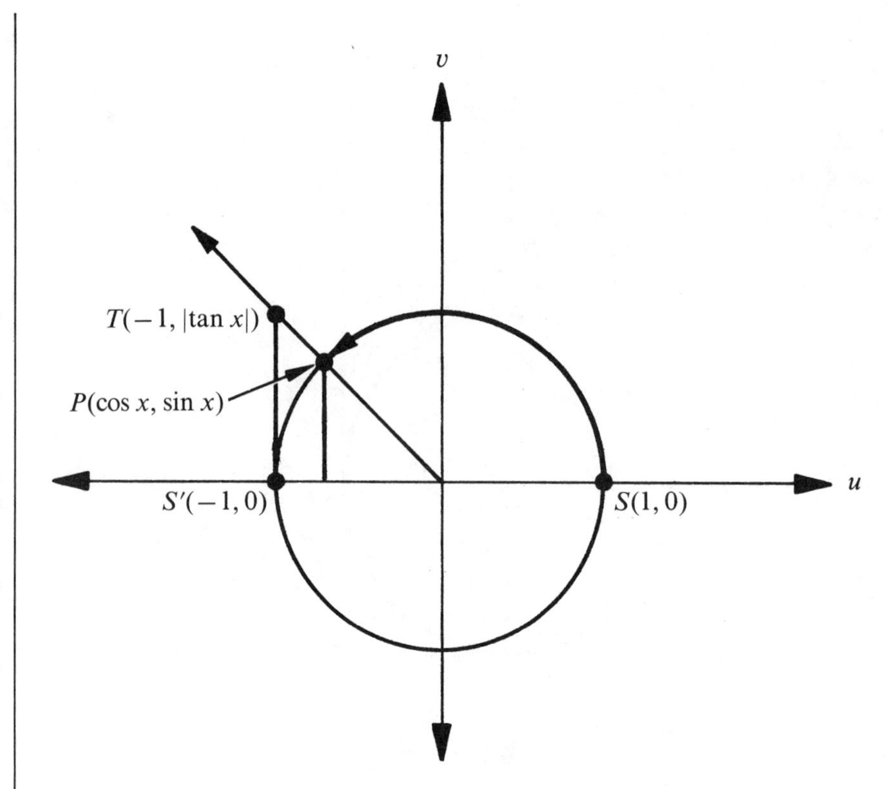

If $\frac{\pi}{2} < x < \pi$, then $P(\cos x, \sin x)$ is in the second quadrant and $\left|\frac{\sin x}{\cos x}\right| = \frac{\overline{TS'}}{\overline{OS'}} = |\tan x|$. Thus $|\tan x|$ is represented by $\overline{TS'}$. The values of $\tan x$ are ________ (positive/negative) for $\frac{\pi}{2} < x < \pi$. Since $\overline{TS'}$ is very long when x is near $\frac{\pi}{2}$ and very short when x is near π, we say that $\tan x$ approaches *negative infinity* as x approaches $\frac{\pi}{2}$ in the second quadrant and $\tan x$ approaches _____ as x approaches π.

As x increases from 0 to $\frac{\pi}{2}$, $\tan x$ increases from ________ through all positive numbers to _______. As x increases from $\frac{\pi}{2}$ to π, $\tan x$ increases from negative infinity through negative numbers to _____.

Make a sketch on the illustrated unit circle, as in the previous two sketches, which shows $\tan x$ as the length of a segment tangent to the unit circle at S' for $\pi < x < \frac{3\pi}{2}$.

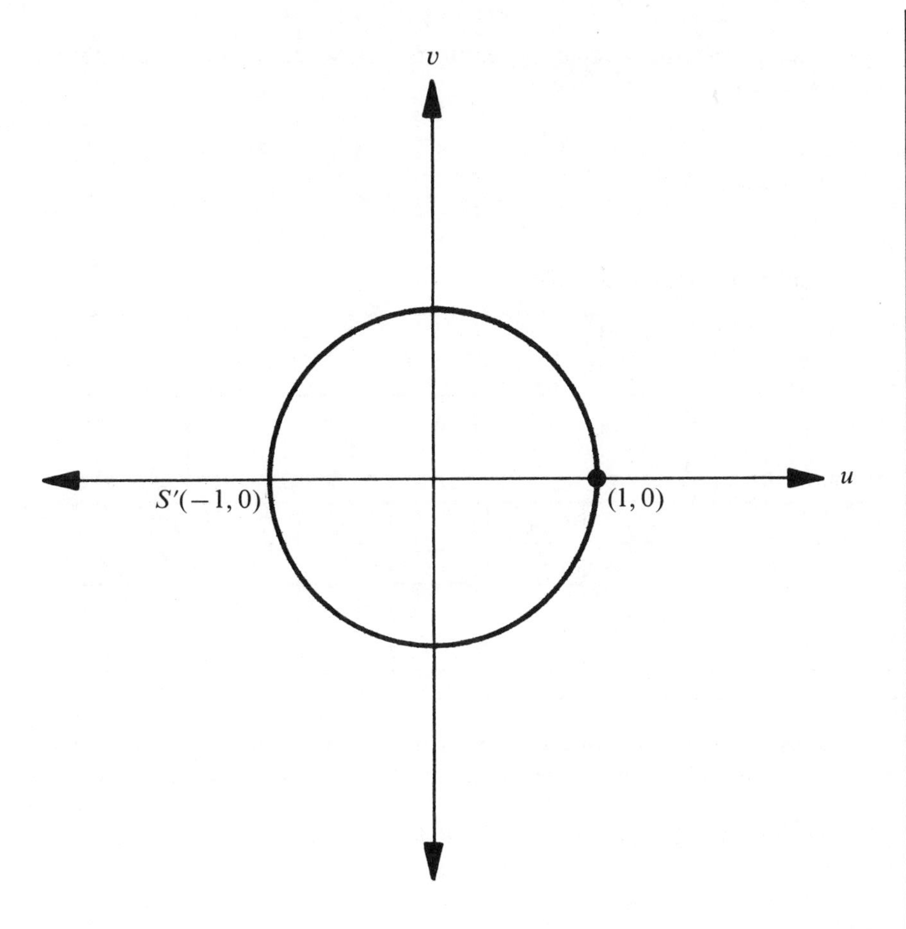

The value of tan x is ______ (positive/negative) for $\pi < x < \frac{3\pi}{2}$. The value of tan x is ______ (increasing/decreasing) as x increases from π to $\frac{3\pi}{2}$. The value of tan x is ______ for $x = \frac{3\pi}{2}$. The value of tan x approaches ______ as x approaches $\frac{3\pi}{2}$.

(cos x, sin x)

In a similar fashion, tan x may be represented by the length of a segment when $\frac{3\pi}{2} < x < 2\pi$, that is, when $P(\cos x, \sin x)$ is in the ______ quadrant. The value of tan x is ______ (positive/negative) for $\frac{3\pi}{2} < x < 2\pi$. The value of tan x approaches ______ as x approaches 2π. As x approaches $\frac{3\pi}{2}$ in this quadrant, tan x approaches negative ______.

increases

very close to zero

undefined

From the discussion in the preceding frames, it can be seen that the range of tan is ___.

$(-\cos x, -\sin x)$

periodic

period

$0 < x \leq \pi$

Values of tan for specific values of x may be calculated from those of $\sin x$ and $\cos x$.

$$\tan\frac{\pi}{6} = \frac{\sin\frac{\pi}{6}}{\cos\frac{\pi}{6}} = \frac{\frac{1}{2}}{\frac{\sqrt{3}}{2}} = \frac{1}{\sqrt{3}} = \frac{\sqrt{3}}{3}.$$

Complete the following tables:

x	0	$\frac{\pi}{6}$	$\frac{\pi}{4}$	$\frac{\pi}{3}$	$\frac{\pi}{2}$	$\frac{2\pi}{3}$	$\frac{3\pi}{4}$	$\frac{5\pi}{6}$	π
$\tan x$									

x	$\frac{7\pi}{6}$	$\frac{5\pi}{4}$	$\frac{4\pi}{3}$	$\frac{3\pi}{2}$	$\frac{5\pi}{3}$	$\frac{7\pi}{4}$	$\frac{11\pi}{6}$	2π
$\tan x$								

Use the ordered pairs of numbers $(x, \tan x)$ determined in the preceding frame to graph the tangent function on the following coordinate system. (Approximate $\sqrt{3}$ by 1.7 and $\frac{\sqrt{3}}{3}$ by 0.6.)

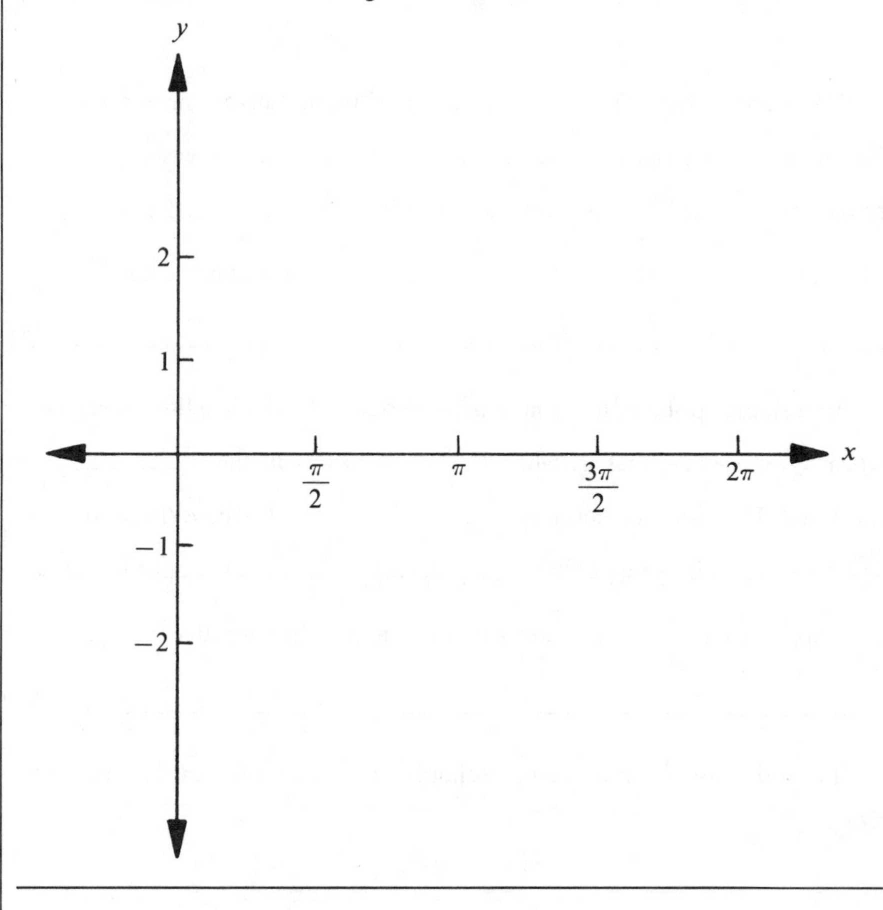

You should see that tan x is undefined whenever $x = \frac{\pi}{2}$ or $\frac{3\pi}{2}$, because $\cos\left(\frac{\pi}{2} = \cos\frac{2}{3\pi}\right) = 0$, but as x approaches $\frac{\pi}{2}$ from the left, tan x ________ (increases/decreases). Furthermore, we can make tan x as large as we desire by choosing x sufficiently close to $\frac{\pi}{2}$.

As x approaches $\frac{\pi}{2}$ from the right, tan x ________ (increases/decreases) without bound.

The graph of a function is **asymptotic** to a line if and only if the distance from a point of the graph to the line continues to decrease toward zero as the point of the graph moves off an infinite distance from the origin.

Because tan x (is/is not) ________ defined for $x = \frac{\pi}{2}$ and tan x gets infinitely large as x approaches $\frac{\pi}{2}$ from the left, we say that tan is **asymptotic** to the line defined by $x = \frac{\pi}{2}$. This line is called an **asymptote** of the tangent function. (See the illustration.)

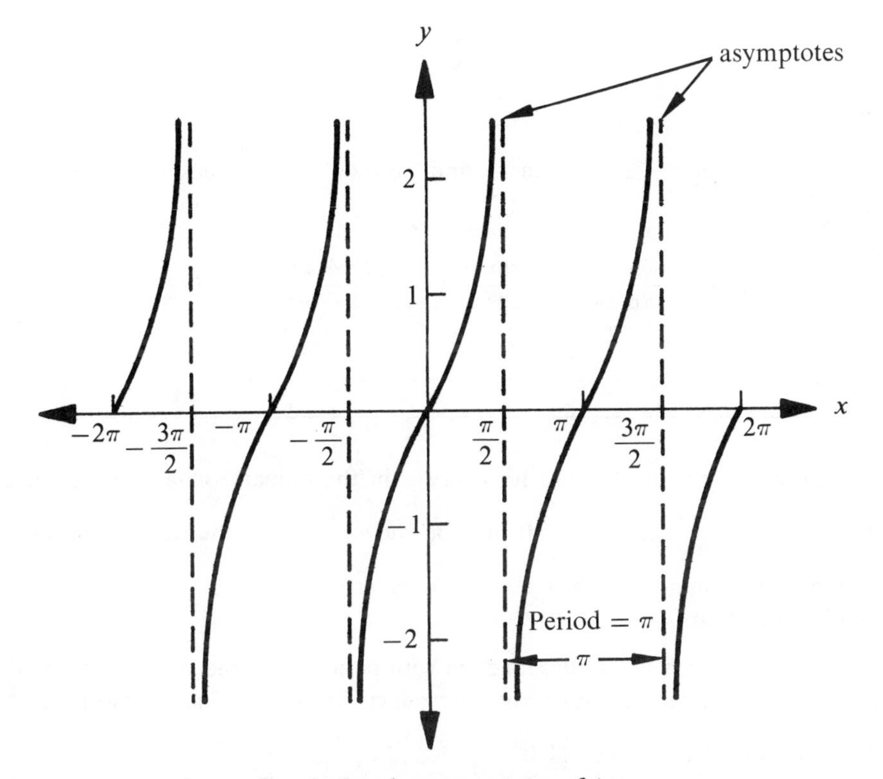

Graph showing asymptotes of tan.

ANSWERS TO PAGE 145

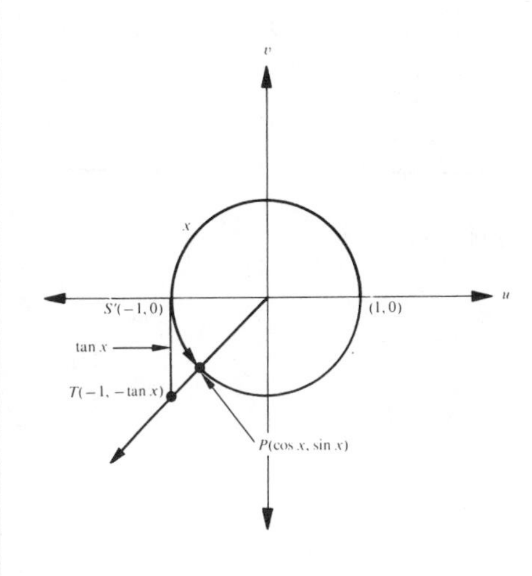

positive

increasing

undefined

infinity

---

fourth

negative

zero

infinity

$\mathscr{R}$

ANSWERS TO PAGE 150

$\frac{-\sin x}{\cos x}$

$-\cot x$

$\frac{-\pi}{2}$	$\frac{-\pi}{3}$	$\frac{-\pi}{4}$	$\frac{-\pi}{6}$	0	$\frac{\pi}{6}$	$\frac{\pi}{4}$
0	$\frac{-\sqrt{3}}{3}$	-1	$-\sqrt{3}$	undef	$\sqrt{3}$	1

$\frac{\pi}{3}$	$\frac{\pi}{2}$	$\frac{2\pi}{3}$	$\frac{3\pi}{4}$	$\frac{5\pi}{6}$	π
$\frac{\sqrt{3}}{3}$	0	$\frac{-\sqrt{3}}{3}$	-1	$-\sqrt{3}$	undef

---

Return to the unit circle (see accompanying illustration). If point B ($\cos x$, $\sin x$) is at a distance $|x|$ along the circle from (1,0), measured counterclockwise if $x > 0$ and clockwise if $x < 0$, then the coordinates of point D, which is located at a distance $(x + \pi)$ along the circle from (1,0), are __________. (This can be verified by showing $\triangle OBA \cong \triangle ODC$.)

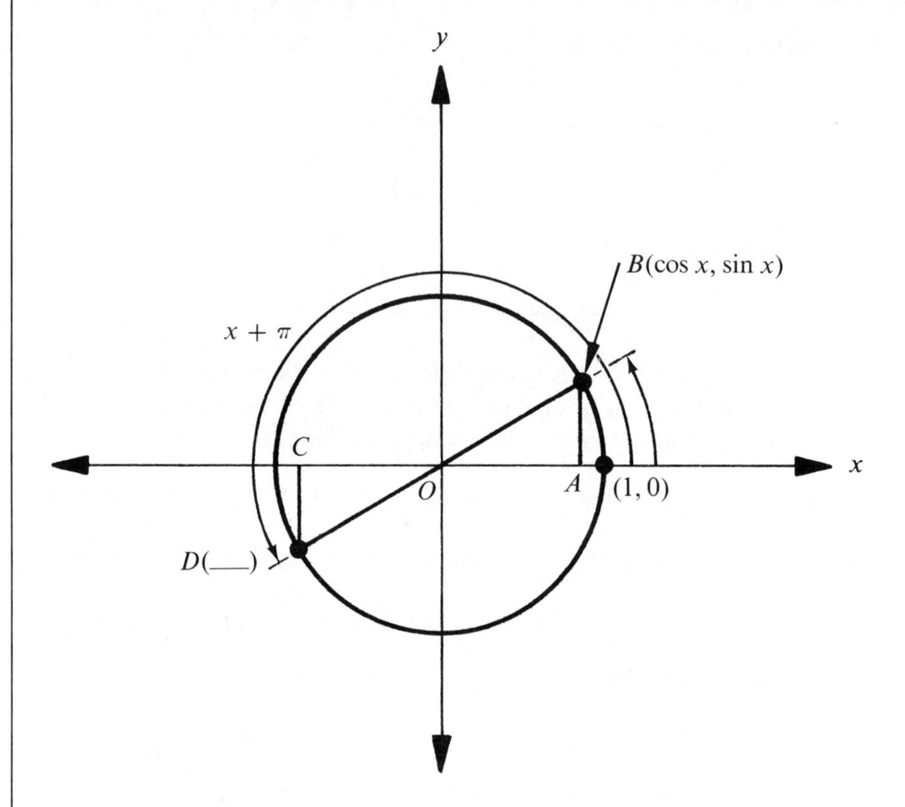

Thus,

$$\sin(x + \pi) = -\sin x \quad \text{and} \quad \cos(x + \pi) = -\cos x.$$

Hence,

$$\tan x = \frac{\sin x}{\cos x} = \frac{-\sin x}{-\cos x} = \frac{\sin(x + \pi)}{\cos(x + \pi)} = \tan(x + \pi),$$

provided $\cos x \neq 0$.

Since $\tan x = \tan(x + \pi)$ for every x in the domain of tan, the tangent function is __________. It may be shown that π is the smallest positive number such that $\tan x = \tan(x + \pi)$. Hence the __________ of the tangent function is π.

Since tangent is a periodic function with period π, all the values of tangent for x in the domain of tan can be determined from the values of the tangent function for x in the interval $0 <$ __________.

Express each of the following in the form tan x for some x such that $0 < x \leq \pi$:

(a) $\tan\left(\frac{\pi}{6} + \pi\right) = \tan$ ______ (b) $\tan \frac{7\pi}{6} = \tan$ ______

(c) $\tan\left(-\frac{5\pi}{6}\right) = \tan$ ______ (d) $\tan \frac{10\pi}{3} = \tan$ ______

DEFINITION:

The **cotangent** function, abbreviated **cot**, is defined as

$$\cot = \left\{(x,y)\colon y = \frac{\cos x}{\sin x}, \sin x \neq 0\right\} \text{ for } x \epsilon \mathcal{R}.$$

It is customary to write **cot** x to denote the values of the cotangent function at x. Thus, $y = \cot x$ if and only if $y = \frac{\cos x}{\sin x}$ and $\sin x \neq 0$. Hence, whenever $\sin x \neq 0$, $\cot x = \frac{\cos x}{\sin x}$.

MOVE TO NEXT FRAME

Since $\cot x =$ ______ whenever $\sin x \neq 0$ and $\tan x =$ ______ whenever $\cos x \neq 0$, cot x and tan x are multiplicative ______ of each other whenever both are defined, i.e., $\tan x = \frac{1}{\cot x}$ and $\cot x = \frac{1}{\tan x}$ whenever $\sin x \neq 0$ and $\cos x \neq 0$.

Cot is defined whenever $\sin x \neq 0$. Thus the set of values of $x \epsilon \mathcal{R}$ for which cot is undefined is ______________.

The domain of cot is ______________. Since $\cot x = \frac{1}{\tan x}$ when $\tan x \neq 0$ and since the range of tan is $\mathcal{R}$, it follows that the range of cot is __.

ANSWERS TO PAGE 147

increases

decreases

is not

ANSWERS TO PAGE 152

$\left\{x : x = (2k+1)\frac{\pi}{2} \text{ for some } k\epsilon J\right\}$

a, b, and c are all true provided $x \neq (2k+1)\frac{\pi}{2}$ for all $k\epsilon J$

x	0	$\frac{\pi}{6}$	$\frac{\pi}{4}$	$\frac{\pi}{3}$	$\frac{\pi}{2}$
$\cos x$	1	$\frac{\sqrt{3}}{2}$	$\frac{\sqrt{2}}{2}$	$\frac{1}{2}$	0
$\sec x$	1	1.2	1.4	2	undef.

Since

$$\sin(-x) = -\sin x \quad \text{and} \quad \cos(-x) = \cos x,$$

$$\tan(-x) = \frac{\sin(-x)}{\cos(-x)} = \frac{(\qquad)}{(\qquad)} = -\tan x$$

and

$$\cot(-x) = \underline{\qquad\qquad}.$$

Complete the following tables. For example,

$$\cot\frac{\pi}{3} = \frac{\cos\frac{\pi}{3}}{\sin\frac{\pi}{3}} = \frac{\frac{1}{2}}{\frac{\sqrt{3}}{2}} = \frac{\sqrt{3}}{3}$$

and

$$\cot\left(\frac{-\pi}{3}\right) = -\cot\left(\frac{\pi}{3}\right) = \frac{-\sqrt{3}}{3}$$

x	$\frac{-\pi}{2}$	$\frac{-\pi}{3}$	$\frac{-\pi}{4}$	$\frac{-\pi}{6}$	0	$\frac{\pi}{6}$	$\frac{\pi}{4}$
$\cot x$							

x	$\frac{\pi}{3}$	$\frac{\pi}{2}$	$\frac{2\pi}{3}$	$\frac{3\pi}{4}$	$\frac{5\pi}{6}$	π
$\cot x$						

Sketch the graph of the cotangent function for x in the interval $-\frac{\pi}{2} \leq x \leq \pi$. Use the ordered pairs found in the above frame and plot them on the following coordinate system.

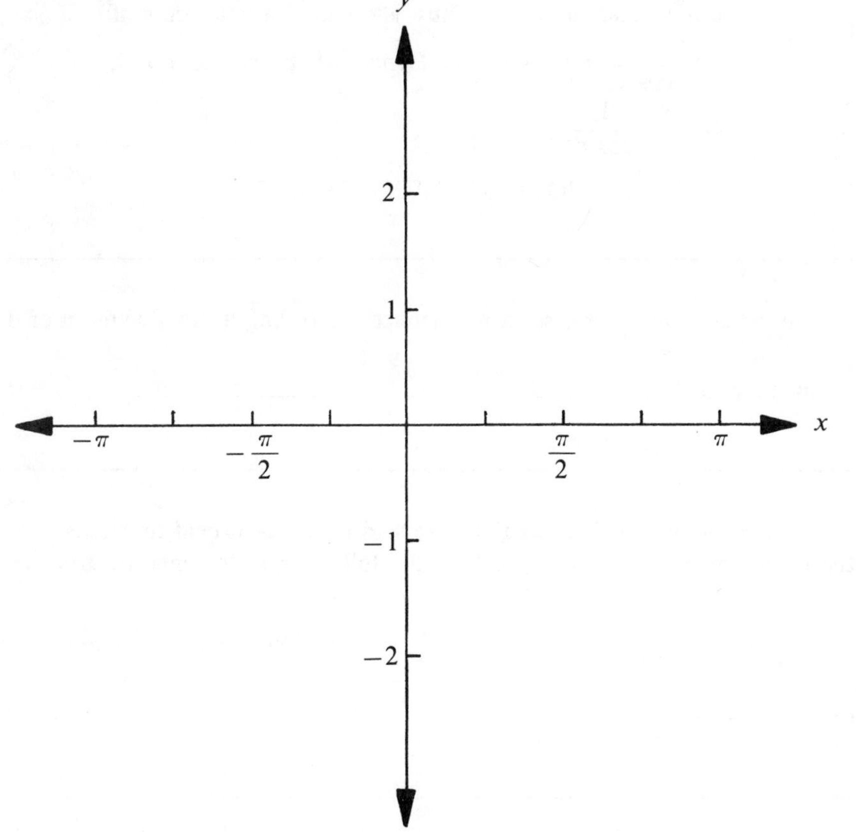

Since $\cos(x+\pi) = -\cos x$ and $\sin(x+\pi) =$ ______, it can be seen that

$$\cot(x+\pi) = \frac{\cos(x+\pi)}{\sin(x+\pi)} = \frac{(\qquad)}{(\qquad)} = \_\_\_\_\_\_,$$
whenever $\sin x \neq 0$.

The function cot is periodic with period __.

ANSWERS TO PAGE 149

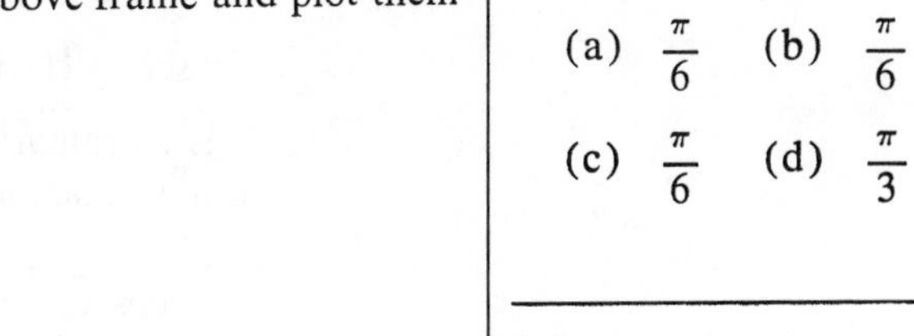

(a) $\frac{\pi}{6}$ (b) $\frac{\pi}{6}$

(c) $\frac{\pi}{6}$ (d) $\frac{\pi}{3}$

$\frac{\cos x}{\sin x}$ $\frac{\sin x}{\cos x}$

inverses

$\{x : x = k\pi \text{ for some } k \in J\}$

$\{x : x \in \mathcal{R}, x \neq k\pi \text{ for all } k \in J\}$

$\mathcal{R}$

---

zero

zero

infinity

asymptotes

$x \in \mathcal{R}$ and $x \neq (2k+1)\frac{\pi}{2}$,

for all $k \in J$.

$\{y : y \in \mathcal{R}$ and $y \geq 1$ or $y \leq -1\}$

sine

cosecant 1

DEFINITION:

The **secant** function, abbreviated **sec**, is defined as

$$\sec = \{(x,y) : y = \frac{1}{\cos x},\ \cos x \neq 0\} \text{ for } x \in \mathcal{R}.$$

It is customary to write **sec** x to denote the value of the secant function at x. Thus $y = \sec x$ if and only if $y = \frac{1}{\cos x}$ and $\cos x \neq 0$. Hence, whenever $\cos x \neq 0$,

$$\sec x = \frac{1}{\cos x}.$$

MOVE TO NEXT FRAME

For what values of x is $\sec x$ not defined, according to the definition of the secant function? ____________________.

The secant and cosine functions are said to be **reciprocal** functions. From the definition of sec, decide which of the following statements are true.

(a) $\cos x = \frac{1}{\sec x}$ __________ (b) $\cos x \sec x = 1$ __________

(c) $\sec x = \frac{1}{\cos x}$ __________

Since the secant and cosine functions are reciprocal functions, *i.e.*, $\sec x = \frac{1}{\cos x}$ when $\cos x \neq 0$, the values for $\sec x$ may be calculated directly from those for $\cos x$. For example, $\sec\frac{\pi}{3} = \frac{1}{\cos\frac{\pi}{3}} = \frac{1}{\frac{1}{2}} = 2.$

MOVE TO NEXT FRAME

Complete the following tables of values for $\sec x$ by first finding the appropriate values of $\cos x$. Change any radicals to decimal approximations to the nearest tenth for the sec values.

x	0	$\frac{\pi}{6}$	$\frac{\pi}{4}$	$\frac{\pi}{3}$	$\frac{\pi}{2}$
$\cos x$					
$\sec x$					

x	$\frac{2\pi}{3}$	$\frac{3\pi}{4}$	$\frac{5\pi}{6}$	π	$\frac{7\pi}{6}$
$\cos x$					
$\sec x$					

x	$\frac{5\pi}{4}$	$\frac{4\pi}{3}$	$\frac{3\pi}{2}$	$\frac{5\pi}{3}$	$\frac{7\pi}{4}$	$\frac{11\pi}{6}$
$\cos x$						
$\sec x$						

Use the values of sec x from the previous frame to sketch the graph of sec on the given coordinate system. The graph of cos is provided so that you may see the reciprocal nature of the two functions.

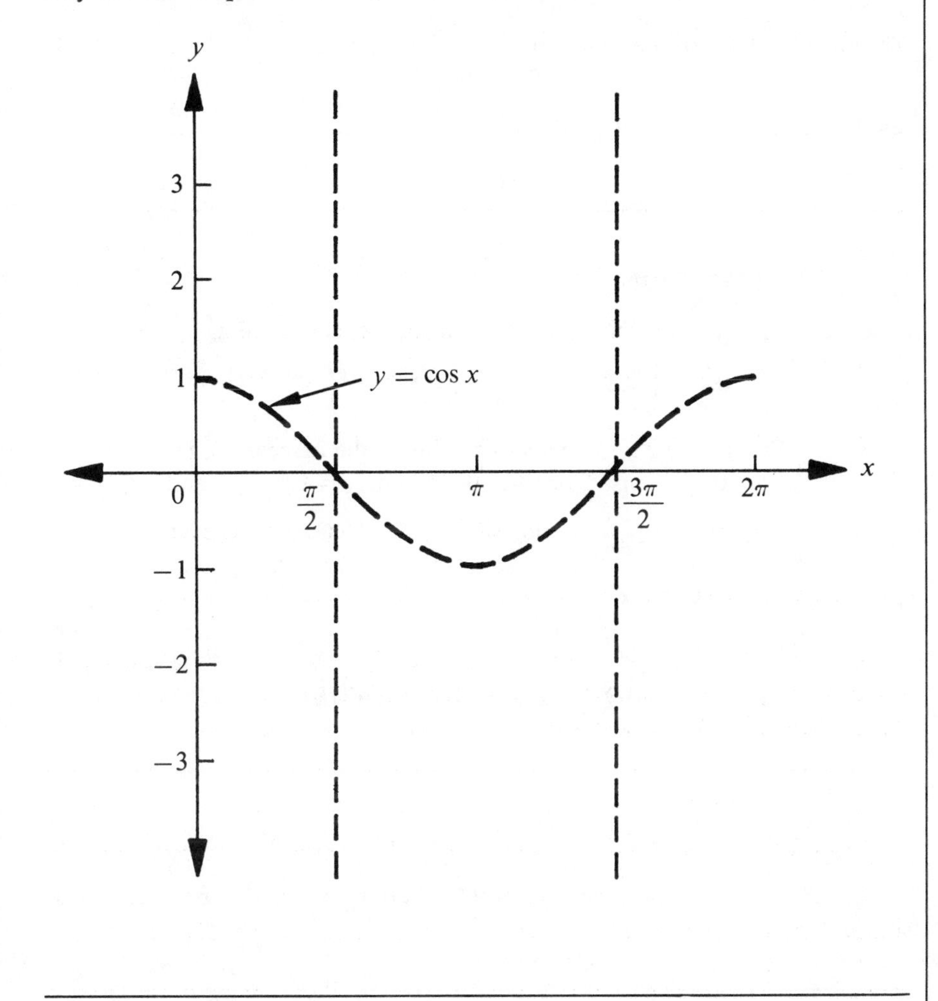

ANSWERS TO PAGE 151

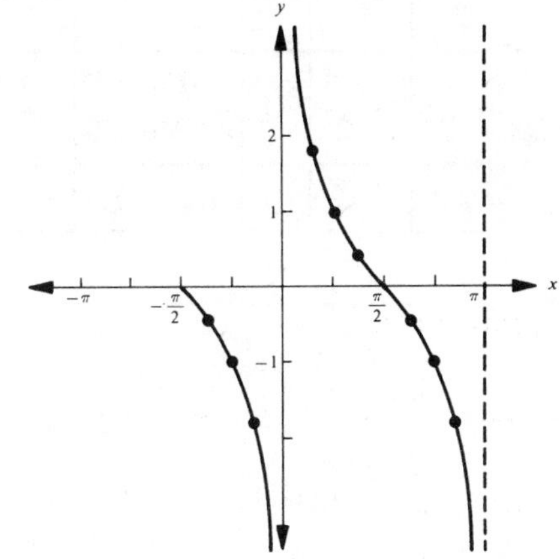

$-\sin x$

$$\frac{-\cos x}{-\sin x} = \cot x$$

π

ANSWERS TO PAGE 156

x	$\frac{3\pi}{4}$	$\frac{5\pi}{6}$	π	$\frac{7\pi}{6}$	$\frac{5\pi}{4}$
$\sin x$	$\frac{\sqrt{2}}{2}$	$\frac{1}{2}$	0	$-\frac{1}{2}$	$-\frac{\sqrt{2}}{2}$
$\csc x$	1.4	2	undef.	-2	-1.4

x	$\frac{4\pi}{3}$	$\frac{3\pi}{2}$	$\frac{5\pi}{3}$	$\frac{7\pi}{4}$	$\frac{11\pi}{6}$
$\sin x$	$-\frac{\sqrt{3}}{2}$	-1	$-\frac{\sqrt{3}}{2}$	$-\frac{\sqrt{2}}{2}$	$-\frac{1}{2}$
$\csc x$	-1.2	-1	1.2	-1.4	-2

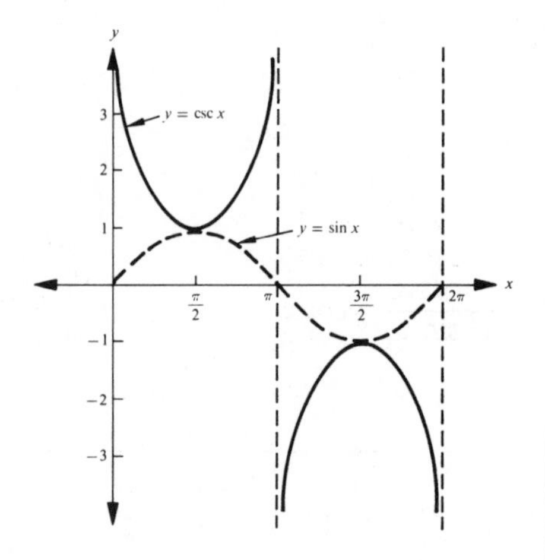

Do you see that the points $(0,1)$, $(\pi,-1)$, and $(2\pi,1)$ in the graph are on both the sec and cos graph? Knowing the graph of the cosine function enables you to graph the secant function.

As x approaches $\frac{\pi}{2}$ from the left, cos x approaches ______ and sec x approaches infinity (becoming increasingly large without bound).

As x approaches $\frac{3\pi}{2}$ from the left, cos x approaches ______ and secant x approaches negative __________.

The lines whose equations are $x=\frac{\pi}{2}$, $x=\frac{3\pi}{2}$, and in general $x=(2k+1)\frac{\pi}{2}$, $k \epsilon J$, are ____________ for the secant function.

The domain of the secant function is $\{x:$____________________$\}$,

and the range of the secant function is ________________.

DEFINITION:

The **cosecant** function, abbreviated **csc**, is defined as

$$\csc = \left\{(x,y) : y = \frac{1}{\sin x}, \sin x \neq 0\right\} \text{ for } x \epsilon \mathcal{R}.$$

We write **csc** x to denote the value of the cosecant function at x. Thus, from the definition, $y = \csc x$ if and only if $y = \frac{1}{\sin x}$ and $\sin x \neq 0$. Hence, whenever $\sin x \neq 0$, $\csc x = \frac{1}{\sin x}$.

MOVE TO NEXT FRAME

From the definition of the cosecant function we see that the ______ and __________ function are reciprocals. Thus, $\csc x \sin x =$ ___, when $\sin x \neq 0$.

Referring to the equation $\csc x = \frac{1}{\sin x}$, $\sin x \neq 0$, it is possible to determine the domain of csc.

Since $\sin x \neq 0, x \notin \{0, \pi, 2\pi, 3\pi, \cdots\}$, the domain of csc is ____.

An analysis of $\frac{1}{\sin x}$ as x varies will enable us to determine the range of csc.

For x very close to zero, $\sin x$ is very close to zero and $\csc x = \frac{1}{\sin x}$ is very ______ (small/large). As x increases to $\frac{\pi}{2}$, $\sin x$ increases from — to __ and $\csc x = \frac{1}{\sin x}$ decreases from large positive numbers to __. Csc $x =$ __ when $x = \frac{\pi}{2}$. As x increases from $\frac{\pi}{2}$ to π, $\sin x$ decreases from __ to __ and $\csc x = \frac{1}{\sin x}$ increases from __ to ________.

An analysis similar to that in the preceding frame will determine that as x increases from π to $\frac{3\pi}{2}$, $\sin x$ decreases from __ to ____ and $\csc x = \frac{1}{\sin x}$ increases from negative infinity to ____. As x increases from $\frac{3\pi}{2}$ to 2π, csc x decreases from ____ to ______________. Csc $x =$ ______ when $x = \frac{3\pi}{2}$.

From the previous frames it may be determined that the range of csc is ____.

Since sin and csc are reciprocal functions, the equation csc $x =$ ______ ____________________ may be used to find values for csc x.

Complete the following tables of values for csc x by first finding values of sin x. Approximate values of csc x to the nearest tenth for graphing.

x	0	$\frac{\pi}{6}$	$\frac{\pi}{4}$	$\frac{\pi}{3}$	$\frac{\pi}{2}$	$\frac{2\pi}{3}$
sin x						
csc x						

ANSWERS TO PAGE 153

x	$\frac{2\pi}{3}$	$\frac{3\pi}{4}$	$\frac{5\pi}{6}$	π	$\frac{7\pi}{6}$
cos x	$-\frac{1}{2}$	$-\frac{\sqrt{2}}{2}$	$-\frac{\sqrt{3}}{2}$	-1	$-\frac{\sqrt{3}}{2}$
sec x	-2	-1.4	-1.2	-1	-1.2

x	$\frac{5\pi}{4}$	$\frac{4\pi}{3}$	$\frac{3\pi}{2}$	$\frac{5\pi}{3}$	$\frac{7\pi}{4}$	$\frac{11\pi}{6}$
cos x	$-\frac{\sqrt{2}}{2}$	$-\frac{1}{2}$	0	$\frac{1}{2}$	$\frac{\sqrt{2}}{2}$	$\frac{\sqrt{3}}{2}$
sec x	-1.4	-2	undef.	2	1.4	1.2

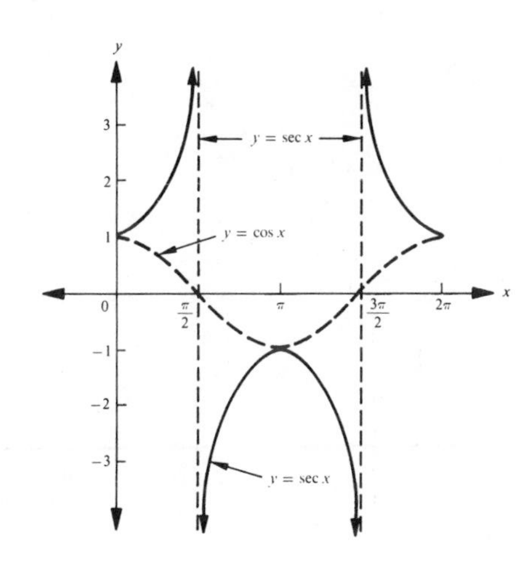

ANSWERS TO PAGE 158

II

a and d

III or IV

x	$\frac{3\pi}{4}$	$\frac{5\pi}{6}$	π	$\frac{7\pi}{6}$	$\frac{5\pi}{4}$
$\sin x$					
$\csc x$					

x	$\frac{4\pi}{3}$	$\frac{3\pi}{2}$	$\frac{5\pi}{3}$	$\frac{7\pi}{4}$	$\frac{11\pi}{6}$
$\sin x$					
$\csc x$					

Use the values found in the previous frame to graph the sin and csc functions over the interval $0 \leq x < 2\pi$. Use the coordinate system provided.

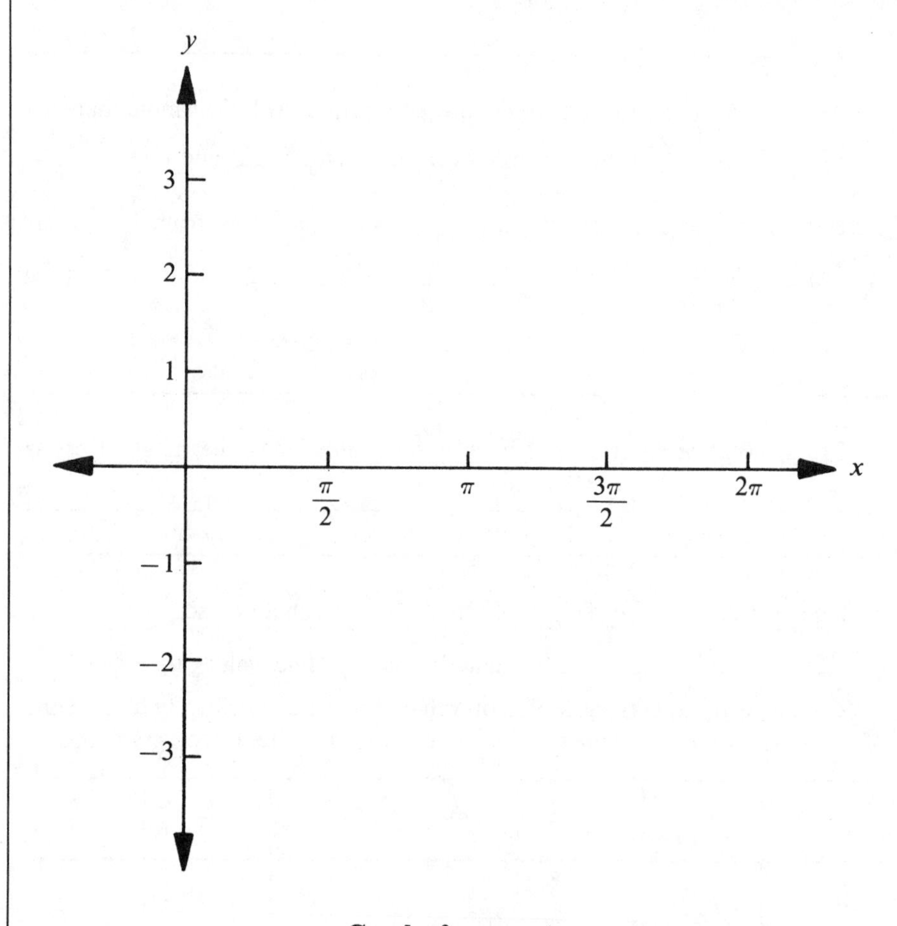

Graph of cosecant.

The lines with equations of the form $x =$ ______________ are asymptotes for the cosecant function.

Since $\sec x = \dfrac{1}{\cos x}$, $\cos x \neq 0$, it follows that

$$\sec(x + 2\pi) = \frac{1}{\cos(x + 2\pi)}$$

Furthermore,

$$\frac{1}{\cos(x + 2\pi)} = \frac{1}{\cos x}$$

by the ______________ of $\cos x$. Therefore, it follows that

$$\sec(x + 2\pi) = \sec x.$$

The secant function is periodic with period ______.

To show that 2π is the least positive period of sec, let $t > 0$ be a period of sec. Then $\sec(x + t) = \sec x$, $\dfrac{1}{\cos(x+t)} = \dfrac{1}{\cos x}$, and $\cos x = \cos(x + t)$.

Therefore, $f \geq 2\pi$ since the cosine function has period ____.

In a like manner it can be shown that csc is periodic with period 2π. This is so because $\csc x =$ ______________, provided $\sin x \neq 0$, by definition and sin has a period of 2π.

In summary, note that the period of the tangent and cotangent functions is ___ and that the period of the sine, cosecant, cosine, and secant functions is ______.

ANSWERS TO PAGE 155

$\{x : x \in \mathcal{R} \text{ and } x \neq k\pi \text{ for all } k \in J\}$

---

large 0

1 1

1

1 0 1 infinity

---

0 −1

−1

−1 negative infinity −1

$\{y : y \in \mathcal{R} \text{ and } y \geq 1 \text{ or } y \leq -1\}$

$\dfrac{1}{\sin x}$, $\sin x \neq 0$

x	0	$\frac{\pi}{6}$	$\frac{\pi}{4}$	$\frac{\pi}{3}$	$\frac{\pi}{2}$	$\frac{2\pi}{3}$
$\sin x$	0	$\frac{\sqrt{2}}{2}$	$\frac{1}{2}$	$\frac{\sqrt{3}}{2}$	1	$\frac{\sqrt{3}}{2}$
$\csc x$	undef.	2	1.4	1.2	1	1.2

ANSWERS TO PAGE 160

$-\frac{\sqrt{3}}{3}$

$\frac{\sin x}{\cos x}$

$\{y: |y| \leq 1\}$

1   0

0

$\frac{1}{|\cos x|} > 1$

$\frac{\sqrt{21}}{5}$

$\frac{-5\sqrt{21}}{10} = \frac{-\sqrt{21}}{2}$

Suppose $P(u,v)$ is a point at a distance $|x|$ along the unit circle from $(1,0)$, measured in a counterclockwise direction if $x > 0$ and a clockwise direction if $x < 0$. We say that x **is in Quadrant I** if and only if P is in Quadrant I. Similarly x is in Quadrant II, Quadrant III, or Quadrant IV if the terminal point of its arc is in the respective quadrant. If P lies on an axis, then it is not said to be in a quadrant. (See the illustration.)

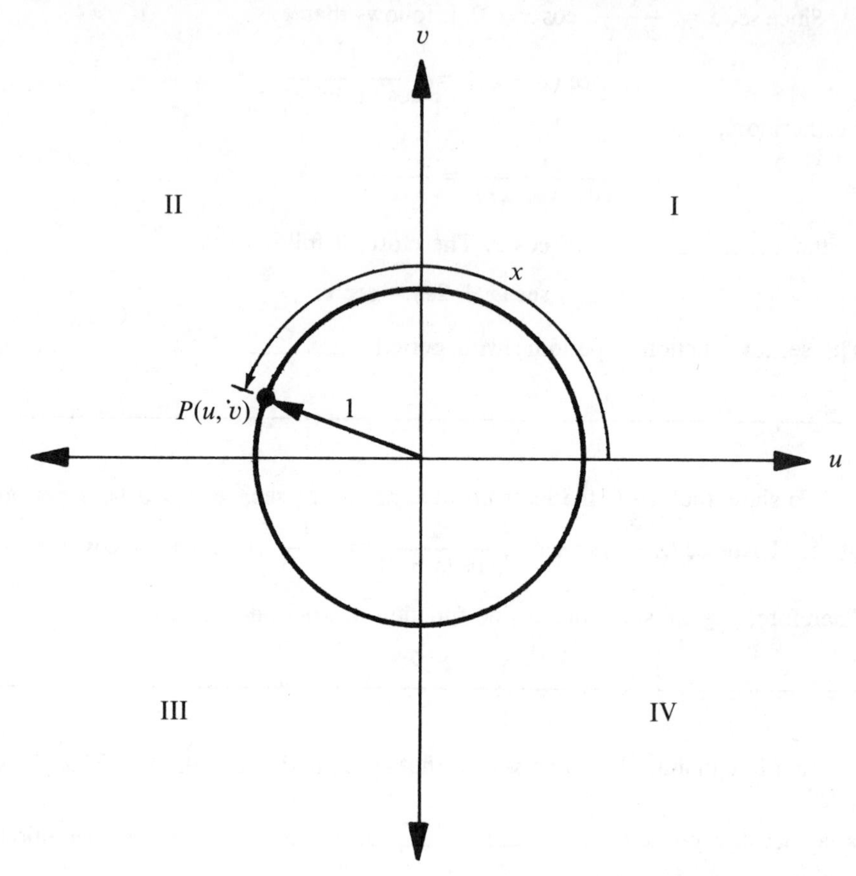

x is in Quadrant ___.

If x is in Quadrant II, which of the following numbers are positive?

(a) $\sin x$ (b) $\cos x$ (c) $\tan x$

(d) $\csc x$ (e) $\sec x$ (f) $\cot x$ ________

If $\csc x < 0$, then x is in Quadrant ______ or ______.

Consider the function $f = \{(x,y): y = 2 \sec x\}$. For every x, the value of y is ____________ that of the value of y in the function $\{(x,y): y = \sec x\}$.

What is the range of f? ____________

Find the set of values of x for which $\csc x = 2$. ____________

(*Hint:* $\csc x = \dfrac{1}{\sin x}$; you must therefore find the values of x for which $\sin x = \dfrac{1}{2}$.)

Find the set of values of x for which $\csc x = \dfrac{1}{2}$. ____________

Find the set of values of x for which $\tan x = -\sqrt{3}$. ____________

(*Hint:* In which quadrant is $\tan x < 0$?)

Problem:

Find $\cos x$ if $\sin x = \dfrac{\sqrt{3}}{2}$ and x is in the first quadrant.

Solution:

Use $\cos^2 x + \sin^2 x = 1$. Thus,

$$\cos^2 x + \left(\frac{\sqrt{3}}{2}\right)^2 = 1,$$

$$\cos^2 x + \frac{3}{4} = 1,$$

$$\cos^2 x = \frac{1}{4},$$

$$\cos x = \frac{1}{2},$$

since x is in Quadrant I. ....

MOVE TO NEXT FRAME

ANSWERS TO PAGE 157

$k\pi, \quad k \epsilon J$

---

periodicity

2π

2π

$\dfrac{1}{\sin x}$

π

2π

---

(6) (a) $\frac{2\pi}{3}$; $\{y:|y| \le 1\}$

(b) $\frac{\pi}{2}$, $\mathcal{R}$

(c) 2π; $\left\{y:|y-3| \le \frac{1}{2}\right\}$

(d) $\frac{4}{3}\pi$; $\{y:y \ge 1 \text{ or } y \le -1\}$

(e) $\frac{\pi}{2}$, $\{y:y \ge 1 \text{ or } y \le -1\}$

(f) $\frac{\pi}{3}$; $\mathcal{R}$

(g) 2π; $\mathcal{R}$

(h) π; $\left\{y:y \le -\frac{1}{2} \text{ or } y \ge \frac{1}{2}\right\}$

(7) (a) I or III

(b) II or III

(c) II or IV

(d) I

(e) not possible

(f) IV

(8) $|\tan x| \ge |\sin x|$ implies

$$\frac{1}{|\cot x|} \ge \frac{1}{|\csc x|}$$

Multiply by $|\cot x| \cdot |\csc x|$ to obtain $|\csc x| \ge |\cot x|$.

Find $\tan x$ if $\sin x = \frac{1}{2}$ and $\tan x < 0$. ______

(*Hint:* Find $\cos x$ by means of the method used in the preceding frames and then use $\tan x = \frac{\sin x}{\cos x}$.)

Problem:

From the definition of the tangent function we know that whenever $\cos x \ne 0$, $\tan x =$ ______________. Use this definition of tan and the properties of sin and cos to prove $|\tan x| \ge |\sin x|$ for all $x \in \mathcal{R}$ for which $\cos x \ne 0$.

Proof:

From the definition of cos we know that the range of cos is __________ ______________. Hence, $|\cos x| \le$ __. If $|\cos x| = 1$, then $|\sin x| =$ __ and $|\tan x| =$ __. Therefore, $|\tan x| = |\sin x|$.

If $|\cos x| < 1$, then $\frac{1}{|\cos x|}$ ____________________ $1(<,>,=)$. Thus $|\sin x|\frac{1}{|\cos x|} > |\sin x|$. Therefore $\frac{|\sin x|}{|\cos x|} > |\sin x|$ and $|\tan x| > |\sin x|$.

The values for sin, cos, tan, cot, sec, and csc have been calculated using certain "special" numbers for x. Numbers for x that are multiples of $\frac{\pi}{6}$, $\frac{\pi}{4}$, or $\frac{\pi}{3}$ have been used as a convenience, since the right triangles determined by these numbers have sides whose ratios are known to us. You are reminded, however, that x may be any real number. Finding values of circular functions for any real number will be considered later in the text.

Problems such as the following may be considered at this time, however.

MOVE TO NEXT FRAME

Problem:

Find $\cot x$ when $\sin x = \frac{-2}{5}$ and x is in the fourth quadrant.

Solution:

Since $\cos^2 x + \sin^2 x = 1$,

$$|\cos x| = \sqrt{1 - \sin^2 x} = \text{\_\_\_\_\_\_}.$$

Since x is in the fourth quadrant $\cos x = \frac{+\sqrt{21}}{5}$.

Now $\cot x = \frac{\cos x}{\sin x} =$ ______ $=$ ______.

EXERCISES. 3.3

1. Find each of the following:

(a) $\tan \frac{5\pi}{4}$ ______ (b) $\cot \frac{29\pi}{3}$ ______

(c) $\sec\left(\frac{-7\pi}{6}\right)$ ______ (d) $\csc \frac{7\pi}{6}$ ______

(e) $\tan\left(\frac{-2\pi}{3}\right)$ ______ (f) $\sec \frac{19\pi}{4}$ ______

2. Find $\tan x$:

(a) When $\cos x = \frac{3}{5}$ and x is in Quadrant IV. ______

(b) When $\sin x = \frac{-2}{3}$ and x is in Quadrant III. ______

(c) When $\sec x = 2\frac{1}{2}$ and x is in Quadrant I. ______

(d) When $\csc x = -1\frac{1}{12}$ and x is in Quadrant IV. ______

3. Prove that $|\cot x| \geq |\cos x|$ whenever $\sin x \neq 0$.

______

______

______

4. State the domain of each of the following functions:

(a) tangent ______

(b) cotangent ______

5. State the range of each of the following functions:

(a) secant ______

(b) cosecant ______

ANSWERS TO PAGE 159

twice

$\{y : y \in \mathcal{R} \text{ and } y \geq 2 \text{ or } y \leq -2\}$

$\{x : x = \frac{\pi}{6} + 2k\pi \text{ or } \frac{5\pi}{6} + 2k\pi$ for some $k \in J\}$

$\emptyset$

$\{x : x = \frac{2\pi}{3} + k\pi \text{ for some } k \in J\}$

ANSWERS TO PAGE 164

(11)

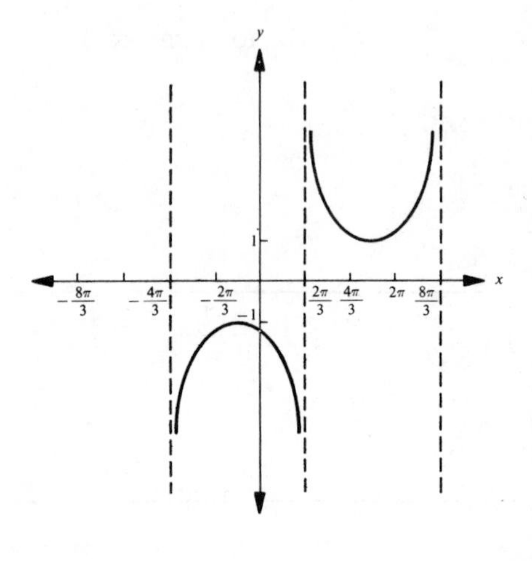

6. State the period and range of the functions defined by each of the following equations:

   (a) $y = \cos 3x$ __________; __________

   (b) $y = 4 \tan 2x$ __________; __________

   (c) $y - 3 = \frac{1}{2} \sin\left(x - \frac{\pi}{2}\right)$ __________; __________

   (d) $y = \csc\left(\frac{3}{2}x + \pi\right)$ __________; __________

   (e) $y = \sec 4x$ __________; __________

   (f) $y = 2 + \cot(3x + \pi)$ __________; __________

   (g) $y = \tan\left(\frac{1}{2}x - \frac{\pi}{2}\right)$ __________; __________

   (h) $y = \frac{1}{2} \sec(2x - 3)$ __________; __________

7. In which quadrants will you find x, if the following statements are true?

   (a) $\tan x > 0$ __________

   (b) $\sec x < -1$ __________

   (c) $\cot x < 0$ __________

   (d) $\sec x > 1$ and $\tan x > 0$ __________

   (e) $\csc x < -1$ and $\sin x > 0$ __________

   (f) $\cot x < 0$ and $\sec x \geq 1$ __________

8. Given that $|\tan x| \geq |\sin x|$, prove that $|\csc x| \geq |\cot x|$.

9. Graph $\{(x,y): y = 3 \tan 2x\}$ over the interval $-\pi \leq x \leq \pi$.

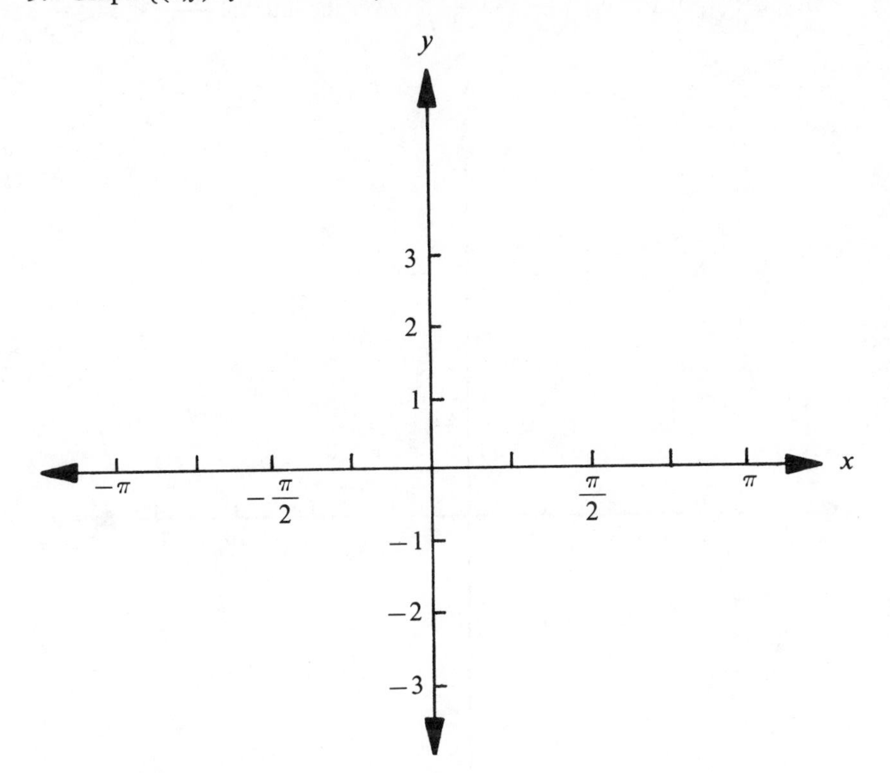

10. Graph $\left\{(x,y): y = -\sec \frac{1}{2}x\right\}$ over the interval $-\pi < x < \pi$.

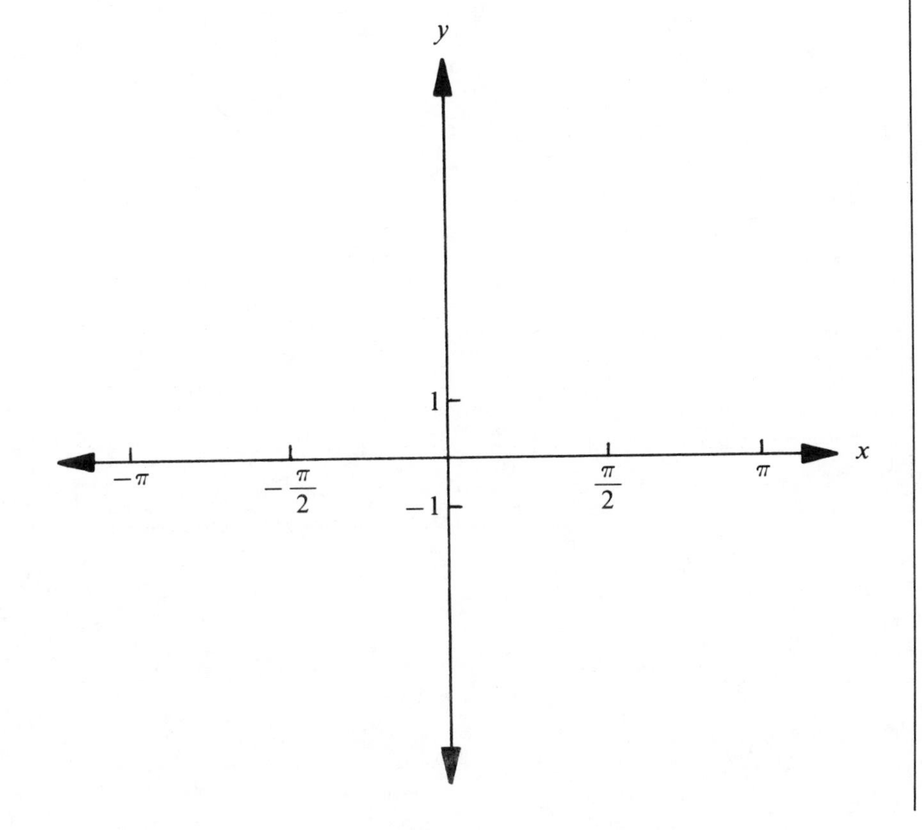

ANSWERS TO PAGE 161

(1) (a) $+1$ (b) $\frac{-\sqrt{3}}{3}$

(c) $\frac{-2\sqrt{3}}{3}$ (d) -2

(e) $+\sqrt{3}$ (f) $+\sqrt{2}$

(2) (a) $\frac{-4}{3}$

(b) $\frac{2\sqrt{5}}{5}$

(c) $\frac{\sqrt{21}}{2}$

(d) $\frac{-12}{5}$

(3) Since $|\cot x| = \frac{|\cos x|}{|\sin x|}$ and $|\sin x| \leq 1, \frac{|\cos x|}{|\sin x|} \geq |\cos x|$ and $|\cot x| \geq |\cos x|$

(4) (a) $\left\{x: x \in \mathcal{R} \text{ and } x \neq (2k+1)\frac{\pi}{2} \text{ for all } k \in J\right\}$

(b) $\{x: x \in \mathcal{R} \text{ and } x \neq k\pi \text{ for all } k \in J\}$

(5) (a) $\{y: y \in \mathcal{R} \text{ and } y \geq 1 \text{ or } y \leq -1\}$

(b) $\{y: y \in \mathcal{R} \text{ and } y \geq 1 \text{ or } y \leq -1\}$

defined

Any choice, such as $x = \frac{\pi}{4}$, for which $\cos x \neq 0$ or $\cos x \neq -\frac{1}{2}$.

---

all x and $y \epsilon \mathcal{R}$

---

substitution

(Cos x is substituted for u and sin x is substituted for v in $u^2 + v^2 = 1$.)

$\csc x \sin x = 1$

---

11. Graph $\left\{(x,y): y = \csc\left(\frac{1}{2}x - \frac{\pi}{3}\right)\right\}$ over the interval $\frac{-4\pi}{3} < x < \frac{8\pi}{3}$.

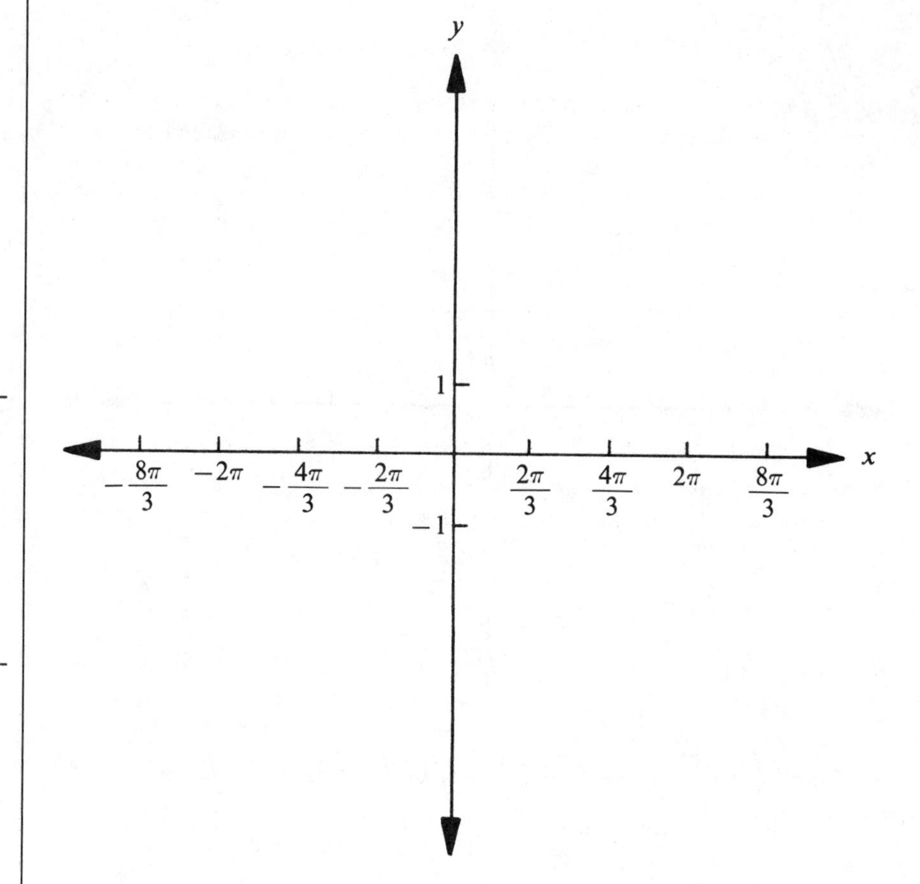

3.4. IDENTITIES

The following derivation was presented in Section 3.1.

Let (u,v) be the coordinates of a point on the unit circle. By the Pythagorean Theorem $u^2 + v^2 = 1$. From the definition of the sine and cosine function $u = \cos x$ and $v = \sin x$. By substitution it follows that ______________ $= 1$.

Because this is the case for all real numbers x, $\cos^2 x + \sin^2 x = 1$ is said to be an **identity.**

DEFINITION:

An **identity** is an equation that holds for all values of the variables for which both members of the equation are defined.

MOVE TO NEXT FRAME

The equation $\cos^2 x + \sin^2 x = 1$ is an ______________, since it holds for all $x \epsilon \mathcal{R}$. Many texts use the symbol $\equiv$ to denote an identity. Thus, $\cos^2 x + \sin^2 x \equiv 1$. We will continue to use the symbol $=$.

$$\frac{2}{x-2} - \frac{1}{x+1} = \frac{x+4}{(x-2)(x+1)}$$

is an identity even though it does not hold for all values of x, because it does hold for all values of the variable for which both members are defined. Each member of the equation is undefined for $x \epsilon$ {______________}. The identity is verified by simply combining the fractions in the left member and noting that the result is identical to the right member.

There are two kinds of equations: **identities** and **conditional equations.**

MOVE TO NEXT FRAME

DEFINITION:

A **conditional equation** is an equation which is not an identity. Thus, a conditional equation does not hold for at least one set of values of the variables for which both members of the equation are defined.

MOVE TO NEXT FRAME

ANSWERS TO PAGE 163

(9)

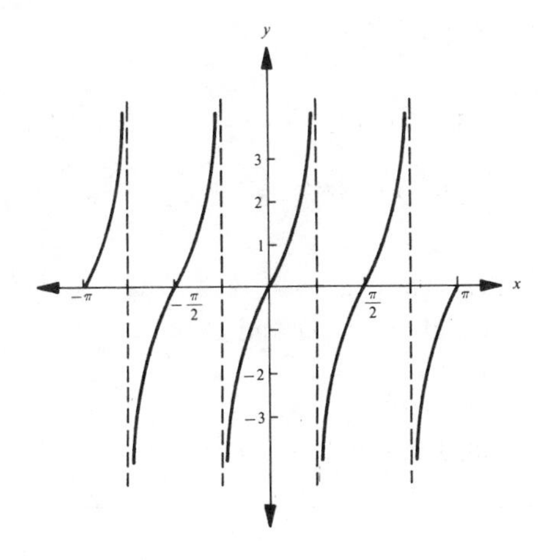

(10)

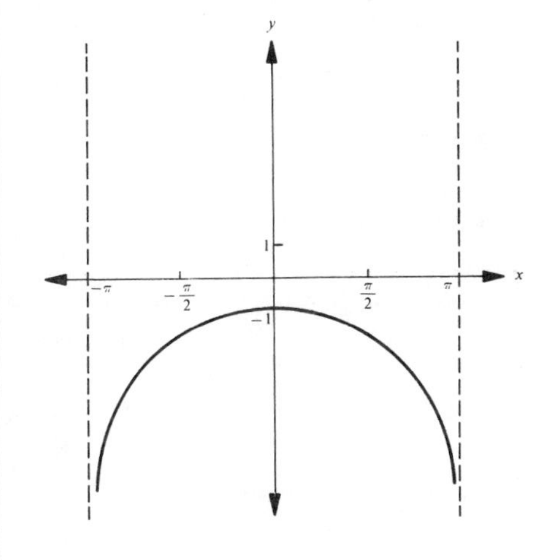

ANSWERS TO PAGE 168

Equations such as

(a) $3x + 4 = 7x - 8$

(b) $x^2 - 3x + 2 = 0$

(c) $2 \cos^2 x = -\cos x$

are conditional equations since, in each case, there are values of x for which the equations do not hold and for which both members are ______________ .

Choose a value of x for which equation (c) does not hold. ______________

I and II III and IV

We will derive and verify several important identities in this section.

$(x + y)^2 = x^2 + 2xy + y^2$ is an identity since it holds for ______________ .
It can be verified by using the properties of the real numbers to expand the left-hand member.

$\cos^2 x + \sin^2 x = 1$ is an identity since it holds for all $x \in \mathcal{R}$. It was verified earlier by use of the definitions of the cos and sin functions and the ______________ principle.

Verification or derivation of identities involving circular functions will depend on their respective definitions and the properties of the real numbers.

I and II

III and IV

MOVE TO NEXT FRAME

Certain identities are said to be **basic identities** because they are definitions or the immediate consequence of the definitions of the circular functions. Thus $\cos^2 x + \sin^2 x = 1$ is a basic identity. Since by definition $\csc x = \dfrac{1}{\sin x}$ whenever $\sin x \neq 0$; multiplication of both members by $\sin x$ results in the basic identity ______________ provided $\sin x \neq 0$.

$$\cos x \sec x = 1$$

is a basic identity. It is derived directly from ______________

and holds for all values of x except ______________.

$$\tan x \cot x = 1$$

is also a basic identity. It can be verified by substituting $\frac{\sin x}{\cos x}$ for ______

and $\frac{\cos x}{\sin x}$ for ______ and simplifying. The equation $\tan x \cot x = 1$ holds

for all x except ______________.

According to the definition of csc, sin and csc are **reciprocal functions.** As a consequence of their respective definitions, there are two other pairs of reciprocal circular functions. They are tan and ____, and cos and ____.

Beginning with the basic identity $\cos^2 x + \sin^2 x = 1$ and dividing both members by $\cos^2 x$, we get

$$\frac{\cos^2 x}{\cos^2 x} + \frac{\sin^2 x}{\cos^2 x} = \frac{1}{\cos^2 x}$$

provided $\cos x \neq 0$. This may be written

$$1 + \left(\frac{\sin x}{\cos x}\right)^2 = \left(\frac{1}{\cos x}\right)^2.$$

Since $\frac{\sin x}{\cos x} =$ ______ and $\frac{1}{\cos x} =$ ______, it follows by substition that

$$1 + \tan^2 x = \sec^2 x$$

is a basic identity which holds for all $x \epsilon \mathcal{R}$ except ______________.

$$\cot^2 x + 1 = \csc^2 x$$

can also be shown to be an identity in a similar fashion. The proof is left as an exercise.

MOVE TO NEXT FRAME

$\cos^2 x + \sin^2 x$

identity

$\{2, -1\}$

By substitution from known identities.

$x = k\pi$ for some $k \epsilon J$

$x = \frac{\pi}{2} + 2k\pi$ or $x = \pi k$ for some $k \epsilon J$

$\csc^2 x - 1 = \cot^2 x$

Identities are useful in expressing the values of a function in terms of the values of another function. For example, they may be used to express sin x in terms of cos x.

$$\cos^2 x + \sin^2 x = 1$$

is a known identity. Thus,

$$\sin^2 x = 1 - \cos^2 x,$$

and

$$\text{(a)}\quad \sin x = \sqrt{1 - \cos^2 x} \quad \text{if } \sin x > 0$$

or

$$\text{(b)}\quad \sin x = -\sqrt{1 - \cos^2 x} \quad \text{if } \sin x < 0.$$

Both solutions (a) and (b) are necessary, since $\sin x > 0$ in Quadrants ________ and $\sin x < 0$ in Quadrants ________. It is conventional to write (a) and (b) together as

$$\sin x = \pm\sqrt{1 - \cos^2 x} \quad \text{or} \quad |\sin x| = \sqrt{1 - \cos^2 x}.$$

Example:

Express tan x in terms of cos x.

Solution:

By definition $\tan x = \frac{\sin x}{\cos x}$ whenever $\cos x \neq 0$. Hence, using the identity from the previous frame,

$$\tan x = \pm\frac{\sqrt{1 - \cos^2 x}}{\cos x}$$

by substitution for sin x, where the plus sign holds if $\sin x > 0$ and the minus sign if $\sin x < 0$.

From our knowledge of sine, we have $\tan x = \frac{\sqrt{1 - \cos^2 x}}{\cos x}$ for x in Quadrants ________ and $\tan x = -\frac{\sqrt{1 - \cos^2 x}}{\cos x}$ for x in Quadrants ________.

To verify that a statement is an identity, you may transform one member into the expression in the other member or transform both members, separately, until a known identity is obtained. You may use the substitution principle, the definitions of the circular functions, and the properties of the real numbers.

MOVE TO NEXT FRAME

Example:

Prove that

$$\frac{1}{1+\sin x}+\frac{1}{1-\sin x}=2\sec^2 x$$

is an identity.

Proof:

Show that the left member is identical to the right member.

$$\frac{1}{1+\sin x}+\frac{1}{1-\sin x}=\frac{1-\sin x+1+\sin x}{(1+\sin x)(1-\sin x)}$$

By the addition of fractions,

$$\frac{1-\sin x+1+\sin x}{(1+\sin x)(1-\sin x)}=\frac{2}{1-\sin^2 x}$$

By simplification,

$$\frac{2}{1-\sin^2 x}=\frac{2}{(\_\_\_\_\_\_)}$$

Since $\cos^2 x+\sin^2 x=1$,

$$\therefore \frac{1}{1+\sin x}+\frac{1}{1-\sin x}=2\sec^2 x,$$

since $\sec x =$ ________ and $\sec^2 x=\dfrac{1}{\cos^2 x}$. Furthermore, we note that both members are undefined for $x\epsilon\{x:$ ____________________________ $\}$.

Example:

Verify that

$$(\tan x+\cot x)^2=\sec^2 x+\csc^2 x$$

is an identity.

Proof:

First note that the left member is defined for all $x\epsilon\mathcal{R}$ except for $\{x:$ ____________________________ $\}$, and the right member is defined for all $x\epsilon\mathcal{R}$ except for $\{x:$ ____________________________ $\}$. Note that the domain of definition for each member is derived directly from the definition of the functions.

By expanding the left member we have

$$\begin{aligned}(\tan x+\cot x)^2&=\tan^2 x+2\tan x\cot x+\cot^2 x\\&=\tan^2 x+2+\cot^2 x.\end{aligned}$$

Why? ________________________________

ANSWERS TO PAGE 167

the definition of secant

$\left\{x:x=(2k+1)\frac{\pi}{2}\text{ for some } k\epsilon J\right\}$

$\tan x$

$\cot x$

$\left\{x:x=\frac{k\pi}{2}\text{ for some } k\epsilon J\right\}$

---

cot sec

$\tan x$ $\sec x$

$\left\{x:x=(2k+1)\frac{\pi}{2}\text{ for some } k\epsilon J\right\}$

ANSWERS TO PAGE 172

(1)(a) T

(b) F since $\sqrt{1 - \cos^2 x} = \sin x$ only in Quadrants I and II.

(c) T

(d) F

(2) $\left\{x: x = \frac{k\pi}{4} \text{ for some } k \epsilon J\right\}$

(3) See Appendix.

$\{x: x \epsilon \mathcal{R} \text{ and } x \neq k\pi, \text{ for all } k \epsilon J\}$

(4) See Appendix.

$\left\{x: x = \frac{k\pi}{2} \text{ for some } k \epsilon J\right\}$

(5)(a) cosecant

(b) secant

(c) cotangent

(6)(a) $-\cos^2 x$

(b) $|\sin x|$

(c) $1, x \neq (2k + 1)\frac{\pi}{2}$ for all $k \epsilon J$

(d) $\cot^2 x, x \neq k\pi$ for all $k \epsilon J$

(e) $0, x \neq k\pi$ for all $k \epsilon J$

$$\tan^2 x + 2 + \cot^2 x = (\tan^2 x + 1) + (1 + \cot^2 x)$$
$$= \sec^2 x + \csc^2 x$$

Why? ______________________________

$$\therefore (\tan x + \cot x)^2 = \sec^2 x + \csc^2 x$$

is an identity.

Carefully consider the logical validity of your proof: Beginning with the statement that you would like to establish as an identity and subsequently using the properties of an equality to transform the statement into one known to be an identity does not, in general, constitute a valid proof.

The reverse procedure—beginning with a known identity and using the properties of equality to arrive at the statement you wish to establish as an identity—does not constitute a valid proof.

A valid proof, however, is often suggested by beginning with the statement which is to be proved. Reversing the steps will then constitute a valid proof. This is known as "working backward" and is illustrated in the next frame.

MOVE TO NEXT FRAME

Example:

Verify that

$$\frac{\csc x + 1}{\cot x} = \frac{\cot x}{\csc x - 1}$$

is an identity. First note that the excluded values of x in the left member are $\{x:$ ______________$\}$ and the excluded values in the right member are

$\{x:$ ______________________$\}$.

Note that multiplying both members of the proposed identity by the lowest common denominator, $\cot x(\csc x - 1)$, yields ______________. This may be rewritten as

$$\csc^2 x = 1 + \cot^2 x,$$

which is a known identity.

Then, replacing the left member by its equal from the identity $\cot^2 x + 1 = \csc^2 x$ (see Exercise 3), we have $\cot^2 x = \cot^2 x$.

This *does not* however constitute a proof that $\frac{\csc x + 1}{\cot x} = \frac{\cot x}{\csc x - 1}$. Rather, it proves that if

$$\frac{\csc x + 1}{\cot x} = \frac{\cot x}{\csc x - 1},$$

then $\csc^2 x = 1 + \cot^2 x$. However, in this case, the steps are reversible. Thus we may start with the known identity $\csc^2 x = 1 + \cot^2 x$ and obtain the desired result as follows.

Assume that $\csc^2 x = \cot^2 x + 1$ is a proved identity. Then,

$$\csc^2 x - 1 = \cot^2 x,$$

and

$$\frac{\csc^2 x - 1}{\cot x\,(\csc x - 1)} = \frac{\cot^2 x}{\cot x\,(\csc x - 1)},$$

provided $\cot x\,(\csc x - 1) \neq 0$. Factoring, we have

$$\frac{(\csc x + 1)\,(\csc x - 1)}{\cot x\,(\csc x - 1)} = \frac{(\cot x)\,(\cot x)}{\cot x\,(\csc x - 1)}.$$

Hence

$$\frac{\csc x + 1}{\cot x} = \frac{\cot x}{\csc x - 1},$$

provided $\csc x$ and $\cot x$ are defined and the denominators are not zero.

Since our transformations introduced no excluded values other than those excluded in the statement initially given, we can conclude that

$$\frac{\csc x + 1}{\cot x} = \frac{\cot x}{\csc x - 1}$$

is an identity.

MOVE TO NEXT FRAME

$\cos^2 x$

$\dfrac{1}{\cos x}$

$\left\{x = (2k + 1)\frac{\pi}{2} \text{ for some } k \epsilon J\right\}$,

i.e., x is an odd multiple of $\frac{\pi}{2}$.

---

x is a multiple of $\frac{\pi}{2}$,

i.e., $x = \dfrac{k\pi}{2}$ for some $k \epsilon J$

$x = \dfrac{k\pi}{2}$ for some $k \epsilon J$

Because $\tan x \cot x = 1$.

ANSWERS TO PAGE 174

(1) 1

(2) (1,0) 2π

(3) (0,1)

(0,−1)

(4) $\frac{5\pi}{3}$

(5) 2π 2π

$\frac{2}{3}$

$\frac{\sqrt{5}}{3}$

(6) no, x might equal $\pi+2k\pi$, for some nonzero $k\epsilon J$.

(7) no, $x_1=\frac{3\pi}{2}+2k\pi$ for some $k\epsilon J$ and $x_2=\frac{3\pi}{2}+2t\pi$, for some $t\epsilon J$. x_1 and x_2 may differ by a multiple of 2π.

(8) 1

(9)(a) (u,v)

(b) $\left(\frac{\sqrt{3}}{2}, \frac{1}{2}\right)$

(c) $\left(\frac{-\sqrt{2}}{2}, \frac{-\sqrt{2}}{2}\right)$

(d) $\left(\frac{-\sqrt{3}}{2}, \frac{1}{2}\right)$

EXERCISES. 3.4

1. *True or False:*

   (a) An identity is a special kind of equation. ____

   (b) The statement $\tan x = \frac{\sqrt{1-\cos^2 x}}{\cos x}$ is an identity for all values of x except

   $$x\epsilon\left\{x : x = (2k+1)\frac{\pi}{2}, \text{ where } k\epsilon J\right\}.$$ ____________

   (c) $\sqrt{1-\sin^2 x} = |\cos x|$. __

   (d) $\frac{1}{\tan x}$ is defined except when $x = (2k+1)\frac{\pi}{2}$ for some $k\epsilon J$. __

2. For what values of x is $\frac{1}{\tan x - \cot x}$ undefined? ____________

3. Derive $\cot^2 x + 1 = \csc^2 x$ and state the values of x for which the statement is true. ____________

4. Prove

   $$\frac{\tan x - \sin x}{\tan x \sin x} = \frac{\tan x \sin x}{\tan x + \sin x}.$$

   For what values of x is the statement not defined. (*Hint:* Multiply numerator and denominator of right member by $\tan x - \sin x$.)

   ____

5. Name the inverse function for each of the following functions:

   (a) sine ____________

   (b) cosine ____________

   (c) tangent ____________

6. Simplify each of the following by appropriate substitutions from one or more basic identities or definitions. (Note restrictions on variable.)

   (a) $\sin^2 x - 1$ ____________

   (b) $\sqrt{1-\cos^2 x}$ ____________

   (c) $\sec^2 x - \tan^2 x$ ____________

   (d) $\csc^2 x - 1$ ____________

   (e) $\sin x \csc x - 1$ ____________

(f) $\tan x \cos x$ ______________________

(g) $\sqrt{1 + \cot^2 x}$ ______________________

(h) $\dfrac{\cos^2 x + \sin^2 x}{\cos x}$ ______________________

(i) $\sin x \sec x \cot x$ ______________________

(j) $\cos^2 x\,(1 + \tan^2 x)$ ______________________

Verify that each of the following are identities. (Note excluded values of the variable.)

7. $\sin x \cot x + \cos^2 x \sec x = 2 \cos x$

8. $\dfrac{\cos x}{1 + \sin x} + \dfrac{\cos x}{1 - \sin x} = 2 \sec x$

9. $\dfrac{\cos x}{1 + \sin x} + \dfrac{1 + \sin x}{\cos x} = 2 \sec x$

Note: Remember that proofs found in the Appendix may not be the only valid proofs, because there may be more than one valid proof of an identity.

10. $\dfrac{\cos x}{\cos x - \sin x} = \dfrac{1}{1 - \tan x}$

11. $\sin^4 x - \cos^4 x = 2 \sin^2 x - 1$

12. $\dfrac{1 - 2\cos^2 x}{\sin x \cos x} = \tan x - \cot x$

13. $\sec x - \tan x = \dfrac{\cos x}{1 + \sin x}$

14. $\sqrt{\dfrac{1 - \cos x}{1 + \cos x}} = |\csc x - \cot x|$

(*Hint:* $\sqrt{a^2} = |a|$)

15. $\sin x + \cos x = \dfrac{\sin x}{1 - \cot x} + \dfrac{\cos x}{1 - \tan x}$

16. $\dfrac{1 - \sin x}{1 + \sin x} = (\sec x - \tan x)^2$

(c) F

(d) F

(e) T

(f) F

(g) T

(h) T

(i) F

(18) (a) $\frac{\sqrt{2}}{2}$ (b) $\frac{1}{2}$

(c) $-\frac{1}{2}$ (d) $\frac{-\sqrt{3}}{2}$

(e) $\frac{4\pi}{3}$ or $\frac{5\pi}{3}$

(f) $\frac{\pi}{3}$ or $\frac{-\pi}{3}$

(19) $\mathcal{R}$
$\{y : y \epsilon \mathcal{R} \text{ and } |y| \leq 1\}$

(20) (a) $\left\{y : |y| \leq \frac{2}{3} \text{ and } y \epsilon \mathcal{R}\right\}$

(b) $\frac{2}{3}$

(c) 4π

(d) $\frac{-\pi}{2}$

(21) (a) $y + 2 = \sin\left(x + \frac{\pi}{4}\right)$

(b) $y + 2 = -\sin\left(x + \frac{\pi}{4}\right)$

(c) $y + 2 = -3\sin\left(x + \frac{\pi}{4}\right)$

(d) $y + 2 = -3\sin \cdot 3\left(x + \frac{\pi}{4}\right)$

CHAPTER 3 REVIEW EXERCISES

1. If O is the origin of a coordinate system and R is a point on the unit circle, then $||\overrightarrow{OR}|| =$ __. (3.1)
2. If a point P starts at (1,0) and travels completely around a unit circle, it returns to ________ and travels a distance equal to ________. (3.1)
3. If a point P starts at (1,0) and travels a distance $\frac{\pi}{2}$, its coordinates are then ________. If it travels a distance from (1,0) equal to $\frac{3\pi}{2}$, its final coordinates are ________. (3.1)
4. The point on the unit circle corresponding to $\cos x = \frac{1}{2}$, and $\sin x = \frac{-\sqrt{3}}{2}$ is at a distance $x =$ ________, measured counterclockwise along the circle from (1,0). (3.1)
5. The period of cosine is ______ and the period of sine is ______. Therefore, if $\cos x = \frac{2}{3}$, then $\cos(x + 2\pi) =$ ______ and if $\sin x = \frac{\sqrt{5}}{3}$, then $\sin(x + 2\pi) =$ ______. (3.1)
6. If $\cos x = -1$ and $\sin x = 0$, can we be sure that $x = \pi$? ________ Why or why not? (3.1) ________________
7. If $\cos x_1 = 0$ and $\sin x_2 = -1$, then is $x_1 = x_2$? Why or why not? (3.1)

   ____

   ____

   ____
8. If ($\cos x$, $\sin x$) corresponds to a point on the unit circle, then $\cos^2 x + \sin^2 x =$ __. (3.1)
9. If p is the function that maps x into (u,v) on the unit circle, as discussed in Section 3.1, then find each of the following:

   (a) $p(x) =$ ____________

   (b) $p\left(\frac{\pi}{6}\right) =$ ____________

   (c) $p\left(\frac{-3\pi}{4}\right) =$ ____________

   (d) $p\left(\frac{17\pi}{6}\right) =$ ____________

10. If f is a periodic function with a period equal to 3, write each of the following in the form $f(x)$ for some $0 \leq x < 3$.

(a) $f(11) =$ ________ (b) $f(-13) =$ ________

(c) $f(6.1) =$ ________ (d) $f(21) =$ ________

11. Find the periods of the functions defined by each of the following: (3.1)

(a) $f(x) = \cos 5x$ ________ (b) $g(x) = \sin \frac{3}{2} x$ ________

(c) $h(x) = \cos 2ax$ ________ (d) $u(x) = \sin\left(-\frac{1}{4}x\right)$ ________

12. Sine and cosine may be said to have a period of 2π, 4π, 6π, or $2k\pi$, $k \epsilon J$, but their ________ period is 2π. (3.1)

13. If g is a periodic function with a period of π, then write each of the following in the form of $g(x)$ for some $0 \leq x < \pi$. (3.1)

(a) $g\left(\frac{3\pi}{2}\right) =$ ________ (b) $g(8\pi) =$ ________

(c) $g\left(\frac{-7\pi}{3}\right) =$ ________ (d) $g\left(\frac{5\pi}{6}\right) =$ ________

(e) $g\left(\frac{23\pi}{4}\right) =$ ________ (f) $g\left(\frac{-\pi}{6}\right) =$ ________

14. To translate the graph of the sine function $\frac{3\pi}{2}$ units to the right and 3 units down it is sufficient to replace x by ________ and y by ________ in the defining equation $y = \sin x$. (3.2)

15. The graph corresponding to $y = \cos 3x$ is said to be a ________ ________ of the graph of $y = -\cos 3x$. (3.2)

16. If f is the function $\{(x,y): y - 2 = +4 \sin(5x + 3)\}$, then find each of the following: (3.2)

(a) vertical shift ________

(b) amplitude ________

(c) phase shift ________

(d) period ________

17. Answer true or false for each of the following: (3.2)

(a) $\cos x = \sin\left(x + \frac{\pi}{2}\right)$ ___

(b) $\sin x = \cos\left(x - \frac{\pi}{2}\right)$ ___

ANSWERS TO PAGE 173

(f) $\sin x, x \neq (2k + 1)\frac{\pi}{2}$ for all $k \epsilon J$

(g) $|\csc x|, x \neq (2k + 1)\frac{\pi}{2}$ for all $k \epsilon J$

(h) $\sec x, x \neq (2k + 1)\frac{\pi}{2}$ for all $k \epsilon J$

(i) $1, x \neq k\frac{\pi}{2}$ for all $k \epsilon J$

(j) $1, x \neq (2k + 1)\frac{\pi}{2}$ for all $k \epsilon J$

(7) See Appendix.

(8) See Appendix.

(9) See Appendix.

(10) See Appendix.

(11) See Appendix.

(12) See Appendix.

(13) See Appendix.

(14) See Appendix.

(15) See Appendix.

(16) See Appendix.

ANSWERS TO PAGE 178

(b) $\mathcal{R}$

$\{y : y \epsilon \mathcal{R} \text{ and } |y| \leq 1\}$

(26) (a) III, IV (b) I, III

(c) I, IV (d) II, III

(27) (a) $\frac{-2\sqrt{13}}{13}$ (b) $\frac{-3\sqrt{13}}{13}$

(c) $\frac{3}{2}$ (d) $\frac{-\sqrt{13}}{3}$

(e) $\frac{-\sqrt{13}}{2}$

(28) (a) $-2\sqrt{2}$

(b) 2

(c) None exists. (*Recall:* $|\cos x| \leq 1$)

(d) $\sqrt{17}$

(e) Undefined

(f) $\frac{4}{3}$ or $\frac{-4}{3}$

(g) $\frac{\pi}{4} + k\pi, k \epsilon J$

(29) $2 \cos^2 x - 1$

(30) Find any x for which both members are defined and for which the statement is not true, *e.g.*, $x = \frac{\pi}{6}$

(31) $\left\{x : x \epsilon \mathcal{R} \text{ and } x \neq \frac{\pi}{2} + k\pi \text{ for all } k \epsilon J\right\}$.

(c) $\sin x = -\cos\left(\frac{\pi}{2} - x\right)$ __

(d) $\sin x = \sin (-x)$ __

(e) $\cos x = \cos (-x)$ __

(f) $\sin (x + 2\pi) = -\sin x$ __

(g) $\cos (x - 2\pi) = \cos x$ __

(h) $\cos (x + \pi) = -\cos x$ __

(i) $\sin (x + \pi) = \sin x$ __

18. Find x for each of the following: (3.2)

(a) $\sin \frac{\pi}{4} = x$ ______ (b) $\sin \frac{5\pi}{6} = x$ ______

(c) $\cos\left(\frac{-2\pi}{3}\right) = x$ ______ (d) $\cos \frac{31\pi}{6} = x$ ______

(e) $\sin x = \frac{-\sqrt{3}}{2}$ and $0 \leq x < 2\pi$ ______

(f) $\cos x = \frac{1}{2}$ and $-\pi \leq x < \pi$ ______

19. The domain of the sine function is __ and the range is __________ ____________________. (3.2)

20. Given the function $f = \left\{(x,y) : y = \frac{2}{3} \cos \left(\frac{x}{2} + \frac{\pi}{4}\right)\right\}$ answer each of the following: (3.2)

(a) The range of f is ______.

(b) The amplitude of f is ______.

(c) The period of f is ______.

(d) The phase shift of f is ______.

21. Write the equation of a sine curve after each of the following modifications are performed in succession upon the defining equation $y = \sin x$. (3.2)

(a) Translated by the vector $\left(\frac{-\pi}{4}, -2\right)$. ____________________

(b) Reflected in the x-axis ____________________

(c) Amplitude changed to 3. ____________________

(d) Period changed to $\frac{2\pi}{3}$. ____________________

22. Sketch the graph defined by $y = 1 + 2\cos\left(\frac{1}{2}x + \pi\right)$ over the interval $-2\pi \leq x \leq 2\pi$. (3.2)

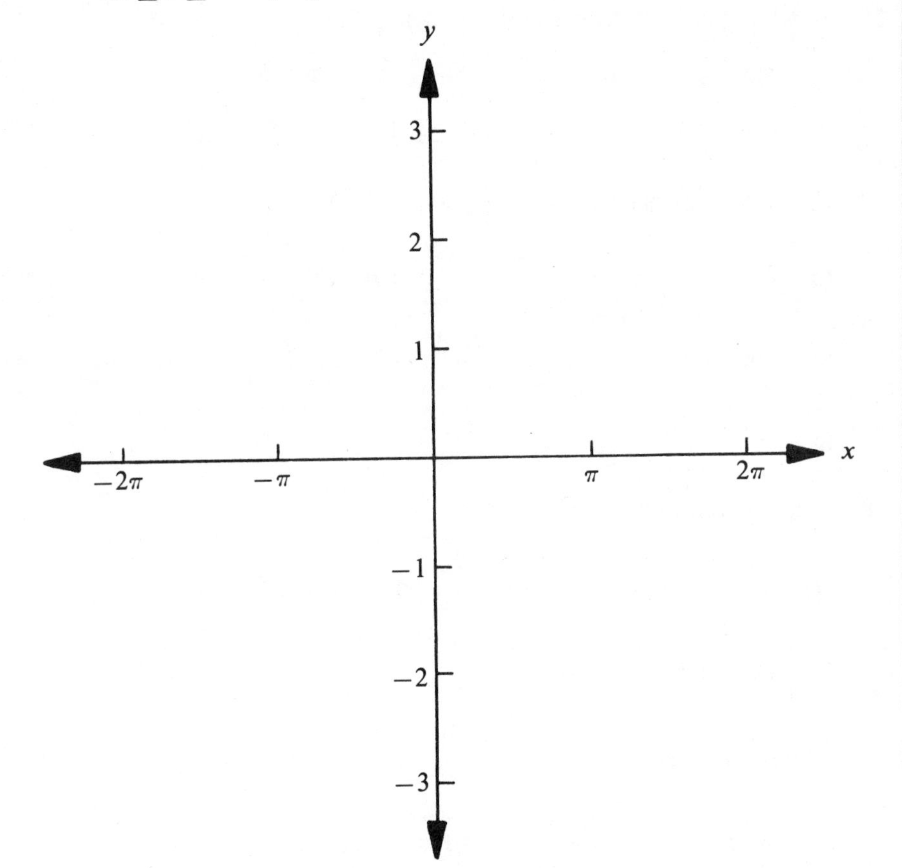

23. One period of the tangent function is 2π. However, its ____________ period is π. (3.3)

24. Find the real number equal to each of the following: (3.1, 3.2, 3.3)

(a) $\cos\frac{-2\pi}{3}$ ______ (b) $\tan\frac{\pi}{6}$ ______

(c) $\sin\frac{5\pi}{6}$ ______ (d) $\cot\frac{-22\pi}{3}$ ______

(e) $\cos 8\frac{1}{6}\pi$ ______ (f) $\sin\left(-21\frac{2}{3}\pi\right)$ ______

25. Specify the domain D and range R of the following functions:

(a) tangent: (3.3) $D =$ ____________________

$R =$ ____________________

ANSWERS TO PAGE 175

(10) (a) $f(2)$ (b) $f(2)$

(c) $f(0.1)$ (d) $f(0)$

(11) (a) $\frac{2\pi}{5}$ (b) $\frac{4\pi}{3}$

(c) $\frac{\pi}{|a|}$ (d) 8π

(12) fundamental

(13) (a) $g\left(\frac{\pi}{2}\right)$ (b) $g(0)$

(c) $g\left(\frac{2\pi}{3}\right)$ (d) $g\left(\frac{5\pi}{6}\right)$

(e) $g\left(\frac{3\pi}{4}\right)$ (f) $g\left(\frac{5\pi}{6}\right)$

(14) $x - \frac{3\pi}{2}$

$y + 3$

(15) reflection about the x axis

(16) (a) 2

(b) 4

(c) $\frac{-3}{5}$

(d) $\frac{2\pi}{5}$

(17) (a) T

(b) T

(b) cosine: (3.1) $D =$ ______________________

$R =$ ______________________

26. In what quadrant does x lie if: (3.1 and 3.3)

(a) $\sin x < 0$ ____________ (b) $\tan x > 0$ ____________

(c) $\cos x > 0$ ____________ (d) $\sec x < 0$ ____________

27. If $\tan x = \frac{2}{3}$ and $3\pi \leq x \leq \frac{7\pi}{2}$, find: (3.3)

(a) $\sin x =$ ____________ (b) $\cos x =$ ____________

(c) $\cot x =$ ____________ (d) $\sec x =$ ____________

(e) $\csc x =$ ____________

28. Find the following: (3.3)

(a) $\cot x$, when $\sin x = \frac{1}{3}$ and x is in Quadrant II. ________

(b) $\csc x$, when $x = \frac{-7\pi}{6}$. __

(c) $\sec x$, when $\cos x = \frac{5}{2}$. ________

(d) $\sec x$, when $\tan x = -4$ and x is in Quadrant IV. ________

(e) $\cot x$, when $x = 3\pi$. ________

(f) $\tan x$, when $\cos x = \frac{-3}{5}$. ________

(g) x, when $\tan x = 1$. ________

29. Write $1 - 2 \sin^2 x$ in terms of $\cos x$. (3.4) ____________

30. Show that $\sin x + \cos x \cot x = \sec x$ is *not* an identity. (3.4)

____

31. For what value of x is

$$\sec x + \tan x = \frac{\cos x}{1 - \sin x}.$$

(3.4) ____

32. Prove the identity $\sec x + \tan x = \dfrac{\cos x}{1 - \sin x}$ and state the values of x for which all terms of the identity are defined. (3.4)

33. Prove the identity

$$(\csc x - 1)(1 + \csc x) = \frac{\csc x \cos x}{\sec x \sin x}.$$

What values of x are excluded from consideration? (3.4)

(22)

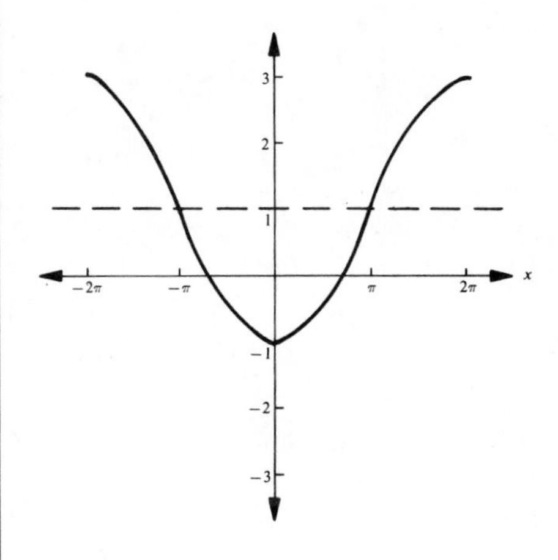

(23) fundamental

(24) (a) $-\dfrac{1}{2}$ (b) $\dfrac{\sqrt{3}}{3}$

(c) $\dfrac{1}{2}$ (d) $\dfrac{-\sqrt{3}}{3}$

(e) $\dfrac{\sqrt{3}}{2}$ (f) $\dfrac{\sqrt{3}}{2}$

(25) (a)

$\left\{x : x \epsilon \mathcal{R} \text{ and } x \neq (2k+1)\dfrac{\pi}{2} \text{ for all } k \epsilon J\right\}$ $\mathcal{R}$

ANSWERS TO PAGE 182

$[\cos(x_1 + x_2), \sin(x_1 + x_2)]$

$[\cos(-x_2), \sin(-x_2)]$

ANSWERS TO PAGE 179

(32) See Appendix.

(33) See Appendix.

CHAPTER 4

Properties of Circular Functions

4.1. CIRCULAR FUNCTIONS OF $(x_1 \pm x_2)$

Show, by counterexample, that the statement

$$\cos(x_1 + x_2) = \cos x_1 + \cos x_2$$

is *false*. Use $x_1 = \frac{\pi}{6}$ and $x_2 = \frac{\pi}{3}$. Thus,

$$\cos(x_1 + x_2) = \cos \_\_ = \_\_$$

and,

$$\cos x_1 + \cos x_2 = \cos\frac{\pi}{6} + \cos\frac{\pi}{3} = \_\_\_\_\_\_ + \_\_.$$

Hence,

$$\cos(x_1 + x_2) = \cos x_1 + \cos x_2 \text{ is } \_\_\_\_\_\_\_\_.$$

(True or False?)

There is a relationship, however, between $\cos(x_1 + x_2)$ and the values of the sine and cosine functions of x_1 and x_2.

MOVE TO NEXT FRAME

Recall the function p described in Section 3.1. For a real number x, begin at the point (1,0) on the unit circle and move along the circle a distance $|x|$ ____________________ (counterclockwise/clockwise) if $x > 0$ and ________________ if $x < 0$. If $P(u,v)$ is the point at which you arrive by this movement, then assigning $(u,v) = (\cos x, \sin x)$ to the real number x creates the function p. Thus $p(x) = (\cos x, \sin x)$.

ANSWERS TO PAGE 184

$\cos a \cos(-b) - \sin a \sin(-b)$

$\cos x_2 \quad -\sin x_2$

$\cos x_1 \cos x_2 + \sin x_1 \sin x_2$

$-1 \quad 0$

Pick any two real numbers x_1 and x_2 and let the coordinates of B equal $p(x_1)$, the coordinates of C equal $p(x_1 + x_2)$, and the coordinates of D equal $p(-x_2)$. Thus $p(x_1) = (\cos x_1, \sin x_1)$, $p(x_1 + x_2) =$ ____________________,

and $p(-x_2) =$ ____________________. (See the illustration.)

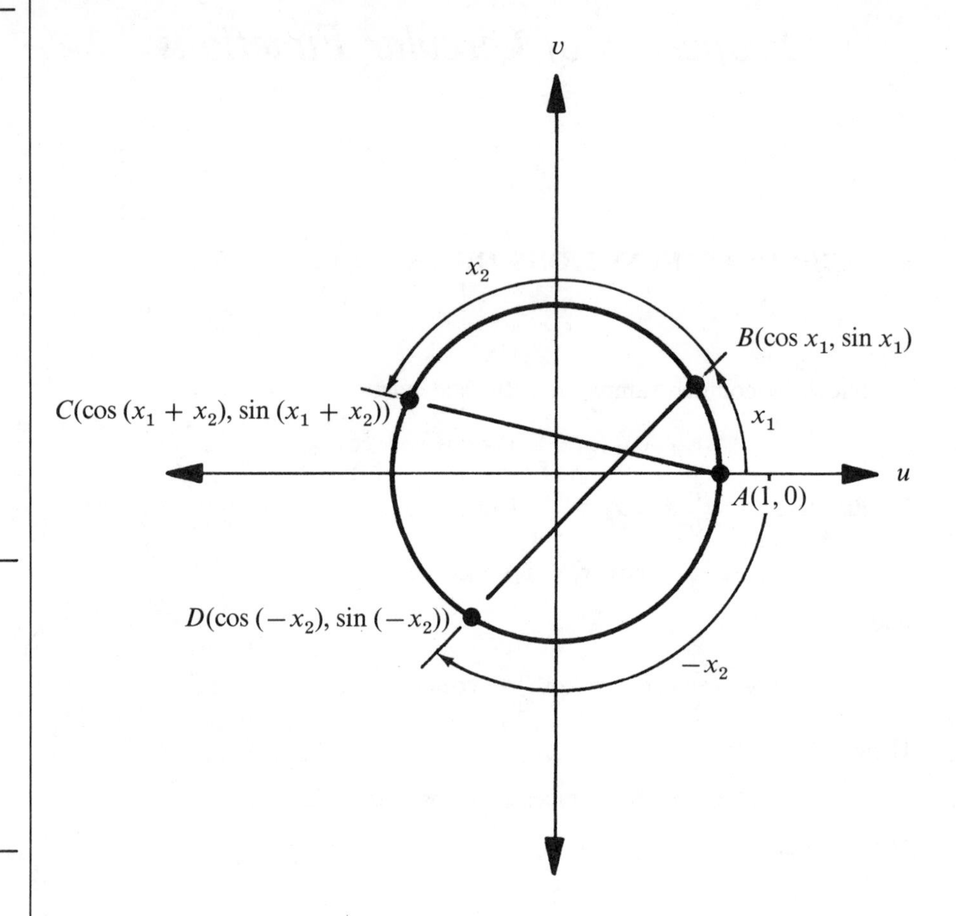

If $m\widehat{XY}$ denotes the arc length of an arc with endpoints X and Y, we have $m\widehat{AC} = m\widehat{AB} + m\widehat{BC} = |x_1| + |x_2|$ and $m\widehat{BD} = m\widehat{BA} + m\widehat{AD} = |x_1| + |-x_2|$. Since $|-x_2| = |x_2|$, $m\widehat{AC} = m\widehat{BD}$.

From geometry, we know if the arcs of a circle have equal lengths, then their corresponding chords have equal lengths. Hence $\|\overrightarrow{AC}\| = \|\overrightarrow{BD}\|$.

We will calculate $\|\overrightarrow{AC}\|$ and $\|\overrightarrow{BD}\|$ by finding the norms of the vectors corresponding to $\overrightarrow{AC}$ and $\overrightarrow{BD}$.

MOVE TO NEXT FRAME

THEOREM:

If $x_1 \in \mathcal{R}$ and $x_2 \in \mathcal{R}$, then

$$\cos(x_1 + x_2) = \cos x_1 \cos x_2 - \sin x_1 \sin x_2.$$

Proof:

Referring to the illustration in the previous frame, if $\vec{v}$ is the vector corresponding to $\overrightarrow{AC}$ and $\vec{w}$ is the vector corresponding to $\overrightarrow{BD}$, then

$$\vec{v} = (\cos(x_1 + x_2) - 1, \sin(x_1 + x_2))$$

and

$$\vec{w} = \rule{6cm}{0.4pt}.$$

Hence

$$||\overrightarrow{AC}|| = ||\vec{v}|| = \sqrt{(\cos(x_1 + x_2) - 1)^2 + (\sin(x_1 + x_2))^2},$$

and

$$||\overrightarrow{BD}|| = ||\vec{w}|| = \sqrt{\rule{5cm}{0.4pt}}.$$

Since $||\overrightarrow{AC}|| = ||\overrightarrow{BD}||$, we have $||\overrightarrow{AC}||^2 = ||\overrightarrow{DB}||^2$ and hence

$$(\cos(x_1 + x_2) - 1)^2 + (\sin(x_1 + x_2))^2$$

$$= \rule{6cm}{0.4pt}.$$

Squaring each term as indicated, we have $\cos^2(x_1 + x_2) - 2\cos(x_1 + x_2) + 1 + \sin^2(x_1 + x_2) = \cos^2(-x_2) - 2\cos(-x_2)\cos x_1 + \cos^2 x_1$

$$+ \rule{6cm}{0.4pt}.$$

Since

$$\cos^2(x_1 + x_2) + \sin^2(x_1 + x_2) = 1,$$

the left member in the above equation becomes $-2\cos(x_1 + x_2) + 2$, and since $\cos^2(-x_2) + \sin^2(-x_2) = 1$ and $\cos^2 x_1 + \sin^2 x_1 = 1$, the right member becomes ____________________________.

$\frac{\pi}{2}$ 0

$\frac{\sqrt{3}}{2} + \frac{1}{2}$

false

Therefore

$$-2\cos(x_1 + x_2) + 2 = 2 - 2\cos(-x_2)\cos x_1 - 2\sin(-x_2)\sin x_1$$

Thus we have, by subtracting two from both members and then dividing both members by -2,

$$\cos(x_1 + x_2) = \cos x_1 \cos(-x_2) + \sin x_1 \sin(-x_2).$$

This finally becomes

$$\cos(x_1 + x_2) = \cos x_1 \cos x_2 - \sin x_1 \sin x_2$$

because

$$\cos(-x_2) = \rule{4cm}{0.4pt}$$

and

$$\sin(-x_2) = \rule{4cm}{0.4pt}.$$

counterclockwise

clockwise

ANSWERS TO PAGE 186

Remember the identity just proved will hold for any real numbers, x_1 and x_2, no matter what they are named. Thus, if $a \in \mathcal{R}$ and $-b \in \mathcal{R}$, we have $\cos(a + (-b)) =$ ____________________________.

See Example 3.

THEOREM:

If $x_1 \in \mathcal{R}$ and $x_2 \in \mathcal{R}$, then

$$\cos(x_1 - x_2) = \cos x_1 \cos x_2 + \sin x_1 \sin x_2$$

Proof:

$$\begin{aligned}\cos(x_1 - x_2) &= \cos(x_1 + (-x_2)) \\ &= \cos x_1 \cos(-x_2) - \sin x_1 \sin(-x_2) \\ &= \cos x_1 \cos x_2 + \sin x_1 \sin x_2,\end{aligned}$$

because

$\cos(-x_2) =$ ______ and $\sin(-x_2) =$ ______.

Since the equations in the two preceding theorems hold for all real numbers x_1 and x_2, they are identities. A number of other useful identities may be obtained from them, as indicated in the following examples.

MOVE TO NEXT FRAME

$\left(\frac{1}{2}\right)\left(\frac{\sqrt{2}}{2}\right)$

$\frac{1}{4}(\sqrt{6} - \sqrt{2})$

Example 1:

Prove the identity

$$\cos(x - \pi) = -\cos x.$$

Proof:

Substituting x for x_1 and π for x_2 in the identity

$\cos(x_1 - x_2) =$ ____________________________,

we have

$$\cos(x - \pi) = \cos x \cos \pi + \sin x \sin \pi.$$

Since $\cos \pi =$ _____ and $\sin \pi =$ __, this reduces to

$$\cos(x - \pi) = -\cos x.$$

Example 2:

Prove the identity $\cos\left(x - \frac{\pi}{2}\right) = \sin x$.

Proof:

$$\cos\left(x - \frac{\pi}{2}\right) = \cos x \cos\frac{\pi}{2} + \sin x \sin\frac{\pi}{2}$$
$$= 0 + \sin x,$$

because $\cos\frac{\pi}{2} =$ ___, and $\sin\frac{\pi}{2} =$ ___.

Example 3:

Prove the identity

$$\sin\left(y - \frac{\pi}{2}\right) = -\cos y.$$

Proof:

Substituting $y - \frac{\pi}{2}$ for x in the identity in Example 2, $\cos\left(x - \frac{\pi}{2}\right) = \sin x$, we have

$$\sin\left(y - \frac{\pi}{2}\right) = \underline{\hspace{6cm}}.$$

But, according to the identity proven in Example 1,

$$\cos(y - \pi) = \underline{\hspace{6cm}}.$$

Therefore $$\sin\left(y - \frac{\pi}{2}\right) = -\cos y.$$

THEOREM:

If $x_1 \epsilon \mathcal{R}$ and $x_2 \epsilon \mathcal{R}$, then

$$\sin(x_1 + x_2) = \sin x_1 \cos x_2 + \cos x_1 \sin x_2.$$

Proof:

$$\sin(x_1 + x_2) = \cos\left[(x_1 + x_2) - \frac{\pi}{2}\right]$$

By the identity proved in Example 2, $\cos\left(x - \frac{\pi}{2}\right) = \sin x$, so

$$\cos\left[(x_1 + x_2) - \frac{\pi}{2}\right] = \cos\left[x_1 + \left(x_2 - \frac{\pi}{2}\right)\right].$$
$$= \cos x_1 \cos\left(x_2 - \frac{\pi}{2}\right) - \underline{\hspace{4cm}}$$

ANSWERS TO PAGE 183

$[\cos(-x_2) - \cos x_1,$
$\sin(-x_2) - \sin x_1]$

$(\cos(-x_2) - \cos x_1)^2$
$+ (\sin(-x_2) - \sin x_1)^2$

$(\cos(-x_2) - \cos x_1)^2$
$+ (\sin(-x_2) - \sin x_1)^2$

$\sin^2(-x_2) - 2\sin(-x_2)\sin x_1$
$+ \sin^2 x_1$

$2 - 2\cos(-x_2)\cos x_1$
$-2\sin(-x_2)\sin x_1$

$\cos x_2$

$-\sin x_2$

ANSWERS TO PAGE 188

$2y$

$\cos^2 y - \sin^2 y$

1

$1 - \cos 2y = 2 \sin^2 y$

$\sqrt{\frac{1 - \cos 2y}{2}}$

$(2k + 1)\pi$, for all $k \in J$

The factor $\cos\left(x_2 - \frac{\pi}{2}\right)$ can be simplified with another application of the identity from Example 2.

$$\cos x_1 \cos\left(x_2 - \frac{\pi}{2}\right) - \sin x_1 \sin\left(x_2 - \frac{\pi}{2}\right)$$
$$= \cos x_1 \sin x_2 - \sin x_1 \sin\left(x_2 - \frac{\pi}{2}\right)$$
$$= \cos x_1 \sin x_2 - (\sin x_1)(-\cos x_2).$$

Why? ____________________

Therefore,

$$\sin(x_1 + x_2) = \sin x_1 \cos x_2 + \cos x_1 \sin x_2$$

THEOREM:

If $x_1 \in \mathcal{R}$ and $x_2 \in \mathcal{R}$, then

$$\sin(x_1 - x_2) = \sin x_1 \cos x_2 - \cos x_1 \sin x_2$$

The proof is left as an exercise.

MOVE TO NEXT FRAME

Problem:

Find $\sin \frac{\pi}{12}$.

Solution:

$$\sin \frac{\pi}{12} = \sin\left(\frac{\pi}{3} - \frac{\pi}{4}\right)$$
$$= \sin\frac{\pi}{3}\cos\frac{\pi}{4} - \cos\frac{\pi}{3}\sin\frac{\pi}{4}$$
$$= \frac{\sqrt{3}}{2}\left(\frac{\sqrt{2}}{2}\right) - (\_\_\_\_\_\_)(\_\_\_\_\_\_)$$
$$= \_\_\_\_\_\_\_\_$$

THEOREM:

If $x_1 \in \mathcal{R}$ and $x_2 \in \mathcal{R}$, then

$$\tan(x_1 + x_2) = \frac{\tan x_1 + \tan x_2}{1 - \tan x_1 \tan x_2}$$

provided $\tan x_1$, $\tan x_2$, and $\tan(x_1 + x_2)$ are defined and $\tan x_1 \tan x_2 \neq 1$.

Proof:

$$\tan(x_1 + x_2) = \frac{\sin(x_1 + x_2)}{\cos(x_1 + x_2)}$$

$$= \frac{(\qquad\qquad\qquad\qquad)}{(\qquad\qquad\qquad\qquad)}$$

Dividing numerator and denominator by $\cos x_1 \cos x_2$, we have

$$\tan(x_1 + x_2) = \frac{\dfrac{\sin x_1 \cancel{\cos x_2}}{\cos x_1 \cancel{\cos x_2}} + \dfrac{\cancel{\cos x_1} \sin x_2}{\cancel{\cos x_1} \cos x_2}}{\dfrac{\cancel{\cos x_1 \cos x_2}}{\cancel{\cos x_1 \cos x_2}} - \dfrac{\sin x_1 \sin x_2}{\cos x_1 \cos x_2}}$$

Since $\dfrac{\sin x_1}{\cos x_1} = \tan x_1$ and $\dfrac{\sin x_2}{\cos x_2} = \tan x_2$,

$\tan(x_1 + x_2) =$ ______________________

0 1

THEOREM:
If $x \epsilon \mathcal{R}$, then

$$\cos 2x = \cos^2 x - \sin^2 x.$$

Proof:

$$\begin{aligned} \cos 2x &= \cos(x + x) \\ &= \cos x \cos x - \sin x \sin x \\ &= \cos^2 x - \sin^2 x. \end{aligned}$$

$$\therefore \cos 2x = \cos^2 x - \sin^2 x.$$

MOVE TO NEXT FRAME

$\cos\left[\left(y - \frac{\pi}{2}\right) - \frac{\pi}{2}\right]$

$-\cos y$

THEOREM:
If $x \epsilon \mathcal{R}$, then

$$\sin 2x = 2 \sin x \cos x.$$

The proof is similar to that in the preceding frame and is left as an exercise.

MOVE TO NEXT FRAME

It is important to recognize that an identity derived for any real number x, x_1, x_2, or θ is true regardless of what we name the real number. For example, we have derived the identity $\sin 2x =$ ____________. This relationship is true for all $x \epsilon \mathcal{R}$. Thus if $y \epsilon \mathcal{R}$, so is $\frac{y}{2}$ and we can let $x = \frac{y}{2}$ in the above identity to obtain another identity: $\sin y = 2 \sin \frac{1}{2}y \cos \frac{1}{2}y$.

$\sin x_1 \sin\left(x_2 - \frac{\pi}{2}\right)$

ANSWERS TO PAGE 190

$a = b$

$\sin x \cos y + \cos x \sin y$

$\sin x \cos y - \cos x \sin y$

$2 \sin x \cos y$

$\frac{1}{2}(x_1 + x_2)$

$\frac{1}{2}(x_1 - x_2)$ $\qquad \frac{1}{2}(x_1 + x_2)$

$\frac{1}{2}(x_1 - x_2)$

$2 \sin \frac{1}{2}(x_1 + x_2) \cos \frac{1}{2}(x_1 - x_2)$

$\sin (x + y)$

Problem:

Prove

$$\cos 4y = \cos^2 2y - \sin^2 2y.$$

Proof:

Substitute $x =$ __ in the identity

$$\cos 2x = \cos^2 x - \sin^2 x$$

Therefore,

$$\cos 4y = \cos^2 2y - \sin^2 2y$$

THEOREM:
If $x \epsilon \mathcal{R}$, then

$$\left|\sin\left(\frac{x}{2}\right)\right| = \sqrt{\frac{1 - \cos x}{2}}$$

Proof:

We know for $y \epsilon \mathcal{R}$, that

(1) $\cos 2y -$ ________________,

and

(2) __ $= \cos^2 y + \sin^2 y.$

Subtracting (1) from (2) results in

$$1 - \cos 2y = \cos^2 y + \sin^2 y - (\cos^2 y - \sin^2 y)$$

or (3) ________________.

Dividing both members of (3) by 2 and solving for $\sin y$ we have

(4) $|\sin y| =$ ________________

Since $\frac{x}{2} \epsilon \mathcal{R}$, we may substitute $\frac{x}{2}$ for y in (4). This gives the desired result.

THEOREM:
If $x \epsilon \mathcal{R}$, then

$$\left|\cos\left(\frac{x}{2}\right)\right| = \sqrt{\frac{1 + \cos x}{2}}.$$

The proof is left as an exercise.

MOVE TO NEXT FRAME

THEOREM:
If $x \epsilon \mathcal{R}$, then

$$\left|\tan\left(\frac{x}{2}\right)\right| = \sqrt{\frac{1 - \cos x}{1 + \cos x}},$$

provided $\cos x \neq -1$ and $x \neq$ ____________.
The proof is left as an exercise.

Identities may be used to find the values of circular functions at certain numbers, as in the following examples. Find $\cos\frac{11\pi}{12}$.

(a) $$\cos\left(\frac{11\pi}{12}\right) = \cos\frac{\frac{11\pi}{6}}{2}$$

Using the identity $\left|\cos\frac{x}{2}\right| =$ __________ and letting $x = \frac{11\pi}{6}$, we have

$$\left|\cos\frac{\frac{11\pi}{6}}{2}\right| = \sqrt{\frac{1+\cos\left(\frac{11\pi}{6}\right)}{2}}$$
$$= \sqrt{\frac{1+(\quad)}{2}}$$
$$= \sqrt{\frac{2+\sqrt{3}}{4}}$$
$$= \frac{1}{2}\sqrt{2+\sqrt{3}}.$$

Since $\frac{11\pi}{12}$ is a second quadrant number, $\cos\frac{11\pi}{12}$ is negative and therefore

$$\cos\frac{11\pi}{12} = \underline{\qquad\qquad\qquad}.$$

(b) The identity $\cos(x_1 + x_2) = \cos x_1 \cos x_2 - \sin x_1 \sin x_2$ could also have been used to find $\cos\frac{11\pi}{12}$ as follows:

$$\cos\frac{11\pi}{12} = \cos\left(\frac{\pi}{4}+\frac{2\pi}{3}\right) = \frac{\sqrt{2}}{2}\left(-\frac{1}{2}\right) - \frac{\sqrt{2}}{2}\left(\frac{\sqrt{3}}{2}\right)$$
$$= \underline{\qquad\qquad\qquad}.$$

In the preceding frame two different methods were used to arrive at $\cos\frac{11\pi}{12}$, with two apparently different results. These results are equal, however. This can be shown, since both are negative, by establishing that their squares are equal.

Squaring the result from (a), we have

$$\left[\left(-\frac{1}{2}\right)\sqrt{2+\sqrt{3}}\right]^2 = \underline{\qquad\qquad\qquad}.$$

Squaring the result from (b), we have

$$\left(\frac{\sqrt{2}+\sqrt{6}}{4}\right)^2 = \frac{\qquad\qquad}{16} = \frac{2+\sqrt{3}}{4}.$$

Thus, $$-\frac{\sqrt{2}+\sqrt{6}}{4} = -\frac{1}{2}\sqrt{2+\sqrt{3}} = \cos\frac{11\pi}{12}.$$

ANSWERS TO PAGE 187

$$\frac{\sin x_1 \cos x_2 + \cos x_1 \sin x_2}{\cos x_1 \cos x_2 - \sin x_1 \sin x_2}$$

$$\frac{\tan x_1 + \tan x_2}{1 - \tan x_1 \tan x_2}$$

$2 \sin x \cos x$

ANSWERS TO PAGE 192

(1) See Appendix.

(2) See Appendix.

(3) (a) $\frac{\sqrt{6}-\sqrt{2}}{4}$ (b) $-(2+\sqrt{3})$

(c) $\frac{1}{2}\sqrt{2-\sqrt{2}}$ (d) $\frac{-1}{2}\sqrt{2-\sqrt{2}}$

(e) $1-\sqrt{2}$ (f) $\frac{1}{2}\sqrt{2+\sqrt{2}}$

(g) $\frac{1}{2}\sqrt{2+\sqrt{3}}$ (h) $\frac{\sqrt{2}-\sqrt{6}}{4}$

(i) $\sqrt{2}-1$ (j) $-2-\sqrt{3}$

(k) $\frac{\sqrt{2-\sqrt{2+\sqrt{3}}}}{2}$

(l) $\frac{1}{2}\sqrt{2+\sqrt{2+\sqrt{2}}}$

(4) See Appendix.

(5) See Appendix.

(6) See Appendix.

In the frame above we use the theorem that if $a^2 = b^2$ and a and b are both positive or both negative, then ________. Note that $a^2 = b^2$ does not always imply $a = b$. For example, $5^2 = (-5)^2$, but $5 \neq -5$.

It is often useful to write a sum of circular functions as a product of circular functions, or to write a product as a sum. Such identities may be derived from the formulas for $(x_1 \pm x_2)$.

MOVE TO NEXT FRAME

THEOREM:

If $x_1 \epsilon \mathcal{R}$ and $x_2 \epsilon \mathcal{R}$, then

$$\sin x_1 + \sin x_2 = 2 \sin \frac{1}{2}(x_1 + x_2) \cos \frac{1}{2}(x_1 - x_2).$$

Proof:

Complete the following identities for any real numbers x and y and add.

(1) $\sin(x + y) =$ ________________

(2) $\sin(x - y) =$ ________________

Adding (1) and (2), we have

(3) $\sin(x + y) + \sin(x - y) =$ ________________

Now let $x + y = x_1$ and $x - y = x_2$.

By solving $\begin{Bmatrix} x + y = x_1 \\ x - y = x_2 \end{Bmatrix}$ simultaneously, we have $x =$ ________ and $y =$ ________. Substituting x_1 for $x + y$, x_2 for $x - y$, ________ for x, and ________ for y in (3), we have

(4) $\sin x_1 + \sin x_2 =$ ________________.

THEOREM:

If $x_1 \epsilon \mathcal{R}$ and $x_2 \epsilon \mathcal{R}$, then

$$\sin x_1 - \sin x_2 = 2 \cos \frac{1}{2}(x_1 + x_2) \sin \frac{1}{2}(x_1 - x_2).$$

This proof is left as an exercise. It is derived by subtracting the identity for $\sin(x - y)$ from the identity for ________________.

There are identities similar to those presented in the preceding frames for the cosine function. They are derived in much the same way as those for the sine functions.

MOVE TO NEXT FRAME

THEOREM:
If $x_1 \epsilon \mathcal{R}$ and $x_2 \epsilon \mathcal{R}$, then

$$\cos x_1 + \cos x_2 = 2 \cos \frac{1}{2}(x_1 + x_2) \cos \frac{1}{2}(x_1 - x_2).$$

Proof:

The following identities for cos have been previously proved.

(1) $\cos(x + y) =$ ____________________,

and

(2) $\cos(x - y) =$ ____________________.

The sum of (1) and (2) is

(3) $\cos(x + y) + \cos(x - y) =$ ____________________.

Again, let $x + y = x_1$ and $x - y = x_2$ so that

$x =$ ________________ and $y =$ ________________.

Substituting these terms for x and y in (3), we have

____.

THEOREM:
If $x_1 \epsilon \mathcal{R}$ and $x_2 \epsilon \mathcal{R}$,

$$\cos x_1 - \cos x_2 = -2 \sin \frac{1}{2}(x_1 + x_2) \sin \frac{1}{2}(x_1 - x_2).$$

The proof is similar to the previous theorem and is left as an exercise.

MOVE TO NEXT FRAME

ANSWERS TO PAGE 189

$\sqrt{\frac{1 + \cos x}{2}}$

$\frac{\sqrt{3}}{2}$

$-\frac{1}{2}\sqrt{2 + \sqrt{3}}$

$-\frac{\sqrt{2} + \sqrt{6}}{4}$

$\frac{1}{4}(2 + \sqrt{3})$

$8 + 4\sqrt{3}$

set of ordered pairs

functions

---

function

EXERCISES. 4.1

1. By using the appropriate sum or difference formula, prove that each of the following is true.

(a) $\cos\left(\frac{\pi}{2}-x\right) = \sin x$ (b) $\sin\left(\frac{\pi}{2}-x\right) = \cos x$

(c) $\cos\left(x+\frac{\pi}{2}\right) = -\sin x$ (d) $\sin\left(x+\frac{\pi}{2}\right) = \cos x$

(e) $\cos(\pi - x) = -\cos x$ (f) $\sin(\pi - x) = \sin x$

(g) $\cos\left(\frac{3\pi}{2}+x\right) = \sin x$ (h) $\sin\left(\frac{3\pi}{2}+x\right) = -\cos x$

(i) $\sin\left(\frac{\pi}{4}+x\right) = \cos\left(\frac{\pi}{4}-x\right)$ (j) $-\tan(\pi - x) = \tan(\pi + x)$

2. Prove

$$\sin(x_1 - x_2) = \sin x_1 \cos x_2 - \cos x_1 \sin x_2.$$

(*Hint:* Use $\sin(x_1 + x_2) = \sin x_1 \cos x_2 + \cos x_1 \sin x_2$.)

3. Use your knowledge of the values of the functions for special real numbers, such as $\frac{\pi}{6}$, $\frac{\pi}{4}$, and $\frac{\pi}{3}$ to find each of the following,

(a) $\sin\frac{\pi}{12}$ ________ (b) $\tan\frac{19\pi}{12}$ ________

(c) $\cos\frac{3\pi}{8}$ ________ (d) $\sin\frac{15\pi}{8}$ ________

(e) $\tan\frac{7\pi}{8}$ ________ (f) $\sin\frac{5\pi}{8}$ ________

(g) $\cos\frac{23\pi}{12}$ ________ (h) $\sin\frac{13\pi}{12}$ ________

(i) $\tan\frac{9\pi}{8}$ ________ (j) $\tan\frac{7\pi}{12}$ ________

(k) $\sin\frac{\pi}{24}$ ________

(l) $\cos\frac{\pi}{16}$ ________

4. Derive an identity for $\tan(x_1 - x_2)$ in terms of $\tan x_1$ and $\tan x_2$.

Hint: Use $\tan(x_1 + x_2) = \dfrac{\tan x_1 + \tan x_2}{1 - \tan x_1 \tan x_2}$

5. Derive an identity for $\cot(x_1 + x_2)$ in terms of $\cot x_1$ and $\cot x_2$.

6. Derive the identity $\sin 2x = 2 \sin x \cos x$.

7. Derive the identity $\left|\cos \frac{x}{2}\right| = \sqrt{\frac{1 + \cos x}{2}}$.

8. Derive the identity $\sin x_1 - \sin x_2 = 2 \sin \frac{1}{2}(x_1 + x_2) \cos \frac{1}{2}(x_1 - x_2)$.

9. Derive the identity $\cos x_1 - \cos x_2 = -2 \sin \frac{1}{2}(x_1 + x_2) \sin \frac{1}{2}(x_1 - x_2)$.

10. Derive an identity for $\sin 3x$ in terms of $\cos x$ and $\sin x$. (*Hint:* Use $\sin 3x = \sin (2x + x)$.)

11. Derive the identity $\left|\tan \frac{x}{2}\right| = \sqrt{\frac{1 - \cos x}{1 + \cos x}}$ and state any values for which it does not hold.

12. Complete each of the following identities by substitution in a previously proved identity.

    (a) $\sin^2\left(\frac{x}{2}\right) + \cos^2\left(\frac{x}{2}\right) =$ ____ .

    (b) $\left|\sin \frac{y}{4}\right| = \sqrt{\text{\_\_\_\_\_\_\_\_}}$.

    (c) $\tan 4t = \frac{2 \tan (2t)}{(\text{\_\_\_\_\_\_})}$.

    (d) $\sin 5x = \sin 2x \cos 3x +$ ____________ .

    (e) $\cos y = 1 -$ ____________ .

    (f) $\sin 4x + \sin 2x =$ ____________ .

    (g) $\sin 4x - \sin 2x =$ ____________ .

13. Prove the identity

$$\left|\sin\left(\frac{\pi}{4} - x\right)\right| = \frac{\cos x - \sin x}{\sqrt{2}}.$$

$\cos x \cos y - \sin x \sin y$

$\cos x \cos y + \sin x \sin y$

$2 \cos x \cos y$

$\frac{1}{2}(x_1 + x_2)$ $\frac{1}{2}(x_1 - x_2)$

$\cos x_1 + \cos x_2$
$= 2 \cos \frac{1}{2}(x_1 + x_2) \cos \frac{1}{2}(x_1 - x_2)$

ANSWERS TO PAGE 196

$\left\{x : x = \frac{\pi}{4} + k\pi \text{ for some } k \in J\right\}$

$y \quad x$

---

all of them

none of them

---

are not

---

one-to-one

4.2. INVERSE CIRCULAR FUNCTIONS

From Chapter 1 recall that a relation is defined as a ______________ ________ of numbers. Furthermore, those relations that have at most one image, or value, for a given element in the domain are called ____________.

The cosine and sine relations are functions, because exactly one point on the unit circle corresponds to each given number x, and the values $\cos x$ and $\sin x$ are the unique coordinates of that point.

MOVE TO NEXT FRAME

Consider this graph of a cosine.

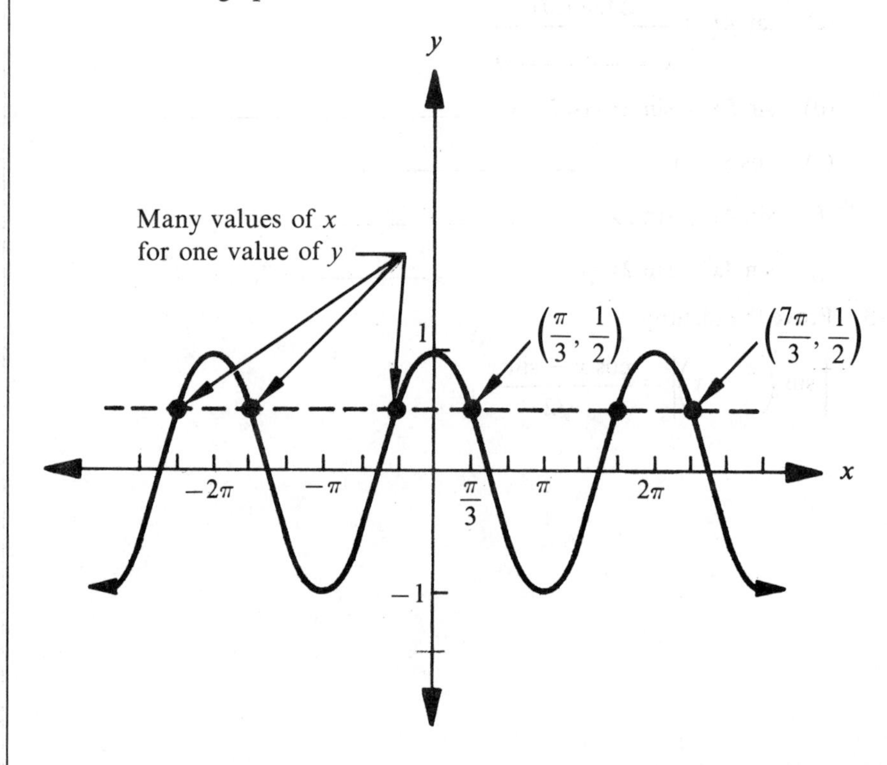

For a given real number x, there is **exactly one** real number y such that $y = \cos x$. Thus $y = \cos x$ defines that kind of relation referred to as a ________________.

The inverse problem, that of finding x when given y, such that $y = \cos x$, is ambiguous. For example, if $y = \cos x = \frac{1}{2}$, x may be any member of the set ______________________________.
This is illustrated in the graph in the preceding frame.

Since there are many values of x which satisfy the equation $y = \cos x$, x is not a function of y.

The infinite set of values of x for which $\cos x = \frac{1}{2}$ is denoted **arccos** $\mathbf{\frac{1}{2}}$ or $\mathbf{\cos^{-1} \frac{1}{2}}$.

The symbol $\arccos \frac{1}{2}$ is read "the set of numbers whose cosine is $\frac{1}{2}$" or "arc cosine $\frac{1}{2}$." when the symbol $\cos^{-1} \frac{1}{2}$ is used, it should not be confused with $\left(\cos \frac{1}{2}\right)^{-1}$, which means $\dfrac{1}{\cos \frac{1}{2}}$.

MOVE TO NEXT FRAME

$$\cos^{-1}u = \arccos u = \{x : x \epsilon \mathcal{R} \text{ and } u = \cos x\}$$

$$\sin^{-1}v = \arcsin v = \{x : x \epsilon \mathcal{R} \text{ and } v = \sin x\}$$

$$\tan^{-1}t = \arctan t = \{x : x \epsilon \mathcal{R} \text{ and } t = \tan x\}$$

$$\cos^{-1}t = \text{arccot}\, t = \{x : x \epsilon \mathcal{R} \text{ and } t = \cot x\}$$

$$\sec^{-1}s = \text{arcsec}\, s = \{x : x \epsilon \mathcal{R} \text{ and } s = \sec x\}$$

$$\csc^{-1}s = \text{arccsc}\, s = \{x : x \epsilon \mathcal{R} \text{ and } s = \csc x\}$$

MOVE TO NEXT FRAME

Find the set of numbers having a value of sine equal to $-\frac{\sqrt{2}}{2}$, i.e., find $\arcsin\left(-\frac{\sqrt{2}}{2}\right)$.

ANSWERS TO PAGE 193

(7) See Appendix.

(8) See Appendix.

(9) See Appendix.

(10) See Appendix.

(11) See Appendix.

(12) (a) 1

(b) $\dfrac{1 - \cos \frac{y}{2}}{2}$

(c) $1 - \tan^2 (2t)$

(d) $\cos 2x \sin 3x$

(e) $2 \sin^2 \left(\frac{y}{2}\right)$

(f) $2 \sin 3x \cos x$

(g) $2 \cos 3x \sin x$

(13) See Appendix.

ANSWERS TO PAGE 198

$\frac{\pi}{2}$ 0

$\frac{\pi}{2}$

Find those values of x for which $\tan x = 1$, *i.e.*, find arctan 1. ______

If we are given a value for x, then there is exactly one value of y paired with that value of x for the function $\cos = \{(x,y): y = \cos x\}$, but if we are given a value for __, then there is an infinite set of values for __ paired with that value of y.

Which of the following circular functions have exactly one value of y in its range paired with each value of x in its domain? ______

(a) sin (b) cos (c) tan (d) cot (e) sec (f) csc

Which of these functions have exactly one value x of its domain paired with y of its range? ______.

This leads to the conclusion that the circular functions (are/are not) ______ one-to-one correspondences as they have been defined in the preceding frames. Thus, as they are defined, they do not have inverse functions.

For a function to have an inverse function, there must be a ______ correspondence between the elements of the domain and the elements of the range.

By a suitable restriction of the domain of each of the circular functions, we can create a new function that is one-to-one and thus has an inverse function.

MOVE TO NEXT FRAME

Notice on the graph of the cosine function, that each value in the range of cos is obtained exactly once if cos x is evaluated for all x in the interval $0 \leq x \leq \pi$. Thus the function

$$\{(x,y): y = \cos x \text{ and } 0 \leq x \leq \pi\}$$

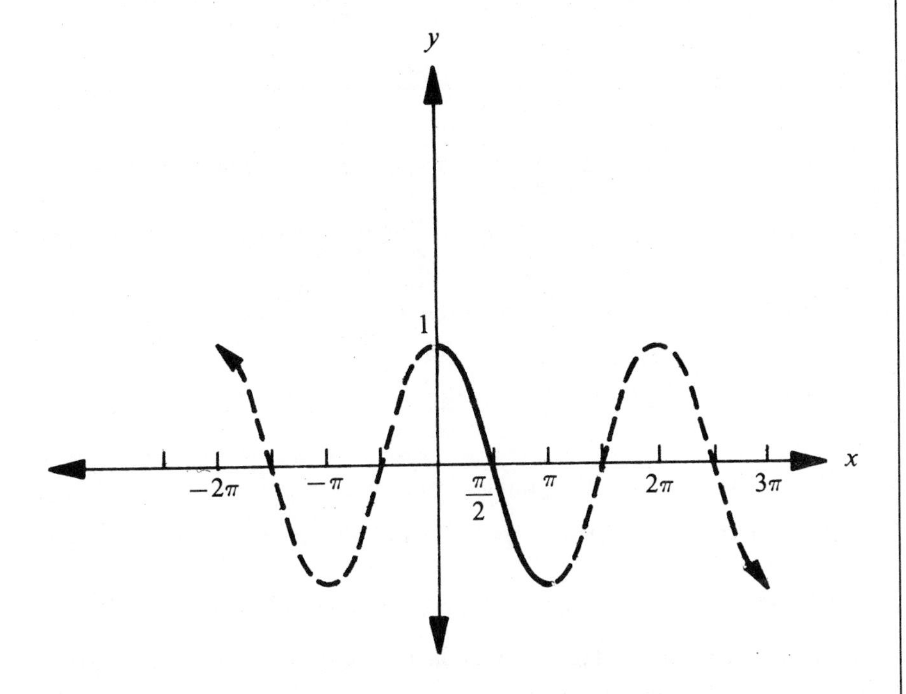

Graph of Cos shown as a restriction of cos.

is a ________________ correspondence. This function is denoted Cos (read "cap-cosine") and is called the **cosine principal value function.**

The function Cos is obtained from the function cos by restricting the domain of the latter function to the interval ____________. Write $y = \text{Cos}\, x$ to indicate $(x,y) \epsilon$ Cos. For example, $\text{Cos}\, \frac{\pi}{3} = \frac{1}{2}$, and $\text{Cos}\, 0 = 1$.

Since Cos is a one-to-one correspondence, it has an inverse function; this function is denoted Arccos or Cos^{-1}. Since Arccos is the inverse of ______, $(x,y) \epsilon$ Arccos if and only if $(y,x) \epsilon$ ______, i.e., if and only if $x = \text{Cos}\, y$. Hence,

$$\text{Arccos} = \text{Cos}^{-1} = \{(x,y): x = \text{Cos}\, y\}.$$

ANSWERS TO PAGE 195

$$\left\{x: x = \frac{\pi}{3} + 2k\pi \text{ or } \frac{5\pi}{3} + 2k\pi \text{ for some } k \epsilon J\right\}$$

$$\left\{x: x = \frac{5\pi}{4} + 2k\pi \text{ or } \frac{7\pi}{4} + 2k\pi \text{ for some } k \epsilon J\right\}$$

ANSWERS TO PAGE 200

$y = x$

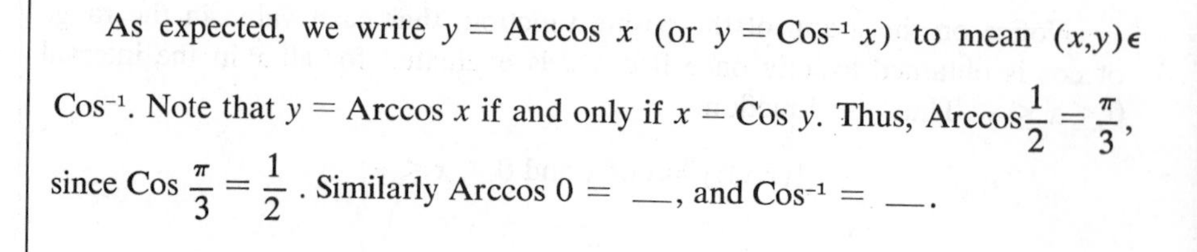

As expected, we write $y = \text{Arccos } x$ (or $y = \text{Cos}^{-1} x$) to mean $(x,y) \in \text{Cos}^{-1}$. Note that $y = \text{Arccos } x$ if and only if $x = \text{Cos } y$. Thus, $\text{Arccos}\frac{1}{2} = \frac{\pi}{3}$, since $\text{Cos } \frac{\pi}{3} = \frac{1}{2}$. Similarly Arccos 0 = __, and $\text{Cos}^{-1} =$ __.

For a given x, the number Arccos x is called the **principal value** of the set arccos x. Thus the principal value of arccos $\frac{1}{2}$ is $\frac{\pi}{3}$; the principal value of arccos 0 is __; and the principal value of $\cos^{-1} \frac{\sqrt{3}}{2}$ is __.

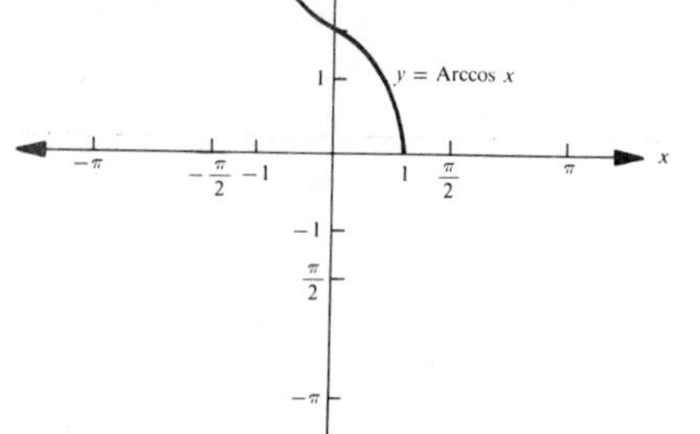

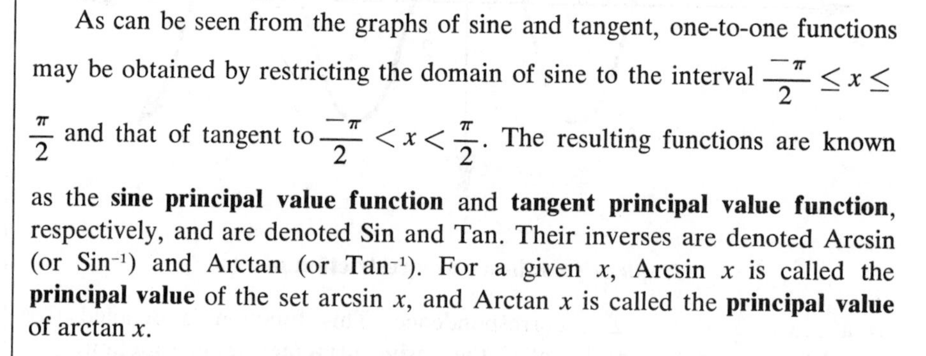

As can be seen from the graphs of sine and tangent, one-to-one functions may be obtained by restricting the domain of sine to the interval $\frac{-\pi}{2} \leq x \leq \frac{\pi}{2}$ and that of tangent to $\frac{-\pi}{2} < x < \frac{\pi}{2}$. The resulting functions are known as the **sine principal value function** and **tangent principal value function**, respectively, and are denoted Sin and Tan. Their inverses are denoted Arcsin (or Sin^{-1}) and Arctan (or Tan^{-1}). For a given x, Arcsin x is called the **principal value** of the set arcsin x, and Arctan x is called the **principal value** of arctan x.

MOVE TO NEXT FRAME

DEFINITIONS:

$$\text{Cos} = \{(x,y): y = \cos x \text{ and } 0 \leq x \leq \pi\};$$

$$\text{Arccos} = \text{Cos}^{-1} = \{(x,y): x = \text{Cos } y\}.$$

$$\text{Sin} = \left\{(x,y): y = \sin x \text{ and } \frac{-\pi}{2} \leq x \leq \frac{\pi}{2}\right\};$$

$$\text{Arcsin} = \text{Sin}^{-1} = \{(x,y) : x = \text{Sin } y\}.$$

$$\text{Tan} = \left\{(x,y) : y = \tan x \text{ and } \frac{-\pi}{2} < x < \frac{\pi}{2}\right\};$$

$$\text{Arctan} = \text{Tan}^{-1} = \{(x,y) : x = \text{Tan } y\}.$$

MOVE TO NEXT FRAME

You will note we have included $x = \frac{\pi}{2}$ and $x = \frac{-\pi}{2}$ in the domain of Sin. Why do you suppose $-\frac{\pi}{2}$ and $\frac{\pi}{2}$ are excluded from the domain of Tan?

Because each of the functions sin, cos, and tan are periodic, we could have selected intervals other than the stated intervals for the domain of definition of the principal value functions, but there is general agreement among mathematicians on those selected.

Are the principal value functions Sin, Cos, and Tan periodic? ______

Find each of the following.

$\text{Arccos} -\frac{1}{2} =$ ______

$\text{Arcsin} \frac{\sqrt{3}}{2} =$ ______

$\text{Arcsin}\left(-\frac{\sqrt{3}}{2}\right) =$ ______

$\text{Tan}^{-1} 1 =$ ______

ANSWERS TO PAGE 197

one-to-one

$0 \leq x \leq \pi$

Cos

Cos

ANSWERS TO PAGE 202

$\frac{-5}{12}$

positive

$0 \leq \text{Arccos}\, x \leq \frac{\pi}{2}$

$0 \leq \text{Arcsin}\, x \leq \frac{\pi}{2}$

0 $\quad \pi$

$\frac{\pi}{2} \leq \text{Arccos}\, x \leq \pi$

$-\frac{\pi}{2} \leq \text{Arcsin}\, x \leq 0$

Remember the graph of the inverse of a function may be obtained by reflecting the graph of the function in the line defined by the equation

______.

That is, if the graph of the function were sketched with some substance that would "come off" on another surface, then the image formed by folding the paper at the line $y = x$ would be that of the reflection, i.e., the inverse of the function. For more accurate sketches, it is necessary to graph the corresponding set of ordered pairs of numbers.

On each of the coordinate systems below, sketch the graph of the inverse of the given function.

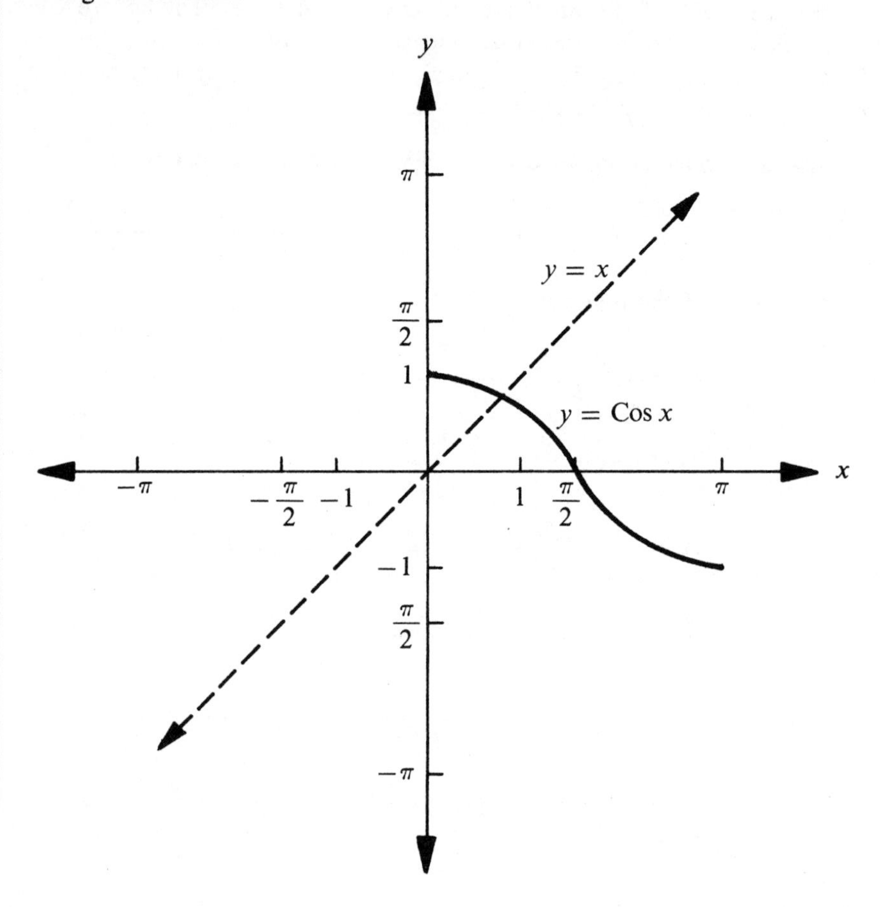

Cos and Arccos

Sin and Arcsin

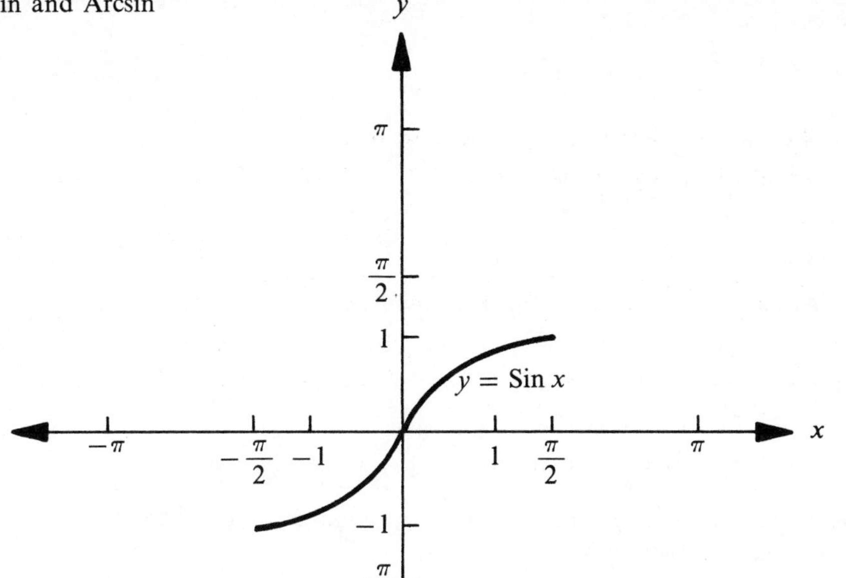

ANSWERS TO PAGE 199

tan x is undefined at $x = \frac{\pi}{2}$ and $x = \frac{-\pi}{2}$

---

no

$\frac{2\pi}{3}$

$\frac{\pi}{3}$

$-\frac{\pi}{3}$

$\frac{\pi}{4}$

Tan and Arctan

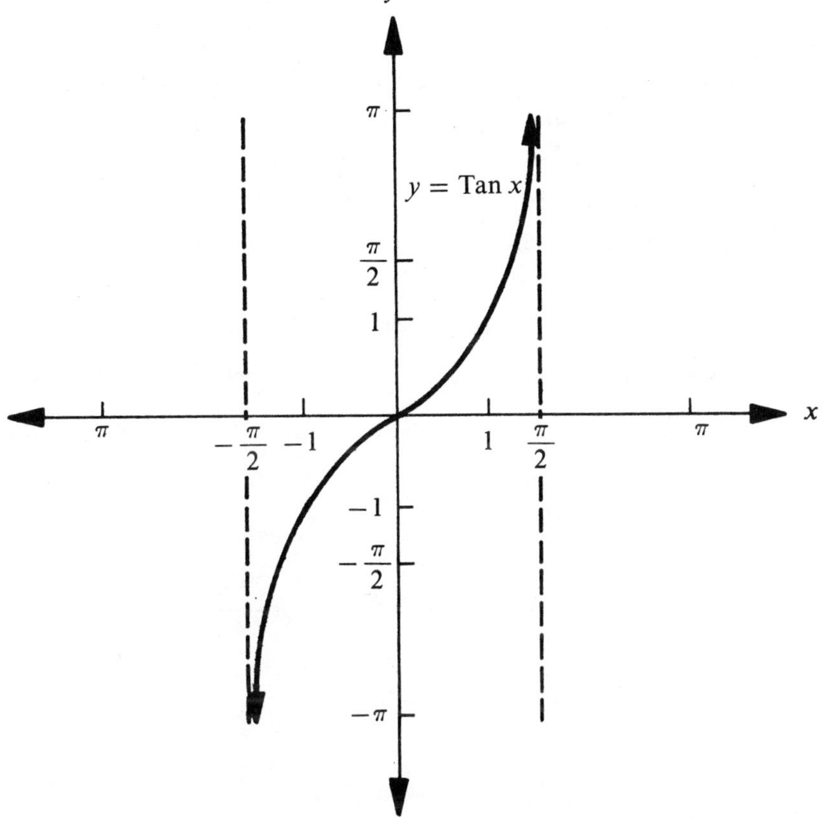

Which of the following relations are defined for all $x \in \mathcal{R}$? ____

(a) $y = \text{Arctan}\, x$ (b) $y = \arctan x$ (c) $y = \tan x$ (d) $y = \text{Tan}\, x$

ANSWERS TO PAGE 204

Example:

Find $\cos\left(\text{Arctan}\dfrac{-5}{12}\right)$.

Solution:

Arctan $\dfrac{-5}{12}$ is some number x for which $\tan x =$ __________ and $\dfrac{-\pi}{2} < x < \dfrac{\pi}{2}$.

$$\tan x = \frac{\sin x}{\cos x} = \frac{-5}{12}.$$

Hence $\sin x$ is some multiple of -5, *e.g.*, $-5t$, and $\cos x$ is the same multiple of 12, i.e., $12t$. Since $\cos^2 x + \sin^2 x = 1$ we have

$$(-5t)^2 + (12t)^2 = 1$$

$$25t^2 + 144t^2 = 1$$

$$t^2 = \frac{1}{169}$$

$$t = \pm\frac{1}{13}$$

However, since $\dfrac{-\pi}{2} < x < \dfrac{\pi}{2}$, $\cos x$ is __________ (positive/negative); therefore,

$$\cos\left(\text{Arctan}\frac{-5}{12}\right) = \cos x = 12\left(\frac{1}{13}\right) = \frac{12}{13}.$$

$\dfrac{\pi}{2} - \text{Arctan}\, x$

It can be shown, as a direct consequence of the definitions of Arccos and Arcsin, that

$$0 \leq \text{Arccos}\, x + \text{Arcsin}\, x \leq \pi.$$

(In the following discussion, it may be helpful to refer to the graphs of Arcsin and Arccos.)

For $x \geq 0$ we know that

$$\_\_\_\_\_\_ \leq \text{Arccos}\, x \leq \_\_\_\_\_\_,$$

and

$$\_\_\_\_\_\_ \leq \text{Arcsin}\, x \leq \_\_\_\_\_\_.$$

Thus,

$$\_\_ \leq \text{Arccos}\, x + \text{Arcsin}\, x \leq \_\_.$$

For $x \leq 0$ we know that

$$\_\_\_\_\_\_ \leq \text{Arccos}\, x \leq \_\_\_\_\_\_,$$

and

$$\_\_\_\_\_\_ \leq \text{Arcsin}\, x \leq \_\_\_\_\_\_.$$

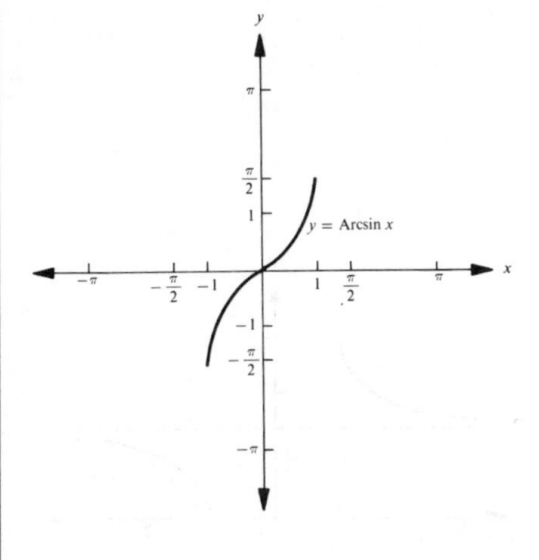

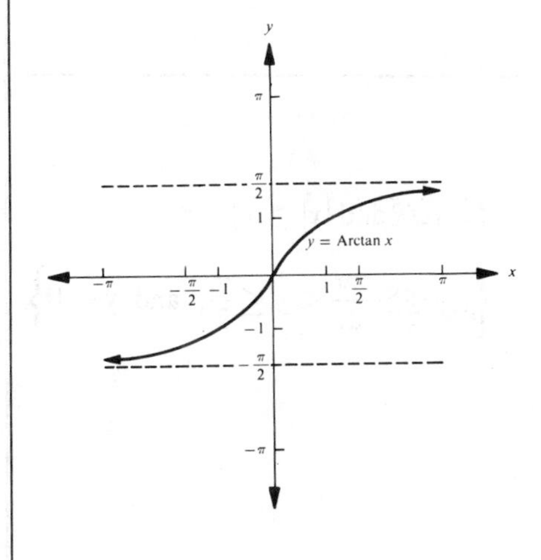

a,b

So that, again,

$$\_\_ \leq \text{Arccos}\, x + \text{Arcsin}\, x \leq \_\_.$$

Therefore, $0 \leq \text{Arcos}\, x + \text{Arcsin}\, x \leq \pi$.

We can also prove

$$\text{Arccos}\, x + \text{Arcsin}\, x = \frac{\pi}{2}$$

with the aid of the result obtained in the previous frame and the identity for $\cos(y_1 + y_2)$.

Let $y_1 = \text{Arccos}\, x$ so that $\cos y_1 = \_\_$ and $0 \leq y_1 \leq \pi$; let $y_2 = \text{Arcsin}\, x$ so that $\sin y_2 = \_\_$ and $\frac{-\pi}{2} \leq y_2 \leq \frac{\pi}{2}$. Now

$$\cos(y_1 + y_2) = \cos y_1 \cos y_2 - \sin y_1 \sin y_2$$

or

$$\cos(y_1 + y_2) = x \cos y_2 - (\sin y_1)\, x.$$

But also, since $\cos y_1 = x$,

$$\sin y_1 = \sqrt{1 - \cos^2 y_1} = \_\_\_\_\_\_\_\_.$$

However, $0 \leq y_1 \leq \pi$. Thus $\sin y_1 \geq 0$; therefore,

$$\sin y_1 = \_\_\_\_\_\_\_\_.$$

Similarly, since $\sin y_2 = x$ and $\cos y_2 \geq 0$,

$$\cos y_2 = \_\_\_\_\_\_\_\_.$$

Thus, by substitution in $\cos(y_1 + y_2) = x \cos y_2 - (\sin y_1)x$,

$$\cos(y_1 + y_2) = \_\_\_\_\_\_\_\_\_\_\_\_\_\_\_\_ = 0.$$

Since it was shown in the preceding frame that $0 \leq \text{Arccos}\, x + \text{Arcsin}\, x \leq \pi$, we have $\text{Arccos}\, x + \text{Arcsin}\, x = \frac{\pi}{2}$, because __ is the only number between 0 and π with a value of cosine equal to zero. Therefore,

$$\text{Arccos}\, x + \text{Arcsin}\, x = \frac{\pi}{2}.$$

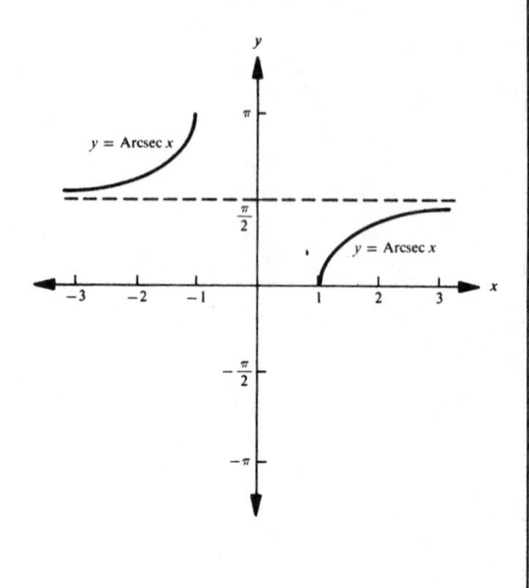

$\{x : x \in \mathcal{R} \text{ and } |x| \geq 1\}$

$\left\{y : y \in \mathcal{R}, \frac{-\pi}{2} \leq y \leq \frac{\pi}{2}, \text{ and } y \neq 0\right\}$

The inverse functions corresponding to Cot, Sec, and Csc are used less often than Arcsin, Arccos, and Arctan. The following are generally accepted as the definitions of Arccot, Arcsec, and Arccsc:

DEFINITIONS:

$$\text{Cot}^{-1} = \text{Arccot} = \left\{(x,y) : y = \frac{\pi}{2} - \text{Arctan}\, x\right\}$$

$$\text{Sec}^{-1} = \text{Arcsec} = \left\{(x,y) : y = \text{Arccos}\frac{1}{x}\right\}$$

$$\text{Csc}^{-1} = \text{Arccsc} = \left\{(x,y) : y = \text{Arcsin}\frac{1}{x}\right\}$$

MOVE TO NEXT FRAME

The definitions stated in the previous frame, though arbitrary, are chosen because each of the following is maintained:

$$(1)\quad \text{Arctan}\, x + \text{Arccot}\, x = \frac{\pi}{2}$$

$$(2)\quad \text{Arcsec}\, x + \text{Arccsc}\, x = \frac{\pi}{2}$$

(1) is an immediate consequence of the definition of Arccot.

(2) follows from the theorem

$$\text{Arccos}\ x + \text{Arcsin}\ x = \frac{\pi}{2}$$

which implies $\text{Arccos}\frac{1}{x} + \text{Arcsin}\frac{1}{x} = \frac{\pi}{2}$ for $|x| \geq 1$.

MOVE TO NEXT FRAME

The definition for Arccot specifies its range when it states

$y =$ ____________________

Since $\frac{-\pi}{2} < \text{Arctan}\ x < \frac{\pi}{2}$ from an earlier definition, it follows that $0 < \text{Arccot}\, x < \pi$.

Proof:

$$\frac{-\pi}{2} < \text{Arctan}\, x < -\frac{\pi}{2}$$

$$\frac{\pi}{2} > -\text{Arctan}\, x > -\frac{\pi}{2}$$

$$\frac{\pi}{2} + \frac{\pi}{2} > \frac{\pi}{2} - \text{Arctan}\, x > \frac{\pi}{2} - \frac{\pi}{2}$$

Therefore $\pi > \text{Arccot}\, x > 0$.

The range of Arcsec may be derived from its definition. In the definition of Arcsec

$$y = \underline{\qquad\qquad}.$$

Since the range of Arccos is $\{y: 0 \le y \le \pi\}$ it follows that the range of Arcsec is the same, providing $y \ne \frac{\pi}{2}$, because if Arcsec $x = \frac{\pi}{2}$, then Arccos $\frac{1}{x} = \frac{\pi}{2}$. This would imply that $\cos \frac{\pi}{2} = \frac{1}{x}$ or $0 = \frac{1}{x}$, which is impossible.

Because the domain of Arccos x is $\{x: |x| \le 1\}$, the domain of Arcsec x is ____________.

Arguments similar to that in the previous frame may be used to establish the domain and range of Arccsc.

MOVE TO NEXT FRAME

Sketch the graph of Arccot.

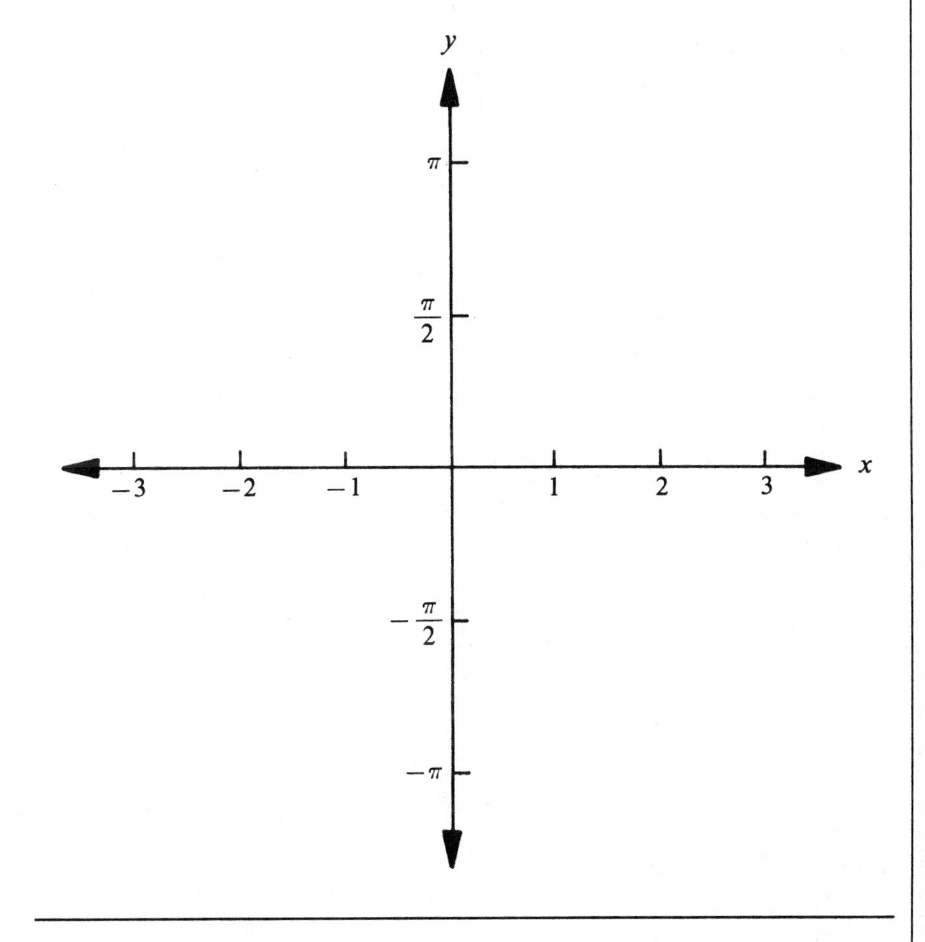

ANSWERS TO PAGE 203

$0 \quad \pi$

---

x

x

$\pm\sqrt{1-x^2}$

$+\sqrt{1-x^2}$

$+\sqrt{1-x^2}$

$x\sqrt{1-x^2} - (\sqrt{1-x^2})\,x$

$\frac{\pi}{2}$

ANSWERS TO PAGE 208

(1) (a) $\left\{\frac{\pi}{6} + 2k\pi \text{ or } \frac{5\pi}{6} + 2k\pi\right\}$

(b) same as (a)

(c) $\left\{\frac{\pi}{3} + k\pi\right\}$

(d) same as (c)

(e) $\left\{\frac{\pi}{4}\right\}$

(f) $\left\{\frac{\pi}{4}\right\}$

(g) $\left\{\frac{5\pi}{4} + 2k\pi \text{ or } \frac{7\pi}{4} + 2k\pi\right\}$

(h) $\left\{\frac{-\pi}{4}\right\}$

(i) $\left\{\frac{-\pi}{6}\right\}$

(j) $\left\{\frac{2\pi}{3}\right\}$

(2) (a) $\frac{2}{3}$

(b) $\frac{\pi}{6}$

(c) $\frac{\sqrt{3}}{2}$

(d) $\frac{\pi}{6}$

(e) $\frac{\pi}{4}$

(f) $\frac{\sqrt{2}}{2}$

(g) $\frac{-7}{25}$

Sketch the graph of Arcsec.

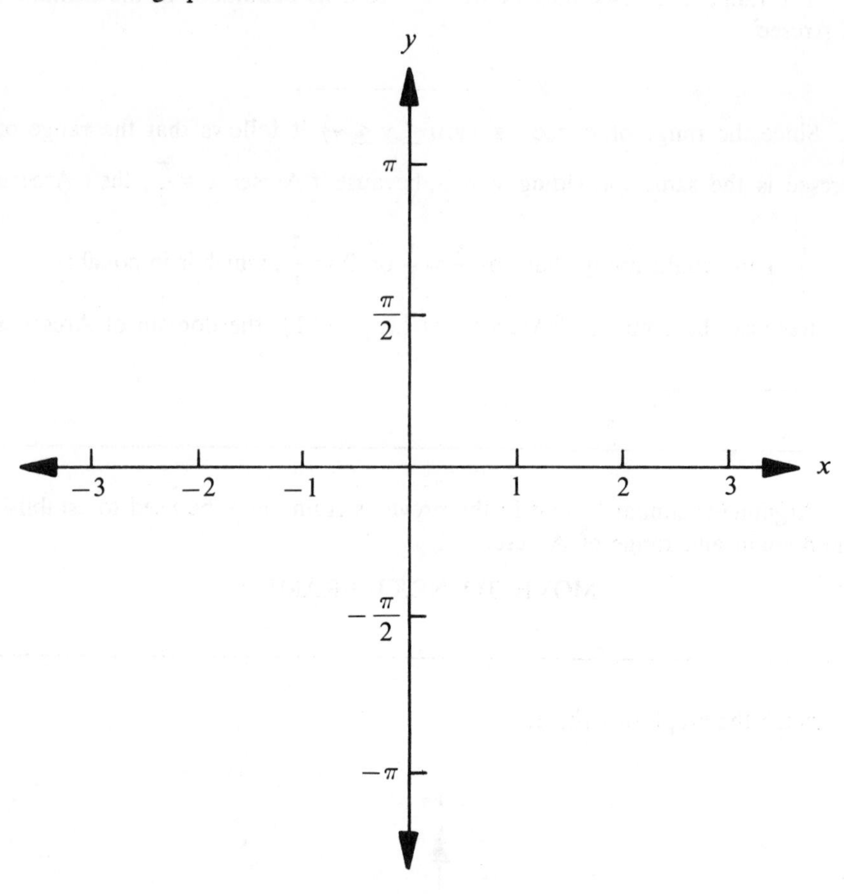

Determine the domain and range of Csc^{-1} and sketch its graph.

Domain = ____________________

Range = ____________________

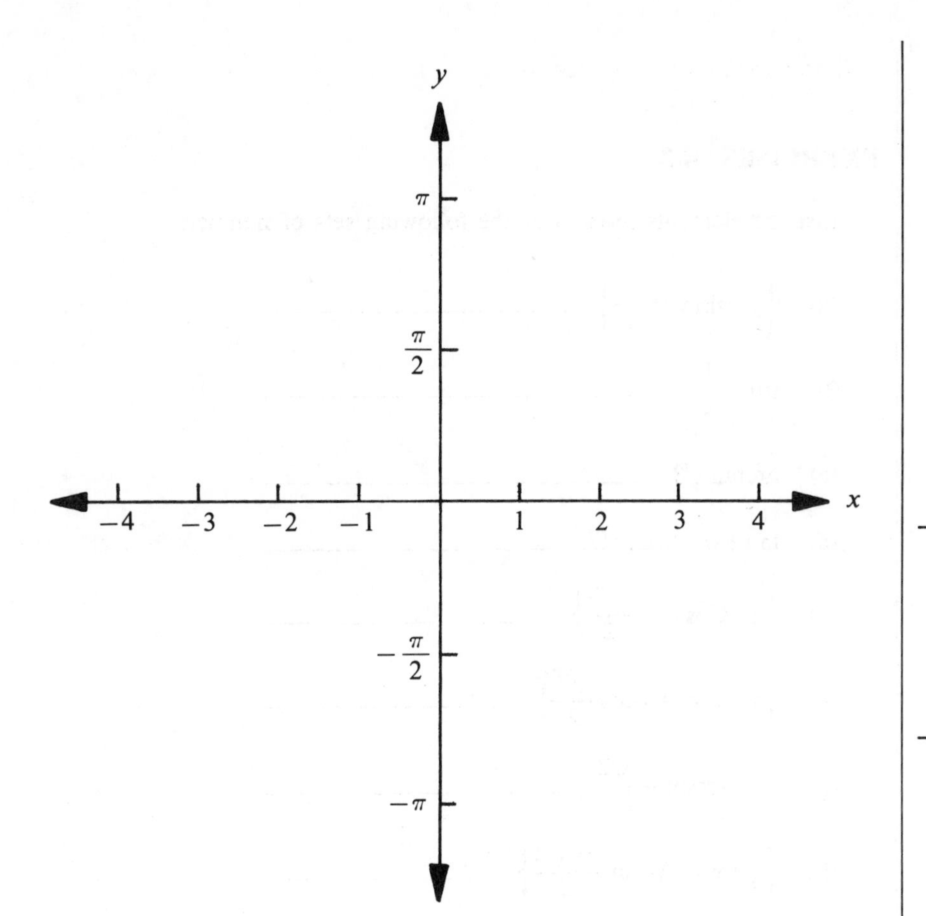

Problem:

Express sin (Arctan x) as an algebraic function of x.

Solution:

Let Arctan $x = y$, then $\tan y = x$ and $\frac{-\pi}{2} < y < \frac{\pi}{2}$. From $\tan y = \frac{\sin y}{\cos y}$ and $\tan y = x$ we have

$$\cos y = \underline{\qquad\qquad},$$

provided $x \neq 0$. Substituting this in the identity $\cos^2 y + \sin^2 y = 1$ we have

$\underline{\qquad\qquad\qquad\qquad\qquad\qquad}$ or

$$\sin^2 y\,(\underline{\qquad\qquad\qquad}) = 1.$$

Solving for $\sin y$,

$$|\sin y| = \frac{x}{\sqrt{1+x^2}}.$$

Since for $\frac{-\pi}{2} < y < \frac{\pi}{2}$, $\sin y$ and $\tan y = x$ are both positive or both negative, $\sin y = \frac{x}{\sqrt{1+x^2}}$. Thus,

$$\sin(\text{Arctan}\, x) = \underline{\qquad\qquad\qquad}.$$

Note that if $x = 0$, the equality holds since both members are zero.

ANSWERS TO PAGE 205

$\text{Arccos}\,\frac{1}{x}$

$\{x : |x| \geq 1\}$

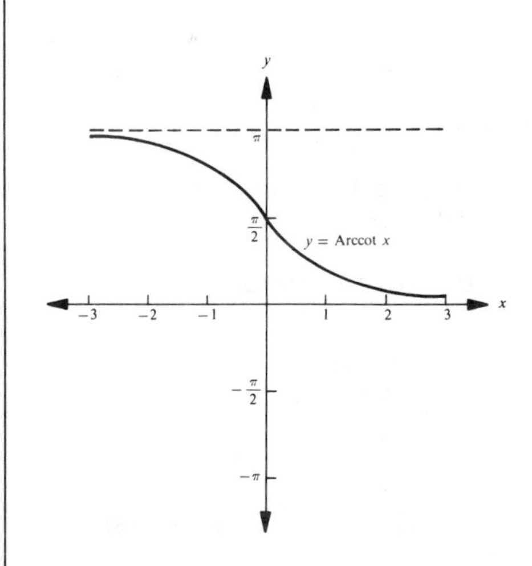

ANSWERS TO PAGE 210

$\arcsin \frac{-\sqrt{3}}{2}$

$\frac{5\pi}{3} + 2k\pi$

$1 - \cos x$

$\sin^2 x = 1 - 2\cos x + \cos^2 x$

$0 = \cos x - \cos^2 x$

$x = (2k+1)\frac{\pi}{2}$ for some $k \epsilon J$

$x = 2k\pi$ for some $k \epsilon J$

$x = \frac{3\pi}{2} + 2k\pi$ for some $k \epsilon J$

EXERCISES. 4.2

1. List the elements in each of the following sets of numbers.

(a) $\left\{y : \sin y = \frac{1}{2}\right\}$ ____________

(b) $\sin^{-1} \frac{1}{2}$ ____________

(c) $\arctan \sqrt{3}$ ____________

(d) $\tan^{-1} \sqrt{3}$ ____________

(e) $\left\{x : \text{Cos}\, x = \frac{\sqrt{2}}{2}\right\}$ ____________

(f) $\left\{y : y = \text{Arccos} \frac{\sqrt{2}}{2}\right\}$ ____________

(g) $x = \arcsin \frac{-\sqrt{2}}{2}$ ____________

(h) $\left\{y : y = \text{Arcsin} \frac{-\sqrt{2}}{2}\right\}$ ____________

(i) $\left\{x : x = \text{Arctan} \frac{-\sqrt{3}}{3}\right\}$ ____________

(j) $\left\{y : y = \text{Arccot} \frac{-\sqrt{3}}{3}\right\}$ ____________

2. Evaluate each of the following:

(a) $\sin\left(\text{Arcsin} \frac{2}{3}\right)$ ______

(b) $\text{Arcsin}\left(\sin \frac{\pi}{6}\right)$ ______

(c) $\sin\left(\text{Arccos} \frac{1}{2} + \text{Arcsin} \frac{\sqrt{3}}{2}\right)$ ______

(d) $\text{Arccsc}\, 2$ ______

(e) $\text{Cot}^{-1}\, 1$ ______

(f) $\cos\,(\text{Arctan}\, 1)$ ______

(g) $\cos\left(2\, \text{Arcsin} \frac{4}{5}\right)$ ______
Hint: Use $\cos 2x$.

(h) $\sin\left(2\,\text{Cos}^{-1}\frac{5}{13}\right)$ ______

(i) $\cos\left(\pi + \text{Arcsin}\,\frac{2}{5}\right)$ ______

Hint: Use $\cos(x + \pi)$.

(j) $\tan\left(\text{Arctan}\,\frac{2}{5} + \frac{\pi}{3}\right)$ ______

Hint: Use $\tan(x_1 + x_2)$.

3. Prove that $\sin(2\,\text{Arctan}\,x) = \dfrac{2x}{1 + x^2}$

4. Express $\tan(2\,\text{Arctan}\,x)$ as an algebraic function of x. ______

5. Express $\cos\left(\frac{1}{2}\,\text{Arcsin}\,x\right)$ as an algebraic function of x. ______

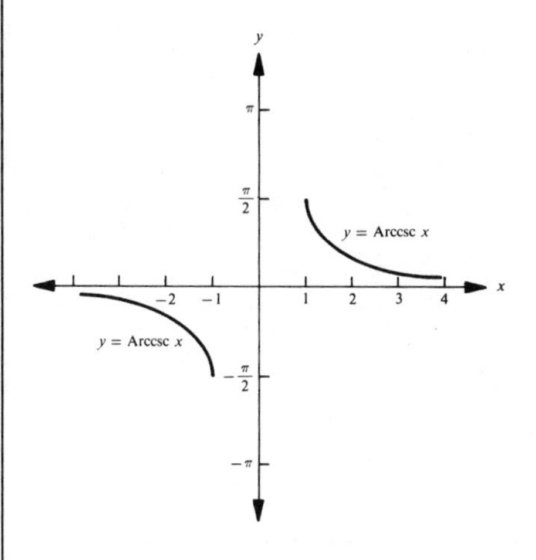

$\dfrac{\sin y}{x}$

$\dfrac{\sin^2 y}{x^2} + \sin^2 y = 1$

$\dfrac{1 + x^2}{x^2}$

$\dfrac{x}{\sqrt{1 + x^2}}$

$\left\{x{:}x = \frac{\pi}{6} + 2k\pi \text{ or } \frac{5\pi}{6} + 2k\pi \text{ for some } k\epsilon J\right\}$

$\frac{\pi}{2} + k\pi$ for some $k\epsilon J$

πk for some $k\epsilon J$

$\frac{\pi}{4} + \frac{k\pi}{2}$ for some $k\epsilon J$

$2 \tan^2 x - 1 = 0$

$|\tan x| = \frac{\sqrt{2}}{2}$ or $\tan x = \frac{\pm\sqrt{2}}{2}$

4.3. CONDITIONAL EQUATIONS AND CIRCULAR FUNCTIONS

We have already solved simple open sentences involving circular functions such as the following.

Example 1: Solve $\sin x = \frac{-\sqrt{3}}{2}$.

The solution is the set corresponding to the inverse relation defined by the expression ________________. This is equal, by the definition in section 4.2, to

$$\left\{x{:}x = \frac{4\pi}{3} + 2k\pi \text{ or } \_\_\_\_\_\_\_\_\_\_ \text{ for some } k\epsilon J\right\}.$$

Each result should be checked in the original equation.

Example 2: Solve $\sin x + \cos x = 1$.

This open sentence is most easily solved by an appropriate substitution. The best substitution is the one that transforms the equation to one involving only $\sin x$ or only $\cos x$.

Solution:

Subtracting $\cos x$ from both members, we have

$$\sin x = \_\_\_\_\_\_\_\_\_\_ .$$

Squaring this, we have

________________________ .

Replacing $\sin^2 x$ with its equal $(1 - \cos^2 x)$ and simplifying, we have

________________________ .

This factors into

$$0 = \cos x\,(1 - \cos x)$$

so that $\cos x = 0$ or $1 - \cos x = 0$. If $\cos x = 0$,

$x\epsilon\{x{:}x =$ ____________________ $\}$.

If $1 - \cos x = 0$, $\cos x = 1$ and

$x\epsilon\{x{:}x =$ ____________________ $\}$.

These are possible solution sets. Performing a check with the original equation, we find that $x\epsilon\{x{:}x =$ ____________________ $\}$ fails to check because, for $k\epsilon J$,

$$\sin\left(\frac{3\pi}{2} + 2k\pi\right) + \cos\left(\frac{3\pi}{2} + 2k\pi\right) = \underline{\qquad} \neq 1.$$

Therefore the solution set is

$$\underline{\qquad\qquad\qquad\qquad}.$$

Example 3:

Solve

$$3 \tan (2x + 1) = \sqrt{3}.$$

Solution:

Set

$$y = 2x + 1.$$

Then

$$3 \tan y = \sqrt{3},$$

$$\tan y = \frac{\sqrt{3}}{3}.$$

Hence

$$y = 2x + 1 = \frac{\pi}{6} + k\pi \text{ for some } k \epsilon J.$$

$$\therefore x = \underline{\qquad\qquad\qquad}$$

Example 4:

Solve $||4 \cos^2 x - 4 \sin x - 1 = 0.||$

Solution:

Substituting ________ for $\cos^2 x$ so that the equation involves only $\sin x$ yields

$$\underline{\qquad\qquad\qquad\qquad}.$$

Factoring,

$$\underline{\qquad\qquad\qquad\qquad}.$$

Thus $2 \sin x - 1 = 0$ or $2 \sin x + 3 = 0$.

From these equations we obtain $\sin x = \frac{1}{2}$ or $\sin x = \frac{-3}{2}$. Remember that the minimum value of $\sin x$ is ________; therefore $\sin x = \frac{-3}{2}$ must be discarded. Find $\arcsin \frac{1}{2}$.

$$\arcsin \frac{1}{2} = \left\{x : x = \frac{\pi}{6} + 2k\pi \text{ or } \underline{\qquad\qquad}\right\}.$$

ANSWERS TO PAGE 209

(h) $\frac{120}{169}$

(i) $\frac{-\sqrt{21}}{5}$

(j) $\frac{40 + 29\sqrt{3}}{13}$

(3) See Appendix

(4) $\frac{2x}{1 - x^2}$

(5) $\sqrt{\frac{1 + \sqrt{1 - x^2}}{2}}$

Checking in the original equation we have both

$$4\left(\frac{\sqrt{3}}{2}\right)^2 - 4\left(\frac{1}{2}\right) - 1 = 0$$

and

$$4\left(\frac{-\sqrt{3}}{2}\right)^2 - 4\left(\frac{1}{2}\right) - 1 = 0.$$

Thus the solution set is ____________________________.

Example 5:

Solve $\tan(2x) - 2 \cot x = 0.$

Solution:

Substituting identities for $\tan 2x$ and $\cot x$ in the original equation, we have

$$\frac{2 \tan x}{1 - \tan^2 x} - \frac{2}{\tan x} = 0.$$

Caution:

This substitution results in an equivalent equation only for those values of x for which the members of the substituted identities are defined.

Thus, values of x for which $\tan x$ is undefined, $\tan x = 0$, and $\tan^2 x = 1$ must be given individual consideration.

(1) When $\tan x$ is undefined, $x \epsilon \{x : x =$ ____________________ $\}$.

(2) When $\tan x = 0$, $x \epsilon \{x : x =$ ____________________ $\}$.

(3) When $\tan^2 x = 1$, $x \epsilon \{x : x =$ ____________________ $\}$.

Of these sets, $\left\{ x : x = \frac{\pi}{2} + k\pi, k \epsilon J \right\}$ satisfies the original equation.

Multiplying $\frac{2 \tan x}{1 - \tan^2 x} - \frac{2}{\tan x} = 0$ by $\tan x(1 - \tan^2 x)$ and simplifying gives us

____________________________.

Solving for $\tan x$

____________________________.

This is satisfied for $x \epsilon \arctan\left(\frac{\pm\sqrt{2}}{2}\right)$. Since we do not now have any simpler way of naming the members in the set $\arctan\left(\frac{\pm\sqrt{2}}{2}\right)$, we will not attempt a different description of this set. Later on, you will learn ways to obtain decimal approximations of the numbers in this set by using tables of trigonometric functions. The original equation is also satisfied by $\arctan\left(\frac{\pm\sqrt{2}}{2}\right)$. Therefore the solution set is $\arctan\left(\frac{\pm\sqrt{2}}{2}\right) \cup \{x:x =$ ________________ $\}$.

Example 6:

Solve $||\text{Arctan } 2x + 3x = \frac{\pi}{4}.||$

Before you begin the solution, note that Arctan $2x$ and Arctan $3x$ are both __________ (positive/negative) when $x > 0$ and both __________ when $x < 0$. Since their sum is $\frac{\pi}{4}$, x must be __________ (positive/negative).

Solution:

Let Arctan $2x = y_1$, then $\tan y_1 =$ ____, and let Arctan $3x = y_2$, then $\tan y_2 =$ ____. Substituting for Arctan, $y_1 + y_2 = \frac{\pi}{4}$, and hence

$$\tan(y_1 + y_2) = \tan\frac{\pi}{4}.$$

Thus,
$$\frac{\tan y_1 + \tan y_2}{1 - \tan y_1 \tan y_2} = \tan\frac{\pi}{4}.$$

Substituting for $\tan y_1$ and $\tan y_z$ gives

$$\frac{2x + 3x}{1 - 2x(3x)} = 1.$$

Simplifying, we have ________________ $= 0$. Solving this by factoring gives $x\epsilon\{$______$\}$. Since we desire $x > 0$, the solution set for Arctan $2x$ + Arctan $3x = \frac{\pi}{4}$ is $\left\{\frac{1}{6}\right\}$.

ANSWERS TO PAGE 211

-1

$\left\{x:x = 2k\pi \text{ or } \frac{\pi}{2} + 2k\pi \text{ for some } k\epsilon J\right\}$

$-\frac{1}{2} + \frac{\pi}{12} + \frac{k\pi}{2}$ for some $k\epsilon J$

$1 - \sin^2 x$

$4\sin^2 x + 4\sin x - 3 = 0$

$(2\sin x - 1)(2\sin x + 3) = 0$

-1

$\frac{5\pi}{6} + 2k\pi$ for some $k\epsilon J$

ANSWERS TO PAGE 216

(18) $\left\{x:x = \frac{\pi}{2} + k\pi \text{ for some } k\epsilon J\right\}$

(19) $\left\{\pm\frac{\pi}{2}, \pm\frac{\pi}{6}, \pm\frac{\pi}{3}\right\}$

(20) no real solution

(21) $\left\{x:x = \frac{11\pi}{12} + k\pi \text{ for some } k\epsilon J\right\}$

(22) $\left\{\frac{\sqrt{5}}{3}\right\}$

(23) $\{13\}$

(24) $\left\{\frac{\sqrt{3}}{2}\right\}$

(25) $\{1\}$

Checking our result is difficult since we don't, as yet, have values for Arctan $\frac{1}{3}$ and Arctan $\frac{1}{2}$. A quick check for reasonableness can be made by referring to this graph of Arctan.

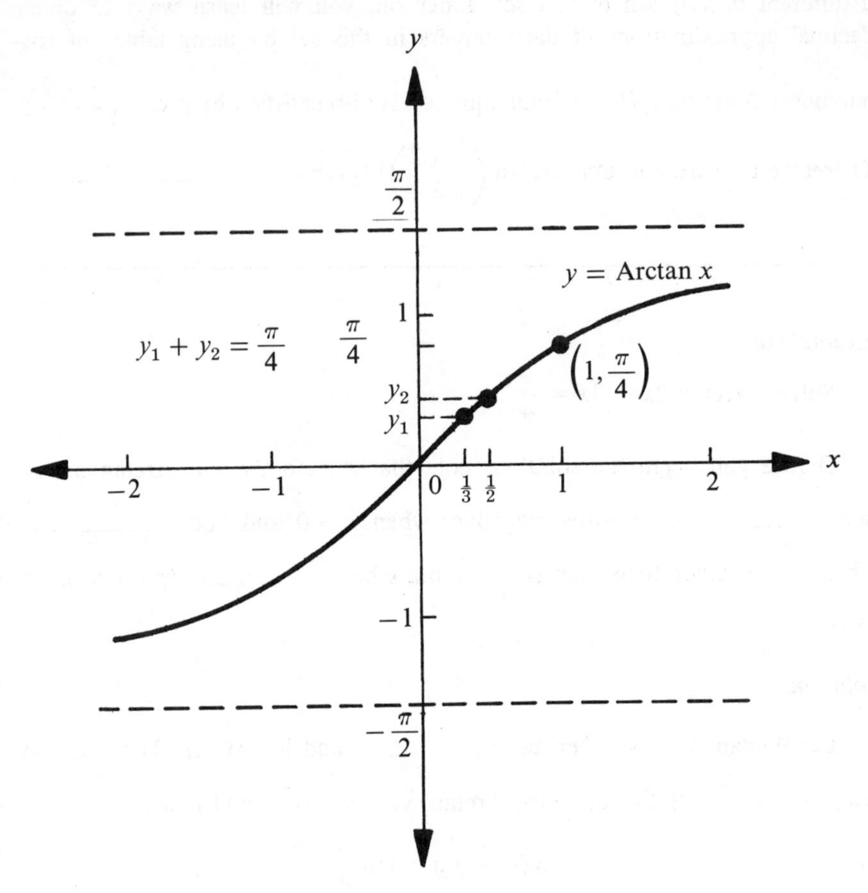

MOVE TO NEXT FRAME

EXERCISES. 4.3

Find the solution sets for each of the following:

1. $\sin x = -\dfrac{1}{2}$ and $0 \leq x < 2\pi$. ____________

2. $3 \tan x - \sqrt{3} = 0$. ____________

3. $\text{Arccos } x = \dfrac{\pi}{6}$. ____________

4. $4 \text{ Arccos } x = 3\pi$. ____________

5. $\text{Arctan } x = \dfrac{-\pi}{6}$. ____________

6. $\arctan \sqrt{3} = y$ and $\dfrac{7\pi}{2} < y < \dfrac{9\pi}{2}$. ____________

7. $2 \arcsin 2x = 3\pi$. ____________

8. $\arccos \dfrac{-\sqrt{3}}{2} = y$. ____________

9. $\sin^2 x = \dfrac{1}{2}$. ____________

10. $\text{Sin } 2x - \cos x = 0$ and $0 \leq x < 2\pi$. ____________

11. $4 \cos 2x + 3 \cos x = 1$. ____________

12. $\sin 2x + \sin x = 0$ and $\pi \leq x < 2\pi$. ____________

13. $\sin^2 x + 2 \sin x = 0$. ____________

14. $4 \tan x + \sin 2x = 0$. ____________

15. $\cos 2x - 1 = \sin x$ and $\dfrac{-\pi}{2} \leq x < \dfrac{\pi}{2}$. ____________

16. $9 \cos^2 x + 6 \cos x = 8$. ____________

17. $4 \sec^2 x = 5 (\tan x + 2)$. ____________

$\dfrac{\pi}{2} + k\pi$ for some $k \epsilon J$

positive negative

positive

$2x$

$3x$

$6x^2 + 5x - 1 = 0$

$\dfrac{1}{6}, -1$

ANSWERS TO PAGE 218

$\{x : x = k\pi \text{ for some } k \epsilon J\}$

(b) $\left\{x : x = (2k+1)\frac{\pi}{4} \text{ for some } k \epsilon J\right\}$

(c) $\left\{x : x = \frac{k\pi}{4} \text{ for some } k \epsilon J\right\}$

(d) $\left\{x : x = \frac{\pi}{4} + k\pi \text{ or } x = (2k+1)\frac{\pi}{2} \text{ for some } k \epsilon J\right\}$

(e) $\left\{x : x = \frac{k\pi}{2} \text{ for some } k \epsilon J\right\}$

(8) See Appendix.

(9) $-\frac{\sqrt{2}+\sqrt{6}}{4}$

(10) $\frac{1}{2}\sqrt{2+\sqrt{2}}$

(11)(a) $\frac{1}{2}\sqrt{2-\sqrt{3}}$

(b) $\frac{\sqrt{6}-\sqrt{2}}{4}$

(c) $\left(\frac{1}{2}\sqrt{2-\sqrt{3}}\right)^2 = \frac{2-\sqrt{3}}{4}$

and $\left(\frac{\sqrt{6}-\sqrt{2}}{4}\right)^2 = \frac{2-\sqrt{3}}{4}$

(12)(a) $\frac{\sqrt{2}}{10}$ (b) $\frac{-7\sqrt{2}}{10}$

(c) $\frac{-336}{625}$ (d) $\frac{527}{625}$

(e) $\frac{-1}{7}$ (f) $\frac{-336}{527}$

18. $\sin^4 x - 1 = 0.$ __________

19. $\cos 5x + \cos 3x + \cos x = 0$ and $\frac{-\pi}{2} \leq x \leq \frac{\pi}{2}.$ __________

20. $\sec x + 3 \cos x = 1.$ __________

21. $\sin\left(x + \frac{\pi}{3}\right) = \cos\left(x + \frac{\pi}{3}\right).$ __________

22. $\tan(\text{Arcsin}\sqrt{1-x^2}) - \sin(\text{Arctan } 2) = 0.$ __________

23. $\text{Arcsin}\frac{5}{x} + \text{Arcsin}\frac{12}{x} = \frac{\pi}{2}$ __________

24. $\text{Arcsin } x - 2 \text{ Arccos } x = 0.$ __________

25. $\text{Arctan } 3x - \frac{3\pi}{4} = \text{Arctan } 2x.$ __________

CHAPTER 4 REVIEW EXERCISES

1. Show by counterexample that

$$\sin(x_1 + x_2) = \sin x_1 + \sin x_2$$

is false. (4.1)

____

____

____

2. Write an identity for $\cos(x_1 + x_2)$.

____

In the proof of this identity, the identity $\cos(-x) =$ ______ and the identity $\sin(-x) =$ ______ were used. (4.1)

3. In the proof of the identity for $\cos(x_1 - x_2)$, $(x_1 - x_2)$ was written as ______________ and the identity for ______________ was used.

4. Prove each of the following identities by using the appropriate sum or difference formula. (4.1)

(a) $\cos\left(\frac{3\pi}{2} - x\right) = -\sin x$ (b) $\sin(x - \pi) = -\sin x$

(c) $\tan(\pi + x) = \tan x$ (d) $\sin\left(x - \frac{3\pi}{2}\right) = \cos x$

(e) $\cos\left(x - \frac{3\pi}{2}\right) = -\sin x$ (f) $\cot\left(\frac{\pi}{4} + x\right) = \frac{\cot x - 1}{\cot x + 1}$

5. Prove that $\tan\frac{x}{2} = \frac{\sin x}{1 + \cos x} = \frac{1 - \cos x}{\sin x}$ is an identity.

6. Prove that $\frac{\cos x}{1 + \sin x} = \sec x - \tan x$ is an identity.

7. State the set of excluded values (values of x for which the statement is undefined) for each of the following:

(a) $$\frac{\sin x}{1 + \cos x} = \frac{1 - \cos x}{\sin x}$$

This statement is undefined for $\sin x = 0$ and ________ $= 0$. Sin $x = 0$ when $x \epsilon \{x : x = k\pi \text{ for some } k \epsilon J\}$ and $1 + \cos x$ is zero when $x \epsilon \{x : x =$ ______________________$\}$. The union of these

(1) $\left\{\frac{7\pi}{6}, \frac{11\pi}{6}\right\}$

(2) $\left\{x : x = \frac{\pi}{6} + k\pi \text{ for some } k\epsilon J\right\}$

(3) $\left\{\frac{\sqrt{3}}{2}\right\}$

(4) $\left\{\frac{-\sqrt{2}}{2}\right\}$

(5) $\left\{\frac{-\sqrt{3}}{3}\right\}$

(6) $\left\{\frac{13\pi}{3}\right\}$

(7) $\left\{-\frac{1}{2}\right\}$

(8) $\left\{y : y = \frac{5\pi}{6} + 2k\pi \text{ or } y = \frac{7\pi}{6} + 2k\pi \text{ for some } k\epsilon J\right\}$

(9) $\left\{x : x = \frac{\pi}{4} + \frac{k\pi}{2} \text{ for some } k\epsilon J\right\}$

(10) $\left\{\frac{\pi}{6}, \frac{\pi}{2}, \frac{5\pi}{6}\right\}$

(11) $\left\{x : x \epsilon \arccos\frac{5}{8} \text{ or } x = (2k + 1)\pi \text{ for some } k\epsilon J\right\}$

(12) $\left\{\pi, \frac{4\pi}{3}\right\}$

(13) $\{x : x = k\pi \text{ for some } k\epsilon J\}$

(14) $\{x : x = k\pi \text{ for some } k\epsilon J\}$

(15) $\left\{\frac{-\pi}{6}\right\}$

(16) $\arccos\frac{2}{3}$

(17) $\arctan\frac{-3}{4}$ or $\arctan 2$

ANSWERS TO PAGE 220

(e) $\frac{-2\sqrt{5}}{5}$

(f) $\frac{\sqrt{3}}{2}$

(18) (a) $x = \arcsin \frac{y}{2}$

(b) $x = \text{Arccos}\, \frac{y}{2}$

(c) $x = 2\, \text{Tan}\, y$

(d) $x = \frac{1}{2} \sin (2y - \pi)$ or

$x = -\frac{1}{2} \sin 2y$

(19) See Appendix.

(20) (a) $\{x : x = \frac{\pi}{2} + k\pi,$

$x = \frac{2\pi}{3} + 2k\pi$, or

$x = \frac{4\pi}{3} + 2k\pi$

for some $k \epsilon J\}$

(b) $\{y : y = \frac{\pi}{2} + 2k\pi$ for some $k \epsilon J\}$

(c) $\{x : x = \frac{\pi}{3} + 2k\pi$ or

$x = -\frac{\pi}{3} + 2k\pi$ for some $k \epsilon J\}$

(d) $\{y : y = \frac{\pi}{3} + k\pi$ or $y =$

$-\frac{\pi}{3} + k\pi$ for some $k \epsilon J\}$

(e) $\{x : x = \frac{\pi}{4} + 2k\pi$ or $y =$

$\frac{5\pi}{4} + 2k\pi$ or $x = \frac{k\pi}{2}$

for some $k \epsilon J\}$

two sets, namely ______________________, constitutes the excluded values of x.

(b) $\tan 2x = \frac{\sin 2x}{\cos 2x}$ ______________________

(c) $\frac{2 \tan x}{1 - \tan^2 x} = \frac{2}{\cot x - \tan x}$ ______________________

(d) $\frac{1}{1 - \tan x} = \frac{\cos x}{\cos x - \sin x}$ ______________________

(e) $\sqrt{\frac{\sec^2 x - 1}{1 - \sin^2 x}} = \frac{\sec x}{\cot x}$ ______________________

8. Prove that $\cos x + 1 = 2 \cos^2 \frac{x}{2}$ for all $x \epsilon \mathcal{R}$. (4.1)

9. Use the fact that $\frac{\pi}{4} + \frac{5\pi}{6} = \frac{13\pi}{12}$ to find $\cos \frac{13\pi}{12}$. (4.1) ____________

10. Use the formula for $\sin \frac{x}{2}$ to find the value of $\sin \frac{5\pi}{8}$. (4.1) ____________

11. (a) Find $\cos \frac{19\pi}{12}$ by using the half-number formula for $\left|\cos \frac{1}{2} x\right|$. (4.1)

____

(b) Find $\cos \frac{19\pi}{12}$ by using the formula for $\cos (x_1 + x_2)$ and the fact that $\frac{\pi}{3} + \frac{5\pi}{4} = \frac{19\pi}{12}$. (4.1) ______________________

(c) Show that the results in (a) and (b) are equal. (4.1) ____________

______________________.

12. If $\cos x = \frac{24}{25}$ and $\frac{3\pi}{2} < x < 2\pi$, find the following: (4.1)

(a) $\sin \frac{1}{2} x =$ ____________ (b) $\cos \frac{1}{2} x =$ ____________

(c) $\sin 2x =$ ____________ (d) $\cos 2x =$ ____________

(e) $\tan \frac{1}{2} x =$ ____________ (f) $\tan 2x =$ ____________

13. Prove the following identities, known as **product formulas**. (4.1)

(a) $\sin x_1 \cos x_2 = \frac{1}{2}[\sin(x_1 + x_2) + \sin(x_1 - x_2)]$

(b) $\cos x_1 \cos x_2 = \frac{1}{2}[\cos(x_1 + x_2) + \cos(x_1 - x_2)]$

(c) $\sin x_1 \sin x_2 = \frac{1}{2}[\cos(x_1 - x_2) - \cos(x_1 + x_2)]$

14. Using the appropriate formula developed in problem 13 above, find the value of $\cos \frac{5\pi}{12} \cos \frac{\pi}{12}$. (4.1) ______

15. Write $\sin x - \sin 3x$ as a product. (4.1) ______

16. Find the solution sets for each of the following: (4.2)

(a) $\tan \frac{5\pi}{6} = y$ ______

(b) $\arcsin\left(\frac{-\sqrt{3}}{2}\right) = y$ ______

(c) $\text{Arccos} \frac{1}{2} = y$ ______

(d) $\cot x = \sqrt{3}$ ______

(e) $y = \text{Sin}^{-1}\left(\frac{\sqrt{2}}{2}\right)$ ______

(f) $\text{Arctan} \frac{-\sqrt{3}}{3} = y$ ______

(g) $\text{Arctan} \sqrt{3} + \text{Arccot} \sqrt{3} = y$ ______

(h) $\text{Arcsin} \frac{\sqrt{3}}{2} + \text{Arccos} \frac{\sqrt{3}}{2} = y$ ______

17. Evaluate each of the following: (4.2)

(a) $\sin(\text{Arcsin}(-1))$ ______

(b) $\sin\left(\text{Arccsc} \frac{5}{4}\right)$ ______

(c) $\tan\left(\text{Arccos} \frac{-5}{13}\right)$ ______

(d) $\tan\left(\arcsin \frac{2}{3}\right)$ ______

(1) Choose an x_1 and x_2 such as $x_1 = \frac{\pi}{2}$ and $x_2 = \frac{\pi}{4}$. Then $\sin\left(\frac{\pi}{2} + \frac{\pi}{4} = \sin\right.$ $\left.\frac{3\pi}{4} = \frac{\sqrt{2}}{2} \neq \sin \frac{\pi}{2} + \sin \frac{\pi}{4}\right)$ $= \frac{2 + \sqrt{2}}{2}$.

(2) $\cos x_1 \cos x_2 - \sin x_1 \sin x_2$

$\cos x$

$-\sin x$

(3) $[x_1 + (-x_2)]$ $\cos(x_1 + x_2)$

(4) See Appendix.

(5) See Appendix.

(6) See Appendix.

(7)(a) $1 + \cos x$

$(2k + 1)\pi$ for some $k \epsilon J$

ANSWERS TO PAGE 222

rays

$\angle SPQ$ $\angle SPR$ $\angle RPQ$

counterclockwise

(e) $\cot\left(\text{Arccos} -\frac{2}{3}\right)$ ______

(f) $\sin\left(2 \text{ Arctan} \frac{\sqrt{3}}{3}\right)$ ______

18. Solve the following for x in terms of y. (4.2)

(a) $y = 2 \sin x$ ______

(b) $y = 2 \text{ Cos } x$ ______

(c) $y = \text{Arctan} \frac{x}{2}$ ______

(d) $2y - \pi = \arcsin 2x$ ______

19. Prove that $\cos(2 \text{ Arctan } x) = \frac{1 - x^2}{1 + x^2}$.

20. Find the solution sets for each of the following: (4.3)

(a) $2 \cos^2 x + \cos x = 0$ ______

(b) $2 \sin y + \cos^2 y = 2$ ______

(c) $3 \cot x = 2 \sin x$ ______

(d) $4 \tan^2 y = 3 \sec^2 y$ ______

(e) $\sin 3x = \sin x (2 \sin 2x - 1)$ ______

CHAPTER 5

Trigonometry I

5.1. ANGLES AND THEIR MEASURE

This sketch represents a **ray**.

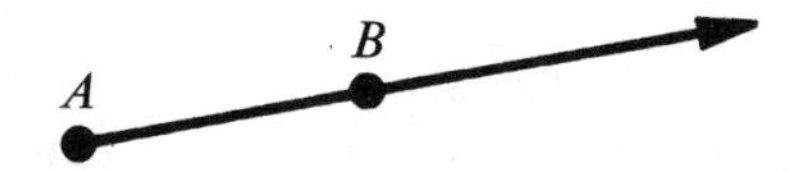

The ray containing point B and having endpoint A is denoted as $\overrightarrow{AB}$ with a double-barbed arrow. $\overrightarrow{AB}$ with a single-barbed arrow denotes the geometric vector or displacement with initial point A and terminal point B. Thus

$\overrightarrow{AB}$ ______ $\overrightarrow{AB}$.
$=$ $\neq$

In geometry the ray $\overrightarrow{AB}$ is defined to be the union of segment $\overline{AB}$ and the set of all points X on line $\overleftrightarrow{AB}$ such that B is between A and X, as illustrated.

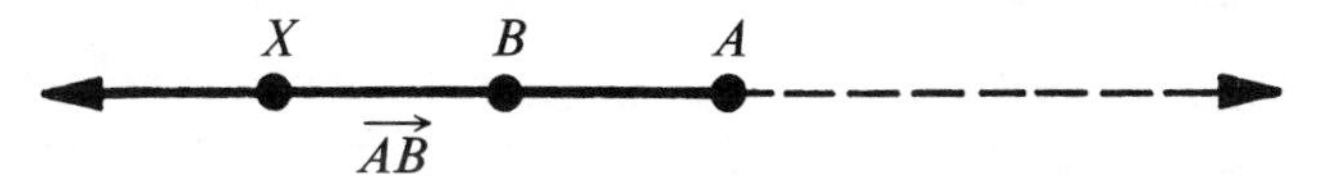

MOVE TO NEXT FRAME

Name or denote each of the following illustrated rays.

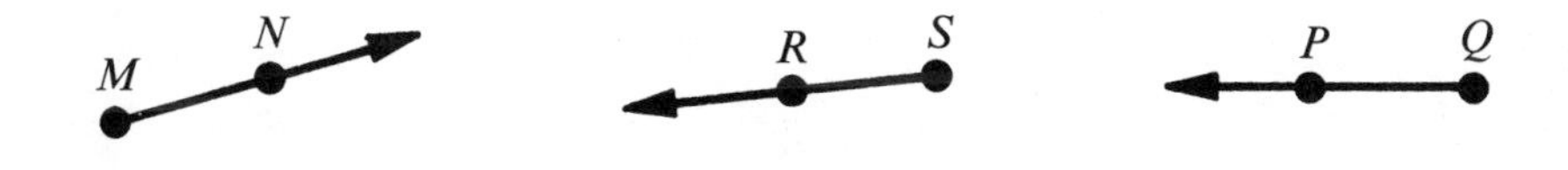

An **angle** is defined to be the union of two rays having a common endpoint.

MOVE TO NEXT FRAME

ANSWERS TO PAGE 219

(13) See Appendix.

(14) Use 13 (b); $\frac{1}{4}$

(15) $-2 \cos 2x \sin x$

(16)(a) $\left\{\frac{\sqrt{3}}{3}\right\}$

(b) $\left\{y : y = \frac{4\pi}{3} + 2k\pi \text{ or } y = \frac{5\pi}{3} + 2k\pi \text{ for some } k \in J\right\}$

(c) $\left\{\frac{\pi}{3}\right\}$

(d) $\left\{x : x = \frac{\pi}{6} + k\pi \text{ for some } k \in J\right\}$

(e) $\left\{\frac{\pi}{4}\right\}$

(f) $\left\{\frac{-\pi}{6}\right\}$

(g) $\left\{\frac{\pi}{2}\right\}$

(h) $\left\{\frac{\pi}{2}\right\}$

(17)(a) -1

(b) $\frac{4}{5}$

(c) $\frac{-12}{5}$

(d) $\frac{2\sqrt{5}}{5}$ or $\frac{-2\sqrt{5}}{5}$

ANSWERS TO PAGE 224

This sketch represents an angle. The **vertex** is point A and the sides are the two ____ denoted by $\overrightarrow{AC}$ and $\overrightarrow{AB}$. The angle is denoted $\angle BAC$ or $\angle CAB$ (with the second letter corresponding to the vertex) or $\angle A$ or $\angle \alpha$, whichever is convenient.

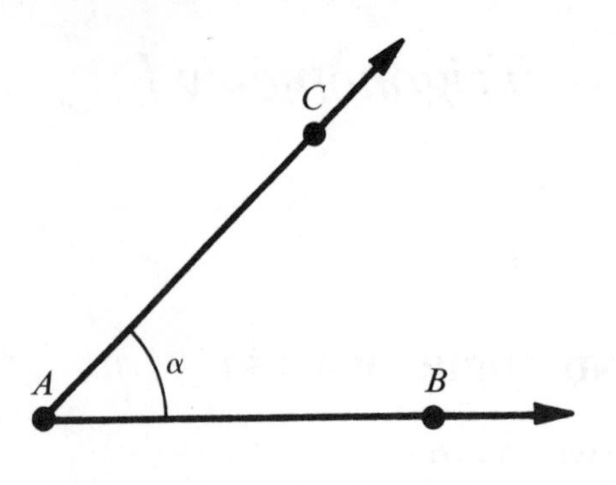

In the event two angles are **adjacent**, that is, they have a common vertex and a common side, the three-letter designation must be used.

Thus the three angles illustrated are denoted ____, ____ and ____.

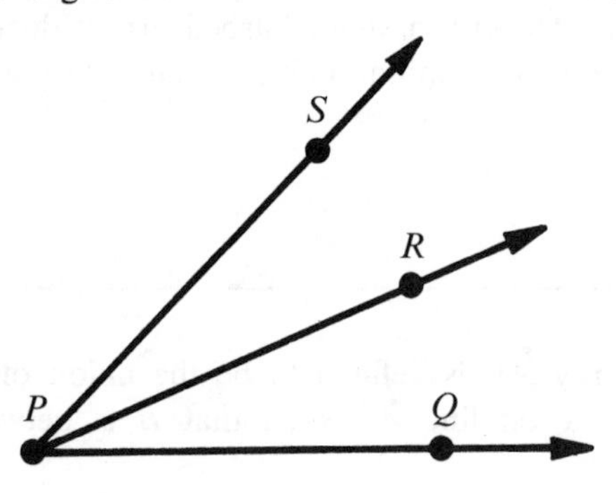

One of the two sides of an angle is called the **initial side** and the other side is called the **terminal side**. Think of the terminal side as the result of a rotation of the initial side about its endpoint, and we will say the angle is formed by this rotation.

In the illustration of an angle, an arrow is used to indicate the direction of rotation. $\angle BAC$ is formed by a ________________ (clockwise/counterclockwise) rotation.

$$\frac{\text{circumference}}{360} = \frac{\pi r}{180}$$

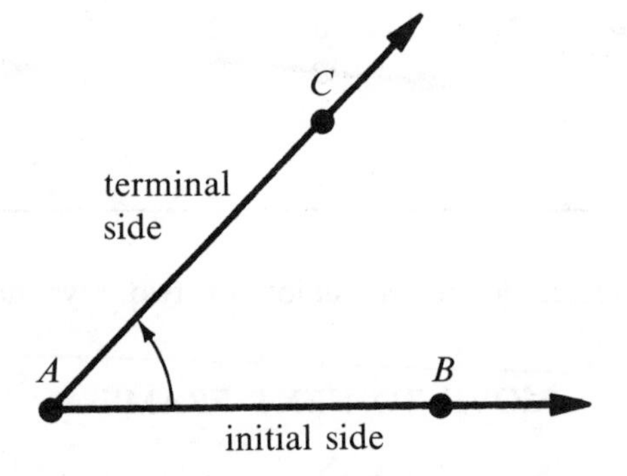

The illustration below represents an angle denoted by $\angle MST$, ______,

____, or ____. It is formed by a ________ rotation in which ____

is the initial side and ____ is the terminal side.

If no indication of rotation is shown, we will assume that the angle is formed by a counterclockwise rotation.

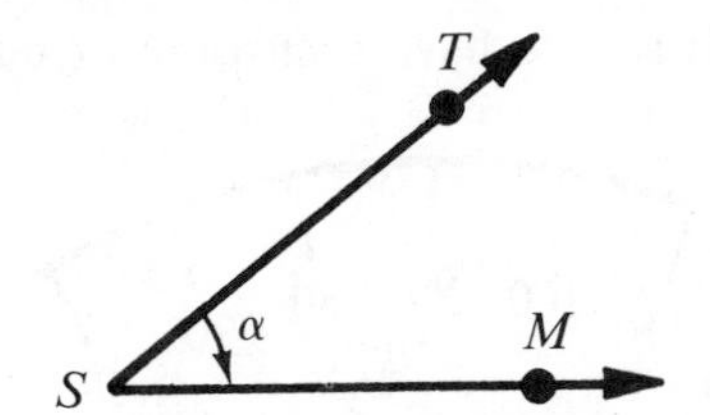

An angle is said to be in **standard position** on a coordinate system if its vertex is the origin and its initial side is that portion of the horizontal axis corresponding to $x > 0$.

Name three angles in the illustration that are in standard position.

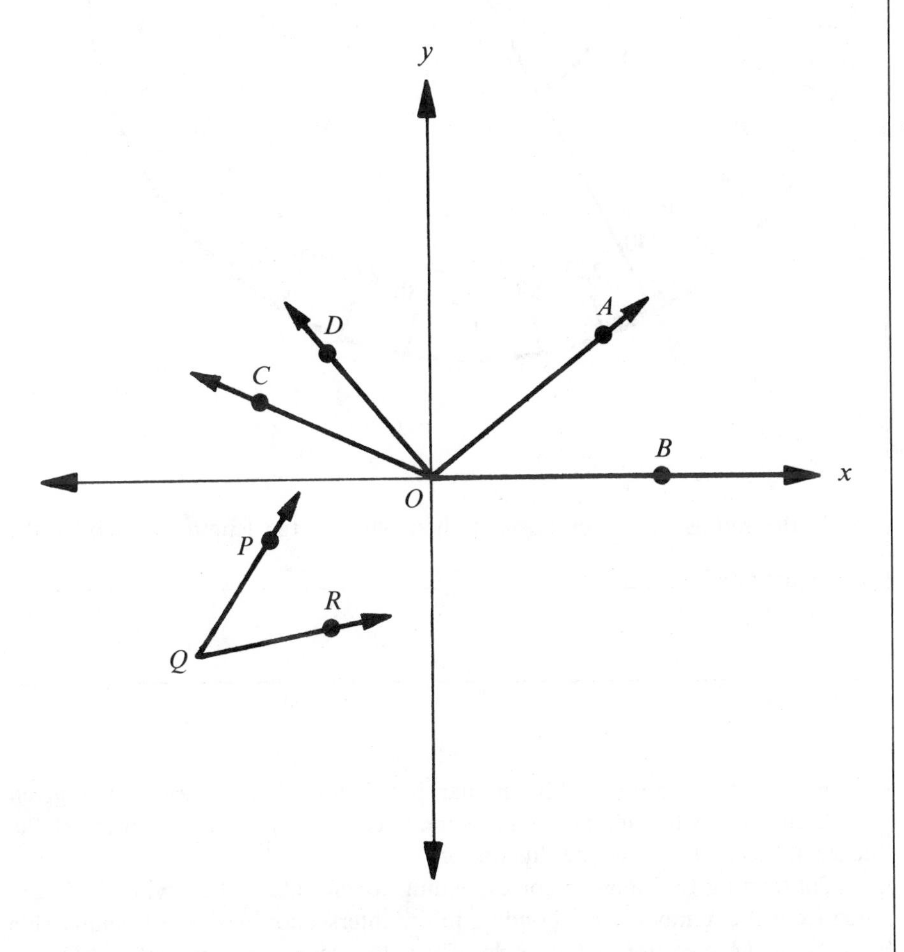

ANSWERS TO PAGE 221

$\neq$

$\overrightarrow{MN}$ $\overrightarrow{SR}$ $\overrightarrow{QP}$

ANSWERS TO PAGE 226

"thirty-six degrees, forty minutes, twenty seconds."

(a) 12070″ (b) 324000″

(a) 1°1′30″ (b) 5°3′20″

405°

A **protractor** is a device used to measure an angle. A protractor may be made out of a circle as follows:

Separate a circle into 360 equal arcs, and number the points separating these arcs from 0 to 359. If the rays of an angle whose vertex is the center of this circle contain the endpoints of an arc $\frac{1}{360}$ the circumference of the circle, then this angle is said to have a measure of **one degree**.

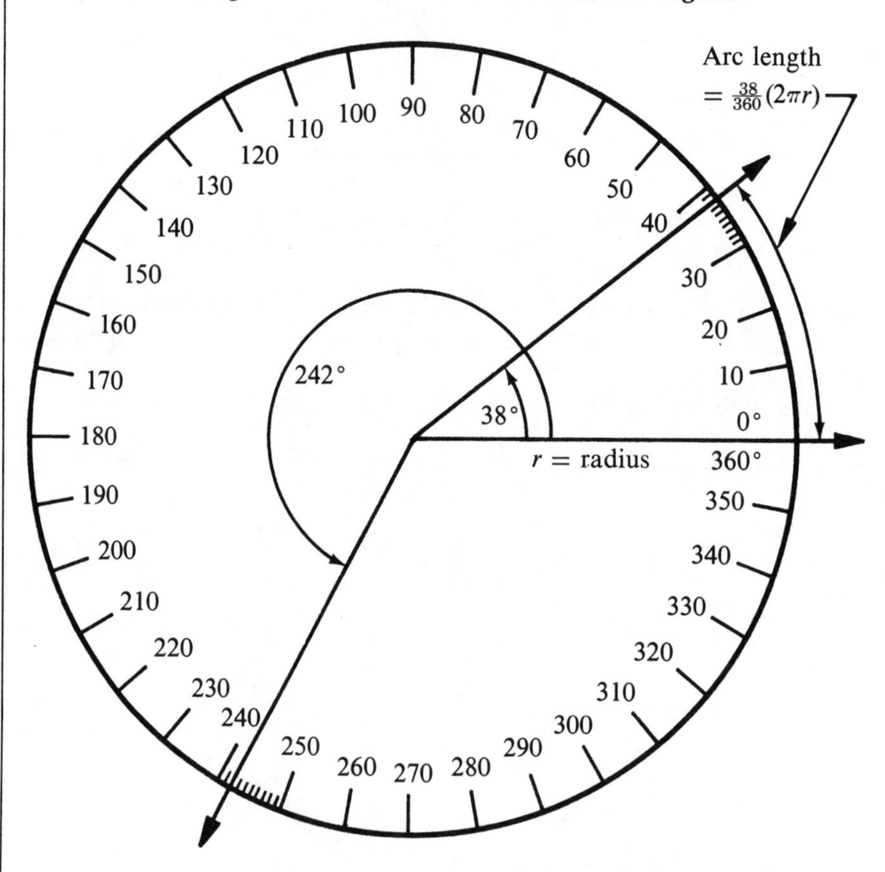

If the radius of the circle is r, then what is the length of each of the 360 equal arcs? __________

Placing the center of this circular protractor on the vertex of a given angle enables us to estimate its measure. The sides of the angle intersect the circle in two points. (See the illustration.)

Subtracting the number corresponding to the intersection with the initial side from the number corresponding to the intersection with the terminal side results in the measure of the angle. Thus, the degree measure of $\angle BOA$ in the illustration is $60° - 30° =$ ______ and the measure of $\angle COD$ is $290° - 330° =$ ______. The degree measure of $\angle ABC$ is denoted by $m° \angle ABC$.

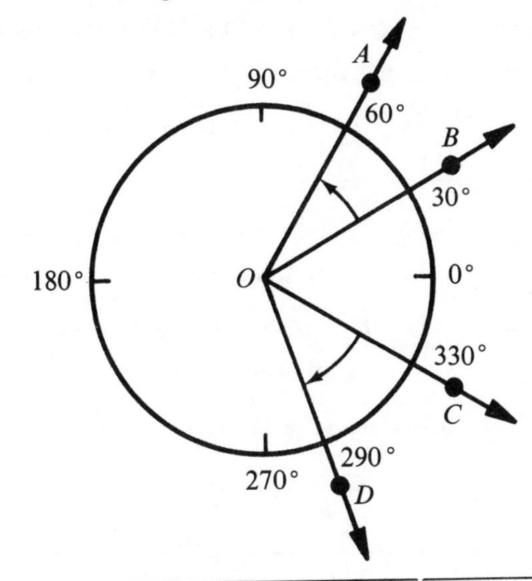

If the angle we are measuring is in standard position, we place the center of our circular protractor at the origin and the point corresponding to zero on the positive portion of the horizontal axis as illustrated.

If the angle is formed by a counterclockwise rotation, its measure may be read directly off of the protractor. If the angle is formed by a clockwise rotation, its degree measure may be found by subtraction.

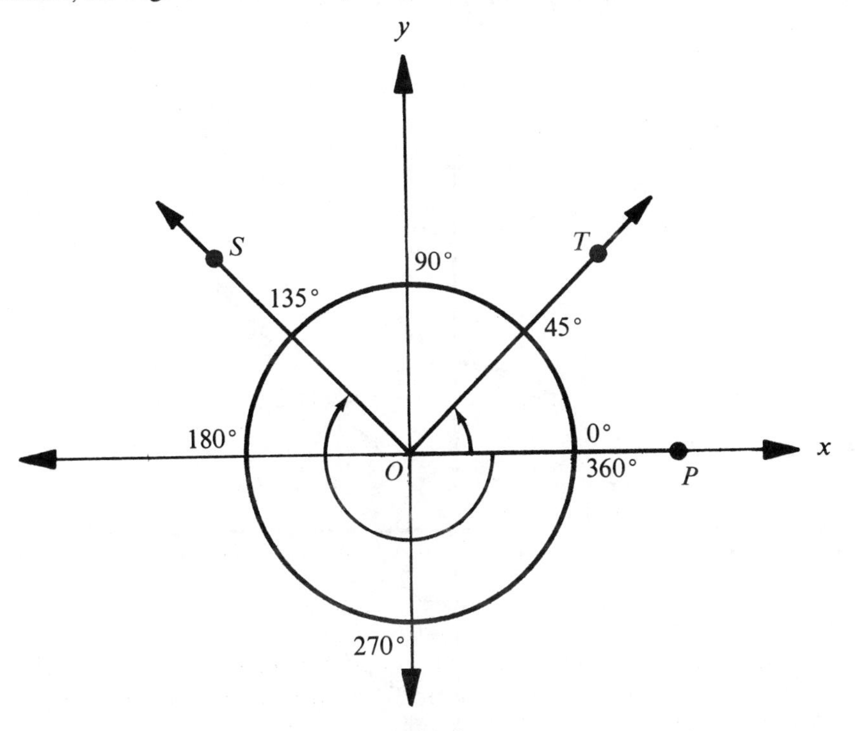

Use the illustration to find the following:

(a) $m° \angle POT =$ ______ (b) $m° \angle POS = 135° - 360° =$ ______.

ANSWERS TO PAGE 223

$\angle TSM$,

$\angle S$, or $\angle \alpha$ clockwise ST

SM

Any angle shown which has $\overrightarrow{OB}$ as its initial side such as $\angle BOD$, $\angle BOC$, or $\angle BOA$.

ANSWERS TO PAGE 228

BC $\angle\gamma$

one degree

To measure an angle with greater exactness, each of the 360 degrees is subdivided into 60 equal arcs, called **minutes**, so that $\frac{1}{60}$ of a degree is equal to one minute, $1'$. Each minute is further subdivided into 60 equal arcs, called **seconds**; $\frac{1}{60}$ of a minute is equal to one second, $1''$. Thus there are angles with measures such as $45'$, read "forty-five minutes," or $36°40'20''$, which is read ____.

What is the measure in seconds of each of the following angular measures?

(a) $3°21'10''$ ________ (b) $90°$ ________

Change each of the following to a measure in degrees, minutes, and seconds.

(a) $3690''$ ________ (b) $18200''$ ________

If the terminal side of an angle is obtained by revolving the initial side through a rotation of more than one complete revolution, then the measure of the angle will be more than $360°$. (See $\angle AOC$ in the illustration.)

To find $m° \angle AOC$, it is necessary to add $360°$ to the $45°$ read from our protractor since 1 revolution corresponds to $360°$. Thus,

$$m° \angle AOC = \_\_\_\_\_\_.$$

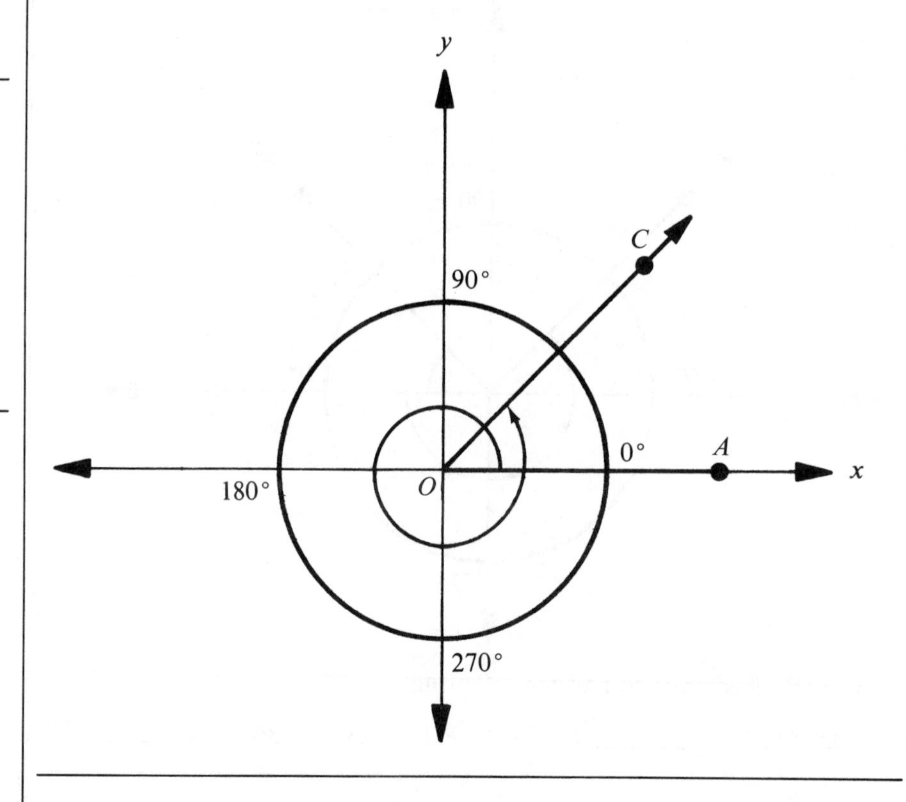

Angles formed by a clockwise rotation are treated in a similar fashion. Find the measure of the angle illustrated.

$m° \angle TOP =$ ____________________ .

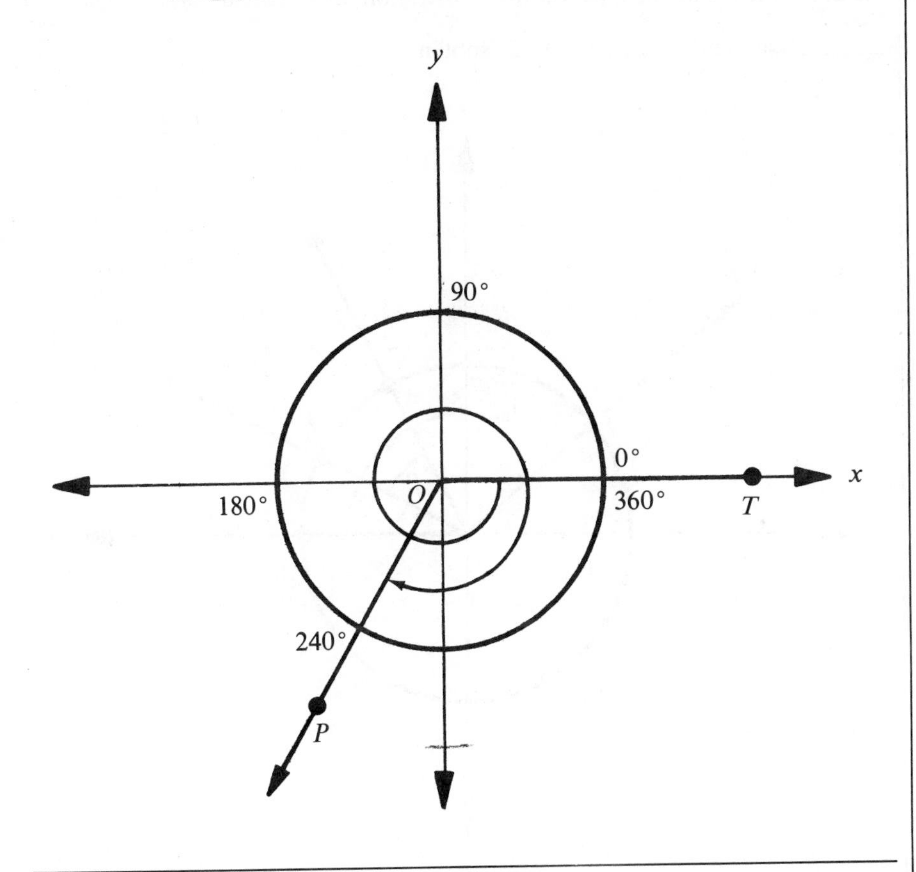

Therefore, knowing the positions of the initial and terminal sides of an angle is not sufficient information for finding the measure of an angle. It is also necessary that we know the direction of rotation and the number of revolutions made in generating the angle.

MOVE TO NEXT FRAME

ANSWERS TO PAGE 225

30°

−40°

(a) 45° (b) −225°

ANSWERS TO PAGE 230

$\pi \quad \frac{\pi}{2}$

A **central angle** of a circle is an angle whose vertex is the center of the circle. An arc of a circle is said to **subtend** a central angle if the sides of the angle contain the endpoints of the arc. A central angle is said to **intercept** an arc which subtends it. In the illustration arc $\widehat{AB}$ subtends angle $\angle\alpha$, ______ subtends $\angle\beta$, and $\widehat{ACD}$ subtends ______ .

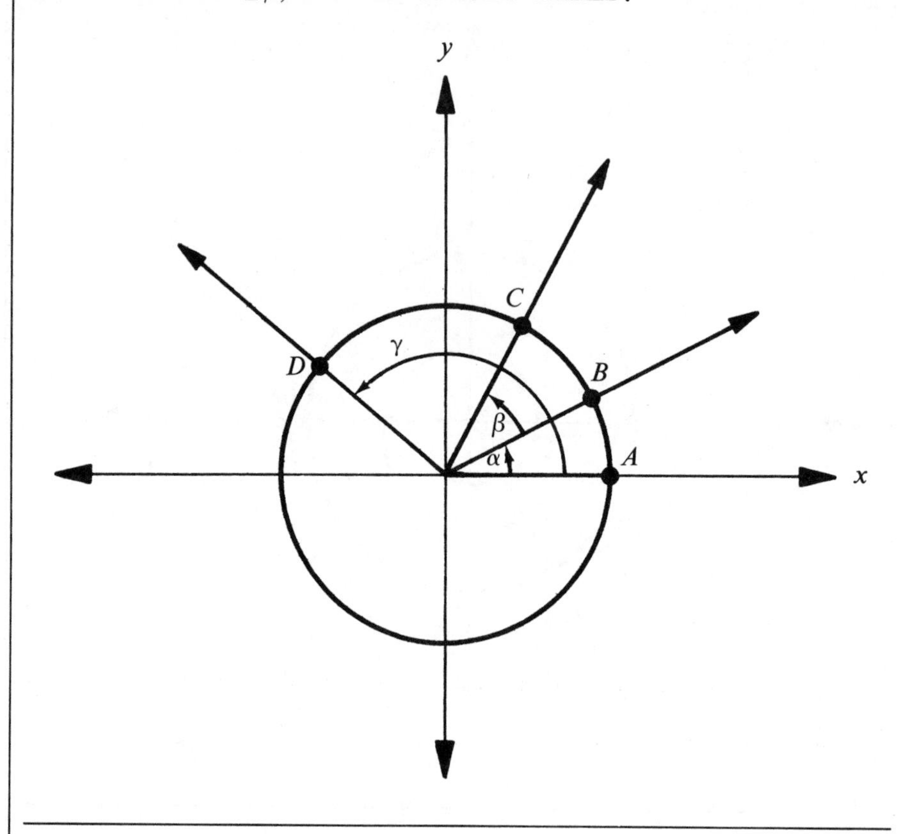

$-120°; 648°; 1530°$

To measure an angle, we have divided a circle into 360 equal arcs. Thus, if the vertex of an angle is placed at the center of a circle and this angle corresponds to a central angle subtended by an arc whose length is $\frac{1}{360}$ of the circumference of the circle, then the measure of that angle is ________ .

(a) $\frac{3\pi}{2}$ (b) $\frac{-\pi}{6}$

(c) $\frac{8\pi}{3}$ (d) $\frac{-7\pi}{12}$

If an angle $\angle \alpha$ is considered as a central angle of a circle whose radius is r and is subtended by an arc of that circle having a length r, then the angle $\angle \alpha$ is said to have one unit of **radian measure.**

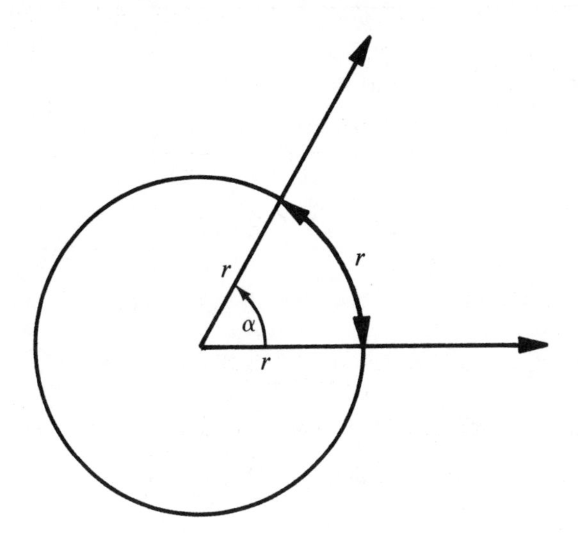

$m < \alpha = 1$ radian

$\angle \beta$ in the illustration is subtended by an arc whose length is $2r$. Therefore the radian measure of $\angle \beta$ is ______________ .

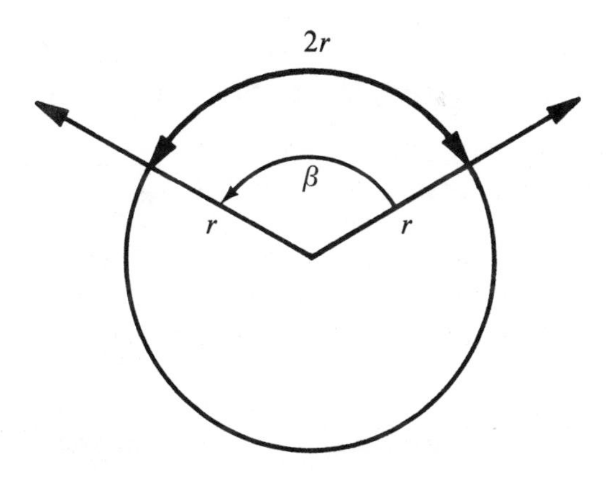

The circumference of a circle having a radius r is ________ , i.e., there are $2\pi \left(\text{approximately } 6\frac{2}{7}\right)$ radii in the circumference of a circle. Therefore, the measure of an angle formed by a rotation of one revolution is 2π radians. How many radians correspond to an angular measure of 360°? ________

ANSWERS TO PAGE 227

$-360° + -(120°) = -480°$

Thus, there are ______ (how many) radians in 180°? 90°?

Radian measure is related to degree measure by

$$1 \text{ radian} = \left(\frac{360}{2\pi}\right)^{\circ} = \left(\frac{180}{\pi}\right)^{\circ},$$

and

$$1^{\circ} = \frac{\pi}{180} \text{ radians.}$$

When working with radian measure it is customary to simply give the measure of an angle as $\frac{\pi}{2}$, rather than $\frac{\pi}{2}$ radians. If we use degree measure, however, the degree symbol will always be written, e.g., 30°, 60°.

MOVE TO NEXT FRAME

$$\frac{\frac{3\pi}{4}}{2\pi} = \frac{3}{8}$$

$\frac{3}{8}$

20π

$$\frac{3}{8}\left(20\pi\right) = \frac{15\pi}{2}$$

Examples:

(a) Change $\frac{3\pi}{2}$ to degree measure.

$$\frac{3\pi}{2}\,(2\pi r) = 270.$$

$$\frac{3\pi}{2} \text{ radians} = 270^{\circ}.$$

(b) Change each of the following to degree measure:

$\frac{-2\pi}{3}$; $\frac{18\pi}{5}$; $8\frac{1}{2}\pi$. ______

Examples:

Change the following degree measure to radian measure.

(a) 270° ______ (b) −30° ______

(c) 480° ______ (d) −105° ______

If an arc of a circle of radius r subtends a central angle of $1°$, then that arc has a length which is $\frac{1}{360}$ of the circumference of the circle or

$$\frac{1}{360}(2\pi r) = \frac{\pi r}{180}.$$

Hence, if it subtends an angle of $40°$, then its arc length s is

$s =$ ______________________.

If it subtends an angle of $m°$, then its arc length s is found as follows.

$$s = m\left(\frac{\pi r}{180}\right)$$

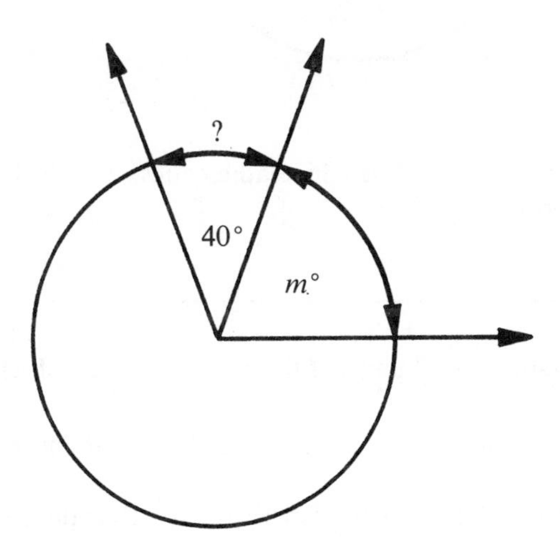

2 radians

Examples:

(a) If a 30° central angle is subtended by a circular arc of radius 6, how long is the subtending arc? ______________

(b) Find the length of the arc of a circle of radius 10 that subtends a central angle of 40°. ________

It is often more convenient to use radian measure to calculate the length of an arc of a circle of radius r.

$2\pi r$

If an arc of a circle of radius r subtends a central angle of one radian, then that arc has length ___. If it subtends an angle of m radians, its length is ______. Thus the length of any arc s subtending a central angle a

2π

is given by

$$s = (m^R \angle \alpha)r,$$

where m^R denotes the measure of the central angle $\angle \alpha$ in radians.

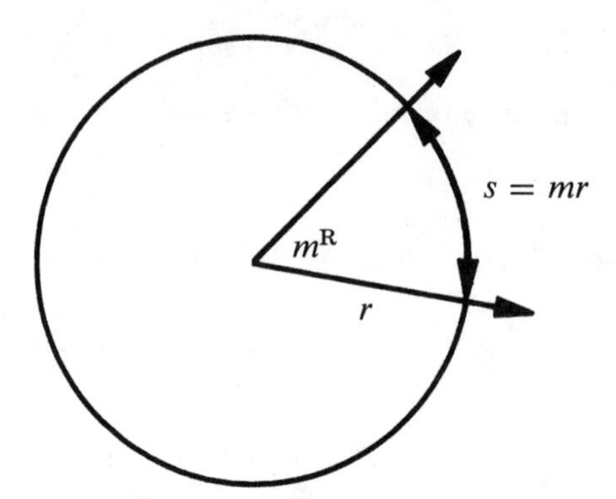

Note: Greek letters are often used in mathematics. A Greek alphabet may be found in the Appendix.

2π

$\frac{m}{2\pi}$

πr^2

A circle has a radius of 10 units. If the measure of one of its central angles is $\frac{3\pi}{4}$, then this angle is ________________ (fraction of) the measure of one complete revolution, and the length of its subtending arc is ______ (fraction of) the circumference of the circle. The circumference is ______ units in length, therefore the length of the arc is ________________ units.

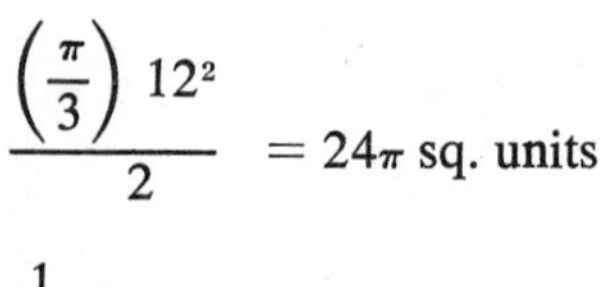

$$\frac{\left(\frac{\pi}{3}\right) 12^2}{2} = 24\pi \text{ sq. units}$$

$\frac{1}{6}$

$\frac{1}{6}$

$233\frac{1}{3}\pi$ sq. units

In general, if $\widehat{AB}$ of a circle subtends central angle α, then we have the following proportion, which relates the length of the arc to the circumference of the circle.

$$\frac{m\widehat{AB}}{\text{circumference}} = \frac{m^\circ \angle \alpha}{360} = \frac{m^R \angle \alpha}{2\pi}.$$

MOVE TO NEXT FRAME

Examples:

Find the length of the arc s that subtends a central angle α in a circle whose radius is r, if:

(a) $m^R \angle \alpha = \frac{\pi}{6}$; $r = 18$; $s =$ ____________

(b) $m^R \angle \alpha = \frac{2\pi}{3}$; $r = 21$; $s =$ ______

(c) $m^R \angle \alpha = 2\pi$; $r = 8$; $s =$ ______

$40\left(\frac{\pi r}{180}\right) = \frac{2\pi r}{9}$

Let $\widehat{AB}$ be the arc of a circle with center P and radius r. Then the **circular sector with boundary arc** $\widehat{AB}$ is the union of all segments $\overline{PX}$ where X is a point of $\widehat{AB}$. The sector whose boundary arc is $\widehat{AB}$ is denoted "sector $\widehat{AB}$": r is called its radius, and central angle $\angle BPA$ is called "the angle of sector $\widehat{AB}$."

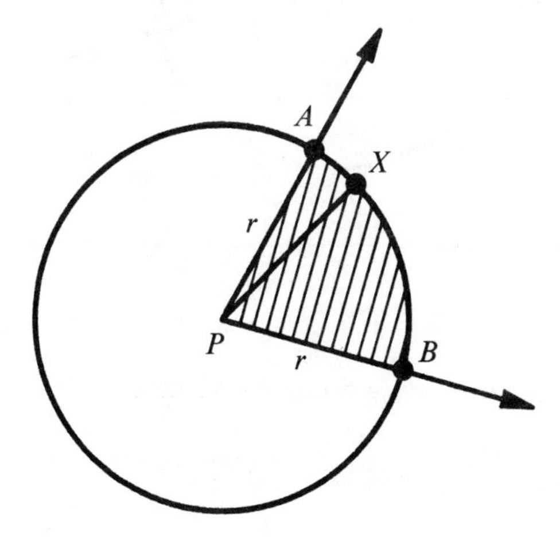

MOVE TO NEXT FRAME

$30\left(\frac{6\pi}{180}\right) = \pi$

$\frac{20\pi}{9}$

---

r

mr

(7) $\frac{4}{5}$

1

(8) $\frac{75\pi}{4}$ sq. units

(9)

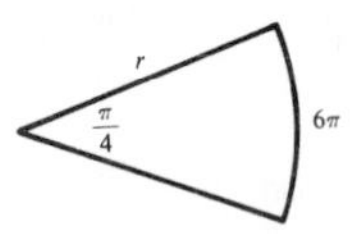

$6\pi = \frac{\pi}{4} \cdot r$

$r = 24$

$A = \frac{\pi}{4}\left(\frac{1}{2}\right) (24)^2$

$A = 72\pi$

(10)

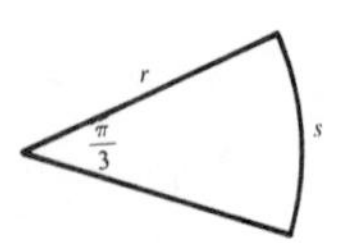

$s = r\left(\frac{\pi}{3}\right)$

$p = s + 2r$

$12 + 2\pi = \frac{\pi r}{3} + 2r$

$r = \dfrac{12 + 2\pi}{2 + \frac{\pi}{3}} = 6$

$A = 6\pi$

(11) $A = \frac{\alpha}{2}\left(\frac{p}{2 + \alpha}\right)^2$

The use of radian measure facilitates the calculation of the **area of a circular sector**. Since there are ______ radians in a circle, a sector having an angle of m radians has an area that is what fraction of that of the total circle?

____

The area of the circle itself is ______. Hence the area of the sector is

$$\frac{m}{2\pi}(\pi r^2) \quad \text{or} \quad A = \frac{m}{2}r^2 .$$

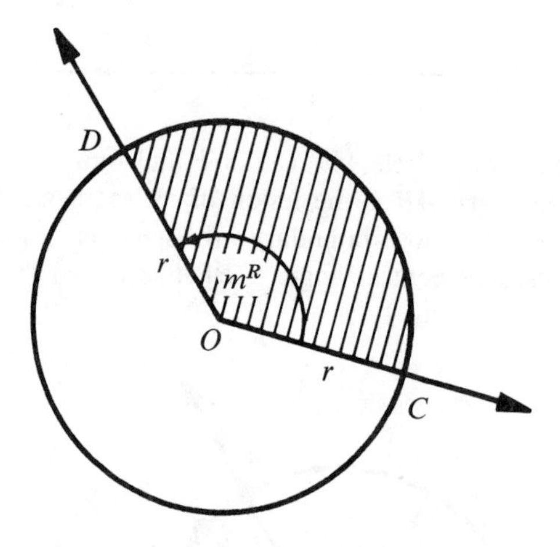

Examples:

(a) If an arc of a circle has a radius of 12 units and a central angle whose measure is $\frac{\pi}{3}$, then the area of the corresponding sector is ______________

____.

You should recognize that the measure of the central angle is __ (fraction of) the measure of one complete revolution; therefore the area of the corresponding sector is __ (fraction of) the area of the entire circle.

(b) If a circle has a radius of 20 units and a central angle has a measure of $\frac{7\pi}{6}$, then the area of the corresponding sector is ______________.

EXERCISES. 5.1

1. Change the following degree measures of angles to their corresponding radian measure.

   (a) 30° ______ (b) 210° ______ (c) 360° ______

   (d) 150° ______ (e) −135° ______ (f) −36° ______

   (g) −900° ______ (h) 30° ______ (i) 100° ______

2. Find the degree measure corresponding to each of the following radian measures.

   (a) $\frac{4\pi}{3}$ ______ (b) π ______ (c) -10π ______

   (d) $\frac{-5\pi}{2}$ ______ (e) $\frac{5\pi}{12}$ ______ (f) $\frac{-13\pi}{4}$ ______

3. In order to find the degree measure of an angle, multiply the radian measure by ______. In order to find the radian measure of an angle, multiply the degree measure by ______.

4. The angle formed by one complete revolution of a ray has a measure in degrees of ______ and a measure in radians of ______.

5. In a circle having a radius of 24, find the lengths of the arcs subtending central angles having the following measures.

   (a) 150° ______ (b) $\frac{3\pi}{2}$ ______

   (c) 330° ______ (d) $\frac{4}{5}\pi$ ______

6. In a circle having a radius of 1 (unit circle), find the lengths of the arcs subtending central angles that have the following measures.

   (a) $\frac{11\pi}{6}$ ______ (b) $\frac{2}{3}\pi$ ______

   (c) 360° ______ (d) π ______

   (e) $\frac{-4\pi}{5}$ ______ (f) −720°

   (g) -20π ______ (h) $3\frac{1}{2}\pi$ ______

ANSWERS TO PAGE 233

(a) $s = \frac{\pi}{6}(18) = 3\pi$

(b) 14π

(c) 16π

ANSWERS TO PAGE 238

(a) $(x,y) = (-1,-2) + t(3,3)$, $t \geq 0$ or $(x,y) = (-1,-2) + t(1,1)$, $t \geq 0$

(b) $(x,y) = (-1,-2) + t(-2,1)$, $t \geq 0$

(c) $(x,y) = (0,0) + t(-1,4)$, $t \geq 0$ or $(x,y) = t(-1,4)$, $t \geq 0$

(d) $(x,y) = t(3,-2)$, $t \geq 0$

(e) $(x,y) = t(1,0)$, $t \geq 0$

7. What is the radian measure of a central angle subtended by an arc 4 units long on a circle having a radius of 5 units? __; of a central angle that is subtended by an arc that is 9 units long on a circle having a radius of 9? __

8. Find the area of a sector of a circle having a radius of 10 units that is formed by a central angle of $\frac{3\pi}{8}$ radians. __________

9. Find the area of a circular sector with arc length 6π and central angle $\frac{\pi}{4}$. __________

10. Find the area of a circular sector whose perimeter p is $12 + 2\pi$ and whose central angle has a measure of $\frac{\pi}{3}$. __________

11. Find the formula for the area of a circular sector whose perimeter is p and whose central angle has a measure of α radians. __________

5.2. TRIGONOMETRIC FUNCTIONS

A ray $\overrightarrow{AB}$ may be described in terms of **vectors.**

Let (x_1,y_1) be the coordinates of point A, and let (a,b) be the vector corresponding to the displacement $\overrightarrow{AB}$. Then (x_1,y_1) is the vector corresponding to the displacement $\overrightarrow{OA}$. (See the illustration.)

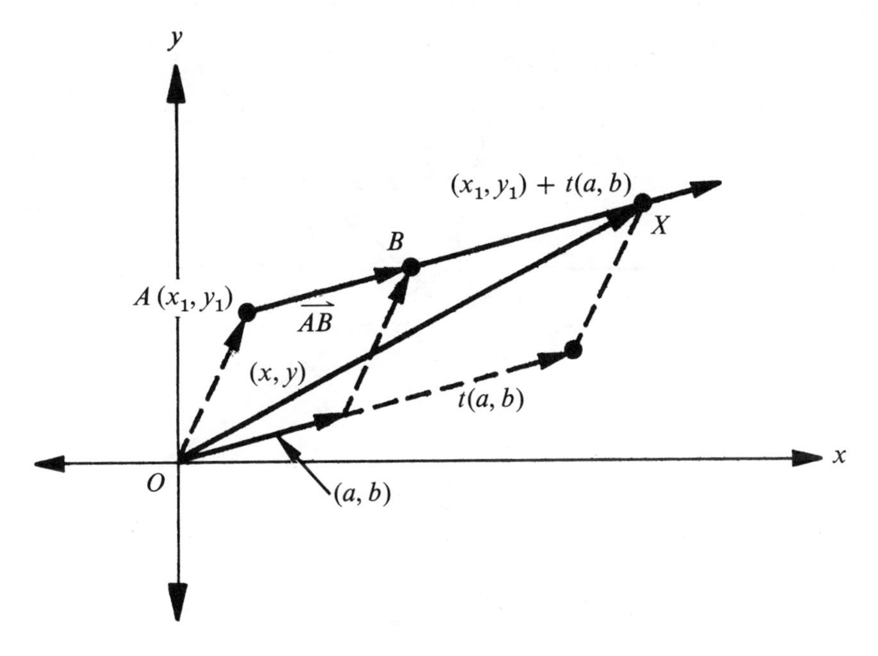

Now a point X with coordinates (x,y) will lie on the ray $\overrightarrow{AB}$ if and only if (x,y) is the sum of (x_1,y_1) and a nonnegative scalar multiple of vector (a,b). That is, $X\epsilon\overrightarrow{AB}$ if and only if $(x,y) = (x_1,y_1) + t(a,b)$ for some $t \geq 0$. Hence, we may describe $\overrightarrow{AB}$ as the set of all points X whose coordinates are members of

$$\{(x,y):(x,y) = (x_1,y_1) + t(a,b), \text{ where } t \geq 0\}.$$

The equation

$$(x,y) = (x_1,y_1) + t(a,b), \quad t \geq 0,$$

is called a **vector equation** of ray $\overrightarrow{AB}$. The vector (a,b) is said to be a **direction vector** of ray $\overrightarrow{AB}$.

MOVE TO NEXT FRAME

---

(1) (a) $\frac{\pi}{6}$ (b) $\frac{7\pi}{6}$ (c) 2π

(d) $\frac{5\pi}{6}$ (e) $\frac{-3\pi}{4}$ (f) $\frac{-\pi}{5}$

(g) -5π (h) $\frac{\pi}{360}$ (i) $\frac{5\pi}{9}$

(2) (a) 240° (b) 180° (c) -1800π

(d) -450π (e) 75° (f) =585°

(3) $\frac{180}{\pi}$

$\frac{\pi}{180}$

(4) 360 2π

(5) (a) 20π (b) 36π

(c) 44π (d) 30π

(6) (a) $\frac{11\pi}{6}$ (b) $\frac{2}{3}\pi$

(c) 2π (d) π

(e) $\frac{4}{5}\pi$ (f) $+4\pi$

(g) -20π (h) $3\frac{1}{2}\pi$

a, c

contained in the right member.

s (because r and s have the same direction).

1

the sets are assumed to be equal

Examples:

Write vector equations for the rays $\overrightarrow{AB}$, $\overrightarrow{AC}$, $\overrightarrow{OP}$, $\overrightarrow{OQ}$, and $\overrightarrow{OR}$ in the illustration.

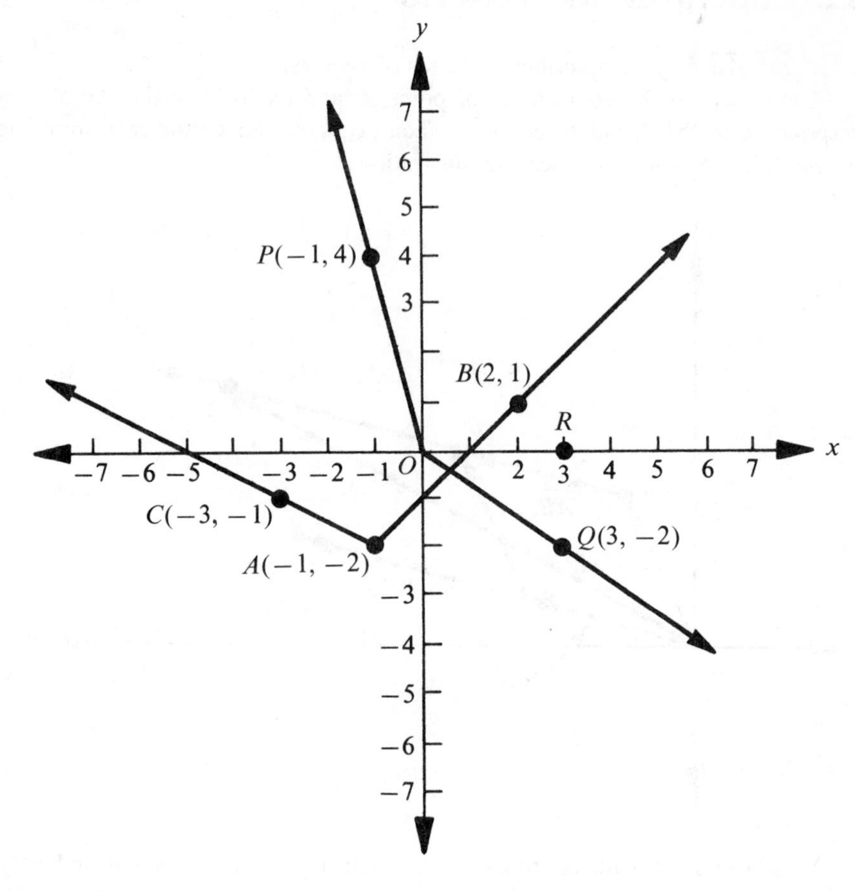

(a) $\overrightarrow{AB}$ __________

(b) $\overrightarrow{AC}$ __________

(c) $\overrightarrow{OP}$ __________

(d) $\overrightarrow{OQ}$ __________

(e) $\overrightarrow{OR}$ __________

There are an infinite number of direction vectors for a given ray. In the theorems which follow, we will prove that any positive scalar multiple of a direction vector of a ray is also a multiple of that ray.

MOVE TO NEXT FRAME

THEOREM:

If $\vec{r}$, $\vec{s}$, and $\vec{v}$ are nonzero vectors and $\vec{r}$ has the same direction as $\vec{v}$ and $\vec{s}$ has the same direction as $\vec{v}$, then $\vec{r}$ has the same direction as $\vec{s}$.

Proof:

$$\vec{r} = t\vec{v} \quad \text{and} \quad \vec{v} = k\vec{s}$$

for some positive real numbers t and k by ____________ of vectors with the "same direction." Therefore

$$\vec{r} = t(k\vec{s}) = (tk)\vec{s}.$$

Again by definition, since tk is a positive real number, $\vec{r}$ has the same direction as $\vec{s}$.

THEOREM:

If (x_1,y_1) are coordinates of a point, $\vec{r}$ is a nonzero vector, and $\{(x_1,y_1) + t\vec{r}$, for some $t \geq 0\}$ corresponds to the points on a ray, then $P(x,y)$ is on the ray if and only if $(x,y) = (x_1,y_1)$ or $(x,y) - (x_1,y_1)$ has the same direction as $\vec{r}$.

Proof:

(1) Suppose $P(x,y)$ is on the ray. That means that

$$(x,y) = (x_1,y_1) + t\vec{r}$$

or

$$(x,y) = (x_1,y_1) = t\vec{r}$$

for some $t \geq 0$. If $t = 0$, $(x,y) = (x_1,y_1)$. Otherwise, by the ____________

of "same direction," $(x,y) - (x_1,y_1)$ has the same direction as __.

(2) Conversely, if $(x,y) = (x_1,y_1)$, then

$$(x,y) = (x_1,y_1) + 0 \cdot \vec{r};$$

if $(x,y) - (x_1,y_1)$ has ____________ as $\vec{r}$, then $(x,y) - (x_1,y_1) = t\vec{r}$ for some $t \geq 0$. Hence

$$(x,y) = \underline{\qquad\qquad\qquad} \quad \text{for some } t \geq 0.$$

Therefore in all cases $P(x,y)$ is on the ray.

ANSWERS TO PAGE 242

(a) $\left(\frac{\sqrt{3}}{2}, \frac{1}{2}\right)$

(b) $\left(\frac{-\sqrt{3}}{2}, -\frac{1}{2}\right)$

(c) $\left(\frac{\sqrt{3}}{2}, -\frac{1}{2}\right)$

(d) $\left(\frac{-\sqrt{2}}{2}, -\frac{\sqrt{2}}{2}\right)$

(e) $\left(\frac{-\sqrt{3}}{2}, -\frac{1}{2}\right)$

(f) $\left(-\frac{1}{2}, \frac{\sqrt{3}}{2}\right)$

αr

α

The previous theorem presents us with a tool to determine whether or not a point is on a given ray.

Example:

$\{(4,5) + t(-3,2)$ for some $t > 0\}$ corresponds to the points of the ray $\overrightarrow{AB}$. Is $P(10,1)$ on $\overrightarrow{AB}$?

Solution:

$$(10,1) - (4,5) = (6,-4)$$

$(6,-4)$ does not equal some positive real multiple of $(-3,2)$, therefore $P(10,1)$ is not on $\overrightarrow{AB}$.

Which of the following points are on $\overrightarrow{AB}$? ____________

(a) $P(1,7)$ (b) $P(-2,3)$ (c) $P(-2,9)$

THEOREM:
If (x_1,y_1) are coordinates of a point and $\vec{r}$ and $\vec{s}$ are nonzero vectors, then

$$\{(x_1,y_1) + t\vec{r} \text{ for some } t \geq 0\} = \{(x_1,y_1) + t\vec{s} \text{ for some } t \geq 0\}.$$

if and only if $\vec{r}$ has the same direction as $\vec{s}$.

Proof:

(1) Suppose $\vec{r}$ and $\vec{s}$ have the same direction. We must show that any point (x,y) contained in the left member is ____________, and conversely. Let

$$(x,y) \in \{(x_1,y_1) + t\vec{r} \text{ where } t \geq 0\}.$$

This implies that $(x,y) = (x_1,y_1) + t\vec{r}$ for some $t \geq 0$. Hence, $(x,y) = (x_1,y_1)$, if $t = 0$, or vector $(x,y) - (x_1,y_1)$ has the same direction as $\vec{r}$. In this case, $(x,y) - (x_1,y_1)$ also has the same direction as ___; hence

$$(x,y) - (x_1,y_1) = t\vec{s} \quad \text{for some } t \geq 0.$$

Thus in all cases, $(x,y) = (x_1y_1) + t\vec{s}$ for some $t \geq 0$, which proves (x,y) is in the right member. In a similar fashion we may show that every (x,y) in the right member is also in the left member.

(2) Conversely, suppose the two sets of ordered pairs in the theorem are equal. Now $(x_1,y_1) + \vec{r}$ is in the left member (if we let $t =$ ___.) Hence $(x_1,y_1) + \vec{r}$ is in the right member, because ____________

____________; therefore,

$$(x_1,y_1) + \vec{r} = (x_1,y_1) + t\vec{s} \quad \text{for some } t \geq 0.$$

Therefore $\vec{r} = t\vec{s}$ for some $t \geq 0$. Since $\vec{r} \neq 0$, $t \neq 0$. Thus $t > 0$ and hence $\vec{r}$ and $\vec{s}$ have the same direction.

The theorem in the preceding frame tells us that if a ray has a direction vector $\vec{r}$, then any nonzero vector having the ______________ as $\vec{r}$ is also a direction vector for the ray.

An angle is formed by the __________ of two rays having the same endpoint. If the vertex of an angle is the origin of a coordinate system and the ______________________ is the x axis, the angle is in __________ position.

The coordinates of any point on the terminal ray of an angle in standard position serve as a direction vector for that ray. Thus one direction vector for the terminal side of the angle in the illustration below is $\vec{v} =$ ________.

Name another direction vector for $\overrightarrow{OB}$ that is twice as long. ________
Name a direction vector for $\overrightarrow{OB}$ that is exactly one unit long. This is the unit vector in the same direction as $\vec{v}$, namely $\dfrac{\vec{v}}{\|\vec{v}\|}$. ______ (See section 2.3.)

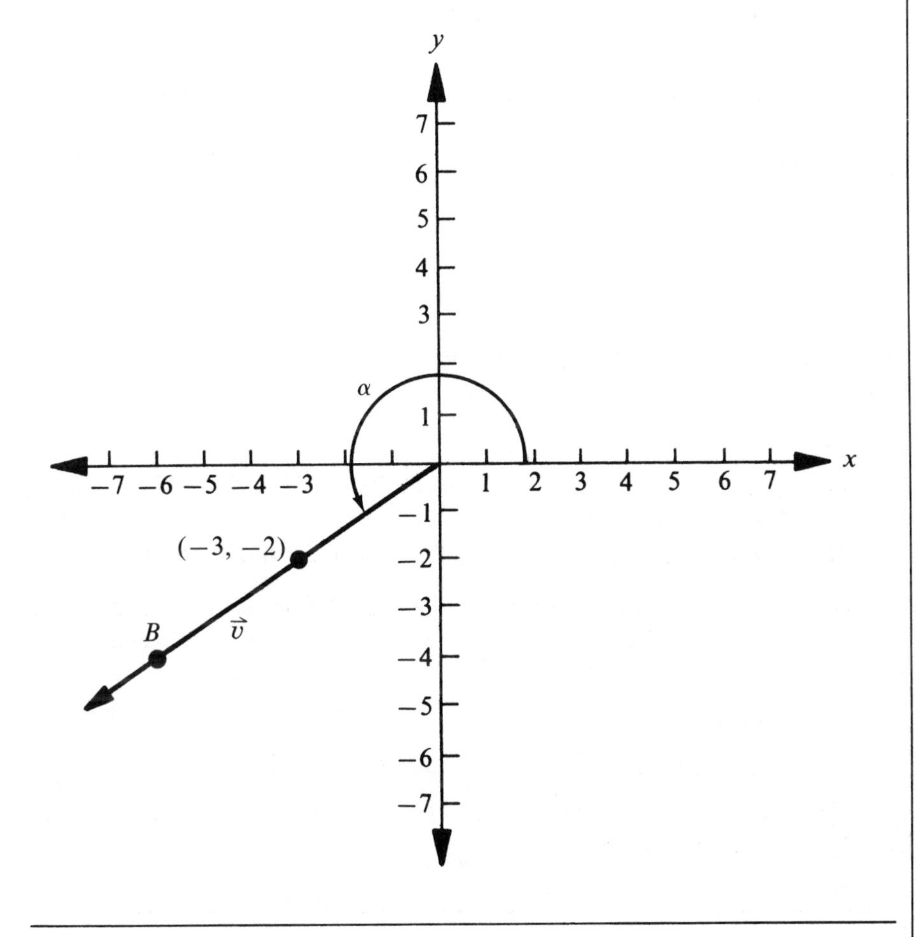

ANSWERS TO PAGE 239

definition

---

definition

$\vec{r}$

the same direction

$(x_1,y_1) + t\vec{r}$

ANSWERS TO PAGE 244

$\frac{-3}{5}$ $\frac{4}{5}$

$\frac{\sqrt{3}}{2}$ $\frac{1}{2}$

$\frac{\pi}{3}$

$\left(\frac{1}{2}, \frac{\sqrt{3}}{2}\right)$

$\left(\frac{1}{2}, \frac{\sqrt{3}}{2}\right)$

$\frac{1}{2}$

$\frac{\sqrt{3}}{2}$

(a) $\frac{\sqrt{3}}{2}$

(b) $-\frac{1}{2}$

(c) $\frac{1}{2}$

DEFINITIONS:

The **unit direction vector** for the terminal ray of any angle α in standard position, having a direction vector $\vec{v}$, is $\frac{\vec{v}}{\|\vec{v}\|}$. The angle α is called the **direction angle** of the vector $\vec{v}$.

MOVE TO NEXT FRAME

Examples:

Find the unit direction vector for the terminal sides of each of the following angles in standard position. (*Hint:* Pick any point P on the terminal ray. Use the coordinates of P as a direction vector $\vec{v}$. Find $\frac{\vec{v}}{\|\vec{v}\|}$.)

(a) 30° ______________

(b) $\frac{7\pi}{6}$ ______________

(c) 330° ______________

(d) $\frac{5\pi}{4}$ ______________

(e) $-150°$ ______________

(f) $\frac{-4\pi}{3}$ ______________

Note: It is customary to refer to an angle by its measure. Thus when we say "the following angles" and simply list their measures, we mean "the angles whose measures are as follows."

Recall that if an arc of a circle of radius r subtends an angle whose radian measure is α, then the length s of the arc is given by $s =$ ______. Thus, if $r = 1$, a central angle whose measure is α radians intercepts an arc that is ___ units long.

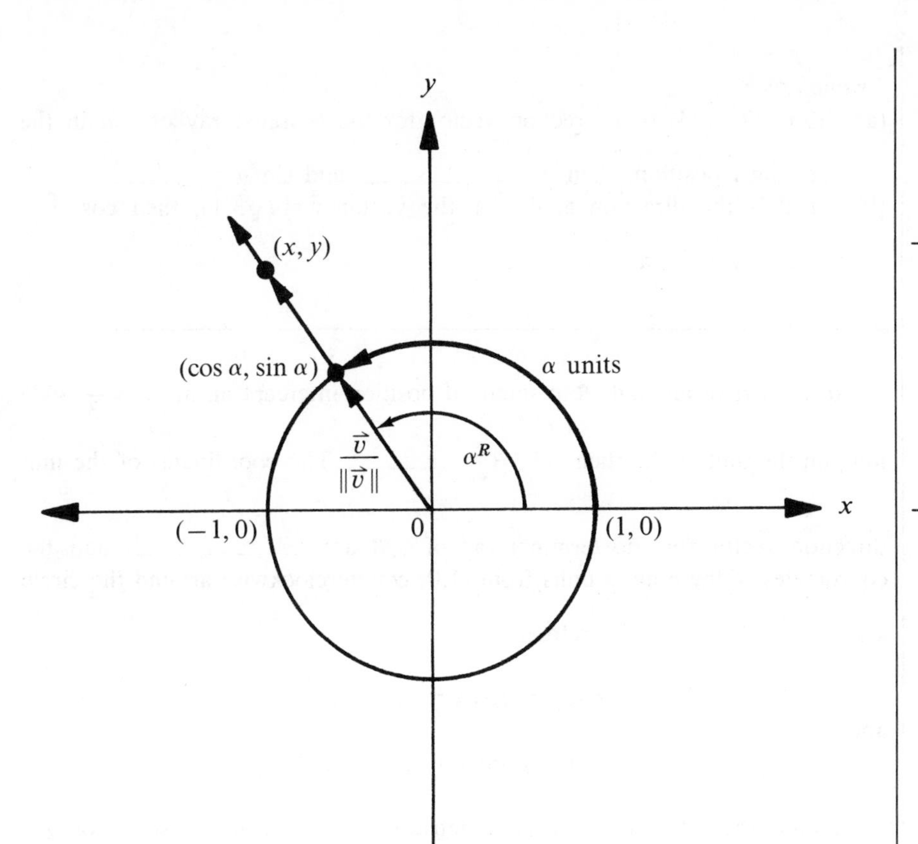

The endpoints of all the unit direction vectors for the terminal rays of angles in standard position lie on the unit circle. Recall that circular functions are defined in terms of points on a unit circle. We have the following definitions of **trigonometric functions** for angle α, which correspond to the circular functions.

MOVE TO NEXT FRAME

DEFINITIONS:

If α is an angle in standard position and $\vec{v} = (x,y)$ is a direction vector of its terminal side, then the

trigonometric cosine $= \left\{(\alpha, \cos \alpha) : \cos \alpha = \right\} \frac{x}{\|\vec{v}\|}$

and the

trigonometric sine $= \left\{(\alpha, \sin \alpha) : \sin \alpha = \frac{y}{\|\vec{v}\|}\right\}$

MOVE TO NEXT FRAME

ANSWERS TO PAGE 241

same direction

---

union

initial side or initial ray

standard

(−3,−2)

(−6,−4)

$\frac{-3\sqrt{13}}{13}, \quad \frac{-2\sqrt{13}}{13}$

Examples:

(a) If $\vec{v} = (-3,4)$ is a direction vector for the terminal ray of $\angle\alpha$ in the standard position, then $\cos\alpha =$ ______ and $\sin\alpha =$ ______.

(b) If β is the direction angle for the vector $\vec{v} = (\sqrt{3},1)$, then $\cos\beta =$ ______ and $\sin\beta =$ ______.

If the rays of an angle β in standard position intercept an arc $x = \frac{\pi}{3}$ units long on the unit circle, then $m^R\angle\beta =$ ______. The coordinates of the unit direction vector for the terminal ray of $\angle\beta$ are ______ and the coordinates of the point x units from (1,0) counterclockwise around the circle are ______. Therefore,

$$\cos\beta = \cos x = \text{\_\_\_\_\_\_},$$

and

$$\sin\beta = \sin x = \text{\_\_\_\_\_\_}.$$

To find the values of the trigonometric functions $\cos\alpha$ and $\sin\alpha$ for $\angle\alpha$ measured in degrees, change the degree measure to radian measure and find the circular functions $\cos x$ and $\sin x$ for $x = m^R\angle\alpha$.

Examples:

(a) $\cos 30° = \cos\frac{\pi}{6} =$ ______.

(b) $\sin 210° = \sin\frac{7\pi}{6} =$ ______.

(c) $\cos -420° = \cos\left(-\frac{7\pi}{3}\right) =$ ______.

The other four trigonometric functions are defined in a manner analogous to their corresponding circular functions as follows:

DEFINITIONS:

trigonometric tangent $= \left\{(\alpha, \tan\alpha) : \tan\alpha = \frac{\sin\alpha}{\cos\alpha}, \cos\alpha \neq 0\right\}$

trigonometric cotangent $= \left\{(\alpha, \cot\alpha) : \cot\alpha = \frac{\cos\alpha}{\sin\alpha}, \sin\alpha \neq 0\right\}$

trigonometric secant $= \left\{(\alpha, \sec\alpha) : \sec\alpha = \frac{1}{\cos\alpha}, \cos\alpha \neq 0\right\}$

trigonometric cosecant $= \left\{(\alpha, \csc\alpha) : \csc\alpha = \frac{1}{\sin\alpha}, \alpha \neq 0\right\}$

MOVE TO NEXT FRAME

$\frac{-9}{-40} = \frac{9}{40}$

ANSWERS TO PAGE 243

From the definition of sin α and cos α, where α is an angle, we have the following useful consequences.

THEOREM:
If $\vec{v} = (x,y)$ is a direction vector of the terminal ray of $\angle\alpha$ in standard position, then

$$\cos\alpha = \frac{x}{\|\vec{v}\|} = \frac{x}{\sqrt{x^2+y^2}}$$

$$\sin\alpha = \frac{y}{\|\vec{v}\|} = \frac{y}{\sqrt{x^2+y^2}}$$

$$\tan\alpha = \frac{\sin\alpha}{\cos\alpha} = \frac{y}{x}, \quad x \neq 0$$

$$\cot\alpha = \frac{\cos\alpha}{\sin\alpha} = \frac{x}{y}, \quad y \neq 0$$

$$\sec\alpha = \frac{1}{\cos\alpha} = \frac{\sqrt{x^2+y^2}}{x}, \quad x \neq 0$$

$$\csc\alpha = \frac{1}{\sin\alpha} = \frac{\sqrt{x^2+y^2}}{y}, \quad y \neq 0$$

MOVE TO NEXT FRAME

Example:
Find the six trigonometric functions of $\angle\alpha$ in the illustration.

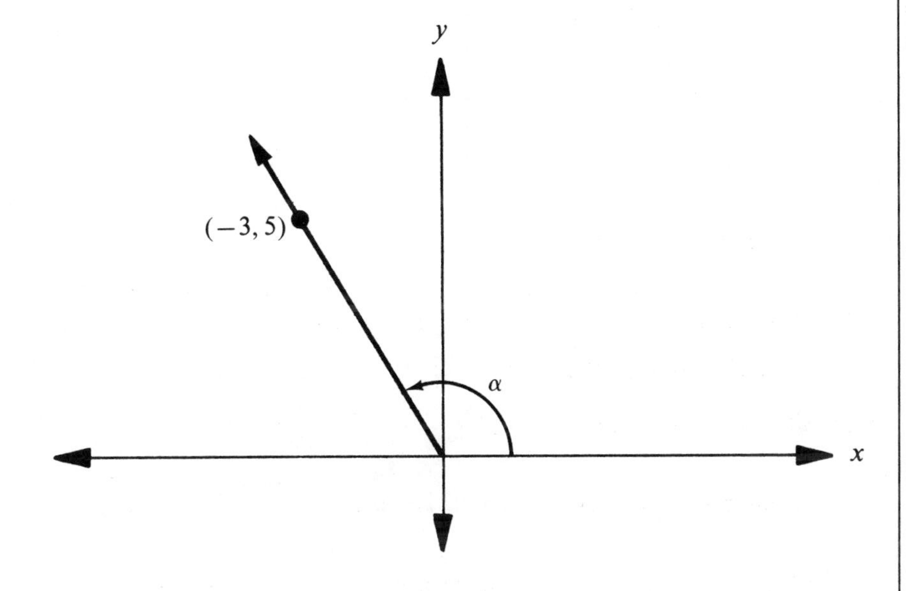

$\cos\alpha = \dfrac{x}{\sqrt{x^2+y^2}} = \dfrac{-3}{\sqrt{34}}$ or $\dfrac{-3\sqrt{34}}{34}$; $\sin\alpha = \dfrac{y}{\sqrt{x^2+y^2}} =$ __________;

$\tan\alpha =$ ______; $\cot\alpha =$ ______; $\sec\alpha =$ ______; $\csc\alpha$ ______.

ANSWERS TO PAGE 248

domains

angles

real numbers

range

An angle is said to be in the "1st, 2nd, 3rd, or 4th quadrant" if the terminal side of the angle lies in the respective quadrant. These quadrants are often denoted QI, QII, QIII, and QIV, respectively.

Example:

$\angle\beta$ lies in Quadrant III and $\sin\beta = \dfrac{-9}{41}$. Find $\tan\beta$. Since we have specified the quadrant for $\angle\beta$, we know that there is exactly one value for $\tan\beta$.

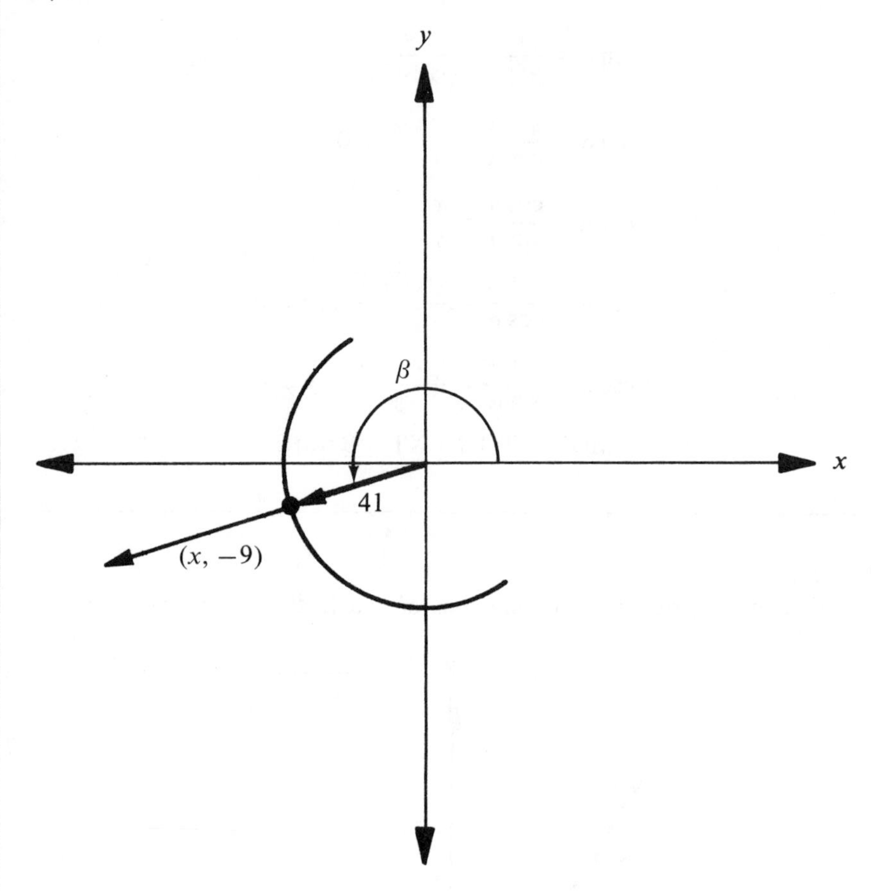

Solution:

$$\sin\beta = \frac{y}{\sqrt{x^2+y^2}} = \frac{-9}{41} = \frac{-9}{\sqrt{x^2+(-9)^2}}.$$

Thus

$$\sqrt{x^2+(-9)^2} = 41;$$

$$x^2 + 81 = 41^2;$$

$$x^2 = 1600;$$

$$x = \pm 40.$$

Since (x,y) is in the third quadrant (see the sketch) and x is negative,

$$\tan\beta - \frac{y}{x} = \underline{\hspace{6cm}}.$$

Example:

If $\tan \beta = \frac{-5}{12}$, sketch β on the given coordinate system and find the values of the remaining five functions. (*Hint:* Use $(12,-5)$ as a direction vector for β in Quadrant IV, then use $(-12,5)$ for a direction vector for β in Quadrant II since tangent is negative in *both* quadrants.)

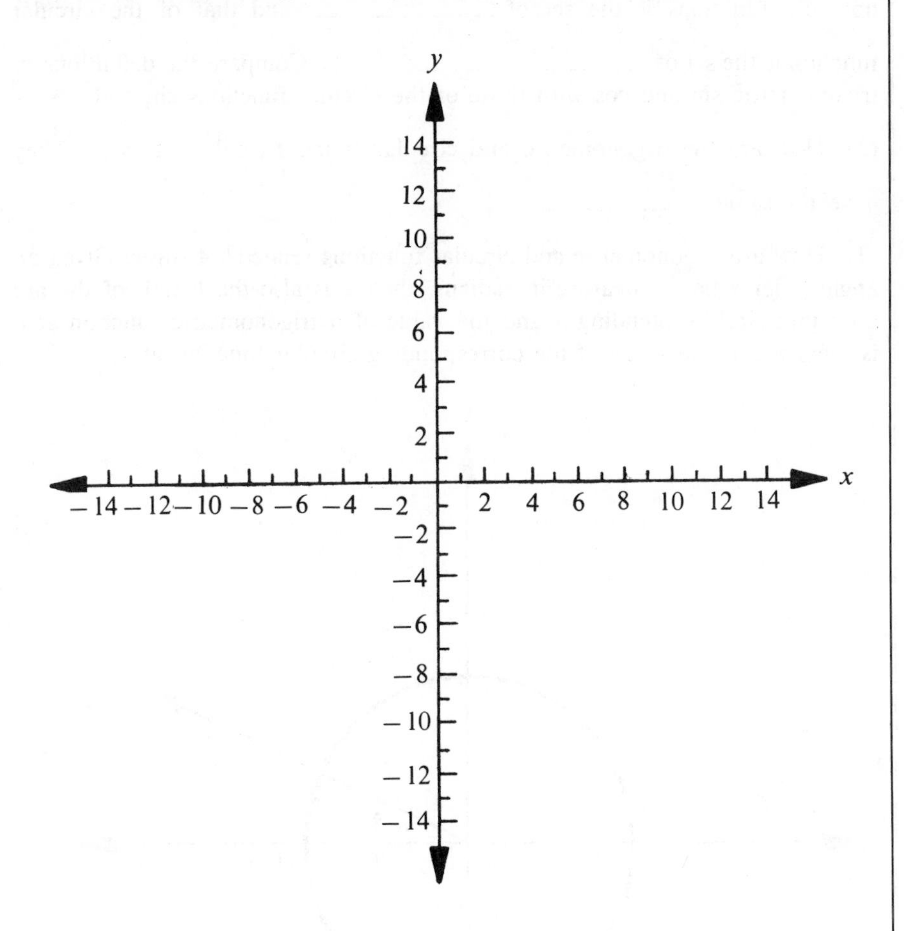

$\cot \beta = \frac{y}{x} =$ ____________

$\sin \beta = \frac{y}{\sqrt{x^2 + y^2}} =$ ____________

$\cos \beta = \frac{x}{\sqrt{x^2 + y^2}} =$ ____________

$\csc \beta = \frac{\sqrt{x^2 + y^2}}{y} =$ ____________

$\sec \beta = \frac{\sqrt{x^2 + y^2}}{x} =$ ____________

Note: When we are given the value of a trigonometric function of an angle, that angle is not uniquely determined. Thus, we must consider all possibilities.

$\frac{5}{\sqrt{34}}$ or $\frac{5\sqrt{34}}{34}$

$\frac{-5}{3}$ $\frac{-3}{5}$ $\frac{-\sqrt{34}}{3}$ $\frac{\sqrt{34}}{5}$

ANSWERS TO PAGE 250

(g) $\frac{-\sqrt{2}}{2}$ (h) $-\sqrt{2}$

(i) $\frac{-\sqrt{3}}{3}$ (j) $-\sqrt{3}$

(k) $\frac{\sqrt{2}}{2}$ (l) $\frac{\sqrt{2}}{2}$

(7) (a) $\frac{-6}{5}$

(b) $\frac{5\sqrt{61}}{61}$

(c) $\frac{-6\sqrt{61}}{61}$

(d) $\frac{-\sqrt{61}}{6}$

(e) $\frac{\sqrt{61}}{5}$

The answers to the following questions explain the relationship between the circular functions previously encountered and the trigonometric functions.

(1) How do trigonometric functions and circular functions differ? *Answer:* These functions differ in their ____________. The domain of the trigonometric functions is the set of ____________ and that of the circular function is the set of ____________. Compare the definitions of trigonometric sin and cos with those of the circular functions sin and cos.

(2) How are the trigonometric and circular functions alike? *Answer:* They have the same ____________.

(3) How are trigonometric and circular functions related? *Answer:* Given an angle α, let x be its measure in radians, then x is also the length of the arc on a unit circle subtending α and the value of a trigonometric function at α is the same as the value of the corresponding circular function at x.

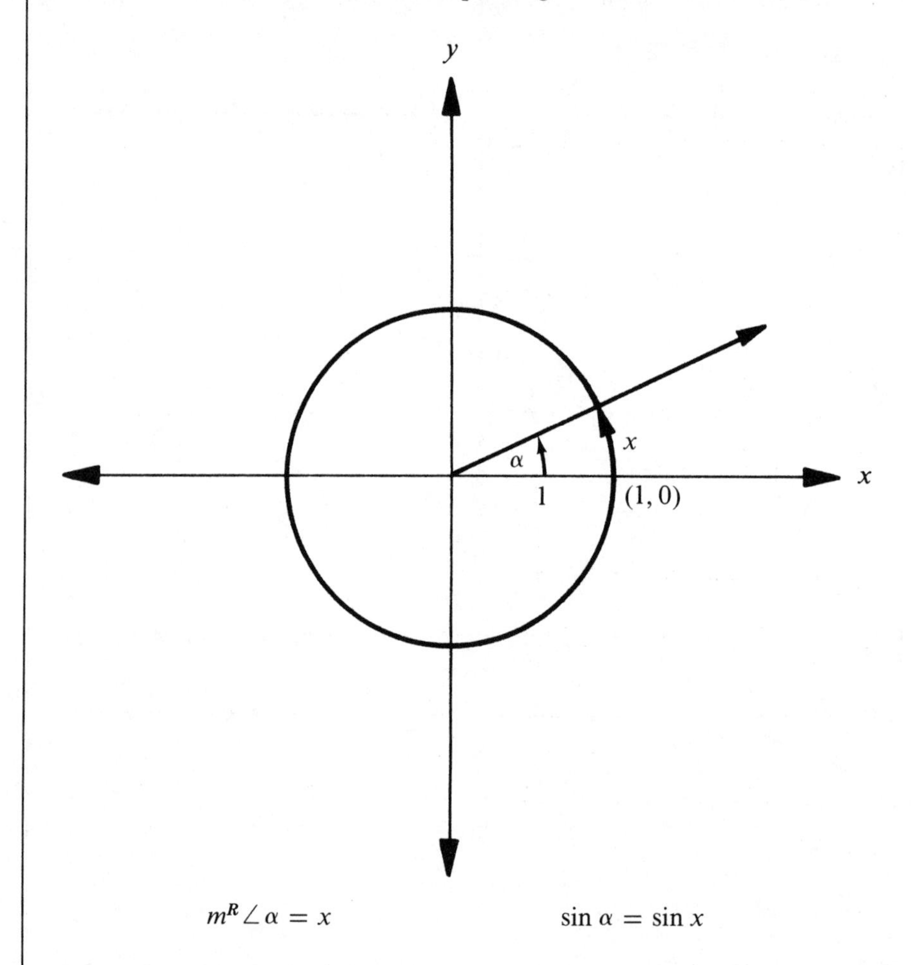

$m^R \angle \alpha = x$ $\sin \alpha = \sin x$

EXERCISES. 5.2

1. If A has coordinates $(-2,5)$ and B has coordinates $(4,1)$, then a vector equation of ray $\overrightarrow{AB}$ is ______.

2. $P(-3,7)$ is a point on the terminal ray of $\angle\beta$ in standard position. A direction vector for the terminal ray $\overrightarrow{OP}$ of $\angle\beta$ is of the form ______.
   The unit direction vector of $\overrightarrow{OP}$ is ______.

3. $\{(x,y):(x,y) = (4,-6) + t(-2,-4),\ t \geq 0\}$ are the coordinates of a ray whose endpoint is ______ and direction vector is ______.
   If α is the direction angle for $(-2,-4)$, then $\sin\alpha =$ ______ and $\tan\alpha =$ ___.

4. Find the unit direction vectors for the terminal rays of each angle, if it is in standard position and its measure is one of the following.

   (a) $210°$ ______ (b) $\frac{-4\pi}{3}$ ______

   (c) $690°$ ______ (d) $\frac{7\pi}{4}$ ______

   (e) $-240°$ ______ (f) $\frac{-5\pi}{6}$ ______

   (g) $-135°$ ______ (h) $\frac{7\pi}{3}$ ______

5. The following are lengths of arcs on a unit circle. For each arc, find the degree measure of the central angle subtended and the value of the tangent function of that angle.

   (a) $\frac{\pi}{6}$ ______; ______ (b) $\frac{\pi}{3}$ ______; ______

   (c) $\frac{\pi}{4}$ ______; ______ (d) $\frac{2\pi}{3}$ ______; ______

   (e) $\frac{5\pi}{6}$ ______; ______ (f) $\frac{7\pi}{6}$ ______; ______

   (g) $\frac{5\pi}{4}$ ______; ______ (h) $\frac{8\pi}{3}$ ______; ______

6. Find each of the following:

   (a) $\sin 210°$ ______ (b) $\cos -150°$ ______

   (c) $\tan 135°$ ______ (d) $\cot 315°$ ______

   (e) $\sec 30°$ ______ (f) $\csc 120°$ ______

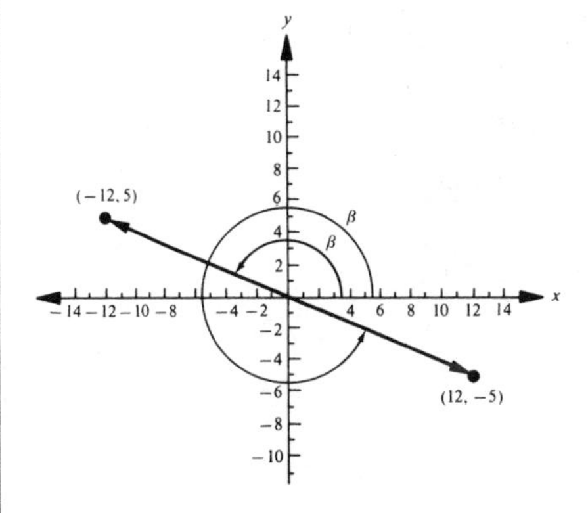

$-\frac{12}{5}$ in QII and QIV

$+\frac{5}{13}$ in QII, $\frac{-5}{13}$ in QIV

$-\frac{12}{13}$ in QII, $\frac{12}{13}$ in QIV

$+\frac{13}{5}$ in QII, $\frac{-13}{5}$ in QIV

$-\frac{13}{12}$ in QII, $\frac{13}{12}$ in QIV

ANSWERS TO PAGE 252

$\cos \alpha \cos \beta - \sin \alpha \sin \beta$

$\cos \alpha \cos \beta + \sin \alpha \sin \beta$

$\sin \alpha \cos \beta + \cos \alpha \sin \beta$

$\sin \alpha \cos \beta - \cos \alpha \sin \beta$

$\dfrac{\tan \alpha + \tan \beta}{1 - \tan \alpha \tan \beta}$

$\dfrac{\tan \alpha - \tan \beta}{1 + \tan \alpha \tan \beta}$

$\cos^2 \theta - \sin^2 \theta$

$2 \sin \theta \cos \theta$

$\dfrac{2 \tan \theta}{1 - \tan^2 \theta}$

$\sqrt{\dfrac{1 + \cos \theta}{2}}$

$\sqrt{\dfrac{1 - \cos \theta}{2}}$

$\sqrt{\dfrac{1 - \cos \theta}{1 + \cos \theta}}$

$2 \sin \frac{1}{2} (\alpha + \beta) \cos \frac{1}{2} (\alpha - \beta)$

$2 \cos \frac{1}{2} (\alpha + \beta) \sin \frac{1}{2} (\alpha - \beta)$

$2 \cos \frac{1}{2} (\alpha + \beta) \cos \frac{1}{2} (\alpha - \beta)$

$-2 \sin \frac{1}{2}(\alpha + \beta) \sin \frac{1}{2} (\alpha - \beta)$

$\frac{1}{2} \sqrt{2 - \sqrt{3}}$

(g) $\sin -45°$ ________ (h) $\csc -45°$ ________

(i) $\tan 150°$ ________ (j) $\cot 330°$ ________

(k) $\sin 45°$ ________ (l) $\cos -45°$ ________

7. Find the values of the other five functions of $\angle \beta$ if $\tan \beta = \dfrac{-5}{6}$ and is in Quadrant II.

(a) $\cot \beta =$ ________________

(b) $\sin \beta =$ ________________

(c) $\cos \beta =$ ________________

(d) $\sec \beta =$ ________________

(e) $\csc \beta =$ ________________

5.3. VALUES FOR TRIGONOMETRIC FUNCTIONS (TABLES AND INTERPOLATION)

Values of trigonometric functions of a few special angles such as 30°, 45°, 60°, and their multiples have been calculated from the properties of isosceles right triangles and 30°-60°-90° triangles. These angles correspond to real numbers such as $\frac{\pi}{6}, \frac{\pi}{4}, \frac{\pi}{3}$, and their multiples on the unit circle.

MOVE TO NEXT FRAME

---

tan 30° = ________, sin 60° = ________, cos 135° = ________, and sec 330° = ________ are examples.

We can also find the values of trigonometric functions of certain other angles using trigonometric identities. **Trigonometric identities** follow directly as a consequence of circular function identities and the definitions of trigonometric functions. Thus, a circular function identity such as $\cos^2 x + \sin^2 x = 1$, where x is an arc length on the unit circle, becomes the trigonometric identity $\cos^2 \theta + \sin^2 \theta = 1$, where θ is an angle by a change of domain from a real number corresponding to arc lengths of angles. The range remains the same.

MOVE TO NEXT FRAME

From your knowledge of corresponding identities for circular functions, complete the following summary of trigonometric identities.

Fundamental Identities

$\tan\theta =$ ________ $(\cos\theta \neq 0)$

$\cot\theta =$ ________ $(\sin\theta \neq 0)$

$\sec\theta =$ ________ $(\cos\theta \neq 0)$

$\csc\theta =$ ________ $(\theta \neq 0)$

$\cos^2\theta + \sin^2\theta =$ ________

$1 + \tan^2\theta =$ ________ $(\cos\theta \neq 0)$

$\cot^2\theta + 1 =$ ________ $(\sin\theta \neq 0)$

ANSWERS TO PAGE 249

(1) $(x,y) = (-2,5) + t(6,-4)$ for some $t \geq 0$

(2) $t(-3,7), t > 0$
$\left(\frac{-3\sqrt{58}}{58}, \frac{7\sqrt{58}}{58}\right)$

(3) $(4,-6)$ $t(-2,-4)$, for some $t > 0$
$\frac{-2\sqrt{5}}{5}$ 2

(4) (a) $\left(\frac{-\sqrt{3}}{2}, -\frac{1}{2}\right)$ (b) $\left(\frac{-1}{2}, \frac{\sqrt{3}}{2}\right)$
(c) $\left(\frac{\sqrt{3}}{2}, -\frac{1}{2}\right)$ (d) $\left(\frac{\sqrt{2}}{2}, \frac{-\sqrt{2}}{2}\right)$
(e) $\left(-\frac{1}{2}, \frac{\sqrt{3}}{2}\right)$ (f) $\left(\frac{-\sqrt{3}}{2}, -\frac{1}{2}\right)$
(g) $\left(\frac{-\sqrt{2}}{2}, \frac{-\sqrt{2}}{2}\right)$ (h) $\left(\frac{1}{2}, \frac{\sqrt{3}}{2}\right)$

(5) (a) $30°; \frac{\sqrt{3}}{3}$ (b) $60°; \sqrt{3}$
(c) $45°; 1$ (d) $120°; -\sqrt{3}$
(e) $150°; \frac{-\sqrt{3}}{3}$ (f) $210°; \frac{\sqrt{3}}{3}$
(g) $225°; 1$ (h) $480°; -\sqrt{3}$

(6) (a) $-\frac{1}{2}$ (b) $\frac{-\sqrt{3}}{2}$
(c) -1 (d) -1
(e) $\frac{2\sqrt{3}}{3}$ (f) $\frac{2\sqrt{3}}{3}$

ANSWERS TO PAGE 254

2nd and 9th

0°00′

45°00′

45°00′

90°00′

(a) 0.3090 (b) 0.7445

(c) 0.9001 (d) 0.8403

(e) 0.2532 (f) 9.255

0° 90°

Sum and Difference Identities

$\cos(\alpha + \beta) =$ ______

$\cos(\alpha - \beta) =$ ______

$\sin(\alpha + \beta) =$ ______

$\sin(\alpha - \beta) =$ ______

$\tan(\alpha + \beta) =$ ______

$\tan(\alpha - \beta) =$ ______

Double-Angle Identities

$\cos 2\theta =$ ______

$\sin 2\theta =$ ______

$\tan 2\theta =$ ______

Half-Angle Identities

$\left|\cos \frac{\theta}{2}\right| =$ ______

$\left|\sin \frac{\theta}{2}\right| =$ ______

$\left|\tan \frac{\theta}{2}\right| =$ ______

Sum to Product Identities

$\sin \alpha + \sin \beta =$ ______

$\sin \alpha - \sin \beta =$ ______

$\cos \alpha + \cos \beta =$ ______

$\cos \alpha - \cos \beta =$ ______

Identities may be used to find the values of trigonometric functions of angles other than the special angles such as 30°, 240°, and 150°, which are easy to calculate directly. A half-angle formula, for instance, may be used to find sin 15°.

$$\sin 15° = \sin \frac{1}{2}(30°) = \sqrt{\frac{1 - \cos 30°}{2}} = \text{\_\_\_\_\_\_}.$$

Use half-angle identities to find each of the following:

(a) $\sin 165° =$ ____________ (b) $\cos 75° =$ ____________

(c) $\tan 22.5° =$ ____________ (d) $\tan\frac{\pi}{8} =$ ____________

(e) $\sin 67.5° =$ ____________ (f) $\cos\frac{7\pi}{12} =$ ____________

Use the suggested sum or difference identity to find each of the following:

(a)

$$\cos 255° = \cos(30° + 225°)$$
$$= \cos 30° \cos 225° - \sin 30° \sin 225°$$
$$= \left(\frac{\sqrt{3}}{2}\right)\left(\frac{-\sqrt{2}}{2}\right) - \left(\frac{1}{2}\right)\left(\frac{-\sqrt{2}}{2}\right) = \text{\_\_\_\_\_\_\_\_\_\_\_\_}$$

(b)

$$\sin 285° = \sin(330° - 45°) = \text{\_\_\_\_\_\_\_\_\_\_\_\_}$$

We have seen how trigonometric identities may be used to find the values of functions at certain angles. Formulas for finding values of trigonometric functions at any angle θ or circular functions at any real number x are derived in a more detailed study of the subject. These formulas usually occur in the form of infinite series such as

$$\sin x = 1 - \frac{x^2}{2!} + \frac{x^4}{4!} - \frac{x^6}{6!} + \cdots + (-1)^{n+1}\frac{x^{2n-2}}{(2n-2)!} + \cdots, \quad x \in \mathcal{R}$$

and

$$\cos x = x - \frac{x^3}{3!} + \frac{x^5}{5!} - \frac{x^7}{7!} + \cdots + (-1)^{n+1}\frac{x^{2n-1}}{(2n-1)!} + \cdots, \quad x \in \mathcal{R}.$$

MOVE TO NEXT FRAME

Values of trigonometric functions for angles at intervals of 10 minutes (10′) are available in table form in the Appendix. These are four significant digit approximations for the values of the functions.

MOVE TO NEXT FRAME

Turn to Table I to answer the following questions.

How many columns are there in the table? ________ In which column(s) do we find the measure in degrees of an angle? ____________

ANSWERS TO PAGE 251

$\frac{\sqrt{3}}{3}$ $\frac{\sqrt{3}}{2}$ $-\frac{\sqrt{2}}{2}$

$\frac{2\sqrt{3}}{3}$

$\frac{\sin\theta}{\cos\theta}$

$\frac{\cos\theta}{\sin\theta}$

$\frac{1}{\cos\theta}$

$\frac{1}{\sin\theta}$

1

$\sec^2\theta$

$\csc^2\theta$

-0.3153

$-\sin 42°10' = -0.6713$

periodic

reduction

In which column(s) do we find the radian measure of an angle and the length of an arc on the unit circle intercepted by that angle? ______________

The first column contains the measure in degrees of an angle whose measure is greater than or equal to ________ and whose measure is less than or equal to ________.

Since $\sin \theta = \cos (90° - \theta)$ the values in Table I of sin for $0° \leq \theta \leq 45°$ are at the same time the values of cos for $45° \leq \theta \leq 90°$. For example, $\sin 8° = \cos (90° - 8°) = \cos 82°$. Similar remarks hold for the remaining trigonometric functions.

Thus for efficient use of Table I, headings are provided at the bottom of the page for the co-functions at the top, and the last column contains measures of angles from 45° to 90° inclusively.

MOVE TO NEXT FRAME

The last column is read from the bottom to the top and contains measures of angles whose measures are greater than or equal to __________ and whose measures are less than or equal to __________.

Use Table I to find approximate values for the following: (Remember that Table I contains functions of real numbers corresponding to arc lengths on the unit circle as well as angles.)

(a) $\sin 18° \approx$ ______________ (b) $\tan 36°40' \approx$ ______________

(c) $\cos 0.4509 \approx$ ______________ (b) $\sin 57°10' \approx$ ______________

(e) $\cos 75°20' \approx$ ______________ (f) $\tan 83°50' \approx$ ______________

Note: The symbol $\approx$ means "approximately equal to."

Table I provides values of trigonometric functions for angles whose measures lie between _______ and _______ inclusively. for angles whose measures are greater than 90° or whose measures are negative, use Table I after using the periodic properties of the functions and enlisting the help of certain additional identities, called reduction formulas, to find functions with equivalent values for angles between 0° and 90°.

For example, consider sin $(-36°20')$. Recall the circular function identity

$$\sin(-x) = \text{\_\_\_\_\_\_\_\_}.$$

Thus, $\sin(-\theta) = -\sin\theta$ and $\sin -36°20' = -\sin 36°20'$. In Table I find $\sin 36°20' \approx$ ________. Thus, $\sin(-36°20') \approx$ ________.

Similarly, recall that $\cos(-\theta) =$ ______ and $\tan(-\theta) =$ ______.

Identities such as $\cos(180° - \theta) = -\cos\theta$ are also an aid. Using the appropriate difference formula, we have

$$\cos(180° - \theta) = \cos 180° \cos\theta + \sin 180° \sin\theta = \text{\_\_\_\_\_\_\_\_}.$$

This is a reduction formula; an example of its use follows.

Find $\cos 140°50'$:

$$\cos 140°50' = \cos(180° - 39°10')$$

$$= -\cos 39°10' \text{\_\_\_\_\_\_\_\_}.$$

The following summarizes some of the most useful **reduction formulas.**

(a) $\sin(-\theta) =$ ________ (b) $\cos(-\theta) =$ ________

(c) $\tan(-\theta) =$ ________ (d) $\sin(180° - \theta) =$ ________

(e) $\sin(180° + \theta) =$ ________ (f) $\cos(180° - \theta) =$ ________

(g) $\cos(180° + \theta) =$ ________ (h) $\tan(180° - \theta) =$ ________

If the measure of the angle is greater than 360°, an appeal to the periodic properties of the circular functions, and hence the periodic properties of the trigonometric functions, is useful. The period of the circular function sine is 2π. Therefore the period of the trigonometric function sine is 2π radians or 360°. Thus,

$$\sin 800° = \sin(720° + 80°)$$

$$= \sin 80° \approx \text{\_\_\_\_\_\_\_\_}.$$

Write the period in degrees for each of the six trigonometric functions.

(a) sine ________ (b) cosine ________

(c) tangent ________ (d) cotangent ________

(e) secant ________ (f) cosecant ________

ANSWERS TO PAGE 253

(a) $\frac{1}{2}\sqrt{2 - \sqrt{3}}$ (b) $\frac{1}{2}\sqrt{2 + \sqrt{3}}$

(c) $\sqrt{2} - 1$ (d) $\sqrt{2} - 1$

(e) $\frac{1}{2}\sqrt{2 + \sqrt{2}}$ (f) $-\frac{1}{2}\sqrt{2 - \sqrt{3}}$

$\frac{-\sqrt{6} + \sqrt{2}}{4}$

$\frac{-\sqrt{2} - \sqrt{6}}{4}$

10

1st and 10th

1.048

1.054

1.049

$AB < AC$

Using periodicity, a reduction formula, and Table I, we can now find the function of any angle.

Examples:

(a) $\tan 1242°30' = \tan (6 \cdot 180° + 162°30') = \tan 162°30'$

$= \tan (180° - 17°30') = -\tan 17°30'$

$\approx$ ______________.

(b) $\sin (582°10') = \sin (360° + 222°10') = \sin 222°10'$

$= \sin (180° + 42°10') \approx$ ______________.

To find the value of a trigonometric function of an angle in the table use the measure of an acute angle (an angle with a measure of less than 90°) having a trigonometric functional value equal to the absolute value of the functional value in question. This acute angle is called a **reference angle.**

To arrive at the appropriate reference angle use the __________ property of the function and/or a __________ formula.

To find the functional value of an angle it is helpful to make a sketch of the angle in standard position. The quadrant in which the terminal side lies determines whether the functional value is positive or negative. Using periodic properties and reduction formulas, the desired value may be expressed in terms of the positive acute angle formed by the terminal side of the given angle and the x axis.

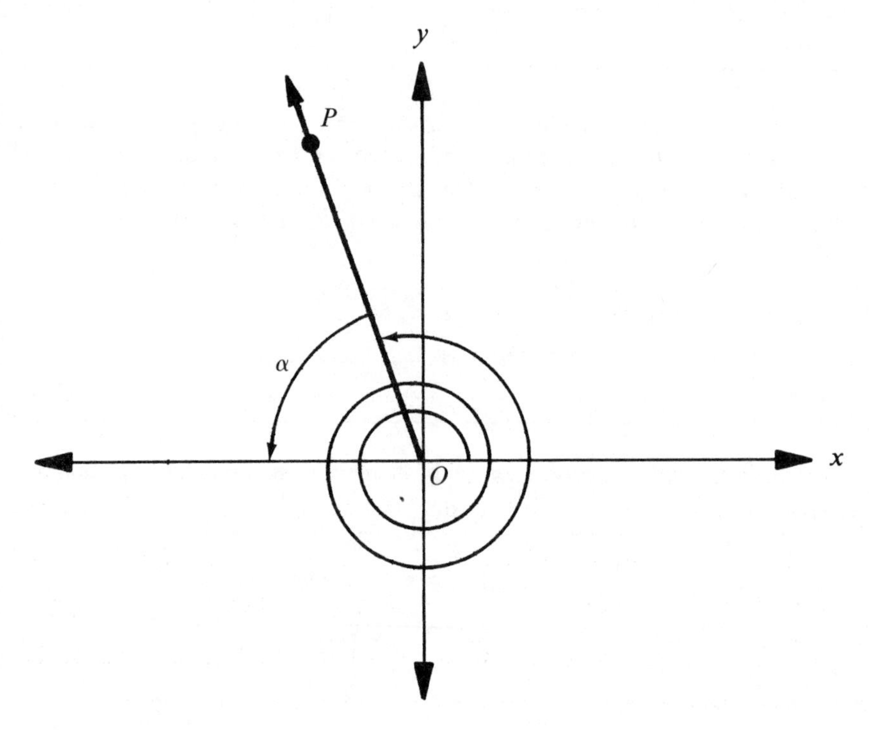

Example:

The angle corresponding to $830°50'$ is sketched on the figure. The terminal side $\overrightarrow{OP}$ is in the ____ quadrant. Therefore, cosine is ________ (positive/negative). The reference angle $\alpha =$ ________.

$\cos 830°50' = \cos(180° - \alpha) = -\cos \alpha = -\cos 69°10' \approx$ ________

$\tan 830°50' = \tan(180° - \alpha) = -\tan \alpha = -\tan 69°10' \approx$ ________

$\sin 830°50' = \sin(180° - \alpha) \approx$ ________

Express each of the following functions of angles whose degree measure is positive and less than 90°.

(a) $\cos 200° =$ ________ (b) $\sin 284° =$ ________

(c) $\sin 190° =$ ________ (d) $\cos 340° =$ ________

(c) $\tan 140° =$ ________ (f) $\cot 146°20' =$ ________

You may desire to find the value of a function at an angle such as $\sin 35°45'$. However, there are not any entries in Table I for $35°45'$, because this table only contains the entries at intervals of $10'$. Since $35°45'$ is halfway between $35°40'$ and $35°50'$, we can make a good approximation for $\sin 35°45'$ by finding the number halfway between $\sin 35°40'$ and $\sin 35°50'$ as follows:

In Table I, we find

$\sin 35°40'$ ________

and

$\sin 35°50'$ ________.

Their difference is ________; half of which is ________. This added to $\sin 35°40'$ gives us

$\sin 35°45' \approx$ ________.

This is a simple form of **linear interpolation.**

Finding the value of the function of an angle that is not exactly halfway between two angles in the table, is done in a similar fashion. If the angle whose functional value you desire is $\frac{1}{10}, \frac{2}{10}, \frac{3}{10}$, or any fractional part of the distance between the angles in the table, its functional value is approximately $\frac{1}{10}, \frac{2}{10}, \frac{3}{10}$, or that respective fractional part of the distance between the tabular entries.

ANSWERS TO PAGE 255

$-\sin x$

0.5925 -0.5925

$+\cos \theta$ $-\tan \theta$

$-\cos \theta$

-0.7753

(a) $-\sin \theta$ (b) $\cos \theta$

(c) $-\tan \theta$ (d) $\sin \theta$

(e) $-\sin \theta$ (f) $-\cos \theta$

(g) $-\cos \theta$ (h) $-\tan \theta$

0.9848

(a) 360° (b) 360°

(c) 180° (d) 180°

(e) 360° (f) 360°

ANSWERS TO PAGE 260

0.6051

Example:

Find tan 46°22′,

tan 46°20′ ≈ ________.

tan 46°22′ is between

tan 46°30′ ≈ ________.

tan 46°30′ − tan 46°20′ ≈ 0.006

46°22′ is $\frac{2}{10}$ the distance from 46°20′ to 46°30′. The difference between tan 46°20′ and tan 46°30′ is 0.006, $\frac{2}{10}$ of which is 0.001 rounded off to the appropriate decimal place. Therefore tan 46°22′ = tan 46°20′ + 0.001 = ________________.

(a) 0.2727 (b) 0.9548

(c) −0.1816 (d) 1.561

(e) −1.178 (f) 0.8575

(g) 0.9888 (h) 1.125

In general, linear interpolation provides a reasonably good approximation of the value of a function when the entries in the table are relatively small. Since Table I has entries at 10′ intervals we can expect linear interpolation to yield reasonable accuracy if we "round off" our results to four significant digits. Linear interpolation approximates a portion of the curve by a line segment. The shorter the segment the better the approximation. See the illustration. $\overline{AB}$ is a better approximation of the curve than $\overline{AC}$ because ________________.

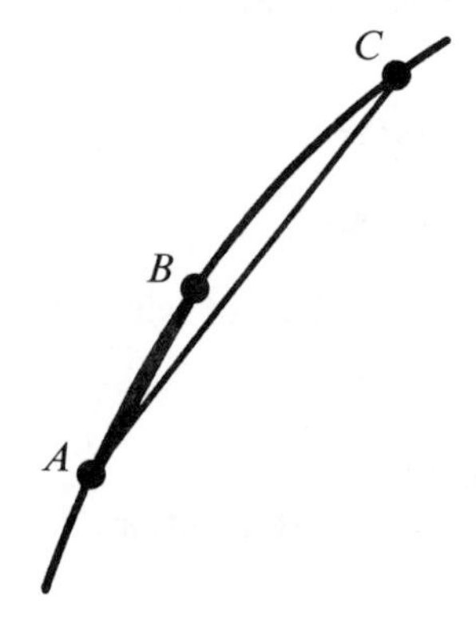

7°30′

{7°30′ + 360k° or
−7°30′ + 360k, $k \epsilon J$}

(a) 18°40′ (b) 25°50′

(c) 47°40′ (d) 69°50′

Linear interpolation is illustrated on the following magnified portion of the graph of the sine function over a 10′ interval.

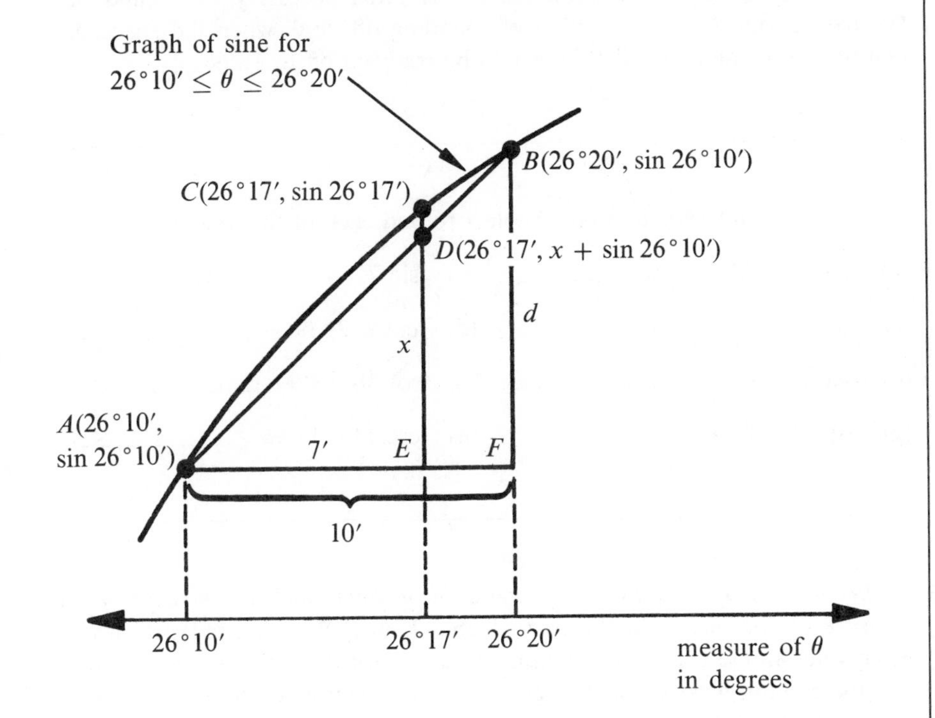

The values of sine at point A and point B are values found in Table I. The value of sine at point C is desired but not found in the table. The ordinate of point D is the interpolated value of sin 26°17′ and CD represents the actual error if linear interpolation is used.

Note that $\triangle ADE$ and $\triangle ABF$ are similar and therefore have proportional parts. Thus, $\frac{x}{d} = \frac{7}{10}$; therefore $x =$ ________, where d is the tabular difference sin 26°20′ − sin 26°10′. Sin 26°10′ + x is a good approximation of sin 26°17′.

The interpolated value of sin 26°17′ = ________.

The data in linear interpolation may be arranged as follows.

Find cos 52°46′.

		θ	$\cos\theta$		
10	6	52°40′	0.6065	x	________
		52°46′	?		
		52°50′	0.6041		

The required proportion is ____________. $x =$ ________ (rounded off to 4 places).

Subtracting x from 0.6065 (cosine is decreasing over this interval) we find that

ANSWERS TO PAGE 257

2nd negative

69°10′

−0.3557

−2.628

sin 69°10′ ≈ 0.9346

(a) −cos 20° (b) −sin 76°

(c) −sin 10° (d) cos 56°

(e) −tan 40° (f) −cot 33°40′

0.5831

0.5854

0.0023 0.0012 (rounded off)

0.5843

$\{x: |x| \leq 1\}$

$\{x: |x| \leq 1\}$

$\mathcal{R}$

(a) 13° (b) 63°50′

(c) 74°50′ (d) $\{\theta: \theta = 63°50' + 360k°$ or $116°10' + 360k\}$

---

real numbers angles

---

cos

0.6670 0.6648

0.6670

0.6648

$\frac{t}{10} = \frac{-18}{-22}$ 8′

$\cos 52°46' \approx$ ________.

Note: In making approximations, it is often necessary to "round off." We have adopted the convention of rounding off "up" when the succeeding digit is 5 or greater, i.e., 1.2675 would be rounded off to 1.268.

Use linear interpolation and Table I to find each of the following:

(a) $\tan 15°15' \approx$ ________ (b) $\sin 72°42' \approx$ ________

(c) $\cos 100°28' \approx$ ________ (d) $\cot 212°39' \approx$ ________

(e) $\sec 148°03' \approx$ ________ (f) $\cos 30°58' \approx$ ________

(g) $\sin 81°24' \approx$ ________ (h) $\csc 117°17' \approx$ ________

We often know the functional value of an angle and desire to know the measure of the angle. In this case, Table I may also be used. Locate the given value in the column containing the appropriate functional value entries, i.e., the column headed sin, cos, etc., and then determine the measure of the corresponding angle.

Example:

Find $m\angle\alpha$ if $\cos \alpha = 0.9914$. Turn to Table I. In the column headed "cos" find 0.9914. The measure of the angle in column 1 corresponding to 0.9914 is ________.

Recall, however, that cosine is a periodic function and that there is an infinite set of angles α having $\cos \alpha = 0.9914$. Table I yields only the reference angle. The complete set is ________.
The conditions of the problem usually indicate which angle of this infinite set is the desired angle.

Find the positive acute angle θ for each of the following:

(a) $\tan \theta = 0.3378$ ________ (b) $\sec \theta = 1.111$ ________

(c) $\sin \theta = 0.7392$ ________ (d) $\cos \theta = 0.3448$ ________

(*Hint:* To find (c) and (d) read up from the bottom of the table.)

Find the angle θ when a functional value of θ, such as $\tan\theta$, is given, is similar to the problem discussed in section 4.2 of finding the real number x when given $\tan x$.

For example, the set of real numbers x for which $\tan x = \sqrt{3}$ is denoted by $x = \arctan\sqrt{3}$ and is equal to ____________________ . Similarly, the set of angles θ for which $\tan\theta = \sqrt{3}$ is denoted by $\theta = \arctan\sqrt{3}$ and is equal to ____________________ .

Just as inverse circular functions were defined by restricting the ________ of the inverse circular relations, inverse trigonometric functions are defined by restricting the ranges of the inverse trigonometric relations.

Complete the following summary of the inverse trigonometric functions, by restricting the inverse trigonometric functions to ranges analogous to the restrictions made for the circular functions.

MOVE TO NEXT FRAME

DEFINITIONS:

$\text{Cos} = \{(\theta,y): y = \cos\theta \text{ and } 0° \leq \theta \leq 180°\};$
$\text{Cos}^{-1} = \text{Arccos} = \{(\theta,y): \theta = \text{Cos } y\}.$

$\text{Sin} = \{(\theta,y): y = \sin\theta \text{ and }$ ____________________ $\};$
$\text{Sin}^{-1} = \text{Arcsin} = \{(\theta,y): \theta = \text{Sin } y\}.$

$\text{Tan} = \{(\theta,y): y = \tan\theta \text{ and }$ ____________________ $\};$
$\text{Tan}^{-1} = \text{Arctan} = \{(\theta,y): \theta = \text{Tan } y\}.$

$\frac{7}{10}d$

0.4428

The capitals are used to distinguish the inverse ____________ from the inverse relation.

0.0024

$\frac{6}{10} = \frac{x}{0.0024}$ 0.0014

ANSWERS TO PAGE 264

(1)(a) $-2-\sqrt{3}$ (b) $-\frac{1}{2}\sqrt{2+\sqrt{3}}$

(c) $\frac{1}{2}\sqrt{2+\sqrt{3}}$ (d) $-\sqrt{2}-1$

(2)(a) $\frac{-\sqrt{6}-\sqrt{2}}{4}$

(b) $\frac{-\sqrt{6}-\sqrt{2}}{4}$

(c) $-2-\sqrt{3}$

(3) See Appendix.

(4)(a) $2 \sin 30° \cos 10°$ or $\cos 10°$

(b) $-2 \sin 35° \sin 15°$

(c) $2 \cos 90° \cos 40°$ or 0

(5)(a) 0.3692 (b) 1.092

(c) 1.550 (d) −0.5422

(e) −8.777 (f) 21.49

(g) 0.2560 (h) 2.211

The ranges of the inverse trigonometric functions may be stated in radians or degrees. The domains are the same as that of the inverse circular functions.

The domain of Arccos is ________.

The domain of Arcsin is ________.

The domain of Arctan is ________.

Use Table I to find each of the following in degrees.

(a) Arctan 0.2309 ________ (b) Arcsin 0.8975 ________

(c) Arccos 0.2616 ________ (d) arcsin 0.8975 ________

Similarly, the inverse trigonometric functions for Cot, Sec, and Csc correspond to the inverse circular functions with the ranges changed from ________ to ________. (See 4.2)

Finding the angle (number) whose trigonometric (circular) function is a given number, may require interpolation. The following example explains a procedure for doing this:

Find θ when $\theta = \text{Arccos } 0.6652$, i.e., find θ such that $\text{Cos } \theta = 0.6652$.

In Table I in the column labeled ______ and reading *up* from the bottom, note that 0.6652 lies between the entries ______ and ______.

Record your tabular values as follows: (t represents the number of minutes to add to $40°10'$ in order to obtain θ.)

$$10'\left\{\begin{array}{l} t\left\{\begin{array}{l} 48°10' = \text{Arcos } \_\_\_\_\_\_ \\ \theta = \text{Arccos } 0.6652 \end{array}\right\} -0.0018 \\ 48°20' = \text{Arccos } \_\_\_\_\_\_ \end{array}\right\} -0.0022$$

The minus signs reflect the decreasing values of cosine.)

The proportion for a linear interpolation is ______ and $t =$ ____.
Therefore $\theta \approx 48°18'$.

Use Table I and linear interpolation to find x or θ for each of the following:

(a) Arcsin $0.3710 = \theta$ ______

(b) Arctan $0.1145 = \theta$ ______

(c) Cos $\theta = 0.9054$ ______

(d) Tan $x = -1.126$ (i.e., ______ Arctan $-1.126 = x$; see 4.2)

(e) arcsin $0.1168 = \theta$ ______

Trigonometric equations are equations having angles as roots. Inverse trigonometric relations or functions and tables such as Table I are useful in finding approximate solutions to these equations.

Example:

Find θ such that $0° \leq \theta \leq 90°$ and

$$80 \sin^2 \theta + 22 \sin \theta - 9 = 0.$$

Factor the equation to get (______)(______) = 0.

This implies that $40 \sin \theta - 9 = 0$ or ______. If $40 \sin \theta - 9 = 0$, then $\sin \theta = \frac{9}{40}$ and $\theta = \text{Arcsin } \frac{9}{40} = \text{Arcsin } 0.2250$. In Table I we find Arcsin $0.2250 =$ ______. If $2 \sin \theta + 1 = 0$, then $\sin \theta = -\frac{1}{2}$, and Arcsin $-\frac{1}{2} =$ ______. Checking in the original conditions, the solution set is ______.

ANSWERS TO PAGE 261

$\left\{x : x = \frac{\pi}{3} + k\pi,\ k \epsilon J\right\}$

$\{\theta : \theta = 60° + 180k°,\ k \epsilon J\}$

---

range

$-90° \leq \theta \leq 90°$

$-90° < \theta < 90°$

---

function

ANSWERS TO PAGE 266

(b) $\arccos \frac{24}{25} = \{\theta : \theta = \pm 16°07' + 360k°\}$

(c) $\arcsin \frac{7}{8} = \{\theta : \theta = 61°03' + 360k°$ or $\theta = 118°57' + 360k°\}$

or $\arcsin \frac{-3}{4} = \{\theta : \theta = 228°35' + 360k°$ or $311°25' + 360k°\}$

EXERCISES. 5.3

1. Use half-angle identities and your knowledge of the functions of common angles to find each of the following:

   (a) $\tan 105°$ ______________ (b) $\cos 165°$ ______________

   (c) $\sin -\frac{5\pi}{12}$ ______________ (d) $\tan \frac{-3\pi}{8}$ ______________

2. Use the suggested sum or difference formula to find each of the following:

   (a) $\cos 165° = \cos (210° - 45°) =$ ______________

   (b) $\sin 195° = \sin (240° - 45°) =$ ______________

   (c) $\tan 285° = \tan (225° + 60°) =$ ______________

3. Prove that the following are trigonometric identities and note any excluded values. (Use the fundamental identities summarized in this section.)

   (a) $\tan 2\theta = \frac{2 \tan \theta}{1 - \tan^2 \theta}$

   (b) $\sec \frac{\alpha}{2} + \csc \frac{x}{2} = \frac{2\left(\sin \frac{\alpha}{2} + \cos \frac{\alpha}{2}\right)}{\sin \alpha}$

   (c) $\sin (\alpha + \beta) \sin (\alpha - \beta) = \sin^2 \alpha - \sin^2 \beta$

   (d) $\sin^2 \theta = \frac{2}{1 + \cos 2\theta}$

4. Express the following as products: (Use the fundamental identities summarized in this section.)

   (a) $\sin 40° + \sin 20°$ ______________

   (b) $\cos 50° - \cos 20°$ ______________

   (c) $\cos 130° + \cos 50°$ ______________

5. Use Table I to find the following functional values.

   (a) $\sin 21°40'$ ______________ (b) $\csc 66°20'$ ______________

   (c) $\tan 57°10'$ ______________ (d) $\cos 122°50'$ ______________

   (e) $\cot 173°30'$ ______________ (f) $\sec 632°40'$ ______________

   (g) $\sin 165°10'$ ______________ (h) $\tan 1.1461$ ______________

6. Use the appropriate sum or difference identity to prove each of the following:

(a) $\sin(270° - \alpha) = -\cos\alpha$ (b) $\cos(270° + \alpha) = \sin\alpha$

(c) $\tan(180° + \alpha) = \tan\alpha$ (d) $\tan(180° - \alpha) = -\tan\alpha$

(e) $\cos(180° + \alpha) = -\cos\alpha$ (f) $\sin(270° + \alpha) = -\cos\alpha$

7. Write the following as a function of an angle θ such that $0 \le \theta \le 90$.

(a) $\sin 326°40' =$ ______

(b) $\cos 132°56' =$ ______

(c) $\tan 170°25' =$ ______

(d) $\cot 246°08' =$ ______

(e) $\sec 620° =$ ______

(f) $\csc 1200° =$ ______

8. Use Table I and linear interpolation to find each of the following functional values.

(a) $\cos 27°32' \approx$ ______ (b) $\csc 33°37' \approx$ ______

(c) $\sin 65°45' \approx$ ______ (d) $\cot 26°28' \approx$ ______

(e) $\tan 20°04' \approx$ ______ (f) $\sin 170°46' \approx$ ______

(g) $\sec 72°29' \approx$ ______ (h) $\cos 170°46' \approx$ ______

9. Use Table I and interpolation to find the degree measure of the angle(s) for each of the following:

(a) $\sin\theta = 0.6248$ ______

(b) $\text{Arctan } 1.185 = \theta$ ______

(c) $\arctan 0.4152 = \theta$ ______

(d) $\text{Arcsin } 0.6230 = \theta$ ______

(e) $\tan\theta = 1.586$ and $0° \le \theta \le 180°$ ______

(f) $\sin\theta = 0.5690$ and $0° \le \theta \le 180°$ ______

10. Solve the following trigonometric equations.

(a) $2\tan^2\theta - 1 = 0$ ______

______

______

(a) $21°47'$

(b) $6°32'$

(c) $\{\pm 25°08' + 360k°\}$

(d) -0.8446

(e) $\{6°42' + 360k°$ or $173°18' + 360k°\}$

$(40\sin\theta - 9)(2\sin\theta + 1)$

$2\sin\theta + 1 = 0$

$13°$

$-30°$

$\{13°\}$

(b) $50 \cos^2 \theta + 27 \cos \theta - 72 = 0$ ______

(c) $32 \cos^2 \theta + 4 \sin \theta - 11 = 0$ ______

$\cos \alpha \cos \beta + \sin \alpha \sin \beta$

$\cos \beta \cos \alpha + \sin \beta \sin \alpha$

$\sqrt{x^2 + y^2}$

5.4. ANGLES BETWEEN LINES

The vector equation of a ray is

$$(x_1,x_2) + t\vec{r}, \quad t \geq 0.$$

In this equation, (x_1,x_2) are the coordinates of the ____________ of the ray and $\vec{r}$ is a ____________ vector of the ray.

The angle ϕ formed by the union of two rays, $\overrightarrow{PA}$ and $\overrightarrow{PB}$, having the same endpoint, is illustrated in the accompanying figure. The respective direction vectors of the rays, $\vec{a}$ and $\vec{b}$, are represented by geometric vectors in standard position.

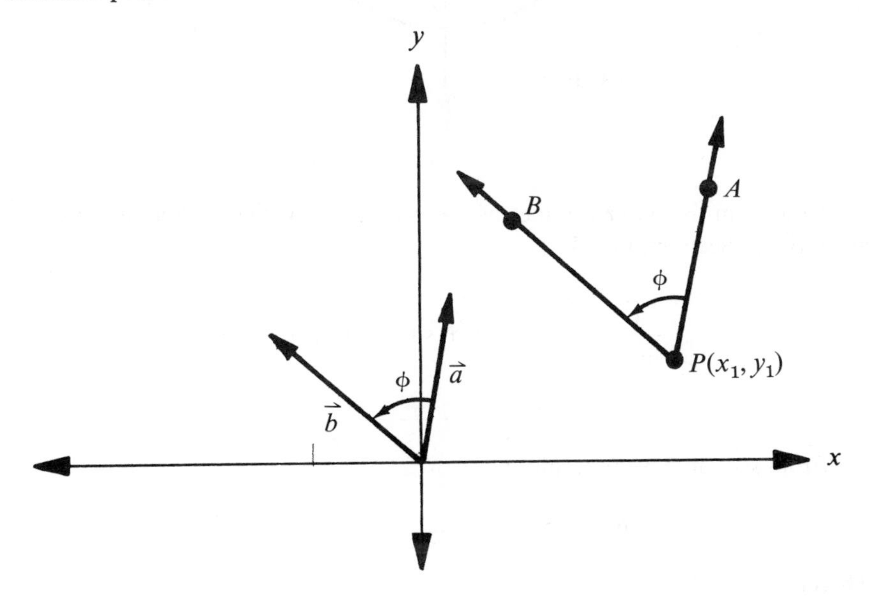

Since these representations of the direction vectors are in the ____________ ____________ as their respective rays, the angle ϕ formed by the rays is congruent to (has the same measure as) the angle formed by these representations of the direction vectors.

Consider the representation, by standard geometric vectors, of two non-zero vectors $\vec{a}$ and $\vec{b}$ in the accompanying illustration. The direction angles of these representations are ____ and ____, respectively. The **angle from** $\vec{a}$ **to** $\vec{b}$ is defined to be the angle β-α; the **angle from** $\vec{b}$ **to** $\vec{a}$ is defined to be the angle α-β. The unit direction vectors corresponding to $\vec{a}$ and $\vec{b}$ are ____________________ and ____________________, respectively.

(See section 5.2.)

ANSWERS TO PAGE 265

(6) See Appendix.

(7) (a) $-\sin 33°20'$

(b) $-\cos 47°04'$

(c) $-\tan 9°35'$

(d) $+\cot 66°08'$

(e) $-\sec 80°$

(f) $\csc 60°$

(8) (a) 0.8867 (b) 1.806

(c) 0.9118 (d) 2.009

(e) 0.3653 (f) 0.1605

(g) 0.3322 (h) -0.9870

(9) (a) $\{\theta{:}\theta = 38°40' + 360k°$ or $141°20' + 360k°\}$

(b) $\{49°50'\}$

(c) $\{\theta{:}\theta = \pm 65°28' + 360k°\}$

(d) $\{38°32'\}$

(e) $\{57°46'\}$

(f) $\{34°41'$ or $145°19'\}$

(10) (a) $\arctan \frac{\sqrt{2}}{2} = \{\theta{:}\theta{:} = 35°16' + 180k°\}$ or $\arctan \frac{-\sqrt{2}}{2} = \{\theta{:}\theta = 144°44' + 180k°\}$

$\sin \phi$

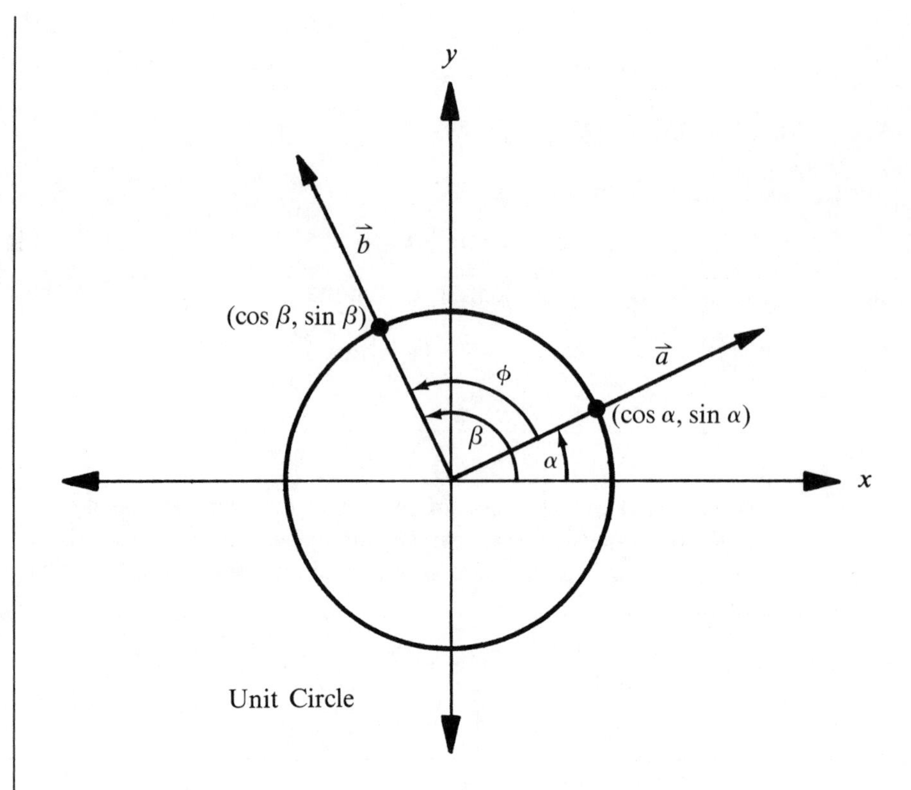

Now form the inner product of the two unit direction vectors for $\vec{a}$ and $\vec{b}$ as follows. (See section 2.4.)

$$\frac{\vec{a}}{||\vec{a}||} \cdot \frac{\vec{b}}{||\vec{b}||} = (\cos \alpha, \sin \alpha) \cdot (\cos \beta, \sin \beta)$$

$$= \_\_\_\_\_\_\_\_\_\_\_\_\_\_\_\_ .$$

From section 5.3 we recall that

$$\cos (\beta - \alpha) = \_\_\_\_\_\_\_\_\_\_\_\_\_\_\_\_\_\_\_\_ .$$

Therefore,

$$\cos (\beta - \alpha) = \frac{\vec{a}}{||\vec{a}||} \cdot \frac{\vec{b}}{||\vec{b}||} .$$

Note that $\cos (\beta - \alpha) = \cos (\alpha - \beta)$. Then if $\phi = \cos \beta - \alpha$, we have

$$\cos \phi = \cos (-\phi) = \frac{\vec{a}}{||\vec{a}||} \cdot \frac{\vec{b}}{||\vec{b}||} .$$

To obtain formulas for $\sin \theta$ and $\sin (-\theta)$, it is helpful to make some observations about a vector and its perpendicular vector. Given vector $\vec{v} = (x,y)$, we will let $\vec{v}_p$ denote the vector $(-x,y)$. Note that $\vec{v} \cdot \vec{v}_p = -xy + xy = 0$. Hence $\vec{v}_p$ is perpendicular to $\vec{v}$. (See section 2.4.) Note that the norm of vector $\vec{v}$,

$$||\vec{v}|| = \_\_\_\_\_\_\_\_\_\_\_\_\_\_\_\_ ,$$

and

$$||\vec{v}_p|| = \underline{\hspace{4cm}}.$$

Thus,

$$||\vec{v}|| = ||\vec{v}_p||.$$

ANSWERS TO PAGE 267

endpoint

direction

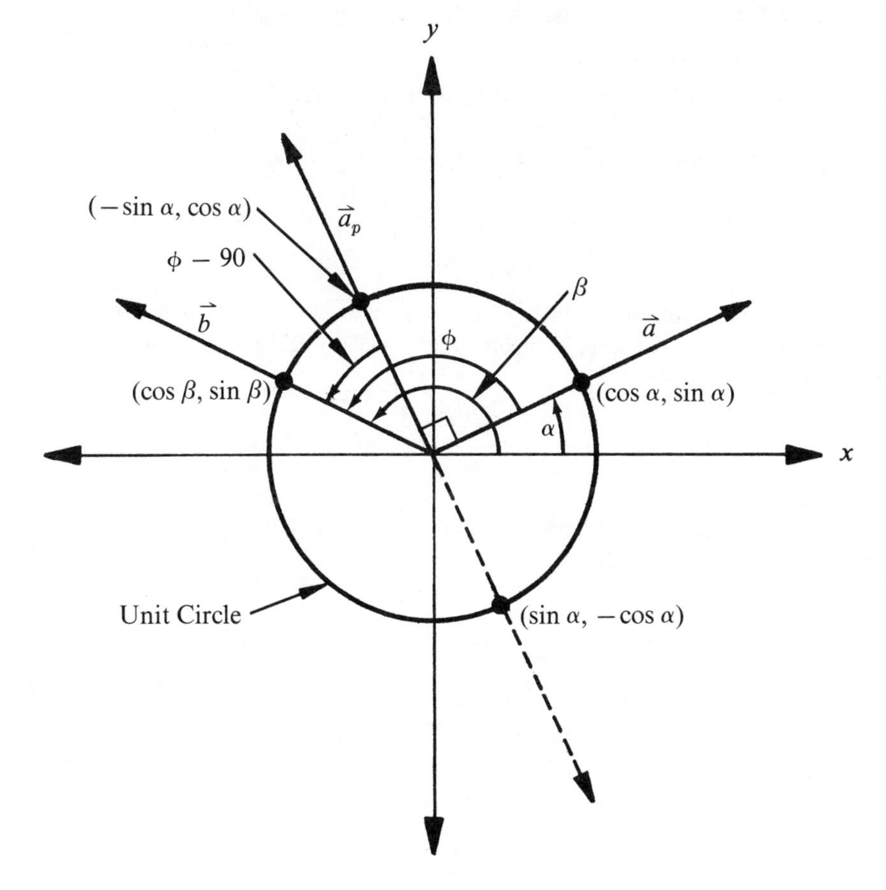

The illustration shows $\vec{a}$, $\vec{b}$, and $\vec{a}_p$. Since $\vec{a}$ is perpendicular to $\vec{a}_p$, and the measure of the angle from $\vec{a}$ to $\vec{b}$ is ϕ, the measure of the angle from $\vec{a}_p$ to $\vec{b}$ is ____________________.

same

direction

The unit vector corresponding to $\vec{a}_p$, in this illustration, is ______________. Note that there is another vector perpendicular to $\vec{a}$, namely $(\sin \alpha, -\cos \alpha)$, and the angle from it to $\vec{b}$ is $(90 + \phi)$.

Using the inner product of the unit direction vectors, we find $\cos(\phi - 90)$.

$$\cos(\phi - 90) = \frac{\vec{a}_p}{||\vec{a}_p||} \cdot \frac{\vec{b}}{||\vec{b}||}$$

$$= -\sin \alpha \cos \beta + \cos \alpha \sin \beta = \underline{\hspace{4cm}}.$$

α β

$$\frac{\vec{a}}{||\vec{a}||} = (\cos \alpha, \sin \alpha)$$

$$\frac{\vec{b}}{||\vec{b}||} = (\cos \beta, \sin \beta)$$

$(x_1,y_1) + t\vec{r}$

union

But

$$\sin(\beta-\alpha) = \_\_\_\_\_\_\_\_\_\_\_\_\_\_\_\_\_\_\_\_ .$$

Thus, $$\sin\phi = \frac{\vec{a}_p}{||\vec{a}_p||}\cdot\frac{\vec{b}}{||\vec{b}||}.$$

From the preceding frames we have the following theorem.

THEOREM:
If ϕ is the angle from a to b, then

(1) $\cos\phi = \frac{\vec{a}}{||\vec{a}||}\cdot\frac{\vec{b}}{||\vec{b}||}$;

(2) $\sin\phi = \frac{\vec{a}}{||\vec{a}_p||}\cdot\frac{\vec{b}}{||\vec{b}||}$.

Note: In this development, if $\vec{a} = (x,y)$, then $\vec{a}_p = (-y,x)$. If we use $\vec{a}_p$ to denote the other perpendicular vector namely, $(y,-x)$, then formula (2) above becomes

$$\sin(-\phi) = \frac{\vec{a}_p}{||\vec{a}_p||}\cdot\frac{\vec{b}}{||\vec{b}||}.$$

MOVE TO NEXT FRAME

Problem:

Find the measurement of $\angle BAC$, if the coordinates of A, B, and C are $(-1,-1)$, $(3,1)$, and $(-2,3)$, respectively. (See the illustration.)

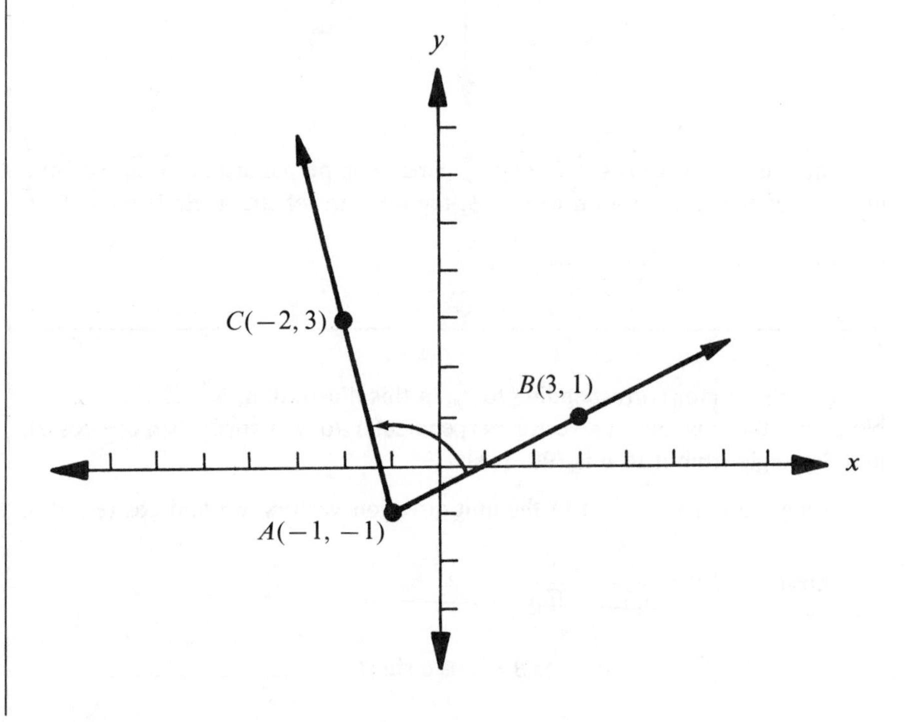

Solution:

The direction vector for $\overrightarrow{AB}$ is

$$(3-(-1), 1-(-1)) = \_\_\_\_\_\_\_\_\_\_$$

and the direction vector for $\overrightarrow{AC}$ is __________.

From the theorem in the preceding frame,

$$\cos \angle BAC = \frac{(4,2)}{2\sqrt{5}} \cdot \frac{(-1,4)}{\sqrt{17}} = \_\_\_\_\_\_\_\_\_\_.$$

The decimal approximation for cos $\angle BAC$, correct to 4 places, is ______.

In Table I, we find that $m \angle BAC \approx$ ________.

Note: There are two angles with measure less than 360° that have the same cosine value, namely ϕ and $360° - \phi$. In this problem we have selected the smallest positive angle since the illustration indicates that the desired angle is less than 180°.

$\sqrt{(-y)^2 + x^2}$

Problem:

Let $\vec{a} = (a_1,a_2)$ and $\vec{b} = (b_1,b_2)$, and use the previous theorem to show that the sine of the angle ϕ from $\vec{a}$ to $\vec{b}$ is the negative of the sine of the angle $(-\phi)$ from $\vec{b}$ to $\vec{a}$.

Solution:

(1) $$\sin \phi = \frac{\vec{a}_p}{\|\vec{a}_p\|} \cdot \frac{\|\vec{b}\|}{\|\vec{b}\|} = \frac{(\qquad\qquad)(\qquad\qquad)}{\sqrt{\qquad\qquad}\ \sqrt{\qquad\qquad}}$$

$$= \_\_\_\_\_\_\_\_\_\_\_\_\_\_\_\_\_\_\_\_.$$

(2) $$\sin(-\phi) = \frac{\vec{b}_p}{\|\vec{b}_p\|} \cdot \frac{\vec{a}}{\|\vec{a}\|} \frac{(\qquad\qquad) \cdot (\qquad\qquad)}{\sqrt{(b_1^2 + b_2^2)}\sqrt{(a_1^2 + a_2^2)}}$$

$$= \frac{(\qquad\qquad\qquad)}{\sqrt{(b_1^2 + b_2^2)(a_1^2 + a_2^2)}}.$$

Therefore, the sine of the angle from $\vec{a}$ to $\vec{b}$ is the negative of the sine of the angle from $\vec{b}$ to $\vec{a}$.

$\phi = 90$

$(-\sin \alpha, \cos \alpha)$

$\sin(\beta - \alpha)$

ANSWERS TO PAGE 274

$(-4,2)$

$(-4,2)$

$(-6,-1)$

$(-2,5)$

$(-6,-1)$ $(-2,5)$

1

-2

$(-4 + 2t, 2 + 3t)$

$3x - 2y = -16$

A line may be described in terms of a vector equation as follows.

Given a line L, let $P(x_1,y_1)$ be any point on L. Let Q be another point on L, and let $\vec{r}$ be a direction vector of ray $\overrightarrow{PQ}$. Then ray $\overrightarrow{PQ}$ is the set of all points X, whose coordinates are in

$$\{(x,y):(x,y) = \_\_\_\_\_\_\_\_\_\_\_\_\_\_, \text{ where } t \geq 0\}.$$

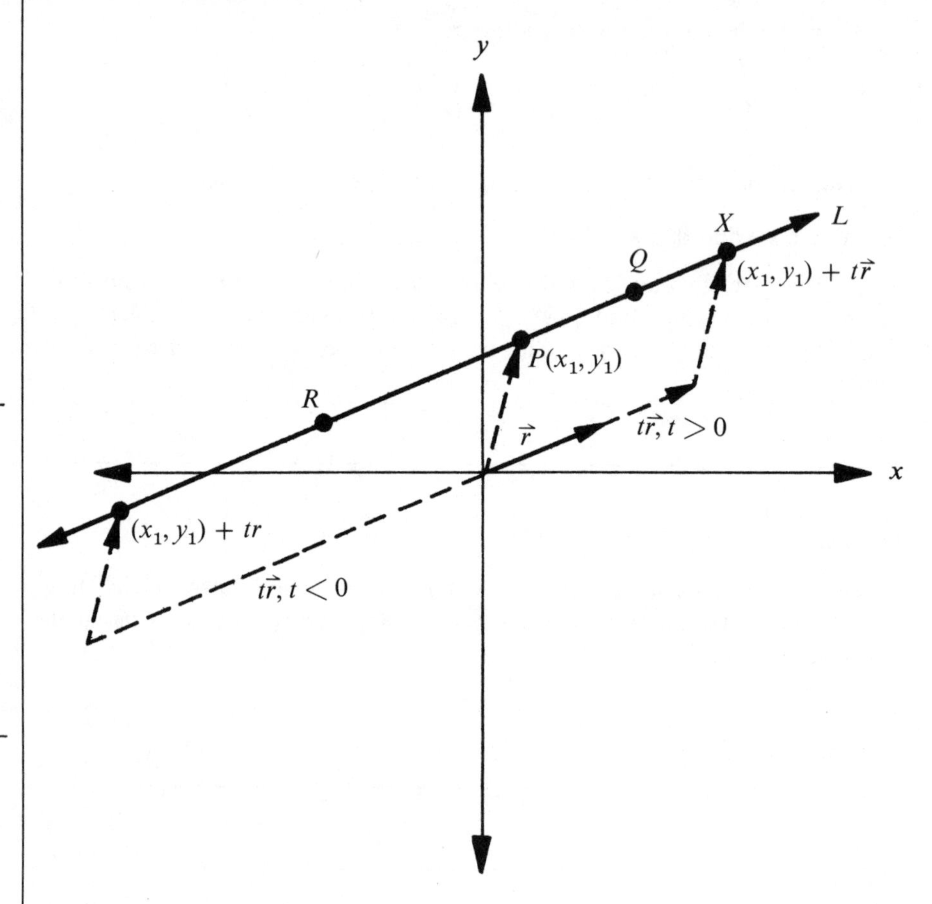

Now consider

$$\{(x,y):(x,y) = (x_1,y_1) + t\vec{r}, \text{ where } t \leq 0\}.$$

This set will consist of the coordinates of all points of the ray opposite $\overrightarrow{PQ}$; call it $\overrightarrow{PR}$ (see the figure). Now L is the __________ of $\overrightarrow{PQ}$ and $\overrightarrow{PR}$. Hence, L may be described as the set of all points whose coordinates are in

$$\{(x,y):(x,y) = (x_1,y_1) + t\vec{r}, \text{ where } t \in \mathcal{R}\}.$$

The equation $(x,y) = (x_1,y_1) + t\vec{r}$, $t \in \mathcal{R}$, is called a **vector equation** of line L. The vector $\vec{r}$ is called a direction vector of line L. Since for any $k \neq 0$, $k\vec{r}$ is a direction vector of a ray contained in L, $k\vec{r}$ is also a direction vector of L. Thus if $\vec{r}$ is a direction vector of L, so is any nonzero scalar multiple of $\vec{r}$.

Examples:

(a) Write a vector equation corresponding to a line containing $P(2,5)$ and having a direction vector $(-3,4)$. ________________

____

(b) Write a vector equation of a line containing $P(-1,-2)$ and $Q(3,-3)$. (*Hint:* Let $\vec{r} = (3,-3) - (-1,-2)$ ________________

____

The answer for Example (b) in the preceding frame suggests the following question: If

(1) $$(x,y) = (x_1,y_1) + t\vec{r}, \text{ where } t \in \mathcal{R}$$

is a vector equation of line L, and if (x_2,y_2) are the coordinates of a point of L, then is

(2) $$(x,y) = (x_2,y_2) + t\vec{r}, \text{ where } t \in \mathcal{R}$$

also a vector equation of L? The answer to the question is ________, because if (a,b) satisfies equation (1), then (a,b) satisfies (2) and conversely.

To show this, suppose (a,b) satisfies equation (1), then $(a,b) =$ ________ for some $t \in \mathcal{R}$, say t_1. To see if this vector satisfies equation (2), we must find $t \in \mathcal{R}$ such that

(3) $$\text{________________} = (x_2,y_2) + t\vec{r}.$$

Subtracting (x_2,y_2) and $t_1\vec{r}$ from both members of (3) results in

$$(x_1,y_1) - (x_2,y_2) - t\vec{r} - t_1\vec{r} \quad \text{or}$$

(4) $$(x_1,y_1) - (x_2,y_2) = (t - t_1)\vec{r}.$$

Now $(x_1,y_1) - (x_2,y_2)$ is a direction vector for line L since both (x_1,y_1) and (x_2,y_2) are points of L. Therefore $(x_1,y_1) - (x_2,y_2) = t_2\vec{r}$ where $t_1 \in \mathcal{R}$. Hence (4) becomes

$$t_2\vec{r} = (t - t_1)\vec{r}.$$

This equation is satisfied when $t = t_2 + t_1$. Hence we conclude that (a,b) satisfies equation (2). Similarly, one may show that if (a,b) satisfies (2), then it also satisfies (1).

The vector (a,b) may be obtained from both equation (1) and (2). However the value of t used to obtain (a,b) in (1) is different from that used in (2).

To find a specific point on a line defined by a given vector equation, substitute a constant for the variable t.

Example:

Suppose $(x,y) = (-4,2) + t(2,3)$ is a vector equation of the line L. Find the coordinates of the points which lie on L obtained by substituting 0, 1, and -1 for t.

(4,2)

(−1,4)

$\frac{4}{2\sqrt{85}}$ or $\frac{2\sqrt{85}}{85}$

0.2169

77°28′

$$\frac{(-a_2,a_1) \cdot (b_1,b_2)}{\sqrt{a_1^2 + a_2^2}\ \sqrt{b_1^2 + b_2^2}}$$

$$\frac{-a_2b_1 + a_1b_2}{\sqrt{(a_1^2 + a_2^2)(b_1^2 + b_2^2)}}$$

$$(-b_2,b_1) \cdot (a_1,a_2)$$

$$-b_2a_1 + b_1a_2$$

ANSWERS TO PAGE 276

(a) $\left(1, -\frac{3}{2}\right)$

(b) $\frac{-3}{2}$

$(1, m_1)$

$(1, m_2)$

Solution:

If $t = 0$, then

$$(x,y) = (-4,2) + 0 = \_\_\_\_\_\_\_\_.$$

Hence the point with coordinates ________ lies on L.

If $t = -1$, then

$$(x,y) = (-4,2) + (-1)(2,3)$$
$$= (-4,2) + (-2,-3)$$
$$= \_\_\_\_\_\_\_\_;$$

and if $t = 1$, then

$$(x,y) = \_\_\_\_\_\_\_\_.$$

Therefore, the points with coordinates ________ and ________ also lie on L.

Example:

(1) $(x,y) = (3,5) + t(4,-1)$, $t \in \mathcal{R}$ and

(2) $(x,y) = (15,2) + t(4,-1)$, $t \in \mathcal{R}$ are vector equations of the same line L.

(7,4) is a point on L. It is obtained from equation (1) by setting $t =$ ___ and from equation (2) by setting $t =$ ______.

Using the definitions of scalar multiplication and vector addition we may write $(-4,2) + t(2,3) = (-4,2) + (2t,3t) = (-4 + 2t, -4 + 3t)$.

Thus the equation

$$(x,y) = (-4,2) + t(2,3)$$

may be written

$$(x,y) = \_\_\_\_\_\_\_\_.$$

Hence by the definition of equality of ordered pairs, we have

$$x = -4 + 2t,$$

and

$$y = 2 + 3t.$$

These equations are called the **parametric equations** of the line. The real number t is called the **parameter**. Replacing t by any real number results in the determination of the x and y coordinates of a point on the line.

Eliminating t from the parametric equations $x = -4 + 2t$ and $y = 2 + 3t$ results in the familiar standard form of the equation of this line. The standard form of this equation is ________.

Problem:

$(x,y) = (6,1) + t(-3,-1)$ is the vector equation of line L. Find each of the following:

(a) Parametric equations for L. ____________ ______________

(b) Standard equation for L. ____________

(c) Equator in slope-intercept form for L. ____________

(d) Slope of L. ____________

THEOREM:

If the vector equation of line L is

$(x,y) = (x_1,y_1) + t(a,b)$ for some $t \in \mathcal{R}$ and $a \neq 0$,

then the slope of L is $m = \frac{b}{a}$, and $\left(1, \frac{b}{a}\right)$ is a direction vector of L.

Proof:

(1) Two points on L are (x_1,y_1) and $(x_1 + a, y_1 + b)$, obtained by replacing t by 0 and 1, respectively. Therefore the slope of L is

$$m = \frac{(y_1 + b) - y_1}{(x_1 + a) - x_1} = \text{\_\_\_}.$$

(2) Since (a,b) is a direction vector of L,

$$\frac{1}{a}(a,b) = \left(\frac{a,b}{a,a}\right) = \text{\_\_\_\_\_\_\_\_\_\_\_\_}.$$

is also a direction vector.

Thus, the direction vector of a line L, which has 1 as its first coordinate, has the ____________ of L as the value of its second coordinate.

DEFINITION:

The fundamental direction vector of a nonvertical line is the vector $(1,m)$, where m is the slope of the line. The fundamental direction vector of a vertical line is $(0,1)$.

MOVE TO NEXT FRAME

$(x,y) = (2,5) + t(-3,4)$, for some $t \in \mathcal{R}$ and others

$(x,y) = (-1,-2) + t(4,-1)$, for some $t \in \mathcal{R}$ or $(x,y) = (3,-3) + t(4,-1)$, $t \in \mathcal{R}$ and others

---

yes

$(x_1,y_1) + t\vec{r}$

$(x_1,y_1) + t_1\vec{r}$

$$\frac{1 + m_1m_2}{\sqrt{(1 + m_1^2)(1 + m_2^2)}}$$

$$\frac{m_2 - m_1}{\sqrt{(1 + m_1^2)(1 + m_2^2)}}$$

$$\frac{m_2 - m_1}{1 + m_1m_2}$$

---

perpendicular

Example:

If $(x,y) = (3,-5) + t(-2,3)$ is a vector equation of line L, then find the following.

(a) The fundamental direction vector of L. __________

(b) The slope of L. __________

If L_1 and L_2 are two nonvertical lines with slopes m_1 and m_2, respectively, then the fundamental direction vectors of L_1 and L_2 are __________ and __________, respectively.

DEFINITION:

Let L_1 and L_2 be two nonvertical lines. Then the **angle from line L_1 to line L_2** is the angle ϕ from $(1,m_1)$ to $(1,m_2)$, where m_1 is the slope of L_1 and m_2 is the slope of L_2. If L_1 has no slope, the angle from L_1 to L_2 is the angle ϕ from $(0,1)$ to $(1,m_2)$; if L_2 has no slope, ϕ is the angle from $(1,m_2)$ to $(0,1)$.

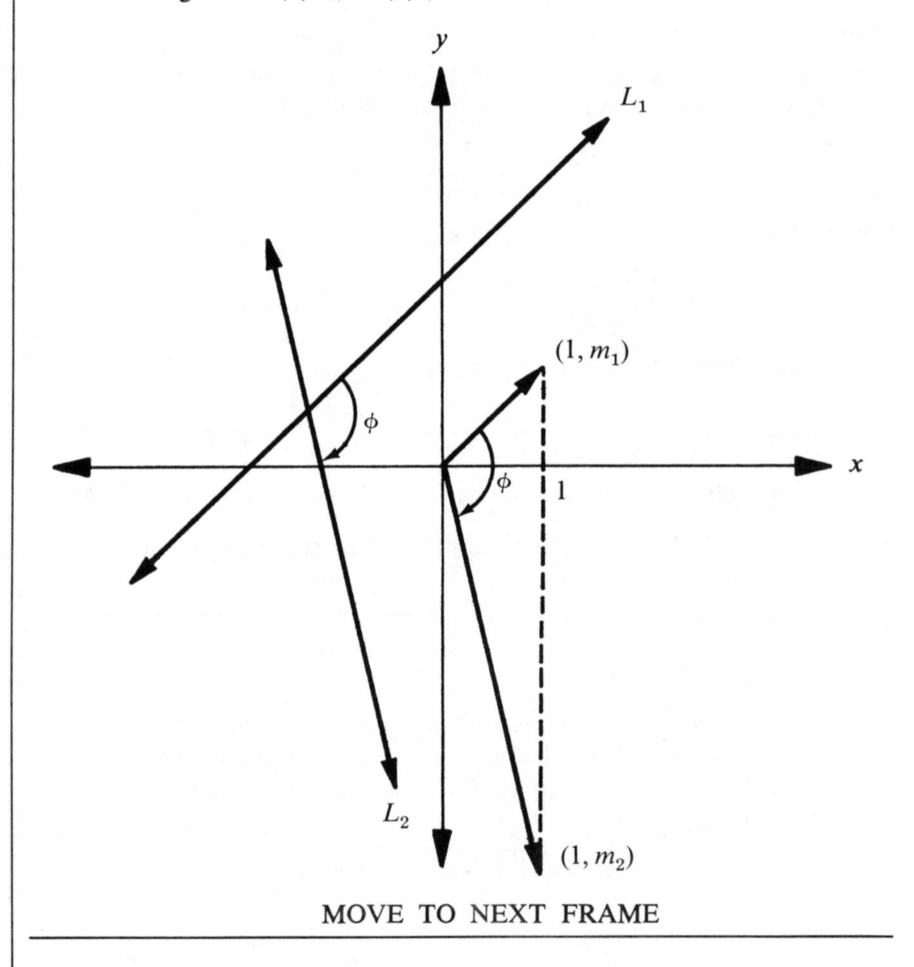

MOVE TO NEXT FRAME

(a) $x = 6 - 3t \qquad y = 1 - t$

(b) $x - 3y = 3$

(c) $y = \frac{1}{3}x - 1$

(d) $\frac{1}{3}$

Problem:

If line L_1 corresponds to $\{(x,y):(x,y) = (4,5) + t(-3,1)\}$, L_2 corresponds to $\{(x,y):(x,y) = (4,2) + t(1,2)\}$, and ϕ is the angle from L_1 to L_2, find $\sin \phi$, $\cos \phi$, and $\tan \phi$.

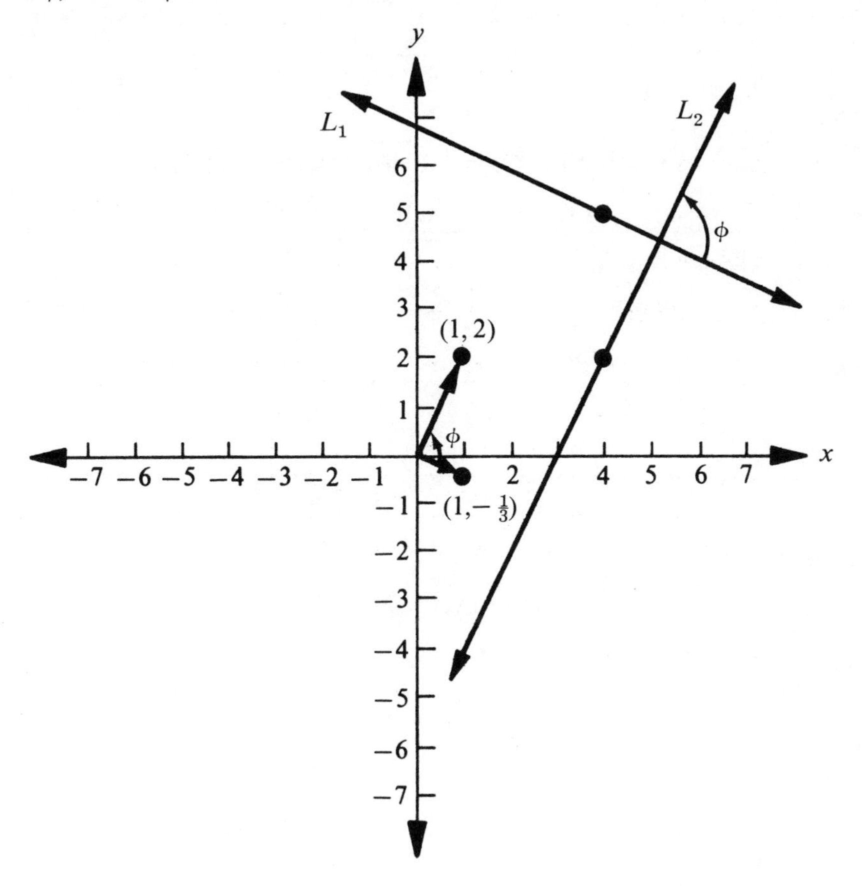

$\frac{b}{a}$

$\left(1, \frac{b}{a}\right)$

Solution:

The fundamental direction vector for L_1 is $\vec{a} =$ ____________, and and the fundamental direction vector for L_2 is $\vec{b} =$ ________. Then using the formulas at the beginning of this section, we have

slope

$$\sin \phi = \frac{\vec{a}_p}{||\vec{a}_p||} \cdot \frac{\vec{b}}{||\vec{b}||} = \frac{(\qquad) \cdot (\qquad)}{\qquad}$$

$$= \underline{\qquad\qquad\qquad}$$

$$\cos \phi = \frac{\vec{a}}{||\vec{a}||} \cdot \frac{\vec{b}}{||\vec{b}||} = \underline{\qquad}.$$

$$\tan \phi = \frac{\sin \phi}{\cos \phi} = \underline{\qquad}.$$

ANSWERS TO PAGE 280

$\frac{2}{5}$ -1

$\frac{-7}{3}$

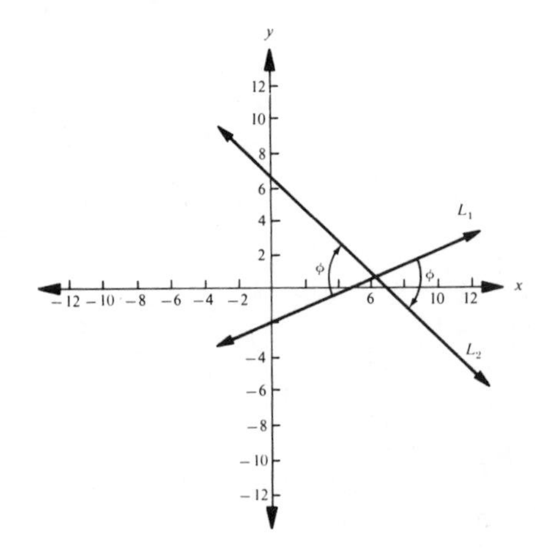

There are two possible inclinations of ϕ.

THEOREM:

If L_1 and L_2 are two nonperpendicular lines with fundamental direction vectors $\vec{a} = (1,m_1)$ and $\vec{b} = (1,m_2)$ respectively, and if ϕ is the angle from L_1 to L_2, then

$$\tan \phi = \frac{m_2 - m_1}{1 + m_1 m_2}.$$

Proof:

Using the formulas at the beginning of this section, we have

$$\cos \phi = \frac{\vec{a}}{||\vec{a}||} \cdot \frac{\vec{b}}{||\vec{b}||} = \frac{(1,m_1) \quad (1,m_2)}{\sqrt{\quad} \quad \sqrt{\quad}} = \_\_\_\_\_\_\_\_\_\_\_\_\_\_\_\_\_\_\_\_ .$$

and $\qquad \sin \phi = \_\_\_\_\_\_\_\_\_\_\_\_\_\_\_\_\_\_\_\_ .$

Thus $\qquad \tan \phi = \frac{\sin \phi}{\cos \phi} = \_\_\_\_\_\_\_\_\_\_\_\_\_\_\_\_\_\_\_\_ .$

If $m_1 m_2 = -1$, then

$$(1,m_1) \cdot (1,m_2) = 0,$$

and we can conclude that L_1 and L_2 are ________________. (See section 2.4).

Example:

L_1 has a direction vector $(-3,5)$ and L_2 has a direction vector $(6,1)$. Use the formula for $\tan \phi$ to find the angle ϕ from L_1 to L_2.

$$m_1 = \_\_\_\_\_\_, \quad m_2 = \_\_\_\_\_\_.$$

$$\tan \phi = \frac{m_2 - m_1}{1 + m_1 m_2} = \_\_\_\_\_\_.$$

$$\phi \approx \_\_\_\_\_\_\_\_\_\_.$$

Sketch the standard geometric representation of the fundamental direction vectors of L_1 and L_2. Indicate angle ϕ on your sketch.

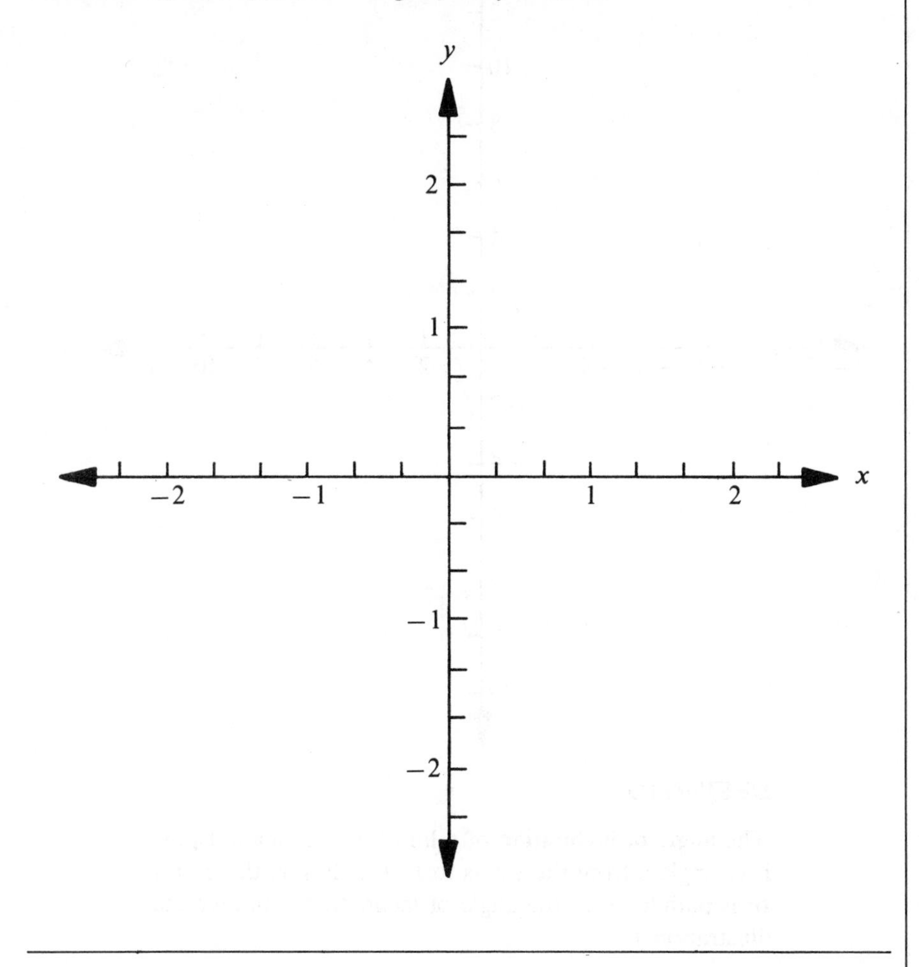

$\left(1, -\frac{1}{3}\right)$

$(1,2)$

$$\frac{\left(\frac{1}{3}, 1\right) \cdot (1,2)}{\sqrt{1 + \frac{1}{9}}\sqrt{1+4}}$$

$\frac{7\sqrt{2}}{10}$

$\frac{\sqrt{2}}{10}$

7

0

Example:

$2x - 5y = 10$ and $x + y = 7$ are equations for lines L_1 and L_2, respectively. Find $\tan \phi$, if ϕ is the angle from L_1 to L_2.

$m_1 =$ ______, $m_2 =$ ______ .

$\tan \phi =$ ______.

Make a sketch of L_1 and L_2 indicating ϕ, the desired angle.

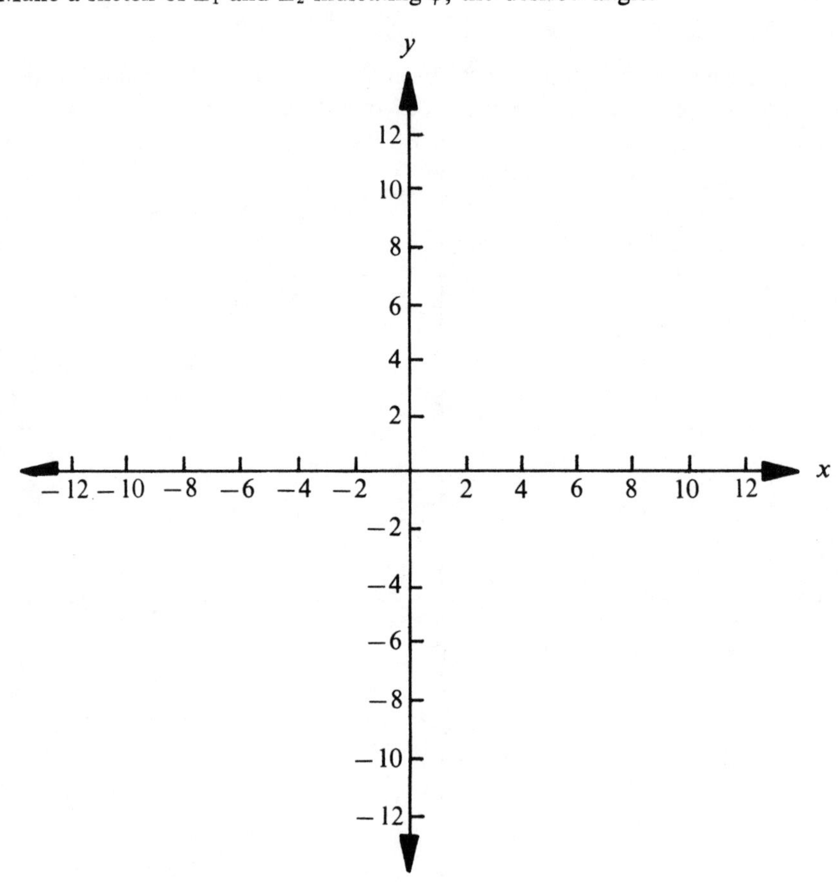

DEFINITION:

The **angle of inclination** of a line L is the smallest positive angle α from the x axis to L. If L lies on the x axis or is parallel to it, the angle of inclination is 0. (See the illustration.)

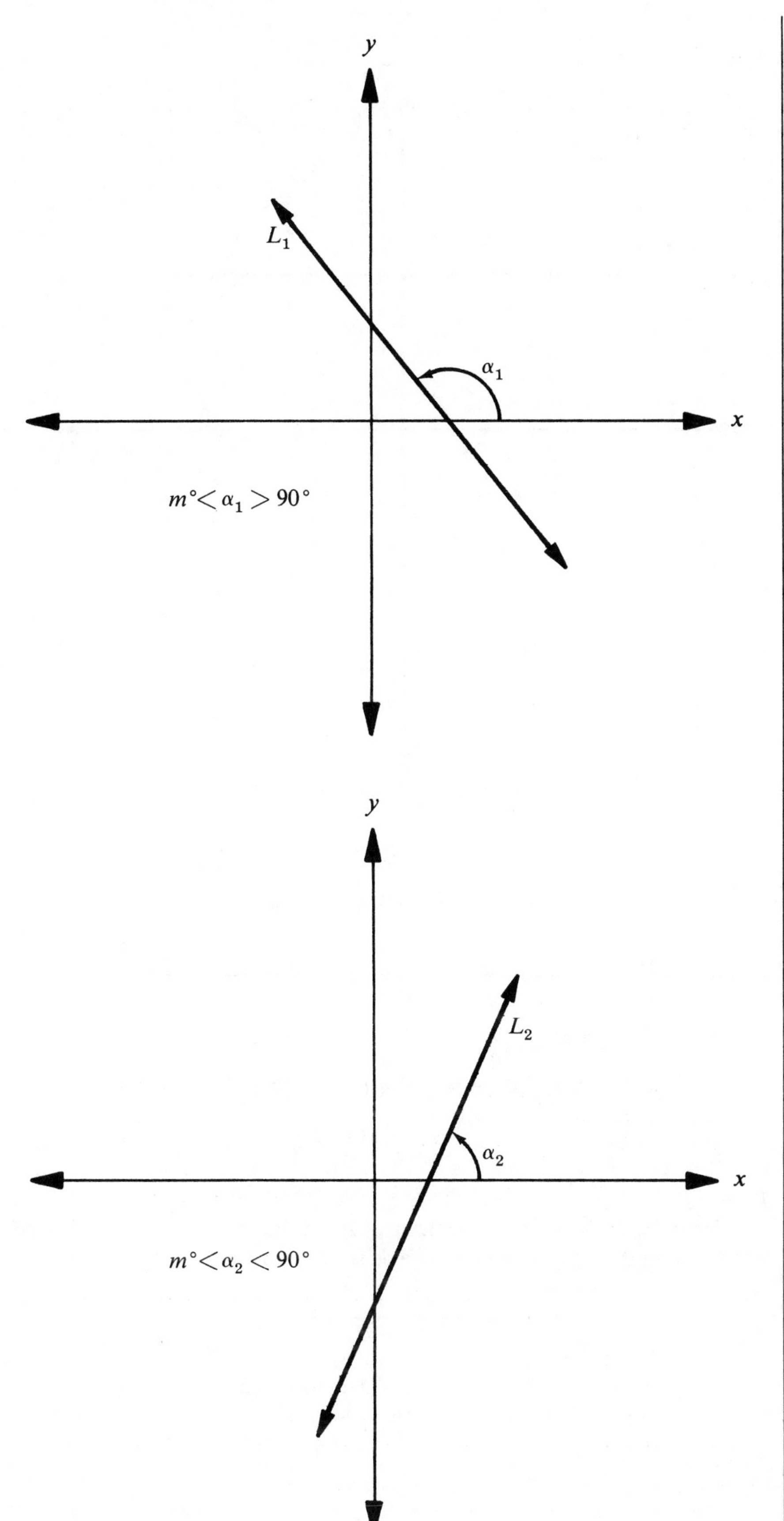
y
L_1
α_1
x
$m^\circ \angle \alpha_1 > 90^\circ$
y
L_2
α_2
x
$m^\circ \angle \alpha_2 < 90^\circ$

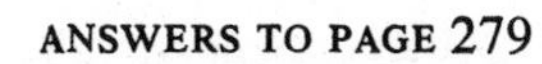
ANSWERS TO PAGE 279

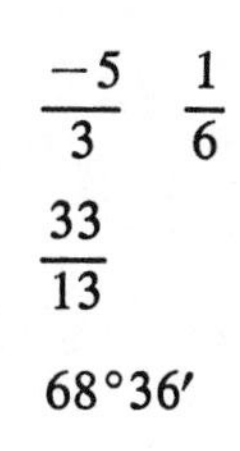
$\frac{-5}{3}$ $\frac{1}{6}$
$\frac{33}{13}$

$68^\circ 36'$

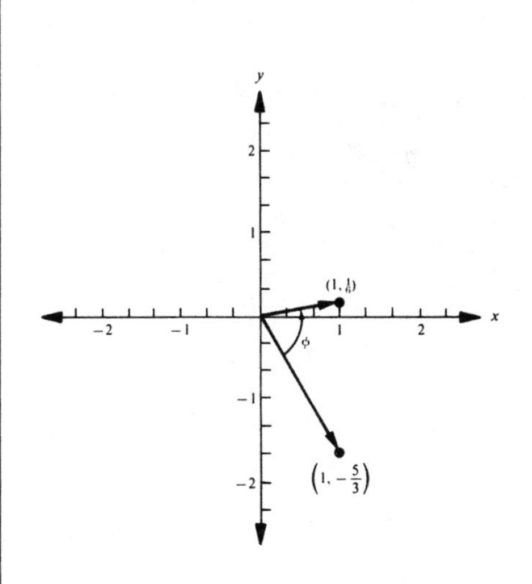
y
x
2
1
−1
−2
$(1, \frac{1}{6})$
ϕ
$(1, -\frac{5}{3})$

(1) 34°42′

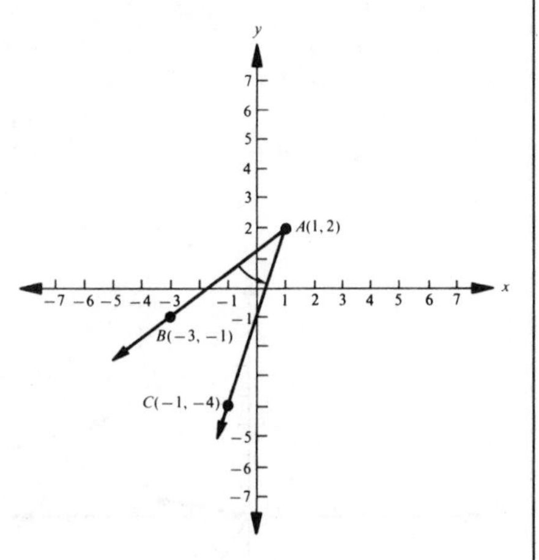

(2) (a) $\dfrac{-2\sqrt{5}}{5}$

(b) $\dfrac{2\sqrt{5}}{5}$

(3) (a) $\dfrac{14}{\sqrt{221}}$ or $\dfrac{14\sqrt{221}}{221}$

(b) $\dfrac{-5}{\sqrt{221}}$ or $\dfrac{-5\sqrt{221}}{221}$

(c) $-\dfrac{14}{5}$

(d) 109°39′

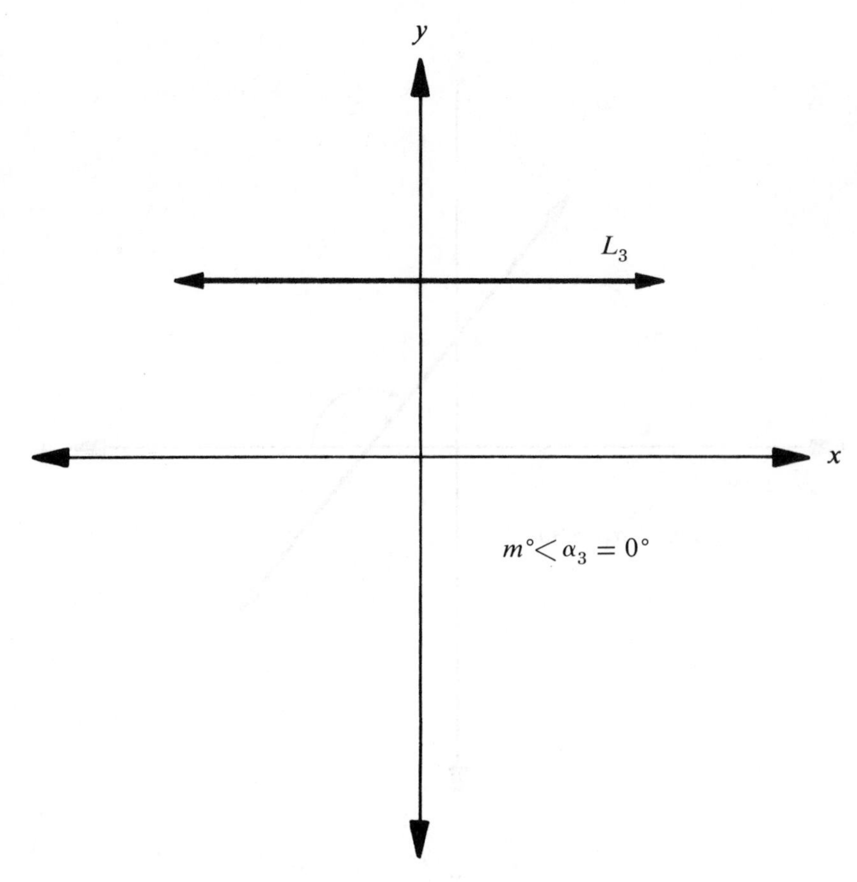

MOVE TO NEXT FRAME

THEOREM:

If line L has slope m and α is the angle of inclination of L, then

$$\tan \alpha = m.$$

Proof:

Using the formula for the tangent of the angle from one line to another and knowing that the slope of the x axis is __, we have

$$\tan \alpha = \frac{m - 0}{1 + m(0)} = \frac{m}{1} = m.$$

MOVE TO NEXT FRAME

Examples:

Find the measure of the angle of inclination for the line corresponding to

$$\{(x,y):(x,y) = (2,4) + t(-3,7)\}.$$

Solution:

$m =$ ______

$\tan \alpha =$ ____________ (decimal approximation)

$\alpha \approx$ ____________

ANSWERS TO PAGE 286

(c) $\frac{-2}{3}$; $\left(1, \frac{-2}{3}\right)$

(d) $\frac{5}{8}$; $\left(1, \frac{5}{8}\right)$

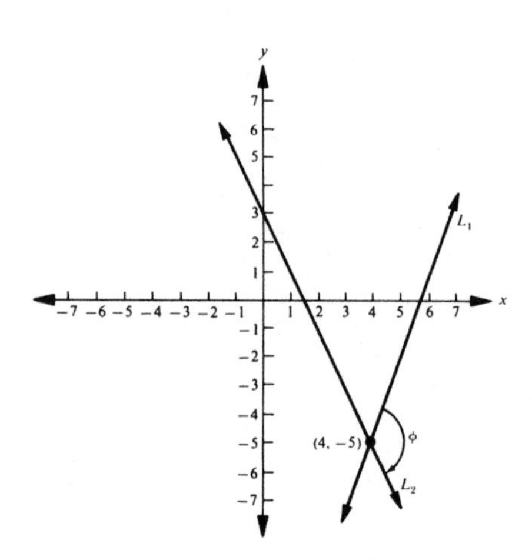

(b) (4,−5)

(13) 45°00′

(14)(a) 59°02′

EXERCISES. 5.4

1. $A(1,2)$, $B(-3,-1)$, and $C(-1,-4)$ are points on a coordinate system. Sketch $\angle BAC$ and find its measure correct to minutes. __________

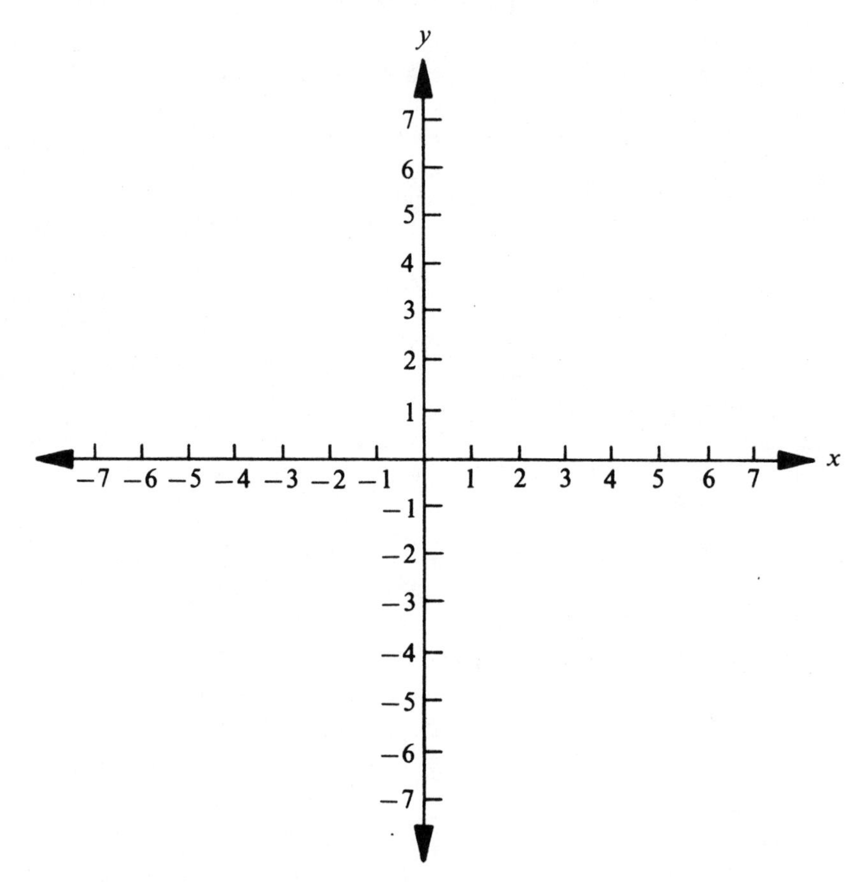

2. $\vec{a} = (-3,3)$ and $\vec{b} = (-1,-3)$ are the direction vectors of an angle.

   (a) Find the sine of the angle from $\vec{b}$ to $\vec{a}$. __________ (b) Find the sine of the angle from $\vec{a}$ to $\vec{b}$. __________

3. If ϕ is the angle from $\vec{r} = (4,1)$ to $\vec{s} = (-2,3)$, find each of the following:

   (a) $\sin \phi =$ __________

   (b) $\cos \phi =$ __________

   (c) $\tan \phi =$ __________

   (d) The measure of ϕ correct to minutes. __________

ANSWERS TO PAGE 283

$-\frac{7}{3}$

-2.333

$113°12'$

---

4. The vertices of a triangle are $A(3,2)$, $B(-1,4)$, and $C(2,-2)$. Find the measures of $\triangle ABC$ correct to the nearest 10 minutes. $\angle A =$ ________

   $\angle B =$ ________ $\angle C =$ ________

5. Write vector equations for the following lines.
   (a) The line containing $P(-5,3)$ and having a direction vector $(1,-2)$.

   ____

   (b) The line containing $P(2,2)$ and $Q(-3,4)$. ________________

   ____

6. If $(x,y) = (2,-4) + t(3,2)$, for some $t \in \mathcal{R}$, is a vector equation of line L, which of the following correspond to points on L? ________
   (a) $(3,-1)$ (b) $(-4,-8)$ (c) $(-1,-2)$ (d) $(5,-2)$ (e) $(2,-4)$.
   (*Hint:* Replace (x,y) in the equation with the ordered pair in question.)

7. Which of the following vector equations define the same line? ________

   (a) $(x,y) = (2,-3) + t(1,-2)$

   (b) $(x,y) = (4,-1) + t(1,-2)$

   (c) $(x,y) = (0,7) + t(1,-2)$

   (d) $(x,y) = (4,-1) + t(-2,4)$

   (e) $(x,y) = (4,-1) + t(-2,-4)$

8. Write $(x,y) = (6,-5) + t(-2,1)$ in (a) parametric form and (b) in standard form.

   (a) ________________ ________________.

   (b) ________________

9. $(x,y) = (3 - 5t, 2t)$ defines the coordinates of the points on a line. Write the equation of the line in standard form. ________________

10. Write a vector equation of the line (a) parallel to the x axis and containing $P(4,-3)$, and (b) parallel to the y axis and containing $P(4,-3)$.

    (a) ________________________________

    (b) ________________________________

11. Find the slope and the fundamental direction vector for the lines with the following equations.

    (a) $(-5,2) + t(-1,1) = (x,y)$ ________ ; ________

    (b) $(x,y) = (2,7) + t(2,5)$ ________ ; ________

ANSWERS TO PAGE 288

(1) 8°52′06″

(2) union

(3) 26,460″

(4) −840°

(5) $\{330 + 360k, k \epsilon J\}$

(6) (a) 30° (b) 660°

(c) 225° (d) −240°

(c) $x = 5 - 3t$ and

$y = -3 + 2t$ ______ ; ______

(d) $5x - 8y = 10$ ______ ; ______

12. (a) Make a sketch and find the measure, correct to minutes, of the angle from L_1 to L_2, if $(x,y) = (4,-5) + t(2,7)$, for some $t \epsilon \mathcal{R}$, and $(x,y) = (1,1) + t(2,-4)$, for some $t \epsilon \mathcal{R}$, are vector equations of L_1 and L_2, respectively.

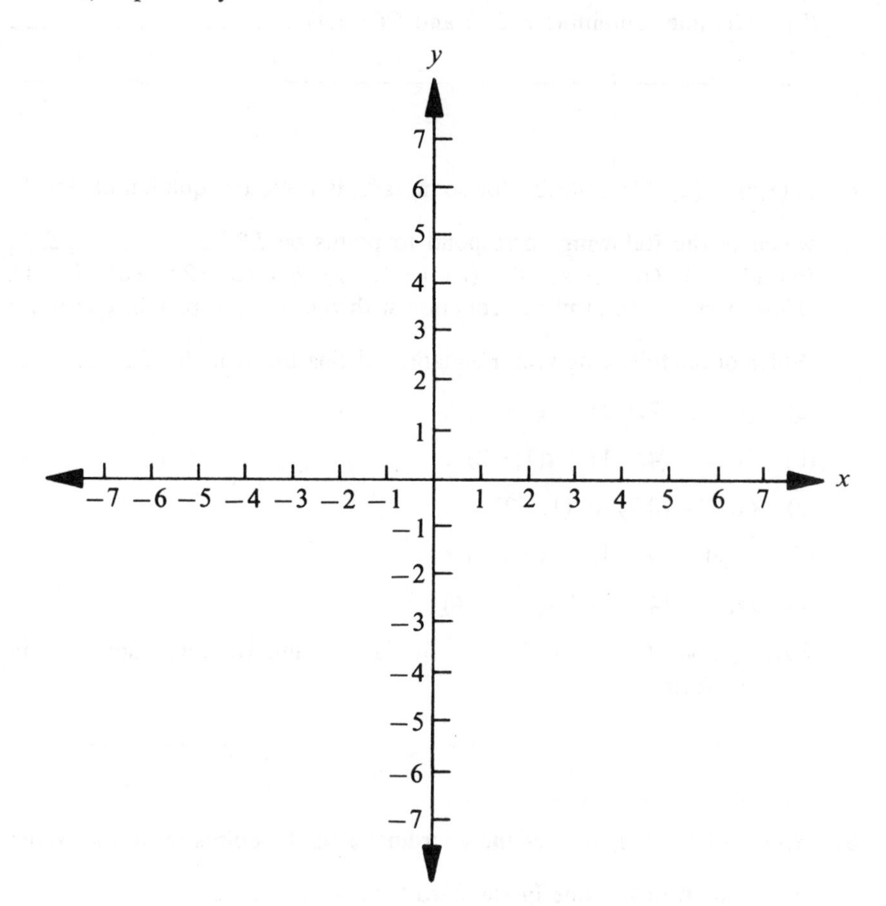

(b) Find the coordinates of the point of intersection of L_1 and L_2.

______

13. Find the measure, correct to minutes, of the least positive acute angle determined by the lines with equations $3x - 6y = 8$ and $2x + 6y = 9$.

______

14. Find the measure of the angle of inclination, correct to minutes, for the lines with the following equations.

(a) $(x,y) = (-3,-2) + t(3,5)$ for some $t \epsilon \mathcal{R}$ ______

(b) $(x,y) = (4,-3) + t(-1,3)$ for some $t \epsilon \mathcal{R}$ ________

(c) $8x + 2y = 9$ ________

15. An angle of intersection of two lines has a measure of 45°. The slope of one of the lines is $\frac{2}{5}$. What is the slope of the other line? ________

16. Line L_1 has the equation $(x,y) = (4,5) + t(-3,2)$ for some $t \epsilon \mathcal{R}$. Line L_2 intersects L_1 at $P(1,7)$. If the angle from L_1 to L_2 is 45°, find the equation in vector form of L_2.

____

ANSWERS TO PAGE 285

(4) 102°30′

36°50′ 40°40′

(5) (a) $(x,y)=(-5,3)+t(1,-2)$ for some $t \epsilon \mathcal{R}$

(b) $(x,y)=(2,2)+t(-5,2)$ or $(x,y)=(-3,4)+t(-5,2)$ for some $t \epsilon \mathcal{R}$ and other equations for the line passing through both points

(6) b, d, e

(7) b, c, d

(8) (a) $x=6-2t \quad y=-5+t$

(b) $x+2y=-4$

(9) $2x+5y=6$

(10) (a) $(x,y)=(4,-3)+t(1,0)$ for some $t \epsilon \mathcal{R}$

(b) $(x,y)=(4,-3)+t(0,1)$ for some $t \epsilon \mathcal{R}$

(11) (a) -1; $(1,-1)$

(b) $\frac{5}{2}$; $\left(1,\frac{5}{2}\right)$

ANSWERS TO PAGE 290

(12) $(x,y) = (7,1) + (-9,3)$, $t \geq 0$ or $(x,y) = (7,1) + t(-3,1)$, $t \geq 0$ and others

(13) $(2,-1)$

$(1,1)$ yes

$\left(\frac{\sqrt{2}}{2}, \frac{\sqrt{2}}{2}\right)$

(14) $\left(\frac{1}{2}, \frac{-\sqrt{3}}{2}\right)$

(15) $\frac{\sqrt{10}}{10}$ $\frac{-3\sqrt{10}}{10}$

(16) (a) $\frac{\sqrt{2}}{2}$ (b) $\frac{-\sqrt{3}}{2}$

(c) $\frac{\sqrt{3}}{3}$ (d) -1

(e) $\frac{\sqrt{3}}{2}$ (f) $-\sqrt{2}$

(g) -2 (h) $-\frac{1}{2}$

(17) (a) -2 (b) $-\frac{1}{2}$

(c) $\frac{-2\sqrt{5}}{5}$ (d) $\frac{-\sqrt{5}}{2}$

(e) $\frac{\sqrt{5}}{5}$ (f) $\sqrt{5}$

(18) (a) $\frac{-\sqrt{5}}{3}$ (b) $\frac{-2\sqrt{5}}{5}$

CHAPTER 5 REVIEW EXERCISES

1. Find the measure in degrees, minutes, and seconds for an angle whose measure is 31,926 seconds. ______________ (5.1)

2. An angle is the ______________ of two rays having a common endpoint. (5.1)

3. Find the measure in seconds of an angle whose measure is 7°21′. ______________ (5.1)

4. Find the measure in degrees of an angle formed by a ray which has rotated through $2\frac{1}{3}$ revolution in a clockwise direction. ________. (5.1)

5. Specify the set of all possible measures of the angle determined by the positive x axis and OT as indicated in the illustration. ______________ ______________ (5.1)

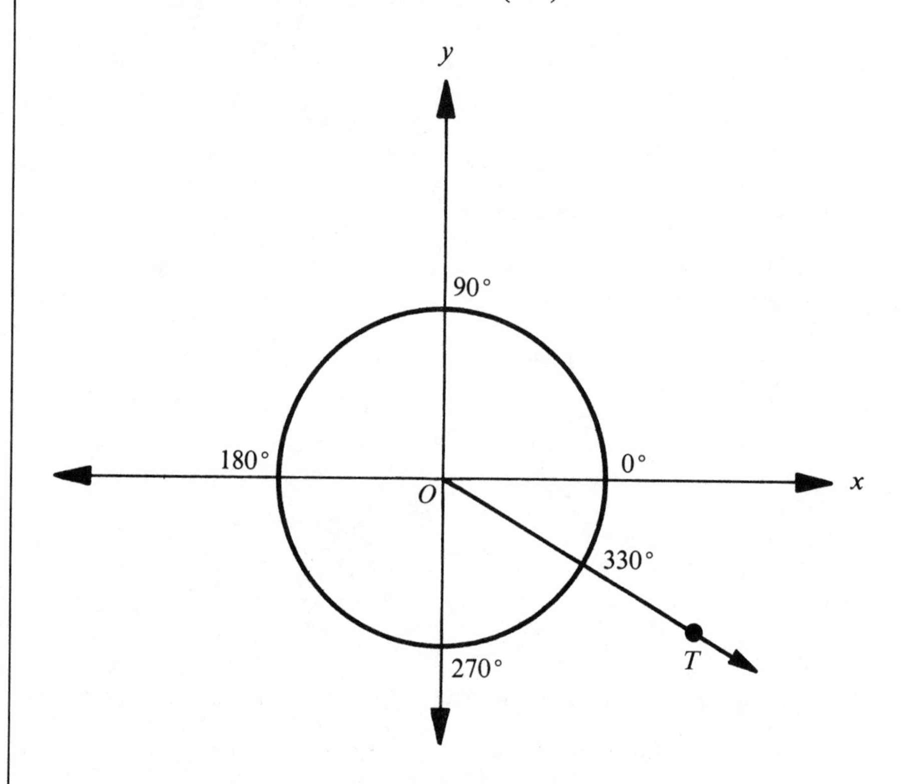

6. Find the degree measure corresponding to each of the following radian measures. (5.1)

(a) $\frac{\pi}{6}$ ______________ (b) $\frac{11\pi}{3}$ ______________

(c) $\frac{5\pi}{4}$ ______________ (d) $\frac{-4\pi}{3}$ ______________

(e) $\frac{7\pi}{12}$ ______________ (f) $\frac{-\pi}{8}$ ______________

7. Change the following degree measure to radian measure. (5.1)

(a) $-450°$ ______________ (b) $-30°$ ______________

(c) $240°$ ______________ (d) $135°$ ______________

(e) $100°$ ______________ (f) $-150°$ ______________

8. Three concentric circles have radii 1 inch, 10 inches, and 12 inches. A given central angle intercepts arcs s_1, s_2, and s_3, respectively, on each of the three circles. (See the illustration.) Find the lengths of the arcs if the central angle has the following measures. (5.1)

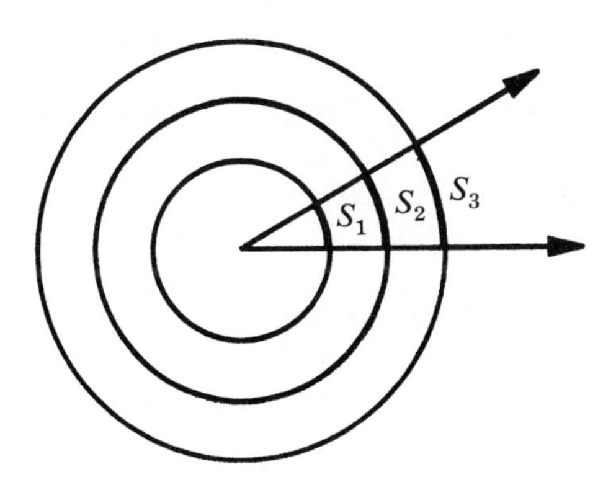

(a) $45°$: $s_1 =$ ______ in., $s_2 =$ ______ in., $s_3 =$ ______ in.

(b) $30°$: $s_1 =$ ______ in., $s_2 =$ ______ in., $s_3 =$ ______ in.

(c) $150°$: $s_1 =$ ______ in., $s_2 =$ ______ in., $s_3 =$ ______ in.

(d) $\frac{\pi}{3}$: $s_1 =$ ______ in., $s_2 =$ ______ in., $s_3 =$ ______ in.

(e) $\frac{7\pi}{4}$: $s_1 =$ ______ in., $s_2 =$ ______ in., $s_3 =$ ______ in.

9. If an arc of a circle has a radius of 14 units and a central angle whose measure is $\frac{5\pi}{6}$, then the area of the corresponding sector is ______________. (5.1)

10. If the measure of a central angle of a circle is $65°$ and the diameter of the circle is 40, the area of the corresponding sector is ________ (5.1)

11. Find the radian measure of a central angle subtended by a 10 inch arc on a circle whose radius is 20. ________ (5.1)

ANSWERS TO PAGE 287

(b) $108°26'$

(c) $104°02'$

(15) $\frac{7}{3}$ or $\frac{-3}{7}$

(16) $(x,y)=(1,7)+t\left(1,\frac{1}{5}\right)$ for some $t \in \mathcal{R}$ and others

ANSWERS TO PAGE 292

(21(a) -0.8225 (b) 0.7285

(c) -1.550

(22) $+2 \cos 50° \sin 30°$ or $-\cos 50°$

(23) See Appendix.

(24) See Appendix.

(25)(a) 0.8806 (b) $+1.182$

(c) 0.9817 (d) -0.6083

(e) 0.2568 (f) -0.2798

(g) 1.039 (h) 0.3286

(26)(a) $\left\{\theta:\theta = k\pi \text{ or } \frac{\pi}{4} + (2k+1)\frac{\pi}{2} \text{ for some } k\epsilon J\right\}$

(b) $\left\{\theta:\theta = \frac{\pi}{6} + 2k\pi \text{ or } \frac{5\pi}{6} + 2k\pi \text{ for some } k\epsilon J\right\}$

(c) no solution

(27)(a) $\frac{17}{\sqrt{290}}$ or $\frac{17\sqrt{290}}{290}$

$\frac{1}{\sqrt{290}}$ or $\frac{\sqrt{290}}{290}$

(b) $\frac{-\sqrt{2}}{2}$

$\frac{-\sqrt{2}}{2}$

12. Write the vector equation of ray $\overrightarrow{AB}$, if A corresponds to (7,1) and B corresponds to (−2,4). ______ (5.2)

13. If $(2,-1) + t(1,1), t \geq 0$ is a vector equation of ray $\overrightarrow{AB}$, then the coordinates of A are ______ and the direction vector of $\overrightarrow{AB}$ is ______. Does (6,3) correspond to a point on $\overrightarrow{AB}$? ______. The unit direction vector for $\overrightarrow{AB}$ is ______.(5.2)

14. The direction angle for $\vec{v}$ has a measure of $\frac{5\pi}{3}$. Find the unit direction vector corresponding to $\vec{v}$. ______ (5.2)

15. α is an angle in standard position. If (2,−6) is a direction vector for the terminal side of α, then cos α = ______ and sin α = ______. (5.2)

16. Find each of the following. (5.2)

(a) sin 45° = ______ (b) cos 150° = ______

(c) tan 210° = ______ (d) cot 315° = ______

(e) sin −240° = ______ (f) sec 135° = ______

(g) csc 330° = ______ (h) sin 330° = ______

17. The terminal side of angle α in standard position contains (3,−6). Find each of the following. (5.2)

(a) tan α = ______ (b) cot α = ______

(c) sin α = ______ (d) csc α = ______

(e) cos α = ______ (f) sec α = ______

18. The terminal side of ∠α lies in Quadrant II and sin α = $\frac{2}{3}$. Find each each of the following. (5.2)

(a) cos α = ______ (b) tan α = ______

(c) $\cot \alpha$ = ________ (d) $\sec \alpha$ = ________

(e) $\csc \alpha$ = ________

19. Use a half-angle formula to find $\sin 22\frac{1}{2}°$. ________ (5.3)

20. Use the identity for $\tan(\alpha - \beta)$ to find $\tan \phi = \tan \alpha - \beta$. (See illustration.) (5.3)

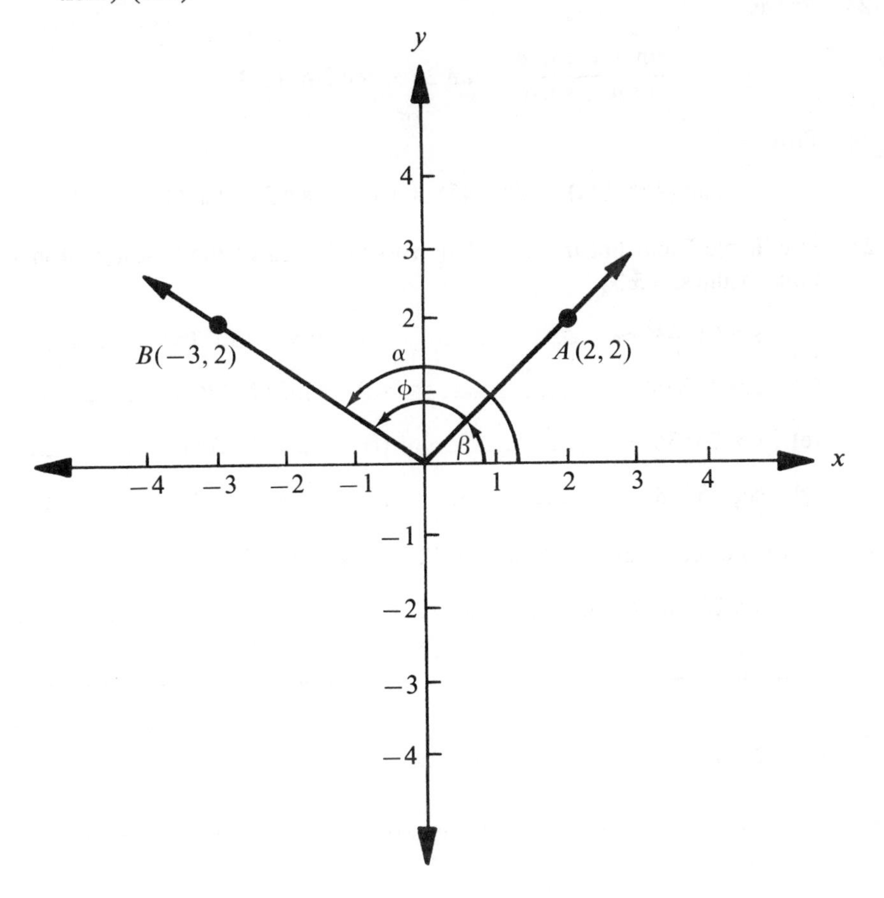

$\tan \alpha$ = ______

$\tan \beta$ = ______

$$\tan(\alpha - \beta) = \frac{\tan \alpha - \tan \beta}{1 + \tan \alpha \tan \beta}$$

= ________

$\therefore \tan \phi$ = ________

ANSWERS TO PAGE 289

(e) 105° (f) $-22\frac{1}{2}°$

(7) (a) $\frac{-5\pi}{2}$ (b) $\frac{-\pi}{6}$

(c) $\frac{4\pi}{3}$ (d) $\frac{3\pi}{4}$

(e) $\frac{5\pi}{9}$ (f) $\frac{-5\pi}{6}$

(8) (a) $\frac{\pi}{4}, \frac{5\pi}{2}, 3\pi$

(b) $\frac{\pi}{6}, \frac{5\pi}{3}, 2\pi$

(c) $\frac{5\pi}{6}, \frac{25\pi}{3}, 10\pi$

(d) $\frac{\pi}{3}, \frac{10\pi}{3}, 4\pi$

(e) $\frac{7\pi}{4}, \frac{35\pi}{2}, 21\pi$

(9) $\frac{245\pi}{3}$ sq. units

(10) $\frac{650\pi}{9}$

(11) $\frac{1}{2}$

ANSWERS TO PAGE 294

(c) 1.118 $48°11'$

(d) undefined $-90°00'$

(34) (a) 1 $45°00'$

(b) undefined $90°00'$

(c) 0 $0°00'$

(d) $\frac{-5}{4}$ $128°40'$

21. Find the functional values, as indicated, for each of the following. (Use Table I in Appendix.) (5.3)

 (a) $\sin 235°20' =$ ________. (b) $\cos 400°40' =$ ________.

 (c) $\tan 122°50' =$ ________.

22. Write $\sin 80° - \sin 20°$ as a product.

 ______________________________ (5.3)

23. Prove

$$\frac{\sin\alpha + \cos\alpha}{\cos\alpha - \sin\alpha} = \tan 2\alpha + \sec 2\alpha. \quad (5.3)$$

24. Prove

$$\cos^2(45° + \alpha) - \sin^2(45° + \alpha) = -\sin 2\alpha. \quad (5.3)$$

25. Use Table I and linear interpolation to find each of the following functional values. (5.3)

 (a) $\sin 61°43' \approx$ ________ (b) $\tan -130°14' \approx$ ________

 (c) $\cos 10°58' \approx$ ________ (d) $\sin 217°28' \approx$ ________

 (e) $\cot 75°36' \approx$ ________ (f) $\tan 164°22' \approx$ ________

 (g) $\sec 15°38' \approx$ ________ (h) $\cos -70°49' \approx$ ________

26. Solve the following equations for all values of θ. (5.3)

 (a) $\sin 2\theta \cos\theta = \sin\theta$ ______________________________

 ____

 (b) $2\sin^2\theta + 13\sin\theta - 7 = 0$ ______________________________

 ____

 (c) $\frac{1}{2}\sin 2\theta = 1$ ______________________________

27. Let ϕ be the angle from $\vec{a}$ to $\vec{b}$ and find $\cos\phi$ and $\sin\phi$ for each of the following: (5.4)

 (a) $\vec{a} = (2,4)$ $\cos\phi =$ ________

 $\vec{b} = (3,7)$ $\sin\phi =$ ________

 (b) $\vec{a} = (1,2)$ $\cos\phi =$ ________

 $\vec{b} = (1,-3)$ $\sin\phi =$ ________

28. Find the angle ϕ, correct to minutes, from $\vec{r}$ to $\vec{s}$ if $\vec{r}=(-4,2)$ and $\vec{s}=(-1,-3)$. __________ (5.4)

29. Write a vector equation for each of the lines determined by the following. (5.4)

(a) Containing $P(8,3)$ and having direction vector $(-8,2)$ __________

(b) Containing $R(-1,5)$ and $S(3,7)$

(c) Parallel to the line defined by $3x - y = 7$ and containing $(-2,3)$.

30. If L corresponds to $\{(x,y):(x,y) = (4,-5) + t(3,1)\}$, determine which of the following are coordinates of points on L. __________ (5.4)

(a) $(1,4)$ (b) $(7,-6)$ (c) $(-2,-7)$ (d) $(1,-6)$

31. Write (a) the parametric equations and thence (b) the standard equation of the line whose vector equation is $(x,y) = (1,-4) + t(2,3)$. (5.4)

(a) __________

(b) __________

32. Find the fundamental direction vectors for each of the following. (5.4)

(a) $\{(x,y):(x,y) = (-4,2) + t(-3,2)\}$ __________

(b) $\{(x,y):(x,y) = (3,-5) + t(1,7)\}$ __________

(c) $\{(x,y):(x,y) = (-1,-4) + t(3,-1)\}$ __________

(d) $\{(x,y):(x,y) = t(7,-6)\}$ __________

(e) $\{(x,y):y = 2x + 5\}$ __________

(f) $\{(x,y):3x - 2y = 6\}$ __________

33. Find $\tan \phi$ and the measure of the angle ϕ from L_1 to L_2, correct to minutes, if the equations for L_1 and L_2, respectively, are as follows. (5.4)

(a) L_1: $(x,y) = (-5,2) + t(-1,2)$
L_2: $(x,y) = (4,4) + t(2,5)$

$\tan \phi =$ __________ : $\phi \approx$ __________

(b) L_1: $x = -4t$, $y = 2 + 3t$
L_2: $x = -5 + 2t$, $y = -7 + t$

$\tan \phi =$ __________ : $\phi \approx$ __________

ANSWERS TO PAGE 291

(c) $\frac{-\sqrt{5}}{2}$ (d) $\frac{-3\sqrt{5}}{5}$

(e) $\frac{3}{2}$

(19) $\frac{1}{2}\sqrt{2-\sqrt{2}}$

(20) $-\frac{2}{3}$

1

$$\frac{-\frac{2}{3} \quad -1}{1+\left(\frac{-2}{3}\right)\ (1)}$$

-5

ANSWERS TO PAGE 296

(0,7)

(−5,−2)   (5,−5)

$\sqrt{29}$ $5\sqrt{2}$

7

(c) L_1: $3x + 4y = 12$
L_2: $x - 5y = 8$

$\tan \phi =$ ________: $\phi \approx$ ________

(d) L_1: $(x,y) = (2,-6) + t(4,1)$
L_2: $(x,y) = (1,1) + t(-1,4)$

$\tan \phi =$ ________: $\phi \approx$ ________

34. Find the slope and the measure of the angle of inclination, correct to minutes, for the lines defined by each of the following. (5.4)

(a) $\{(x,y):(x,y) = (1,-7) + t(1,1)\}$

m: ________ α: ________

(b) $\{(x,y):(x,y) = (9,-2) + t(0,1)\}$

m: ________ α: ________

(c) $\{(x,y):(x,y) = (-6,1) + t(1,0)\}$

m: ________ α: ________

(d) $\{(x,y):(x,y) = (3,2) + t(-4,5)\}$

m: ________ α: ________

CHAPTER 6

(28) 98°08′

Trigonometry II

(29) (a) $(x,y) = (8,3) + t(-8,2)$ or $(x,y) = (8,3) + t(-4,1)$

(b) $(x,y) = (-1,5) + t(4,2)$ or $(x,y) = (3,7) + t(2,1)$ and others

(c) $(x,y) = (-2,3) + t(1,3)$

6.1. THE RIGHT TRIANGLE

The sides of a triangle may be thought of as geometric vectors. In this case the norms of the corresponding vectors would then be the **lengths of the sides.** If the vertex of a triangle is denoted by a capital letter, say X, then the vector corresponding to the opposite side will be denoted $\vec{x}$, and its length $\|\vec{x}\|$ will simply be denoted by x. Thus the length of the side opposite B in $\triangle ABC$ is

$$\|\vec{b}\| = \_\_\_\_\_\_\_\_\_\_.$$

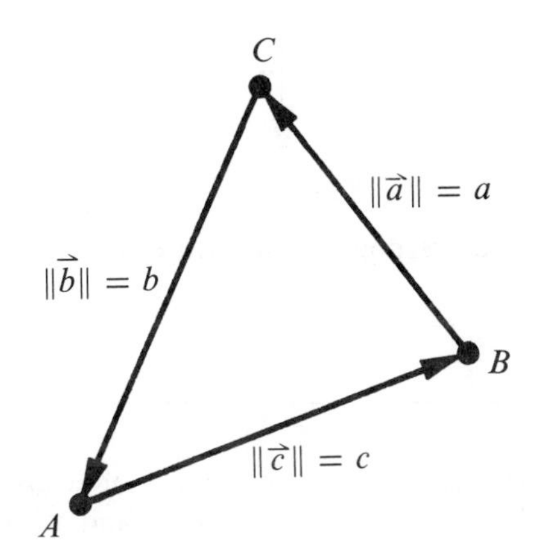

(30) c, d

(31) (a) $x = 1 + 2t$, $y = -4 + 3t$

(b) $3x - 2y = 11$

(32) (a) $\left(1, -\frac{2}{3}\right)$

(b) (1,7)

(c) $\left(1, -\frac{1}{3}\right)$

(d) $\left(1, \frac{-6}{7}\right)$

(e) (1,2)

(f) $\left(1, \frac{3}{2}\right)$

The geometric vectors corresponding to the sides of a triangle will always be directed so that the interior of the triangle lies to the left of the vector as it is transversed from its initial point to its terminal point. This is illustrated in the preceding frame. The sum of the corresponding vectors would therefore be ______.

(33) (a) −1.125   131°38′

(b) 2.000   63°26′

ANSWERS TO PAGE 298

$\overrightarrow{EF}$

$\overrightarrow{ED}$

zero

$(-6,4)$

$(4,-7)$

$(2,3)$

$\angle K$

$(-6,4)$ and $(-2,-3)$

zero

180°

90°

90°

complementary

acute

In $\triangle ABC$, as illustrated, the vector corresponding to side $\overline{AB}$ is ______, to $\overline{BC}$ is ______, and to $\overline{CA}$ is ______.

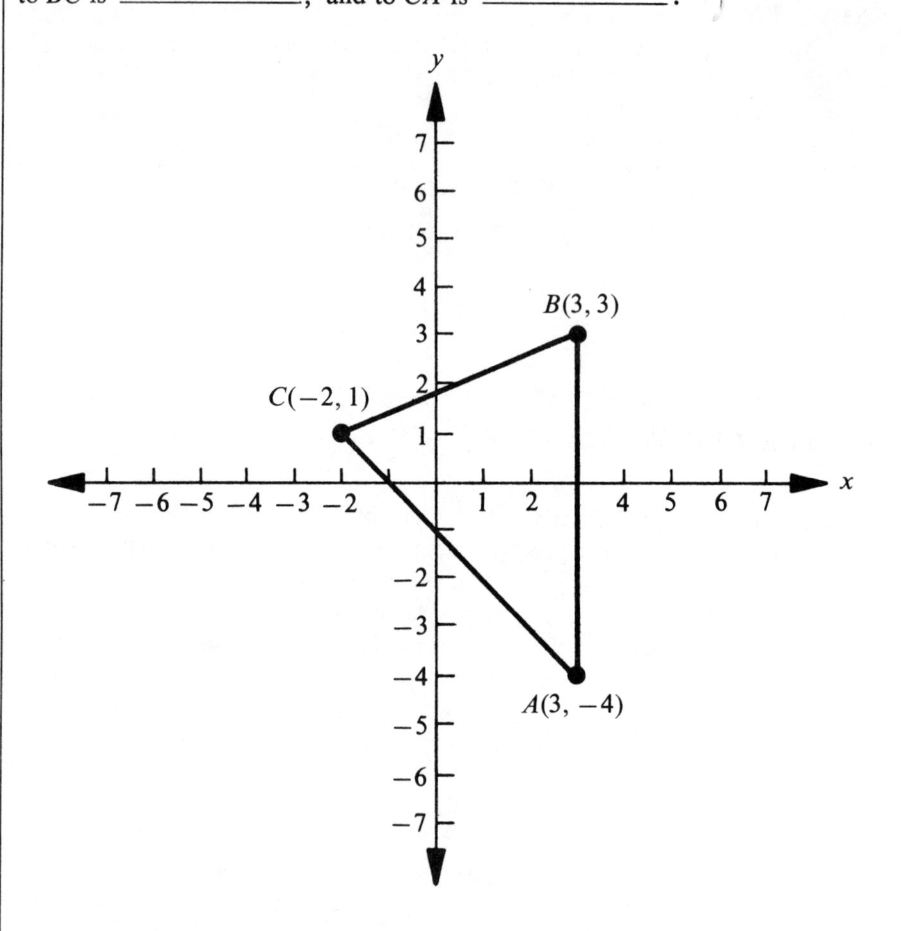

The lengths of the corresponding sides are $a =$ ______, $b =$ ______, and $c =$ ______.

An **angle of a triangle** is a positive angle of degree measure less than 180°, whose vertex is a vertex of the triangle and whose sides contain the other two vertices.

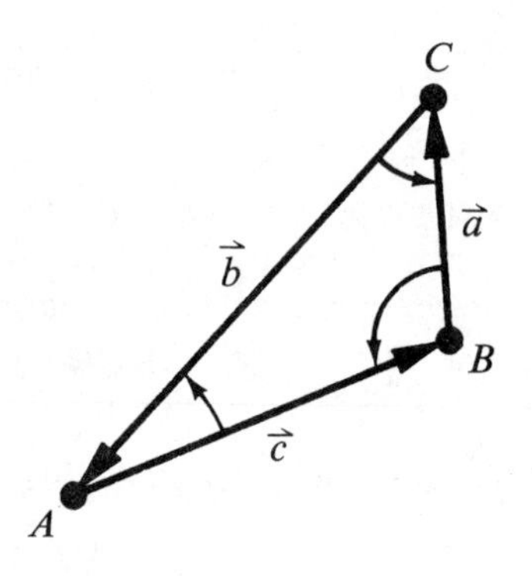

The angles are considered to be formed by a counter-clockwise rotation. This being the case, $\angle B$, in the illustration, is the angle from ray ______ to ray ______. Direction vectors for the rays forming $\angle B$ are ______ for $\overrightarrow{BC}$ and ______ for $\overrightarrow{BA}$.

b

Referring to $\triangle RST$ as illustrated, find each of the following.

$\vec{r} =$ ______; $r =$ ______

$\vec{s} =$ ______; $s =$ ______

$\vec{t} =$ ______; $t =$ ______

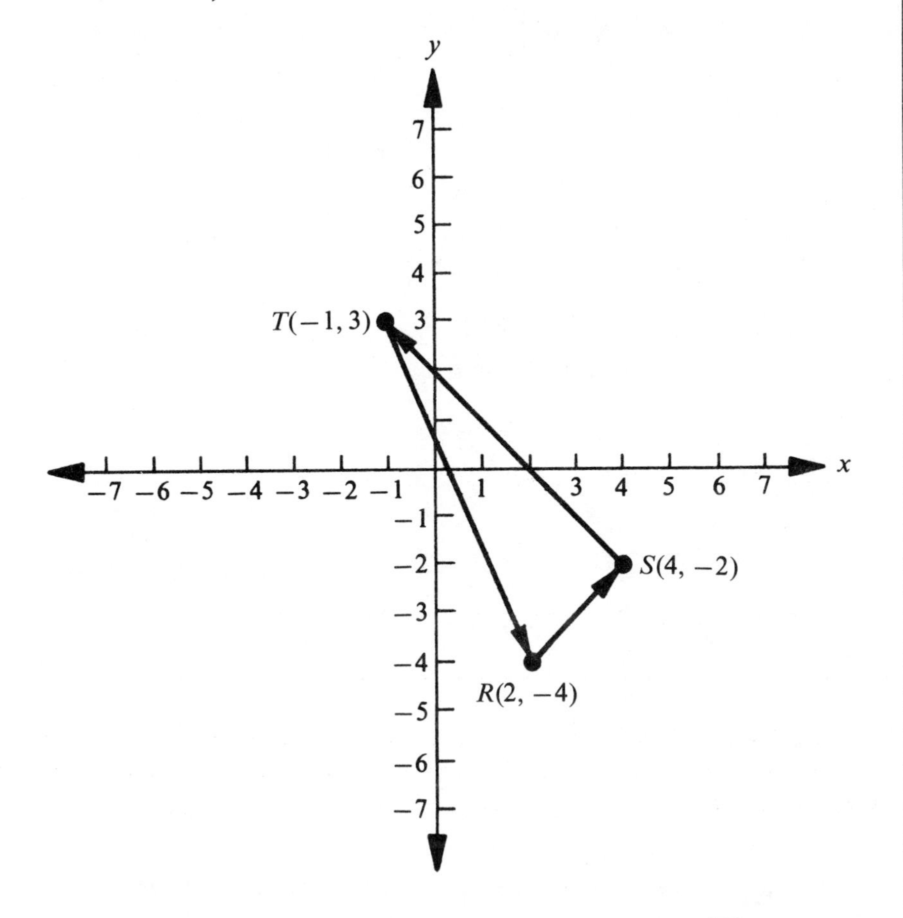

Direction vectors for the sides of $\angle T$ are ______ for $\overrightarrow{TS}$ and ______ for $\overrightarrow{TR}$.

If one of the angles of a triangle is a right angle, then the triangle is said to be a right triangle. The degree measure of a right angle is ______.

0

0

$\frac{b}{c}$

$\frac{a}{c}$

$\frac{b}{c}$

$\frac{a}{b}$

$\frac{b}{a}$

$\triangle DEF$ is a right triangle with $m° \angle E = 90°$. This means rays ______ and ______ are perpendicular, and the inner product of their corresponding vectors $\vec{d} \cdot \vec{f}$ is ________. (See section 2.4.)

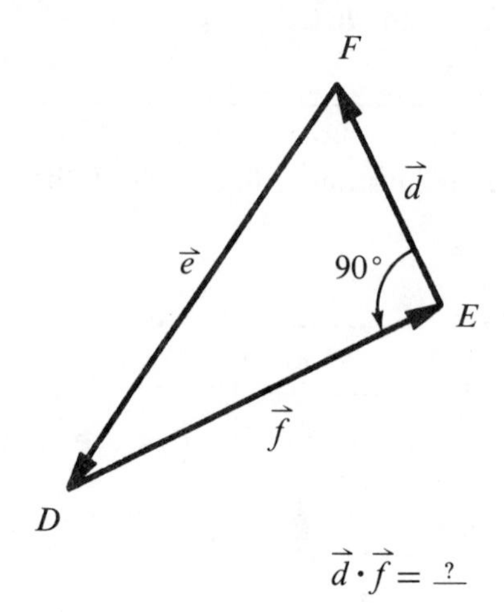

$\vec{d} \cdot \vec{f} = \underline{?}$

$T(-3,5)$, $K(3,1)$, and $G(1,-2)$ are the vertices of right $\triangle GKT$. The vectors corresponding to each side are:

$\vec{g} =$ ____________________,

$\vec{k} =$ ____________________,

and

$\vec{t} =$ ____________________.

Which angle is the right angle? ________ What are the direction vectors for the sides of the right angle? ____________________ The inner product of these direction vectors is ________.

Since the sum of the degree measures of the angles of a triangle is ______, and since the right angle in a right triangle has a degree measure of ______, the sum of the degree measures of the remaining two angles is ________.

Therefore, the two remaining angles are said to be ______________ angles. They are also referred to as ____________ angles since each of their measures is less than 90°.

In $\triangle ABC$ as illustrated, ______ is a right angle and $\angle C$ and ______ are complementary acute angles. Find each of the following. (See section 5.4.)

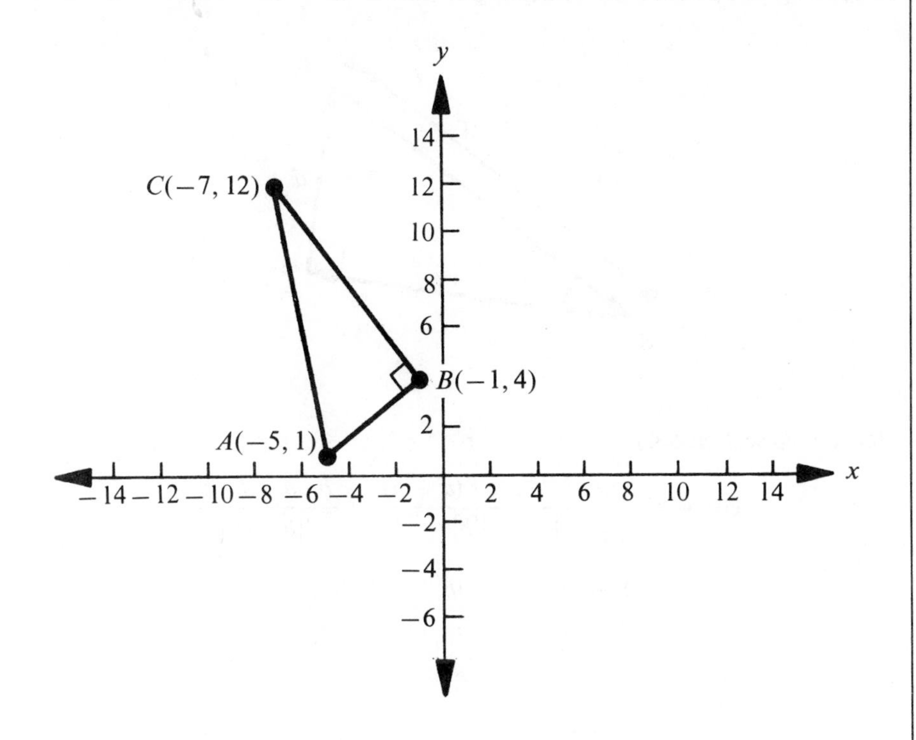

(a) $\cos A =$ ______ $\quad \sin C =$ ______

(b) $\sin A =$ ______ $\quad \cos C =$ ______

Observe in the preceding frame that since $m^\circ \angle C = 90^\circ - m^\circ \angle A$,

$$\sin C = \sin (90^\circ - A) = \cos A.$$

Also,

$$\cos C = \cos (90^\circ - A) = \text{______}.$$

Since $\angle C$ and $\angle A$ are complementary angles, the sine of an angle is equal to the cosine of its complement, and the cosine of an angle is equal to the sine of its complement. Sin and cos are called **co-functions.** Tan and cot are also co-functions, as are sec and csc. It may be verified that

$$\tan A = \cot (90^\circ - A), \quad \cot A = \tan (90^\circ - A),$$

$$\sec A = \csc (90^\circ - A) \text{ and } \csc A = \sec (90^\circ - A).$$

Thus, in every case, we may say that the value of a trigonometric function at an angle is equal to the value of the co-function at the complementary angle.

ANSWERS TO PAGE 297

$\overrightarrow{BC}$

$\overrightarrow{BA} \quad \vec{a}$

$-\vec{c}$

$(-5,5) \quad 5\sqrt{2}$

$(3,-7) \quad \sqrt{58}$

$(2,2) \quad 2\sqrt{2}$

$(5,-5) \quad (3,-7)$

90°

---

tan 40°

0.8391 15.10

---

c

e

$\frac{e}{c}$ $\frac{e}{c}$

$\frac{f}{c}$ $\frac{e}{f}$ $\frac{e}{f}$

(a) 60° 10 $10\sqrt{3}$ or 17.32

Let $\angle C$ be the right angle in $\triangle ABC$ as illustrated. If the vectors corresponding to the sides are as indicated, then $\vec{a} \cdot \vec{b} =$ ______.

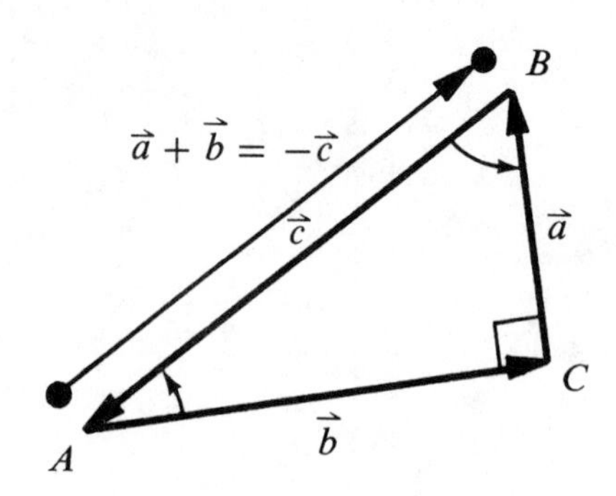

Hence (see section 5.4)

$$\cos A = \frac{\vec{b} \cdot (-\vec{c})}{||\vec{b}||\ ||\vec{c}||} = \frac{\vec{b} \cdot (\vec{a} + \vec{b})}{||\vec{b}||\ ||\vec{c}||} = \frac{\vec{b} \cdot \vec{a} + \vec{b} \cdot \vec{b}}{||\vec{b}||\ ||\vec{c}||}$$

$$= \frac{0 + \vec{b} \cdot \vec{b}}{||\vec{b}||\ ||\vec{c}||} = \frac{||\vec{b}||^2}{||\vec{b}||\ ||\vec{c}||} = \frac{||\vec{b}||}{||\vec{c}||}$$

$$= \text{\_\_\_\_\_\_}.$$

and

$$(\vec{b} \cdot \vec{b} = ||\vec{b}||^2; \text{ see section 2.4})$$

Similarly,

$$\sin A = \frac{\vec{b}_p \cdot (-\vec{c})}{||\vec{b}_p||\ ||\vec{c}||}.$$

However since $\vec{a} \perp \vec{b}$, $\vec{b}_p = k\vec{a}$ for some $k > 0$. Thus,

$$\sin A = \frac{k\vec{a} \cdot (-\vec{c})}{||k\vec{a}||\ ||\vec{c}||} = \frac{k\vec{a} \cdot (\vec{a} + \vec{b})}{k||\vec{a}||\ ||\vec{c}||}$$

$$= \frac{\vec{a} \cdot \vec{a} + \vec{a} \cdot \vec{b}}{ac} = \frac{a^2 + 0}{ac} = \text{\_\_\_\_\_\_\_\_\_\_\_\_}.$$

In the previous frame we have shown that if $\angle C$ is a right angle in $\triangle ABC$, then $\sin A = \frac{a}{c}$ and $\cos A =$ ______.

Using the definition of tan and cot, we have

$$\tan A = \frac{\sin A}{\cos A} = \text{\_\_\_\_\_\_\_\_\_\_\_\_}$$

and

$$\cot A = \text{\_\_\_\_\_\_\_\_\_\_\_\_}.$$

Also from their definitions

$$\sec A = \frac{c}{a} \quad \text{and} \quad \csc A = \frac{c}{b}.$$

We have established the following theorem.

THEOREM:

If $\angle C$ is a right angle in $\triangle ABC$, then

$$\sin A = \frac{a}{c}, \quad \cos A = \frac{b}{c},$$

$$\tan A = \frac{a}{b}, \quad \cot A = \frac{b}{a},$$

$$\sec A = \frac{c}{b}, \quad \csc A = \frac{c}{a}.$$

MOVE TO NEXT FRAME

Note that a is the length of the leg opposite $\angle A$, b is the length of the leg adjacent to $\angle A$, and c is the length of the hypotenuse. Thus, the above theorem may be recalled by remembering that if A is an acute angle in a right triangle, then:

$$\sin A = \frac{\text{side opposite}}{\text{hypotenuse}}$$

$$\cos A = \frac{\text{side adjacent}}{\text{hypotenuse}}$$

$$\tan A = \frac{\text{side opposite}}{\text{side adjacent}}$$

$$\cot A = \frac{\text{side adjacent}}{\text{side opposite}}$$

$$\sec A = \frac{\text{hypotenuse}}{\text{side adjacent}}$$

$$\csc A = \frac{\text{hypotenuse}}{\text{side opposite}}$$

MOVE TO NEXT FRAME

Concerning ourselves with $\angle B$ rather than $\angle A$ in the right triangle described in the previous frames, we have:

$\sin B =$ ____________ $\csc B =$ ____________

$\cos B =$ ____________ $\sec B =$ ____________

$\tan B =$ ____________ $\cot B =$ ____________

ANSWERS TO PAGE 299

$\angle B$ $\angle A$

(a) $\frac{\sqrt{5}}{5}$ $\frac{\sqrt{5}}{5}$

(b) $\frac{2\sqrt{5}}{5}$ $\frac{2\sqrt{5}}{5}$

$\sin A$

ANSWERS TO PAGE 304

Example:

In right $\triangle ABC$, $\angle C$ is a right angle, $m^\circ \angle B = 40^\circ$, and $a = 18$. Find b.

Solution:

$\tan B = \frac{b}{a}$, hence $\tan 40^\circ = \frac{b}{18}$ and $b = 18($ $)$. From Table I, $\tan 40^\circ \approx$ ________. Thus, $b \approx (0.8391)18$, and $b \approx$ ______. (Correct to hundredths.)

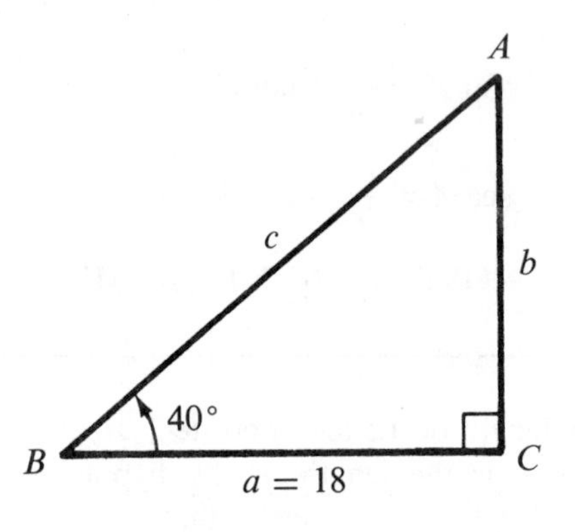

$\frac{h}{1000}$

approx. 364 yds

In $\triangle CEF$, as illustrated, $\angle C$ is a right angle. The hypotenuse is ____. The side adjacent to $\angle F$ is____.

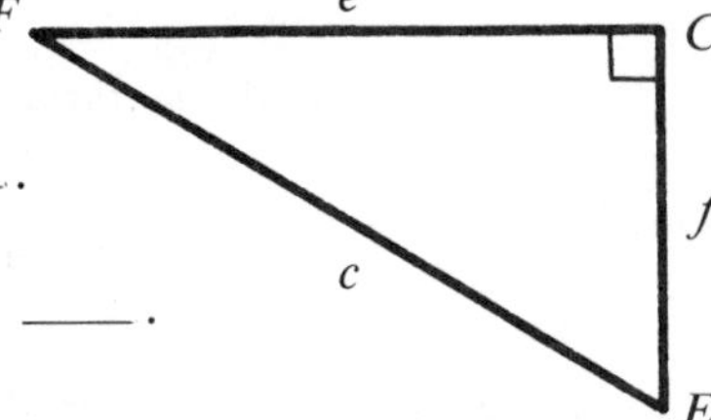

Complete the following.

$\sin F = \frac{f}{c}$; $\cos F =$ ____; $\sin E =$ ____.

$\cos E =$ ____; $\tan E =$ ____; $\cot F =$ ____.

The **parts** of a triangle are the three angles and the three sides. To solve a triangle is to find the measures or the lengths of these parts.

MOVE TO NEXT FRAME

Examples:

Solve each of the following right triangles. (Use Table I for those triangles that do not contain 30° or 45° angles.)

(a) $\triangle ABC$ with $m^\circ \angle C = 90^\circ$, $c = 20$, and $m^\circ \angle A = 30^\circ$.

$m^\circ \angle B =$ ______; $a =$ ______; $b =$ ______________.

41.2 miles

(b) $\triangle FAT$ with $\angle A$ a right angle, $t = 12$, and $m° \angle F = 45°$.

$m° \angle T =$ ______ ; $a =$ ______ ; $f =$ ______ .

(c) $\triangle ABC$ with $m° \angle B = 90°$, $m° \angle C = 24°$, and $c = 10$.

$m° \angle A =$ ______ ; $a =$ ______ ; $b =$ ______ ;

Selecting the "best" functions for the solution of a triangle can minimize computations and errors. For example, in exercise (c) of the previous frame the length b can best be found by noting that since $\csc c = \dfrac{\text{hypotenuse}}{\text{opp. side}}$,

$$\csc 24° = \frac{b}{10} \quad \text{or} \quad b = 10 \csc 24° = 10(2.459) = 24.59;$$

b could also be found by using sin, since

$$\sin 24° = \frac{10}{b} \quad \text{or} \quad b = \frac{10}{\sin 24} = 24.59.$$

However, use of the latter method would require division rather than the simple multiplication required in the first method.

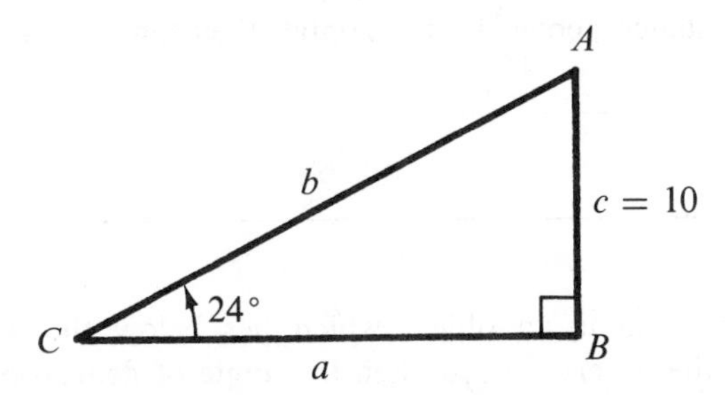

If an observer sights an object which lies above the horizontal plane passing through the observer's eye, then the **angle of elevation** of the object is the angle measured from the horizontal to the line of sight.

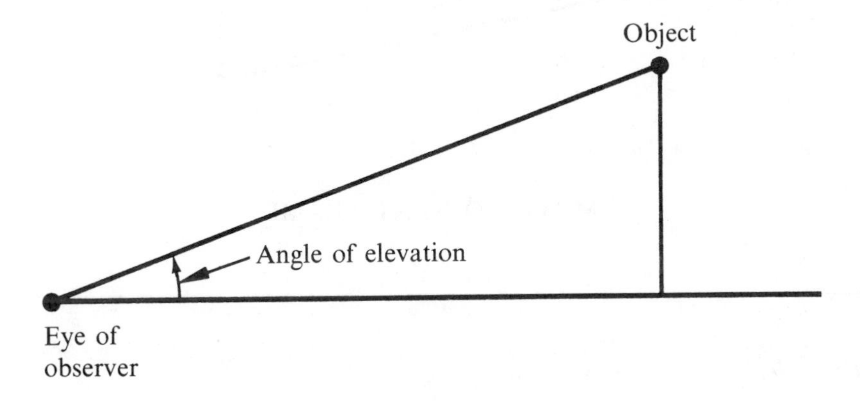

MOVE TO NEXT FRAME

$\frac{b}{c}$ $\frac{c}{b}$

$\frac{a}{c}$ $\frac{c}{a}$

$\frac{b}{a}$ $\frac{a}{b}$

ANSWERS TO PAGE 306

26°34′

Example:

A surveyor observes that the angle of elevation of a prominent landmark, from a distance of 1000 yards, is 20°. How much higher than the horizontal is the landmark?

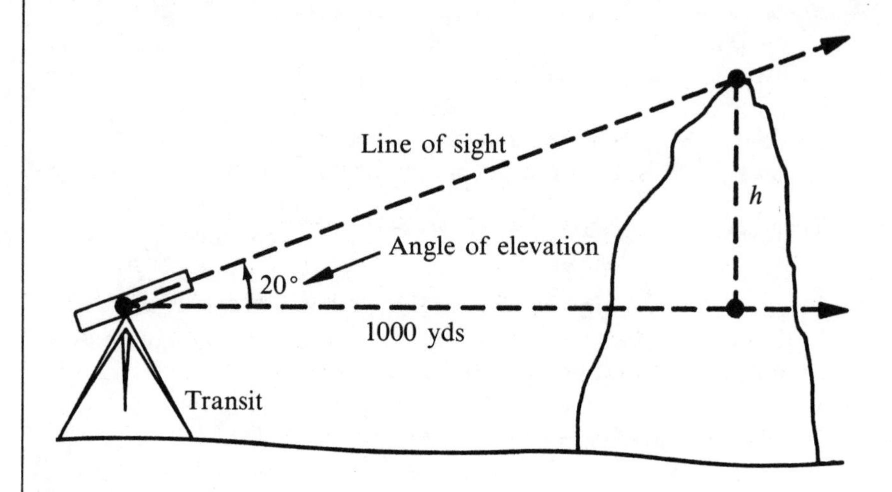

Solution:

If h is the distance above the horizontal, then $\tan 20° \approx$ ________.

$h \approx$ ________________.

If an observer sights an object which lies below the horizontal plane passing through the observer's eye, then the **angle of depression** of the object is the angle measured from the horizontal to the line of sight.

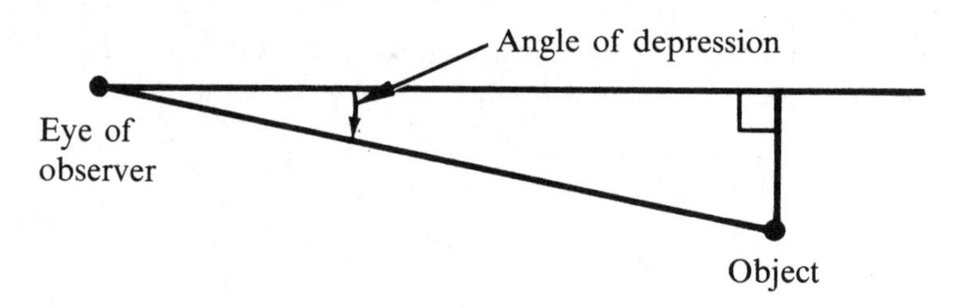

MOVE TO NEXT FRAME

Example:

An aircraft's radar antenna is tilted down 11° when a target appears at a distance of 42 miles. What is the horizontal distance, correct to the nearest tenth of a mile, to a point directly over the target? ________________

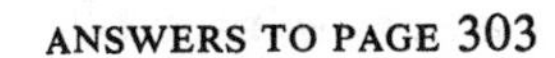

ANSWERS TO PAGE 303

(b) 45° $12\sqrt{2}$ or 16.97 12

(c) 66 22.46 24.59

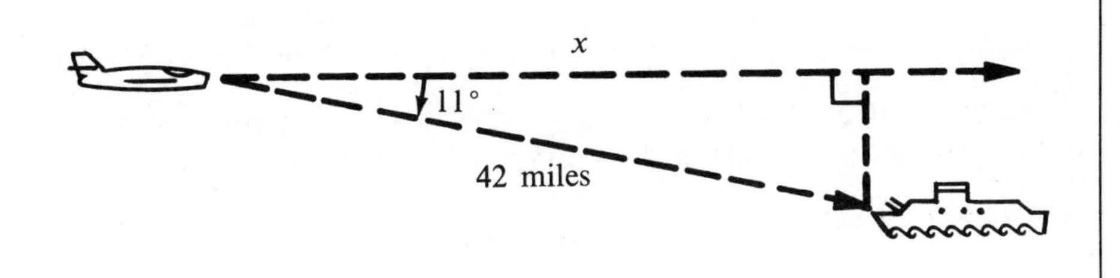

$$x = 42(\_\_\_)$$

A **force** may be thought of as a "push" or "pull" in a certain direction by a given "amount" or "magnitude." Vectors are used to solve certain problems in physics involving forces. Assumptions regarding operations on vectors are analogous to those involving operations on forces.

MOVE TO NEXT FRAME

The following assumptions are made concerning vectors and forces.

A. Every force may be represented by a vector having the same direction as the force and whose norm is the magnitude of the force.

B. The sum of all the forces acting at a single point is equal to a single force, called their resultant. The vector representing the resultant force is the sum of the vectors representing the forces acting on the point.

MOVE TO NEXT FRAME

Example:

Two forces of 50 pounds and 100 pounds act on an object at right angles to each other. What is the resultant force and its direction with respect to the 100 pound force?

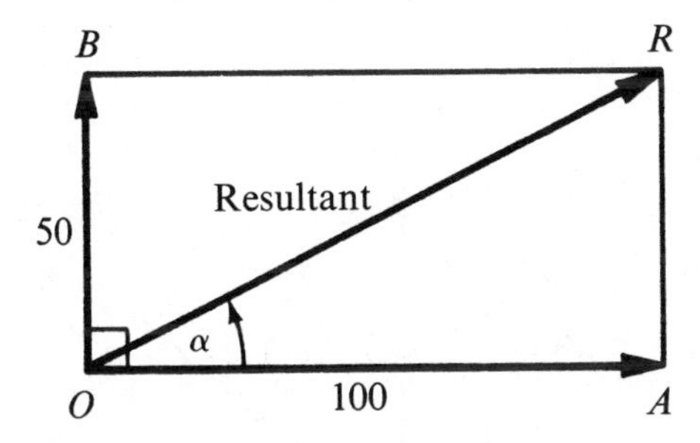

Solution:

A force has magnitude and direction and may be represented by a geometric vector. Let $\overrightarrow{OB}$ represent the 50 pound force and $\overrightarrow{OA}$ the 100 pound force as in the illustration. $\overrightarrow{OB}$ and $\overrightarrow{OA}$ determine a parallelogram. The geometric vector $\overrightarrow{OR}$ corresponding to the diagonal of the parallelogram represents the resultant of the two forces. Since the forces are at right angles, this parallelogram is a rectangle and the Pythagorean Theorem may be used to find the magnitude $||\overrightarrow{OR}||$ of the resultant force. (See sections 2.1 and 2.2.) Since $||\overrightarrow{OB}|| = 50$ and $||\overrightarrow{OA}|| = 100$, $||\overrightarrow{OR}|| = \sqrt{50^2 + 100^2} = \sqrt{12{,}500}$; $||\overrightarrow{OR}|| = 50\sqrt{5} \approx 111.8$. Thus the magnitude of the resultant force is approximately 111.8. To find the angle α that the resultant makes with the 100 pound force, we note that $\tan \alpha = \dfrac{||\overrightarrow{AR}||}{||\overrightarrow{OA}||} = \dfrac{50}{100} = 0.5$.

Therefore $\alpha \approx$ ______________, from Table I.

Example:

Two cables support a weight of 1000 pounds as shown in the figure. The cable, represented by $\overline{BC}$, makes an angle of 40° with the horizontal. The cable represented by $\overline{AB}$ makes an angle of 50° with the horizontal. What is the magnitude, correct to tenths, of the force that each cable exerts at the junction B?

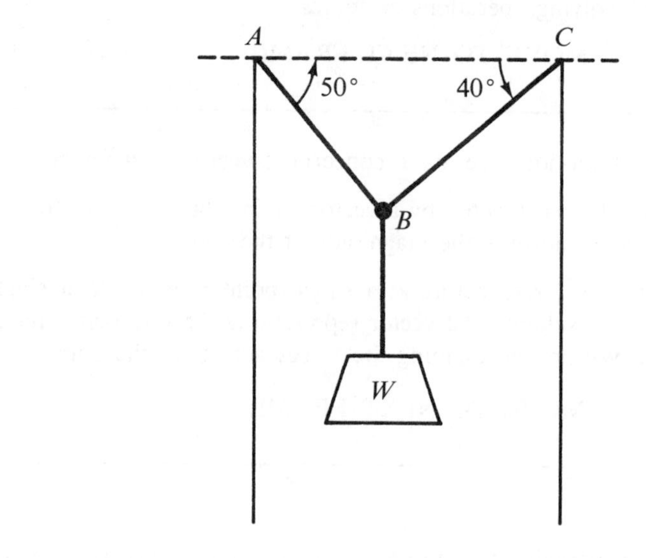

200 sin 20° ≈ 68.4

200 cos 20° ≈ 187.9

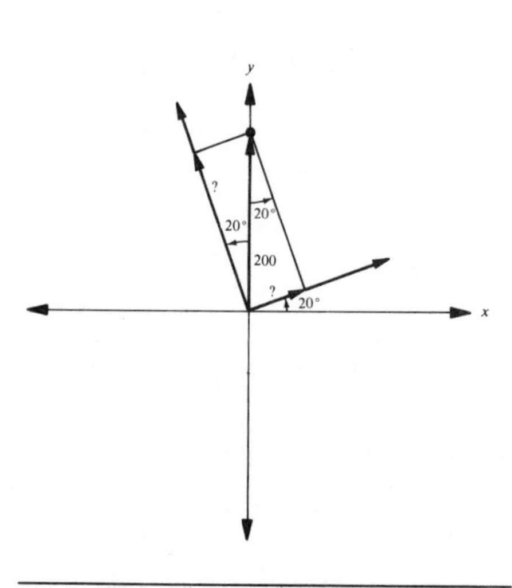

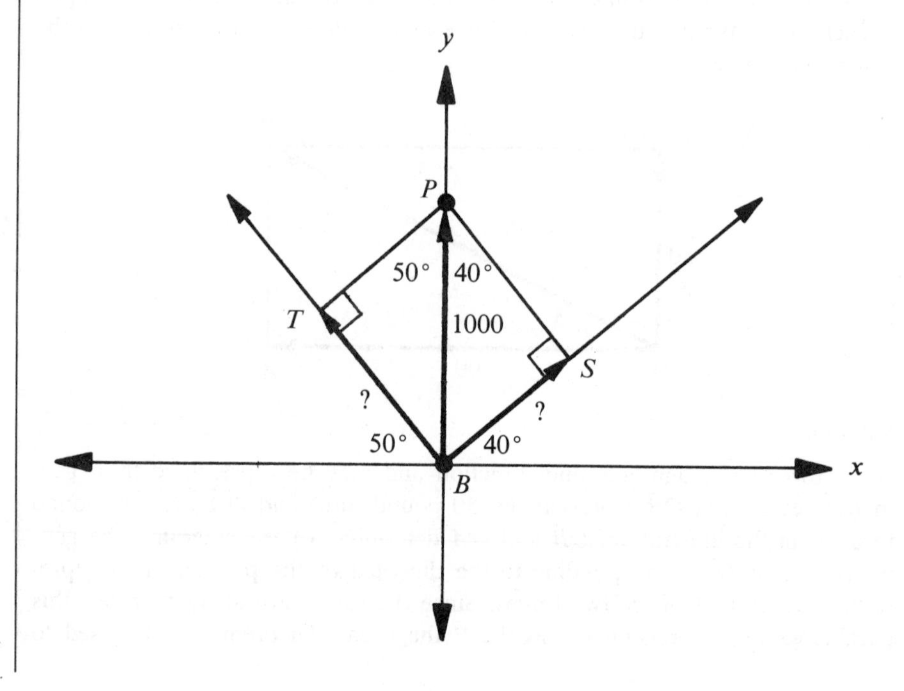

Solution:

In order to support the weight there must be a force of 1000 pounds in a direction opposite to the pull of the weight. Place the origin of a coordinate system at junction B, with the vector corresponding to the required 1000 pound resultant force on the positive y axis. (See the illustration.) The required magnitudes are the lengths of $\overrightarrow{BT}$ and $\overrightarrow{BS}$. The parallelogram having resultant $\overrightarrow{BP}$ as a diagonal, is a rectangle. Thus, right triangles are involved and

$$\sin 40° = \frac{||\overrightarrow{BS}||}{1000};\ ||\overrightarrow{BS}|| \approx \_\_\_\_\_\_\_\_ \text{ pounds.}$$

$$\sin 50° = \_\_\_\_\_\_\_\_;\ ||\overrightarrow{BT}|| \approx \_\_\_\_\_\_\_\_ \text{ pounds.}$$

An object placed on an inclined plane, such as an automobile on a downhill grade or a box on a loading ramp, is subjected to the force of gravity directed toward the center of the earth with a magnitude equal to the weight of the object. (See the illustration.)

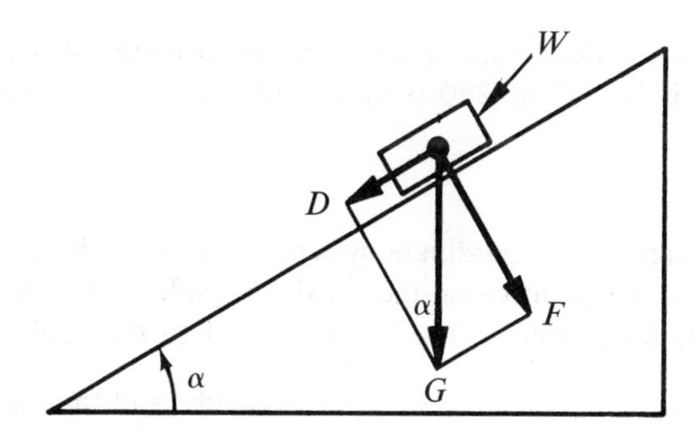

Ignoring the friction of the object on the inclined plane, the force of gravity, represented by $\overrightarrow{WG}$ in the illustration, is resolved into two perpendicular components of force represented by $\overrightarrow{WD}$ and $\overrightarrow{WF}$. The force represented by $\overrightarrow{WD}$ tends to move the object down the plane, and the force represented by $\overrightarrow{WF}$ is exerted against the plane. If w is the weight of the object, then the magnitude of the force tending to move the object down the plane is $w \sin \alpha$. If the object is not moving, then there is a restraining force equal in magnitude to $w \sin \alpha$ in the opposite direction.

MOVE TO NEXT FRAME

ANSWERS TO PAGE 310

(1) $\overline{CF}$ $\overline{FA}$ $\overline{AC}$

(2) $(-3,-3)$ $3\sqrt{2}$

$(7,0)$ 7

$(-4,3)$ 5

0

(3)(a) $\vec{w}$ $-\vec{r}$

(b) $\vec{t}$ $-\vec{w}$

(c) $\vec{r}$ $-\vec{t}$

(4) $\angle V$ $\overline{TA}$

$\overline{VT}$

$\vec{a}$

(5)(a) $\frac{d}{s}$ (b) $\frac{a}{s}$

(c) $\frac{a}{s}$ (d) $\frac{d}{s}$

(e) $\frac{d}{a}$ (f) $\frac{a}{d}$

Example:

An object W is held in position on an inclined plane by a force parallel to the plane and another perpendicular to it. (See the illustration.)

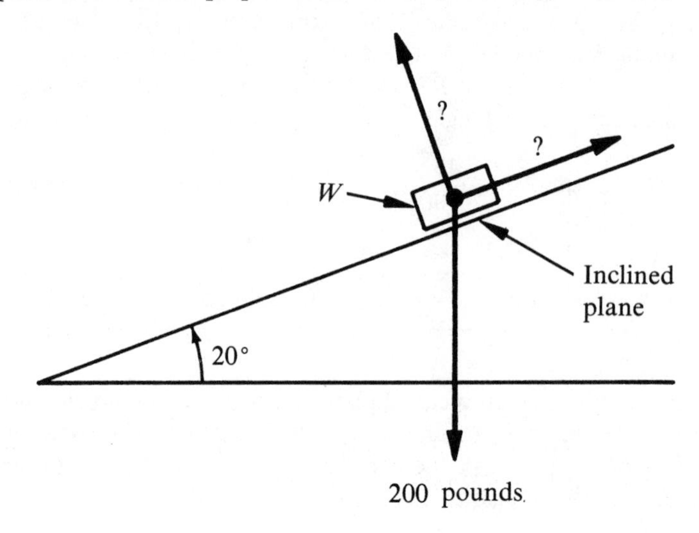

Find the magnitudes of the forces, correct to tenths of a pound, holding W in position, if W weighs 200 pounds and the angle of inclination of the plane is 20°.

Solution:

Place the origin of a coordinate system on W with the representation of the resultant 200 pound force on the y axis. Complete the required parallelogram in the adjoining sketch. The force parallel to the inclined plane has a magnitude of ________________ pounds, and the force perpendicular to the plane has a magnitude of ________________ pounds.

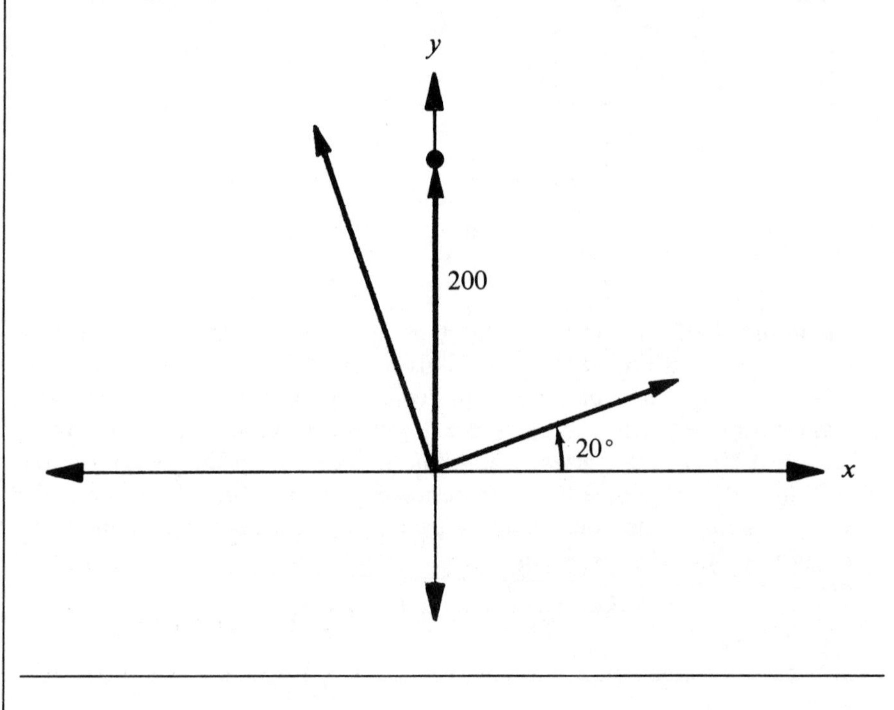

Velocities may be represented by geometric vectors in the same manner as forces since they also have magnitude and direction. The following example illustrates the use of geometric vectors in air navigation.

MOVE TO NEXT FRAME

Example:

An aircraft is flying with a true heading of north and a true airspeed of 300 knots. Throughout its flight its course is influenced by a 50-knot wind from the west. What is the aircraft's course and groundspeed?

(*Note:* In air navigation, "true heading" and "true airspeed" refer to the actual heading of the longitudinal axis of the aircraft and the actual speed of the aircraft through the air mass. The aircraft's "course" and "groundspeed" refer to the actual track over the ground.)

The course and groundspeed vector is the resultant of the vector corresponding to the wind's force and direction, and the vector corresponding to the aircraft's true heading and true airspeed.

Solution:

First, make a representative sketch. Since bearings and course measurements for navigational purposes are measured clockwise from the north and are positive, the measure of $\angle\theta$ is the desired course.

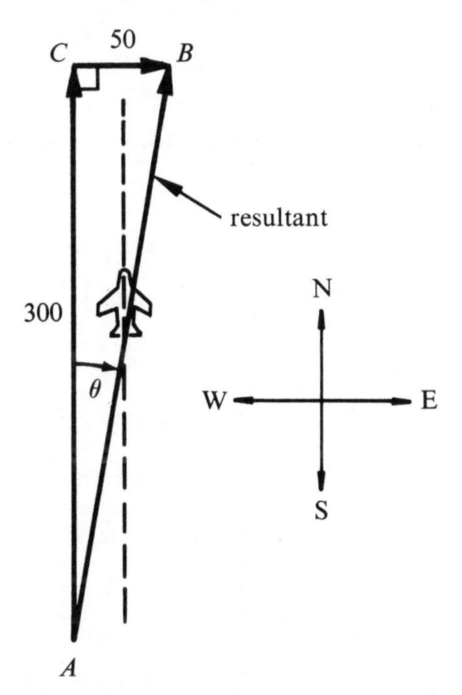

Thus, $\tan\theta \approx$ ____________ (correct to 4 places), and $\theta \approx$ ________ (correct to 30, from Table I).

Since this is a right triangle, the Pythagorean Theorem may be used to determine the groundspeed, represented by the resultant vector. Therefore

groundspeed $= \sqrt{300^2 + 50^2} \approx$ __________ (correct to knots).

642.8

$\overrightarrow{BT}$ 766.0

1000

ANSWERS TO PAGE 312

(9)(a) 3°26′ (b) 3,168 ft.

(10) 23.0 inches

(11) 540.9 pounds

EXERCISES. 6.1

1. Name the line segment in $\triangle FAC$ whose length is denoted by the following letters.

   a: ______ c: ______ f: ______

2. The vertices of $\triangle ABC$ are $A(-2,1)$, $B(5,1)$, and $C(1,4)$. Find each of the following.

   $\vec{b} =$ __________ $b =$ __________

   $\vec{c} =$ __________ $c =$ __________

   $\vec{a} =$ __________ $a =$ __________

   $\vec{a} + \vec{b} + \vec{c} =$ __________.

3. Write the direction vectors for each of the angles in $\triangle TRW$.

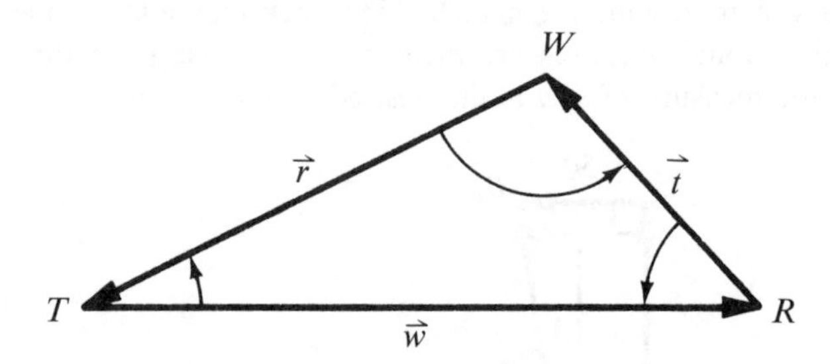

   (a) $\angle T$ has direction vectors ______ and ______.

   (b) $\angle R$ has direction vectors ______ and ______.

   (c) $\angle W$ has direction vectors ______ and ______.

4. In $\triangle VAT$, $\vec{a} \cdot \vec{t} = 0$. Therefore $\triangle VAT$ is a right triangle. Which angle is the right angle? ______. Which side is the hypotenuse? ______. Which side is adjacent to $\angle T$? ______. Write the correct designation for the vector corresponding to $\overline{VT}$. ______.

5. $\triangle DAS$ is a right triangle with $m^\circ \angle S = 90^\circ$. a, s, and d denote the lengths of the sides. Find the appropriate ratio in terms of the lengths of the sides, for each of the following.

   (a) $\sin D =$ __________ (b) $\sin A =$ __________

   (c) $\cos D =$ __________ (d) $\cos A =$ __________

   (e) $\tan D =$ __________ (f) $\cot D =$ __________

6. Solve each of the following right triangles. (Compute lengths of sides to the nearest tenth and measures of angles to the nearest ten minutes.)

   (a) $\triangle ABC$ with $\angle C$ a right angle, $m^\circ \angle A = 51°30'$, and $a = 112$.

   $m^\circ \angle B =$ ________; $b \approx$ ________; $c \approx$ ______.

   (b) $\triangle DEF$ with $\angle D$ a right angle, $e = 100$, and $f = 136$.

   $m^\circ \angle E \approx$ ________; $m^\circ \angle F \approx$ ________; $d \approx$ ________.

   (c) $\triangle GHQ$ with $\angle H$ a right angle, $h = 1760$, and $m^\circ \angle G = 10°20'$.

   $m^\circ \angle Q \approx$ ________; $q \approx$ ________; $g \approx$ ________.

   (d) $\triangle JKM$ with $m^\circ \angle K = 90°$, $k = 45$, and $j = 20$.

   $m^\circ \angle J \approx$ ________; $m^\circ \angle M \approx$ ________; $m \approx$ ________.

7. Two strong searchlights may be used to measure the heights of the bases of low level clouds at night. (See the illustration.) Searchlights A and B are 300′ apart on a horizontal surface. Searchlight B with a vertical beam projects a spot of light on the cloud base. Searchlight A elevates its beam until its projected spot coincides with that of searchlight B. If the resulting beam elevation is 70°, find the height of the cloud base to the nearest 50 feet. ________________.

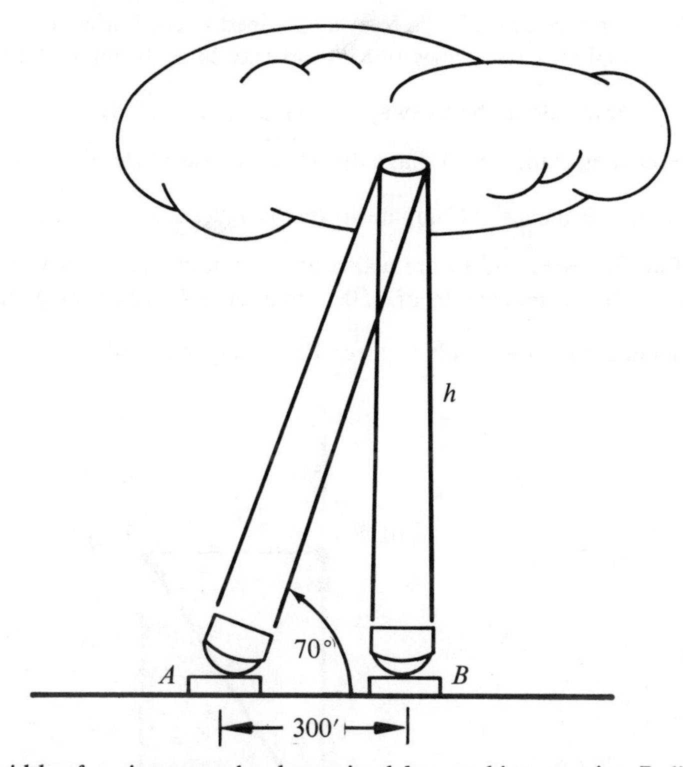

0.1667   9°30′

8. The width of a river may be determined by marking a point P directly across the river from a prominent landmark, T. From P measure 100 feet along the perpendicular from $\overline{TP}$ to a point S. At S measure $\angle TSP$. (See the illustration.) How wide is the river, to the nearest tenth, if the $m^\circ \angle TSP = 55°12'$? ________________

304 knots

(14) (a) 342.3 pounds
(b) 734.1 pounds

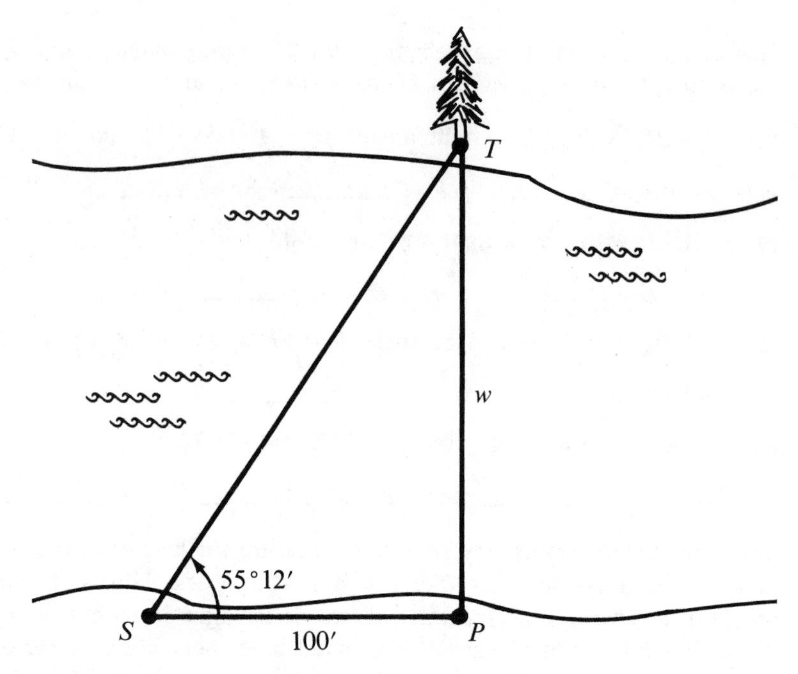

9. A certain freeway near Los Angeles has a 6% grade. (6% grade denotes an average rise of 6 feet for every 100 feet of horizontal measurement.)

   (a) At what angle is the freeway inclined to the horizontal, and (b) how high (in feet) does one rise in traveling 10 miles (52,800 ft) upgrade along the freeway? (a) ________ (b) ________

10. How long is the chord that subtends a central angle of 66° in a circle of radius 20 inches? (Compute to tenths.) ____________

11. Two forces F_1 and F_2 are acting on a point at right angles to each other. If F_1 has a magnitude of 450 pounds and F_2 has a magnitude of 300 pounds, then the resultant force has a magnitude of ____________

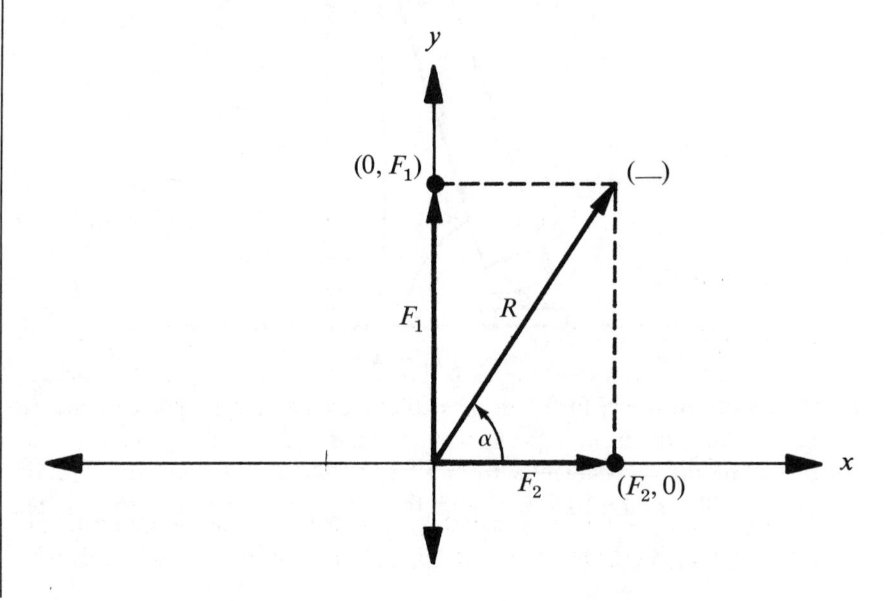

and acts at an angle of __________ with F_2. (Compute magnitude to pounds and angle measure to ten minutes.)

12. Find the true heading to the nearest degree and true airspeed to the nearest knot for an aircraft that must follow a course of 090° at a groundspeed of 450 knots, if there is a reported wind from the south (180°) of 60 knots. (*Hint:* Sketch a figure showing the required groundspeed and course as the resultant.) True Heading = ________. (Compute to nearest degree.) True Airspeed = ________. (Compute to the nearest knot.)

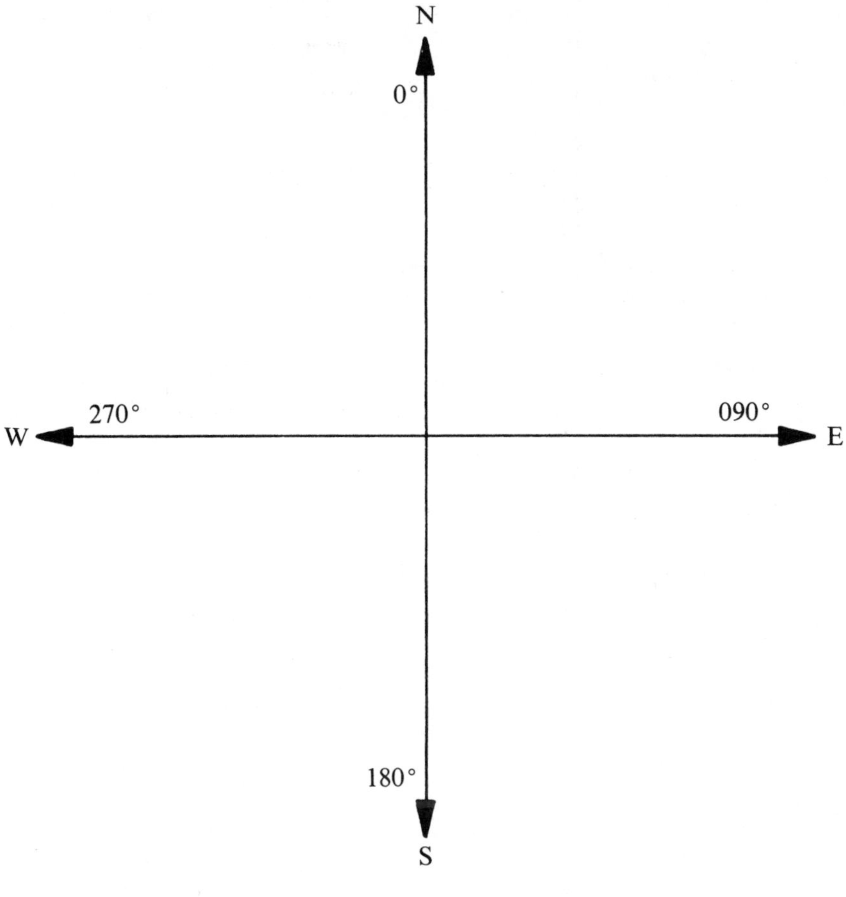

If the same wind was from the west (270°), then the required true airspeed would be ______________knots.

13. A 720 pound weight is resting on a plane inclined at an angle of 18° with the horizontal. Find the magnitude, to the nearest tenth of a pound, of the force parallel to the plane that is necessary to prevent the weight from moving. ____________________

14. An 810 pound weight is suspended by two cables, as indicated in the illustration. The cables form angles with measures 25° and 65° with

ANSWERS TO PAGE 311

(6)(a) 38°30′ 89.1 143.1

(b) 36°20′ 53°40′ 168.80

(c) 79°40′ 1731.5 314.2

(d) 26°20′ 63°40′ 40.3

(7) 800 feet

(8) 143.9 ft.

ANSWERS TO PAGE 316

$2\,\vec{c}\cdot\vec{b}$

$-||\vec{c}||\ ||-\vec{b}||\cos A$

$-2||\vec{c}||\ ||-\vec{b}||\cos A$

$c^2 + b^2 - 2cb\cos A$

---

the horizontal. Find the magnitude of the force pulling (a) the cable at 25° with the horizontal and (b) the cable at 65° with the horizontal.

(a) ______________ (b) ______________

(Compute to the nearest tenth.)

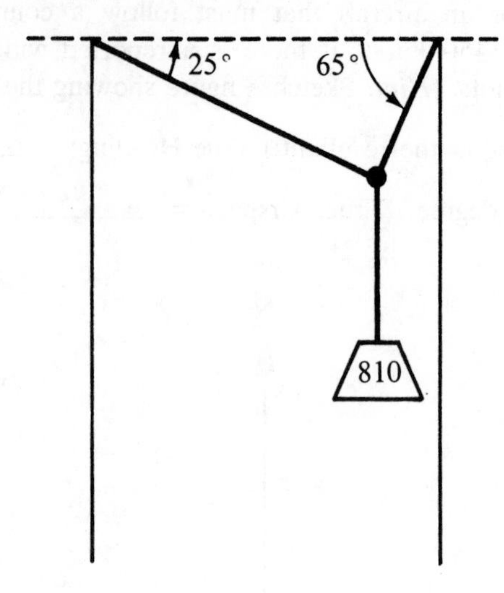

6.2. LAW OF COSINES AND LAW OF SINES

In the previous section we used right triangles to solve certain problems. The **Law of Cosines** enables us to solve problems involving any triangle in which we are given the measures of (a) two sides and the included angle, or (b) three sides.

MOVE TO NEXT FRAME

Consider $\triangle ABC$. Let the vectors corresponding to the sides be assigned as shown in the illustration.

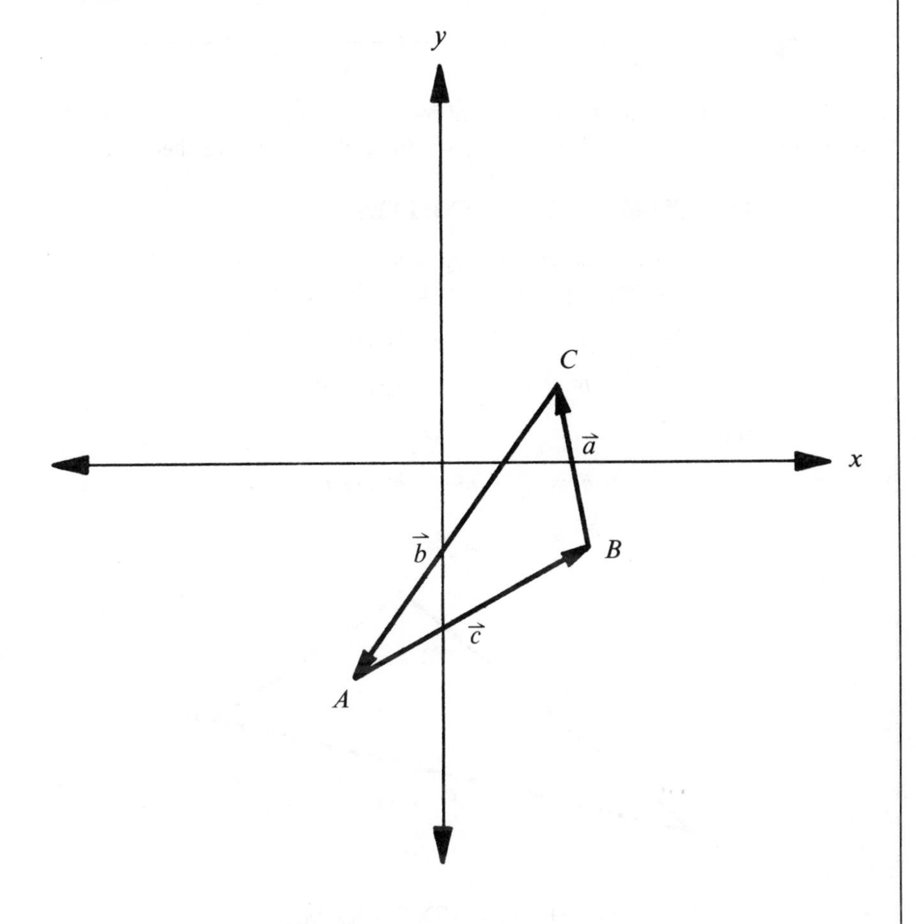

The sum of the corresponding vectors is

$$\vec{c} + \vec{a} + \vec{b} = \_\_.$$

Therefore, it follows that

$$-\vec{a} = \vec{c} + \vec{b}, \quad \text{and} \quad ||-\vec{a}|| = ||\vec{c} + \vec{b}||.$$

ANSWERS TO PAGE 313

56°20′

(12) 098°

455 knots

390 knots

(13) 222.5 pounds

Now square both norms.

(1) $$||-\vec{a}||^2 = ||\vec{c}||^2 + \text{\_\_\_\_\_\_} + ||\vec{b}||^2.$$

(See Ex. 6, section 2.4.) Recalling that $\cos A = \dfrac{\vec{c} \cdot (-\vec{b})}{||\vec{c}||\,||-\vec{b}||}$ and that $\vec{c} \cdot (-\vec{b}) = -(\vec{c} \cdot \vec{b})$, we have

$$||\vec{c}||\,||-\vec{b}|| \cos A = \vec{c} \cdot (-\vec{b}) = -(\vec{c} \cdot \vec{b})$$

or (2) $$\vec{c} \cdot \vec{b} = \text{\_\_\_\_\_\_\_\_\_\_\_\_}.$$

Substituting (2) into (1),

(3) $$||-\vec{a}||^2 = ||\vec{c}||^2 + ||\vec{b}||^2 + \text{\_\_\_\_\_\_\_\_\_\_\_\_}$$

Since $||-\vec{a}|| = ||\vec{a}|| = a$, $||\vec{c}|| = c$, and $||-\vec{b}|| = ||\vec{b}|| = b$, a substitution in (3) yields

$$a^2 = \text{\_\_\_\_\_\_\_\_\_\_\_\_}$$

A statement similar to the one above for a^2 may be established for b^2 and c^2 by the same procedure. Thus, we have the following theorem.

THEOREM: LAW OF COSINES

For any triangle having sides whose lengths a, b, and c are opposite angles A, B, and C, respectively,

$$a^2 = b^2 + c^2 - 2bc \cos A,$$

$$b^2 = a^2 + c^2 - 2ac \cos B,$$

and

$$c^2 = a^2 + b^2 - 2ab \cos C.$$

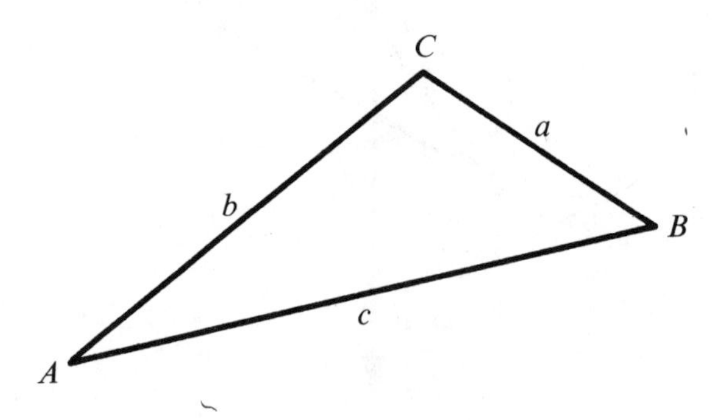

MOVE TO NEXT FRAME

Example: (Two sides and included angle)

Find the length of the third side of $\triangle ABC$, given that $m^\circ \angle A = 40^\circ$, $b = 75$, and $c = 90$.

70°

$200^2 - 2(120)(200) \cos 70°$

195 miles

$\dfrac{200^2 + 195^2 - 120^2}{}$ 0.8157

35°

285°

Solution:

From the Law of Cosines

$$a^2 = 75^2 + 90^2 - \underline{\hspace{6cm}},$$

$$a = \sqrt{\underline{\hspace{5cm}}},$$

$\therefore a \approx$ ________________. (Compute to the nearest tenth.)

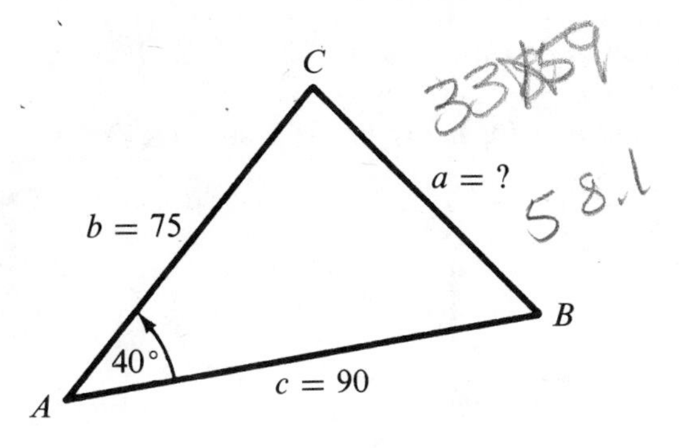

Example: (Three sides)

The sides of a triangle have lengths 8, 12, and 15. Find the measure of the angle opposite the side whose length is 8.

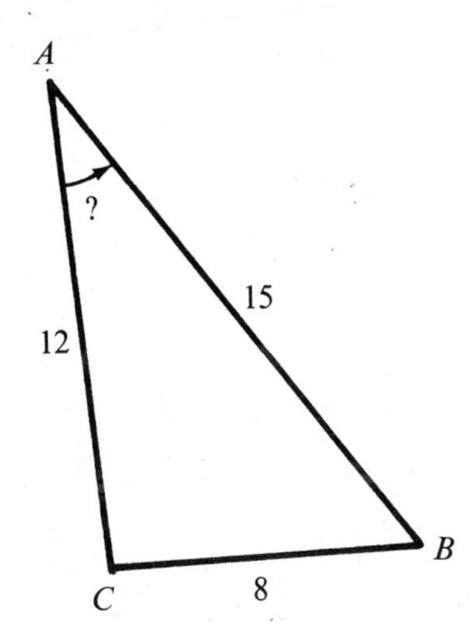

Solution:

Label the triangle ABC and use the Law of Cosines to solve for cos A. Thus,

$$a^2 = b^2 + c^2 - 2bc \cos A \quad \text{and} \quad \cos A = \underline{\hspace{4cm}}.$$

Since $a = 8$ (because it is opposite $\angle A$), $b = 12$, and $c = 15$,

$$\cos A = \frac{12^2 + 15^2 - 8^2}{2(12)(15)} \approx \underline{\hspace{3cm}}. \text{ (Correct to 4 places.)}$$

$\therefore m^\circ \angle A \approx$ ________________ (Compute to the nearest minute.)

Similarly, $m^\circ \angle B$ and $m^\circ \angle C$ may be found. A check for your results is

$$m^\circ \angle B + m^\circ \angle c + m^\circ \angle A = 180^\circ$$

when all three angles have been calculated.

Example:

A search aircraft flys a course of 030° from Point Oboe for 120 miles, then a course of 140° for 200 miles, and finally returns to Point Oboe. Find the course and distance for the return trip to Point Oboe.

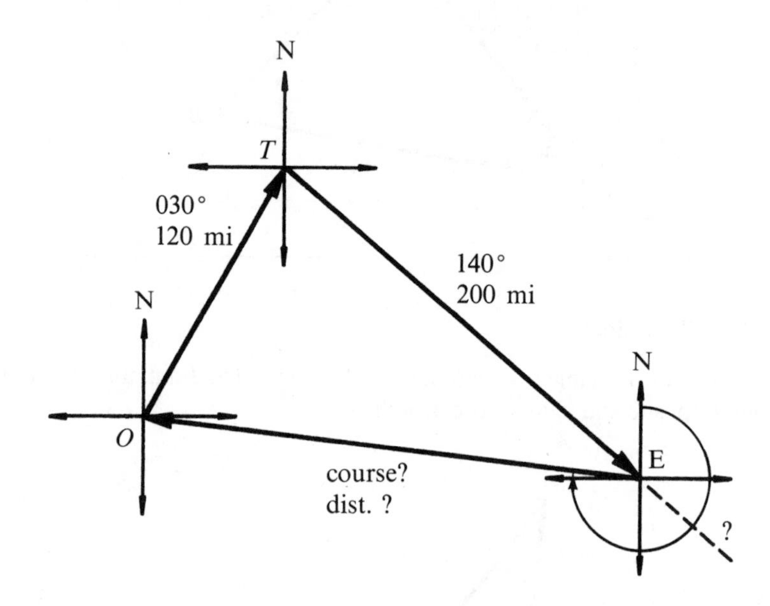

$a^2 + b^2 + 2ab \cos \alpha$

$a^2 + b^2 - 2ab \cos \alpha$

Solution:

The illustration shows how course measurements are made from true north with $\triangle OTF$ indicating the track of the aircraft. The measure of $\angle T$ in $\triangle OTF$ is ______. With the Law of Cosines we can calculate the return distance t from F to O.

two sides and the included angle

$$t^2 = 120^2 + \text{\_\_\_\_\_\_\_\_\_\_\_\_\_\_\_\_},$$

and $t \approx$ ____________ . (To the nearest mile)

To find the required return course, calculate $m^\circ \angle F$ in $\triangle OTF$ with the Law of Cosines; then add its supplement to 140°.

$a^2 + b^2 - 2ab \cos C$

$$\cos F = \frac{\text{\_\_\_\_\_\_\_\_\_\_\_\_}}{2(200)(195)} \approx \underset{\text{4-place decimal}}{\text{\_\_\_\_\_\_\_\_}}.$$

0

$m^\circ \angle F \approx$ ______ (To the nearest degree.)

$\therefore$ Course to Point Oboe: ______

$a^2 + b^2$

ANSWERS TO PAGE 317

$2(75)(90)\cos 40°$

3384

58.2

Example:

Two forces acting on a point P determine an angle with a measure of 42°. If the magnitudes of the forces are 30 pounds and 40 pounds, find the magnitude b of the resultant force and the measure of the angle determined by it and the 40-pound force.

Solution:

Sketch a parallelogram showing the resultant as a diagonal. (From geometry recall that consecutive angles in a parallelogram are ____________.)

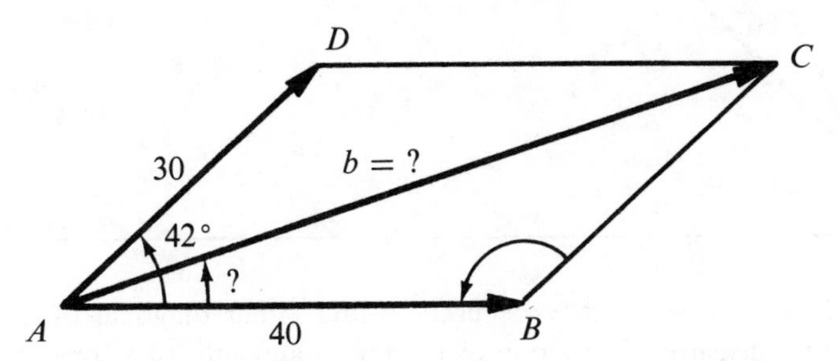

Since $m° \angle A = 42°$ in $\square ABCD$, $m° \angle B =$ ________, and the resultant is represented by the side opposite the 138° angle in $\triangle ABC$. Using the Law of Cosines,

$$b^2 = 30^2 + \text{\_\_\_\_\_\_\_\_\_\_\_\_\_\_\_\_\_\_\_\_}.$$

Because $\cos 138° = -\cos 42°$ the equation becomes

$$b^2 = 30^2 + \text{\_\_\_\_\_\_\_\_\_\_\_\_\_\_\_\_\_\_\_\_},$$

and

$b \approx$ ____________________ (To the nearest tenth.)

Let θ be the angle determined by the resultant and the 40-pound force. Again using the Law of Cosines,

$$\cos \theta = \frac{b^2 + 40^2 - 30^2}{\text{\_\_\_\_\_\_\_\_\_\_}}.$$

From Table I,

$\theta \approx$ ______ (To the nearest degree.)

$$\frac{b^2 + c^2 - a^2}{2bc}$$

0.8472

32°05′

Which of the following triangles, with the given information indicated, may be solved by the direct use of the Law of Cosines? ____________

a)

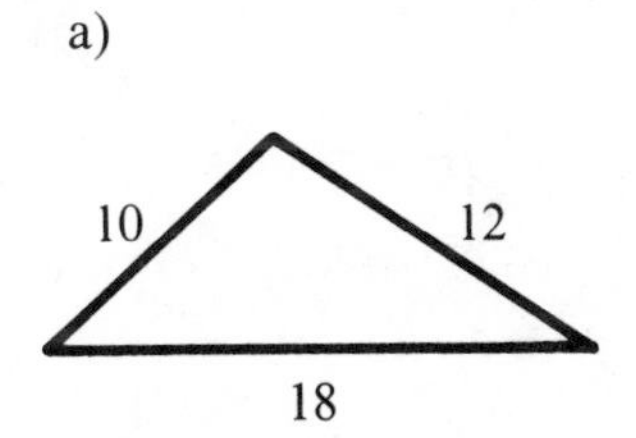

b)

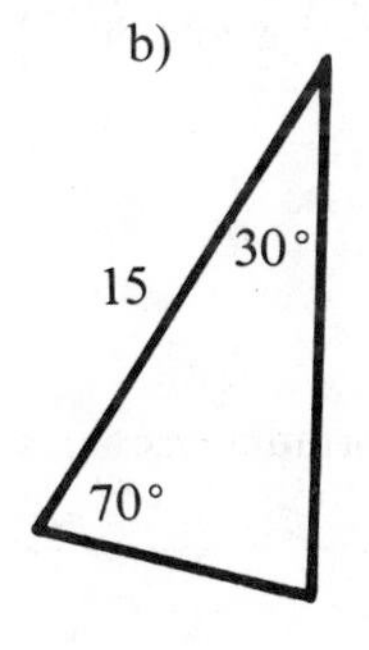

ANSWERS TO PAGE 322

0 0

$$\frac{\sin B}{b} = \frac{\sin A}{a}$$

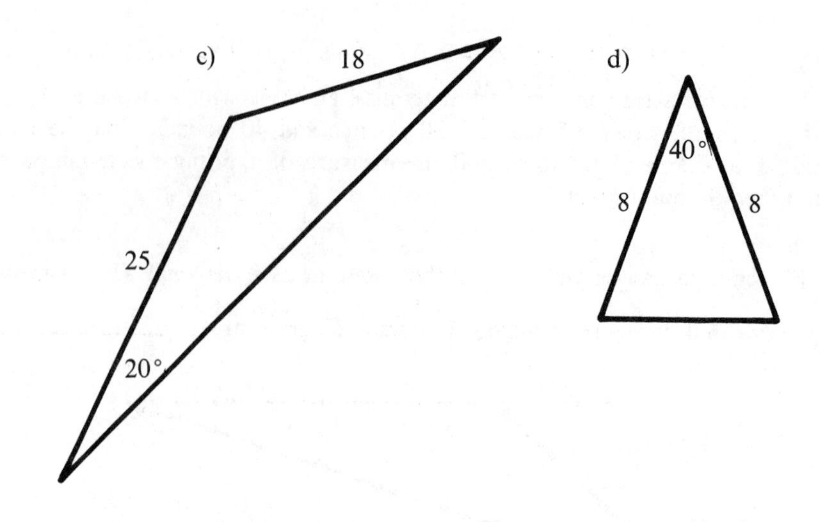

The Law of Cosines may be used to find either diagonal of a parallelogram, if the measure of any one of its angles and any two consecutive sides are given. Write formulas for the diagonals d_1 and d_2 in the parallelogram illustrated, if a and b are the lengths of consecutive sides and α is an acute angle.

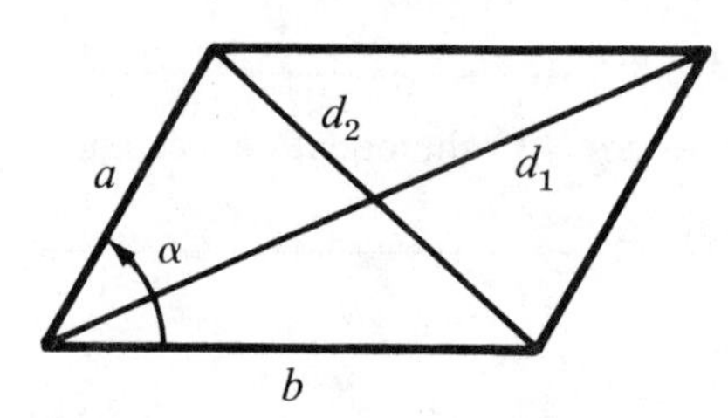

$d_1^2 =$ ____________________

$d_2^2 =$ ____________________

The Law of Cosines is useful when three sides of a triangle are given or

________________________________ of a triangle are given.

Apply the Law of Cosines to the right triangle illustrated to find c in terms of a and b.

$c^2 =$ ____________________

Since

$\cos C = \cos 90° =$ ___,

the formula becomes

$c^2 =$ ____________________.

You should see from this example that the Pythagorean Theorem is a special case of the Law of Cosines when the included angle is 90°.

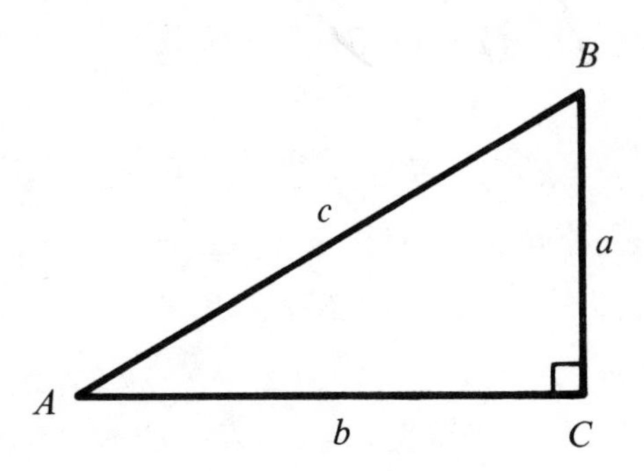

To solve triangles when two angles and the length of one side of a triangle are given, we will develop another law.

MOVE TO NEXT FRAME

Consider any $\triangle ABC$. Let $\vec{a}$, $\vec{b}$, and $\vec{c}$ correspond to the sides so that $\vec{a}+\vec{b}+\vec{c}=\vec{0}$. From section 5.4, we have

sin A = ______________ ($\angle A$ is the angle from $\vec{c}$ to $-\vec{b}$.)

Knowing that $||\vec{c}_p|| = c$, $||-\vec{b}|| = b$ and $\vec{c}_p \cdot (-\vec{b}) = -(\vec{c}_p\vec{b})$,

(1) $-(\vec{c}_p \cdot \vec{b}) = -(\vec{b} \cdot \vec{c}_p) =$ ______________ and

sin $(-B)$ = ______________. ($\angle(-B)$ is the angle from $-\vec{c}$ to $\vec{a}$.)

Thus

$-(\vec{c}_p \cdot \vec{a}) =$ ______________,

and since $\sin(-B) = -\sin B$,

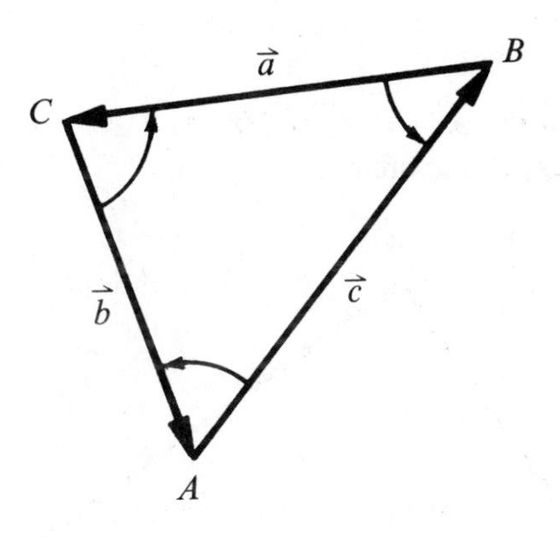

(2) $\vec{c}_p \cdot \vec{a} = \vec{a} \cdot \vec{c}_p =$ ______________.

ANSWERS TO PAGE 319

supplementary (since their sum is is 180°)

138°

$40^2 - 2(40)(30)\cos 138°$

$40^2 + 2(40)(30)\cos 42°$

65.4 pounds

$\overline{2(b)(40)}$

18°

---

a d

s

$$\frac{32}{\sin 25°} = \frac{40}{\sin S}$$

0.5283

31°53′ 148°07′ 123°07′

6°53′

63.42 9.08

ambiguous

Since

$$\vec{a} + \vec{b} + \vec{c} = \vec{0}$$

$$(\vec{a} + \vec{b} + \vec{c}) \cdot \vec{c}_p = \vec{0} \cdot \vec{c}_p,$$

or

$$\vec{a} \cdot \vec{c}_p + \vec{b} \cdot \vec{c}_p + \vec{c} \cdot \vec{c}_p = \vec{0} \cdot \vec{c}_p,$$

Recalling that $\vec{c} \cdot \vec{c}_p =$ __ and $\vec{0} \cdot \vec{c}_p =$ __,

$$\vec{a} \cdot \vec{c}_p + \vec{b} \cdot \vec{c}_p = 0$$

or

(3) $$\vec{a} \cdot \vec{c}_p = -(\vec{b} \cdot \vec{c}_p).$$

Substituting equations (1) and (2) into (3) results in

$$ac \sin B = bc \sin A.$$

Dividing each member by abc results in

____________________________.

The same procedure as that used in the preceding frame could be followed with $\angle B$ and $\angle C$ to obtain $\frac{\sin B}{b} = \frac{\sin C}{c}$. Thus, we have the following theorem.

THEOREM: LAW OF SINES

In any triangle having sides of lengths a, b, and c, with opposite angles, $\angle A$, $\angle B$, and $\angle C$, respectively.

$$\frac{\sin A}{a} = \frac{\sin B}{b} = \frac{\sin C}{c}.$$

MOVE TO NEXT FRAME

Example:

Given $\triangle ABC$ with $m°\angle A = 34°20'$, $b = 200$, and $m°\angle C = 53°10'$, find a and c to the nearest hundredth.

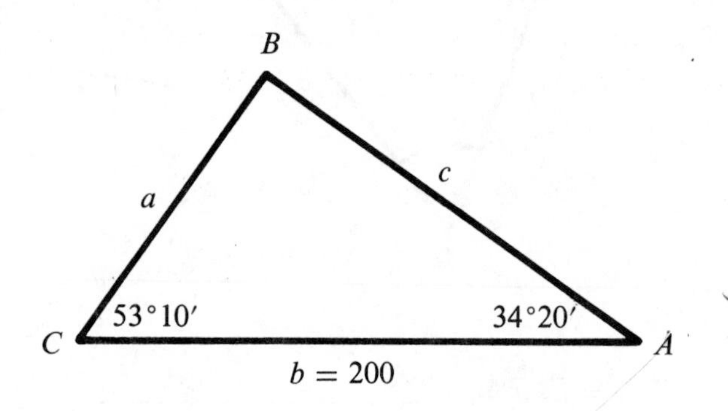

Solution:

Sketch and label an illustration of $\triangle ABC$ as indicated; note that $m\angle B = 180 - (m^\circ \angle A + m^\circ \angle C)$. Thus,

$$\sin B = \sin (A + C).$$

Why? ______

Since the triangle has *angle-side-angle* given use the Law of Sines, which states: ______. By substitution in the Law of Sines,

$$\frac{a}{\sin 34^\circ 20'} = \frac{200}{\_\_\_\_\_\_}.$$ Recall that $\sin B = \sin (A + C)$.

87 130°

Solve to find a. $a \approx$ ______.

To find c substitute again in the Law of Sines.

$$\frac{c}{\sin 53^\circ 10'} = \_\_\_\_\_\_.$$

$$\therefore c = \_\_\_\_\_\_.$$

Since

$$\frac{a}{\sin A} = \frac{b}{\sin B}, \quad \frac{a}{b} = \frac{\sin A}{\sin B}.$$

Therefore, another way of stating the Law of Sines is to say that in any triangle, the lengths of the sides are proportional to the ______ ______.

Thus it is emphasized that the lengths of the sides are *not* proportional to the measures of the angles.

If we have a triangle for which three parts are given, and not all are angles, we can solve the triangle. This solution is unique if we are given three sides, two sides and the included angle, or two angles and any side.

However, if we are given two sides and an angle **opposite** one of the sides, then the solution may be ambiguous.

MOVE TO NEXT FRAME

$$\frac{\vec{c}_p \cdot (-\vec{b})}{\|\vec{c}_p\| \, \|-\vec{b}\|}$$

$bc \sin A$

$$\frac{(-\vec{c}_p) \cdot \vec{a}}{\|-\vec{c}_p\| \, \|\vec{a}\|}$$

$ac \sin (-B)$

$ac \sin B$

Example: (Ambiguous case)

Solve $\triangle RST$ for t, $m\angle S$, and $m\angle T$, given that $r = 32$, $s = 40$, and and $m\angle R = 25°$.

Solution:

Sketch $\triangle RST$ indicating all possible solutions. $m\angle S$ may be found by using the Law of Sines.

$$\frac{r}{\sin R} = \frac{\quad}{\sin S}.$$

Substituting known values, we have ____________________.

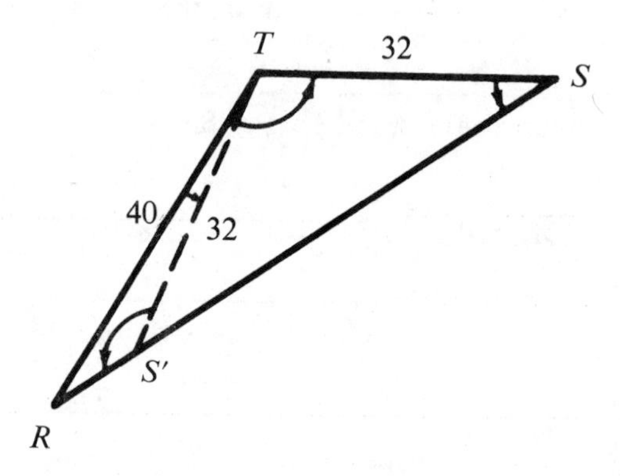

Use Table I to find sin 25° and calculate sin S. Sin $S =$ ________________. Since there are two angles S such that $0° \leq m°\angle S \leq 180°$ and $\sin S = 0.5258$, we must consider each possibility. This is the so-called ambiguity.

Thus, $m°\angle S =$ __________ or __________, and $m°\angle T =$ __________ or __________, respectively.

To find t use the Law of Sines again.

$$\frac{t}{\sin T} = \frac{r}{\sin R}.$$

Since there are two possible measures for $\angle T$ use the Law of Sines twice, finding both values of t, i.e., $t =$ _______ when $\angle T$ is obtuse and $t =$ _______ when $\angle T$ is acute.

Since the Law of Sines was used throughout the example above, the Law of Cosines should be used as a check.

MOVE TO NEXT FRAME

Even though "two sides and the angle opposite one of them" is referred to as the ____________________ case, there are situations in which it yields unique solutions.

If in $\triangle ABC$, a, b, and $\angle A$ are given, and $\frac{a}{b} = \sin A$, then, from the Law of Sines,

$$\frac{\sin B}{b} = \frac{\sin A}{a} \text{ or } \frac{\sin B}{b} = \frac{1}{b}.$$

Hence,

$$\sin B = 1.$$

Does this situation yield a unique situation? ______ (See the illustration.)

Why? ____

____.

Note in this case $\triangle ABC$ is a right triangle.

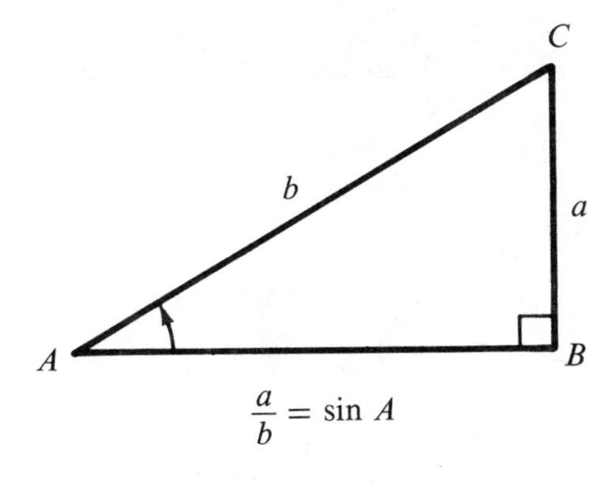

$\frac{a}{b} = \sin A$

In $\triangle ABC$, a, b, and $\angle A$ are given, and $a \geq b$. Does this situation yield a unique solution? ______ (See the illustrations.)

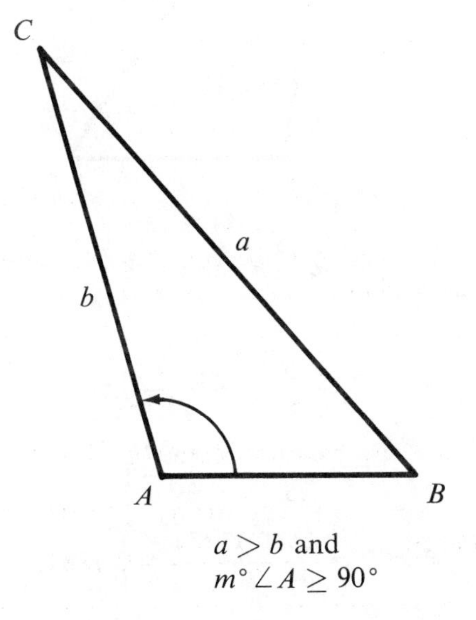

$a > b$ and
$m° \angle A \geq 90°$

ANSWERS TO PAGE 323

$\sin[180° - (A + C)] = \sin(A + C)$

$$\frac{a}{\sin A} = \frac{b}{\sin B} = \frac{c}{\sin C}$$

$\sin 87°30'$

112.91

$$\frac{200}{\sin 87°30'}$$

160.24

sine of the respective opposite angles.

no

$\triangle ABC$ $\triangle AB'C$

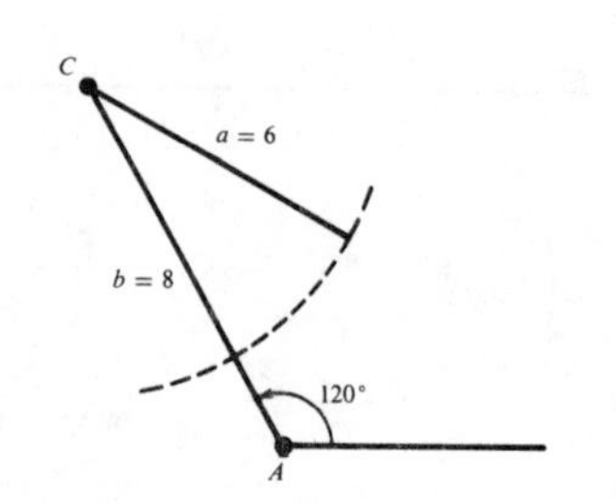

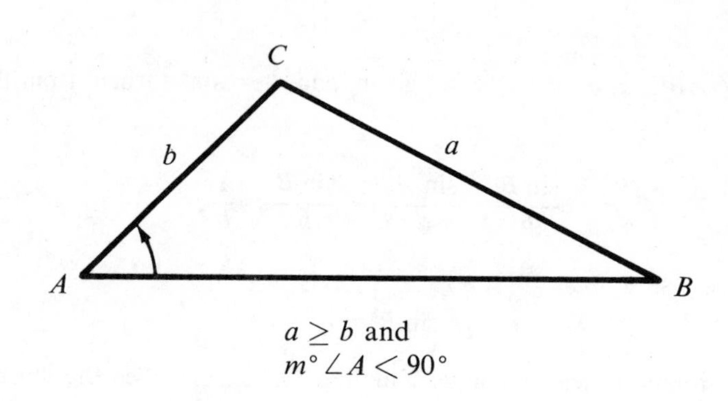

$a \geq b$ and
$m° \angle A < 90°$

Example:

In $\triangle ABC$, $a = 30$, $b = 25$, and $m° \angle A = 110°$. Find $m° \angle B$.

Solution:

By the Law of Sines,

$$\frac{\sin B}{b} = \frac{\sin A}{a}.$$

Thus,

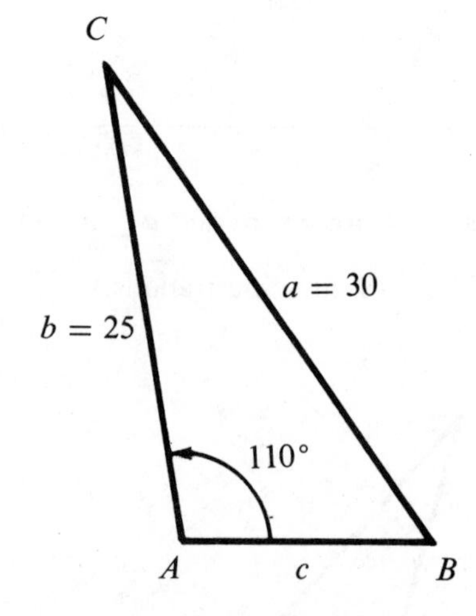

$a > b$ and $m° \angle A > 90°$

$$\frac{\sin B}{25} = \frac{\sin 110°}{30};$$

$$\frac{\sin B}{25} = \frac{0.9397}{30};$$

$$\sin B = \frac{25(0.9397)}{30} = 0.7831.$$

ANSWERS TO PAGE 325

Since $0° < m° \angle B < 180°$, and $\sin B = 0.7831$, there are two possible values for $m° \angle B$, namely, __________ or __________. Only one of these may be used, however, and that is __________. Why? __________

____

____

____

yes

There is only one $\angle B$ such that $0° < m° \angle B < 180°$ and $\sin B = 1$, namely, $m° \angle B = 90°$.

Similarly, if in $\triangle ABC$, $a > b$, and $m° \angle A < 90°$, we have a unique solution.

Example:

In $\triangle ABC$, $a = 40$, $b = 36$, and $m° \angle A = 52°$. Find $m° \angle B$.

Solution:

Apply the Law of Sines.

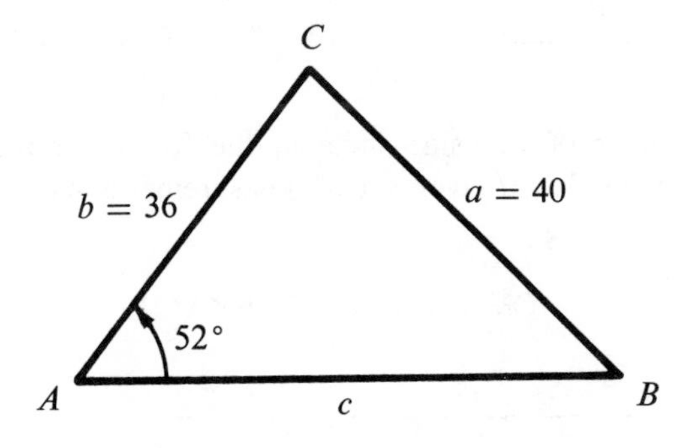

$a > b$ and $m° \angle A < 90°$

yes

$\frac{\sin B}{36} =$ __________, and $\sin B =$ __________.

Thus there are two possible values for $m° \angle B$, namely, __________ or __________. But again the only one that can be used is __________

because ______________________________

____

____

If $a = b$ in $\triangle ABC$, then we have an __________ triangle, and therefore a unique solution.

____

ANSWERS TO PAGE 330

b

a

a

b

b

b

b

a

c

In $\triangle ABC$, a, b, and $\angle A$ are given, $a < b$ and $\frac{a}{b} > \sin A$. Does this situation yield a unique solution? ______. (See the illustration.) There are two possible triangles that could result from this set of given information. They are __________ and ____________________.

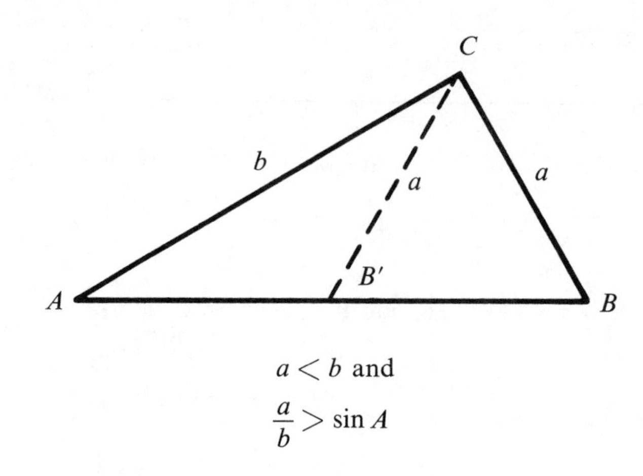

$a < b$ and

$\frac{a}{b} > \sin A$

Each of the cases of side-side-angle in the frames above presumed the existence of a triangle, but a given set of measurements may not determine a triangle.

MOVE TO NEXT FRAME

Sketch $\triangle ABC$ given $m° \angle A = 120°$, $a = 6$, and $b = 8$.

The preceding frame illustrates that if $\angle A$ is obtuse and a ______ b, ($\leq$, $\geq$) then no triangle is determined.

Sketch $\triangle ABC$ given that $m^\circ \angle A = 60^\circ$, $a = 12$, and $b = 20$.

In the illustration, note that the perpendicular distance from C to line $\overleftrightarrow{AB}$ is $b \sin A$. Thus we conclude that if $\angle A$ is acute and a ______ $b \sin A$, ($<$, $>$) then no triangle is determined.

If $a = b \sin A$, then $\triangle ABC$ is a ______ ______ and there is a unique solution.

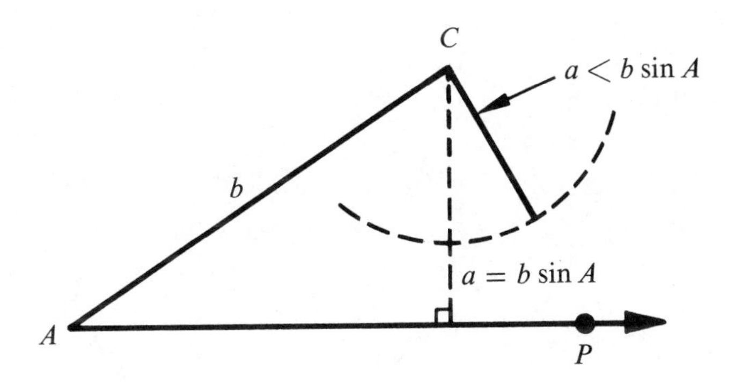

ANSWERS TO PAGE 327

128°27′ or 51°33′

51°33′

Since the sum of the measures of the angles of a triangle is 180°, it cannot have two obtuse angles.

$\frac{\sin 52^\circ}{40}$ 0.7092

45°10′

134°50′ 45°10′

the sum of the measures of the angles of a triangle is 180°.

---

isosceles

ANSWERS TO PAGE 332

(6) See Appendix.

(7) 150°

$$\frac{a-b}{a+b} = \frac{\tan\frac{1}{2}(A-B)}{\tan\frac{1}{2}(A+B)}$$

$$\frac{20-12}{20+12} = \frac{\tan\frac{1}{2}(A-B)}{\tan\frac{1}{2}\,(150°)}$$

0.9330

43°01′

86°02′

118°01′

31°59′

For each of the following, determine whether there is (a) no triangle, (b) a unique triangle, or (c) two triangles which fit the given description of $\triangle RST$.

(1) $\angle S$ is obtuse and $s > r$. ______

(2) $\angle S$ is obtuse and $s < r$. ______

(3) $\angle S$ is obtuse and $s = r$. ______

(4) $\angle S$ is a right angle and $s > r$. ______

(5) $\angle S$ is acute and $s = r$. ______

(6) $\angle S$ is acute and $s > r$. ______

(7) $\angle S$ is acute and $s = r \sin S$. ______

(8) $\angle S$ is acute and $s < r \sin S$. ______

(9) $\angle S$ is acute and $r > s > r \sin S$. ______

$\leq$

EXERCISES. 6.2

1. Use the Law of Cosines to solve for the indicated part in each of the following triangles. (Calculate lengths of sides to the nearest tenth and measures of angles to the nearest ten minutes.)

   (a) $\triangle ABC$ with $a = 40$, $b = 20$, and $m^\circ \angle C = 34^\circ$. $c \approx$ ______.

   (b) $\triangle DEF$ with $d = 17$, $e = 30$, and $f = 22$. $m^\circ \angle E \approx$ ______.

   (c) $\triangle RST$ with $r = 121$, $s = 70$, and $m^\circ \angle T = 105^\circ 10'$. $t \approx$ ______.

2. Use the Law of Sines to solve for the indicated part in each of the fol-following triangles. (Calculate lengths of sides to the nearest tenth and measures of angles to the nearest ten minutes.)

   (a) $\triangle PQR$ with $m^\circ \angle P = 20^\circ 40'$, $m^\circ \angle Q = 72^\circ$, and $p = 45$. $r \approx$

   ______.

   (b) $\triangle STP$ with $s = 68$, $t = 100$, and $m^\circ \angle S = 42^\circ 10'$. $m^\circ \angle T \approx$

   ______.

   (c) $\triangle DOC$ with $m^\circ \angle D = 50^\circ$, $d = 82$, and $c = 50$. $m^\circ \angle C \approx$ ______

   ______.

   (d) $\triangle FAX$ with $m^\circ \angle A = 114^\circ 30'$, $a = 28$, and $f = 32$. $m^\circ \angle F \approx$

   ______.

3. Use the Law of Cosines or the Law of Sines to solve for the indicated parts of the following triangles. (Calculate lengths of sides to the nearest hundredth and measures of angles to the nearest ten minutes.)

   (a) $\triangle BAM$ with $b = 12$, $a = 8$, and $m^\circ \angle M = 30^\circ 40'$. $m \approx$ ______,

   $m^\circ \angle B \approx$ ______, and $m^\circ \angle A \sim$ ______.

   (b) $\triangle TAC$ with $t = 32$, $a = 42$, and $c = 64$. $m^\circ \angle A \approx$ ______.

   $m^\circ \angle C \approx$ ______, $m^\circ \angle T \approx$ ______.

   (c) $\triangle SAR$ with $m^\circ \angle S = 94^\circ 20'$, $a = 72$, and $m^\circ \angle R = 22^\circ 40'$. $r \approx$

   ______ and $s \approx$ ______.

   (d) $\triangle PFG$ with $f = 24$, $g = 50$, and $m^\circ \angle G = 85^\circ 30'$. $p \approx$ ______,

   $m^\circ \angle F \approx$ ______, and $m^\circ \angle P \approx$ ______.

4. In $\triangle ABC$, show that $c = b \cos A + a \cos B$.

5. Express the length of the base b of an isosceles triangle as a function of the vertex angle θ. Let s be the length of the congruent sides. (*Hint:* Use the Law of Cosines and a half-angle formula.)

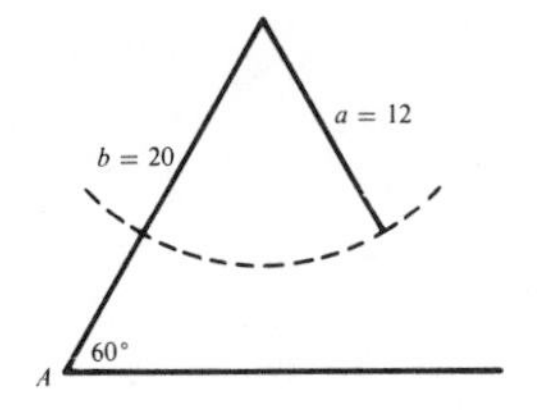

no such triangle exists

$<$

right triangle

(16) See Appendix.

(17) See Appendix.

6. Given $\triangle ABC$, use the properties of proportions and the Law of Sines to show that $\frac{a-b}{a+b} = \frac{\sin A - \sin B}{\sin A + \sin B}$. Subsequently use the product formulas to show that $\frac{a-b}{a+b} = \frac{\tan\frac{1}{2}(A-B)}{\tan\frac{1}{2}(A+B)}$.

This final result is called the **Law of Tangents** and is useful in finding $\angle A$ and $\angle B$ of $\triangle ABC$ when given two sides and the included angle $\angle C$.

7. In $\triangle ABC$, $a = 20$, $b = 12$, and $m^\circ \angle C = 30°00'$. Use the Law of Tangents in Ex. 6 above to find $m^\circ \angle A$ and $m^\circ \angle B$.

Solution:

Since $m^\circ \angle C = 30°00'$,

$$m^\circ \angle A + m^\circ \angle B = \underline{\hspace{5cm}}.$$

The Law of Tangents is

$$\underline{\hspace{8cm}}.$$

Substituting given values results in

$$\underline{\hspace{8cm}}.$$

Use Table I and solve to get

$$\tan\frac{1}{2}(A-B) \approx \underline{\hspace{4cm}}$$

(Four decimal places)

From Table I and interpolation

$$\frac{1}{2}(m^\circ \angle A - m^\circ \angle B) \approx \underline{\hspace{4cm}},$$

so that

$$m^\circ \angle A - m^\circ \angle B \approx \underline{\hspace{4cm}}.$$

Knowing that $m^\circ \angle A + m^\circ \angle B \sim 150°00'$, solve the equations simultaneously for the sum and difference of $m^\circ \angle A$ and $m^\circ \angle B$ to find

$$m^\circ \angle A = \underline{\hspace{4cm}},$$

and

$$m^\circ \angle B \approx \underline{\hspace{4cm}}.$$

8. Find $m^\circ \angle R$ and $m^\circ \angle S$ in $\triangle RST$, given that $r = 50$, $s = 30$, and $m^\circ \angle T = 70°40'$. Use Table I and interpolate to find the measures to the nearest minute.

$m^\circ \angle R \approx$ ________________,

and

$m^\circ \angle S \approx$ ________________.

9. Two consecutive sides of a parallelogram have lengths 16 and 22. The shorter diagonal has a length of 18. Find the length to the nearest tenth of the longer diagonal. ________________

10. Two forces having magnitudes of 46 pounds and 82 pounds, respectively, act on a point. The angle determined by these forces is 36°30′. (a) Find the magnitude to the nearest pound of the resultant force. (b) Find the measure of the angle to the nearest ten minutes, as determined by the resultant and the 82 pound force.

(a) Resultant = ____________. (b) Angle = ____________

11. Find (a) the course to the nearest degree and (b) the groundspeed to the nearest knot of an aircraft that flies a true heading of 160° and a true airspeed of 240 knots. The wind throughout the flight is 30 knots from 220°.

Course = ____________. Groundspeed = ____________

12. Use vectors to prove that if the lengths of two consecutive sides of a parallelogram are a and b and the length of one of the diagonals is c, then the length of the other diagonal is $d = \sqrt{2a^2 + 2b^2 - c^2}$.

13. The desired course and groundspeed of an aircraft is 030° at 360 knots. What is the true heading and true air speed required to maintain this course and the groundspeed when the wind is 40 knots from 225°?

True Heading = ________________
(Compute to the nearest degree.)

True Airspeed = ________________
(Compute to the nearest knot.)

14. Two forces having magnitudes of 200 pounds and 140 pounds, respectively, act on a point. If the angle determined by the two given forces is acute and the angle determined by the resultant force and the larger force is 39°10′, find the magnitude to the nearest pound of the resultant force. ________________

15. The true heading and true airspeed of an aircraft is 160° at 400 knots. The wind is from 290°. If the resulting course is 155° find the groundspeed and wind velocity to the nearest knot. Groundspeed = ________.

Wind = ____________.

ANSWERS TO PAGE 331

(1) (a) 26.0

(b) 99°50′

(c) 154.8

(2) (a) 127.4

(b) 80°50′ or 99°10′ (ambiguous)

(c) 27°50′

(d) no solution

(3) (a) 6.55

110°50′ 38°30′

(b) 35°

119° 26°

(c) 31.34 80.57

(d) 45.75

28°40′ 65°50′

(4) See Appendix.

(5) $b = s\sqrt{2(1-\cos\theta)}$ or

$b = 2s \sin\frac{\theta}{2}$

16. Two angles, $\angle A$ and $\angle B$, and the included side c of $\triangle ABC$ are given. Use the Law of Sines to find the altitude h to side c in terms of $\angle A$, $\angle B$, and side c. ______

______

______

17. Use the results of Exercise 16 to show that the area R of $\triangle ABC$, given $\angle A$, $\angle B$, and c, is

$$R = \frac{c^2 \sin A \sin B}{2 \sin (A + B)}$$

$\sqrt{2^2 + (2\sqrt{3})^2} = 4$

$\frac{\pi}{3}$

$\left(4, \frac{\pi}{3}\right)$

6.3. POLAR COORDINATES

If $P(x,y)$ is a point in a coordinate plane, the vector $\vec{r} = (x,y)$ is called the **radius vector** of P. The length r of $\vec{r}$ is $r = ||\vec{r}|| =$ ______________. The direction angle θ of $\vec{r}$ is the angle determined by $\vec{r}$ and the ______________. (See section 5.2)

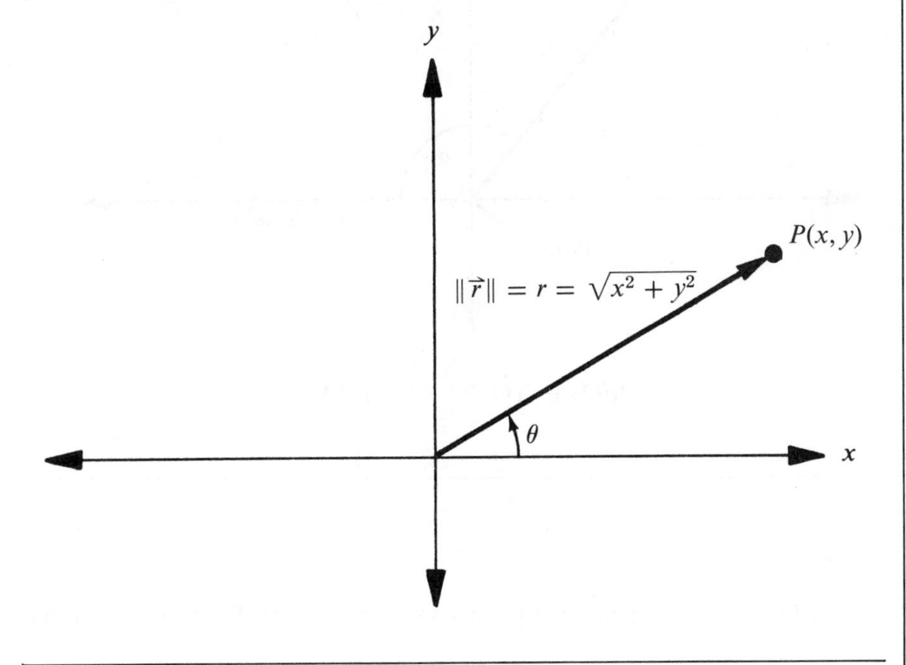

A point $P(x,y)$ can be completely described by giving the length and direction angle of its radius vector. A closely related method of describing a point is to give a set of **polar coordinates** for the point. These are defined in the following frame.

MOVE TO NEXT FRAME

DEFINITIONS:

Let $P(x,y)$ be a point in a plane coordinate system. An ordered pair of real numbers (ρ,θ) is called a pair of **polar coordinates** for $P(x,y)$ if and only if θ is an angle in standard position coterminal with the direction angle of its radius vector $\vec{r} = (x,y)$ and $|\rho| = \sqrt{x^2 + y^2}$. "$\rho$" and "$\theta$" are the Greek letters "rho" and "theta," respectively. The real number ρ is called the **radial coordinate** of P or sometimes the **directed distance** of P, since it may be positive or negative. θ is called a **polar angle** and is usually measured in radians. When using polar coordinates, the origin is called the **pole** and the positive x axis is called the **polar axis.**

ANSWERS TO PAGE 333

(8) 74°06′

35°14′

(9) 34

(10)(a) 122 pounds (b) 13°00′

(11)(a) 153° (b) 226 knots

(12) See Appendix.

(13) 028°

322 knots

(14) 215

(15) 433 knots

49 knots

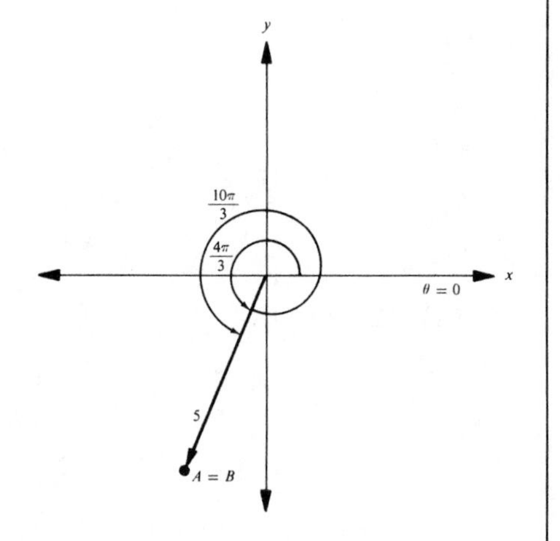

an infinite number

exactly one

(a) −4 (b) 4

(c) −4 (d) 4

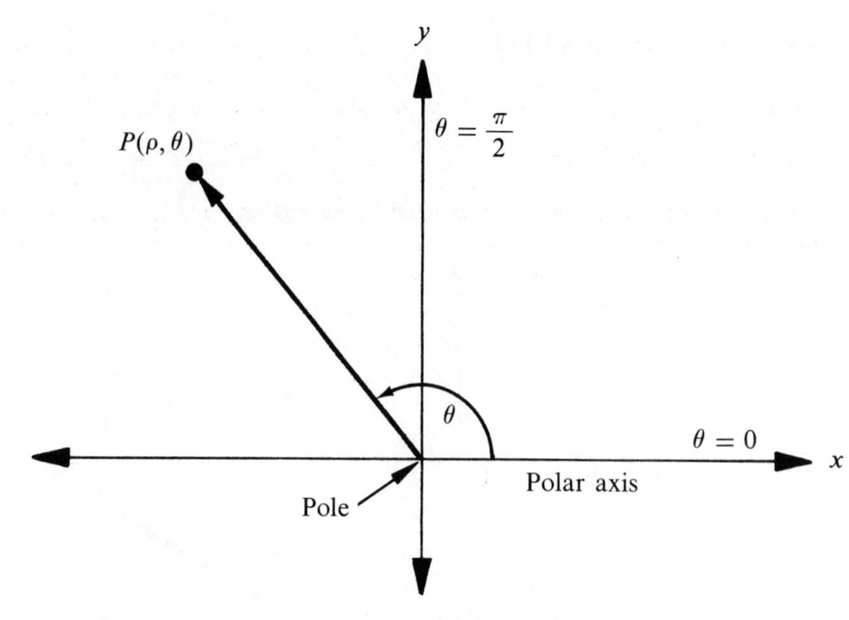

MOVE TO NEXT FRAME

Example:

Let $P(2,2\sqrt{3})$ be a point in a plane coordinate system. From the definition,

$\rho =$ ________________,

and

$\theta =$ ________________.

Thus a pair of polar coordinates for point P is ________________.

To sketch a point P on a coordinate system, when given polar coordinates for P, you first sketch the terminal ray of the given polar angle θ. Then if $\rho > 0$, P is the point on the terminal ray of θ (when in standard position), which is ρ units from the pole. If $\rho < 0$, then P is the point on the terminal side of $\theta + \pi$ (when in standard position) at a distance $|\rho|$ from the pole. Note that the terminal sides of θ and $\theta + \pi$ are opposite rays.

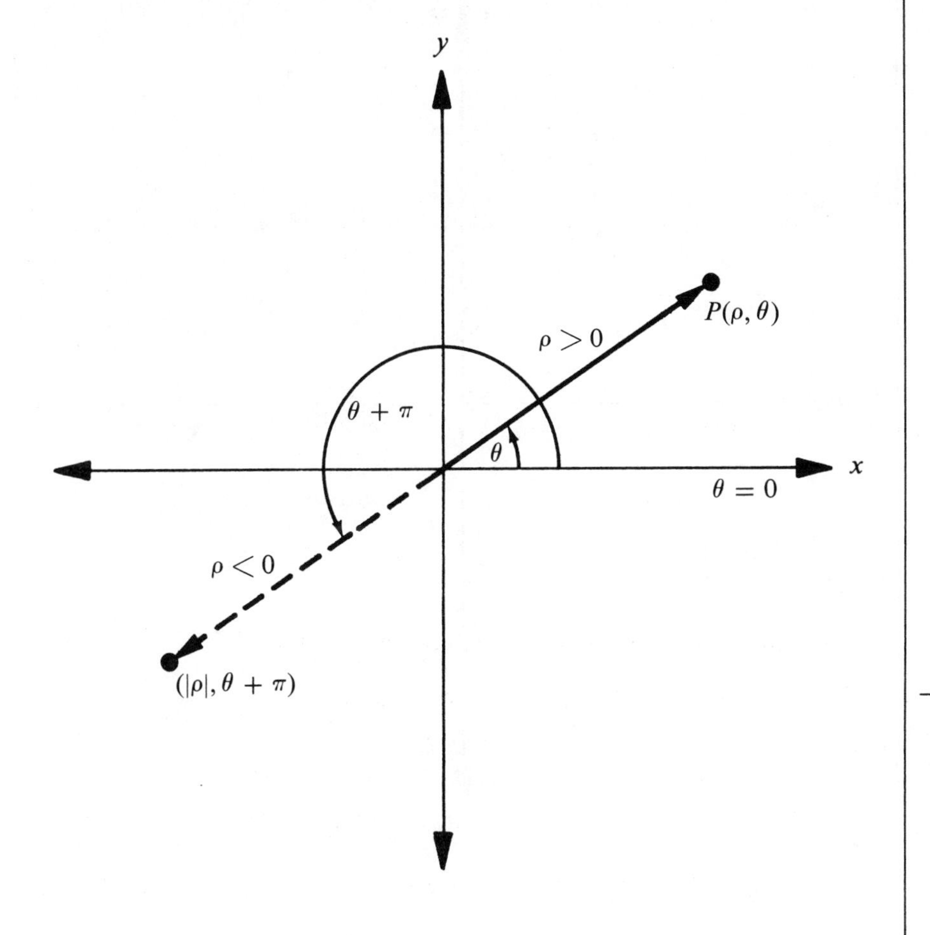

MOVE TO NEXT FRAME

ANSWERS TO PAGE 335

$\sqrt{x^2 + y^2}$

positive x axis

straight line through the pole with an angle of inclination from the horizontal of $\frac{\pi}{3}$.

Use the adjacent coordinate system to sketch the location of point A and point B, if A and B have polar coordinates $\left(5, \frac{4\pi}{3}\right)$ and $\left(5, \frac{10\pi}{3}\right)$ respectively.

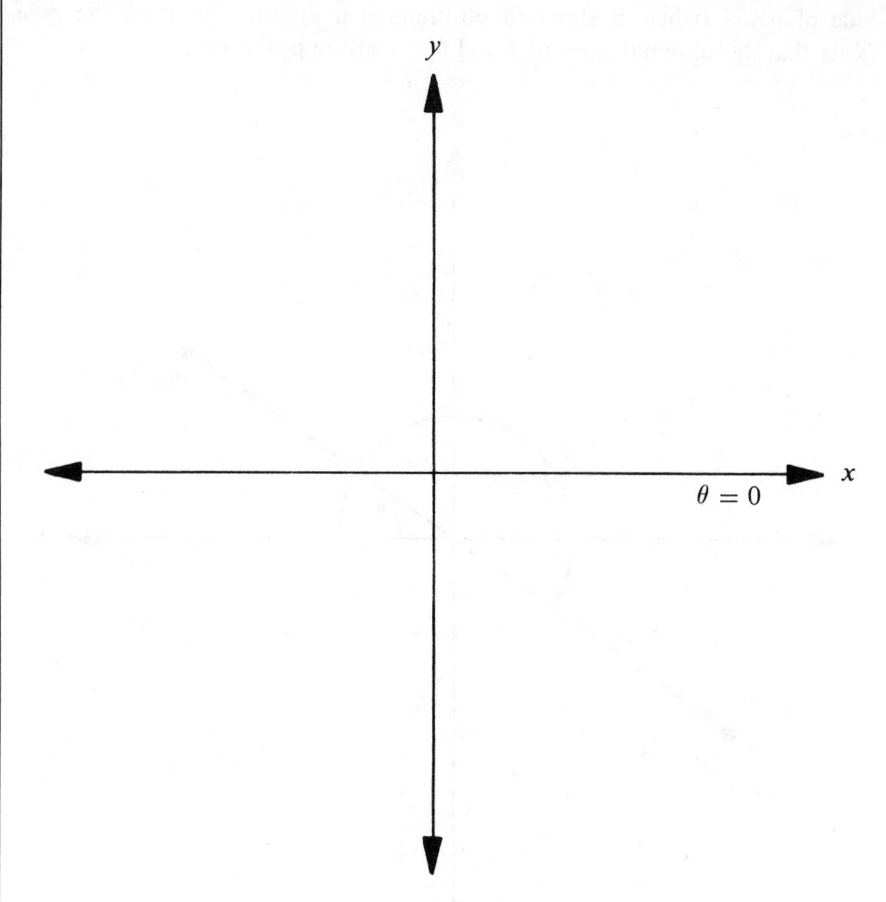

The preceding frame illustrates a fundamental characteristic of the polar coordinates of a point. For a given point there exist(s) ____________ (exactly one, two, an infinite number of) pair(s) of polar coordinates. For a given pair of polar coordinates there exist(s) ____________ (exactly one, two, an infinite number of) point(s).

A pair of polar coordinates for point P is $\left(4, \frac{\pi}{9}\right)$. Complete the following ordered pairs so that they are also polar coordinates for P.

(a) $\left(\_\_\_\_, \frac{7\pi}{6}\right)$ (b) $\left(\_\_\_\_, \frac{13\pi}{6}\right)$

(c) $\left(\_\_\_\_, \frac{19\pi}{6}\right)$ (d) $\left(\_\_\_\_, \frac{25\pi}{6}\right)$

Notice that if (ρ,θ) is a pair of polar coordinates for P, then $[-\rho,\theta + (2k + 1)\pi]$ or $(\rho,\theta + 2k\pi)$ for all $k\epsilon J$ are also polar coordinates for P.

The pole (origin) is assigned any pair of polar coordinates $(0,\theta)$ where θ is any real number.

A relation in x and y may be represented by a graph in the rectangular coordinate plane. For example, the graph of $x = 2$ is a ______________, and the graph of $x^2 + y^2 = 4$ is a ______________. A relation in ρ and θ may also be represented by a graph in a **polar coordinate system.**

Consider the graph of the relation defined by $\rho = 4$. No restriction is placed on the polar angle θ by the equation $\rho = 4$; so as θ takes all real number values, the point P, which is 4 units from the pole on the terminal side of θ, traces out a circle whose radius is ________. Similarly, if $\rho = c$, where c is a nonzero constant, this constant relation describes a circle. What is the graph of $\rho = -4$ in the polar coordinate system? ______________.

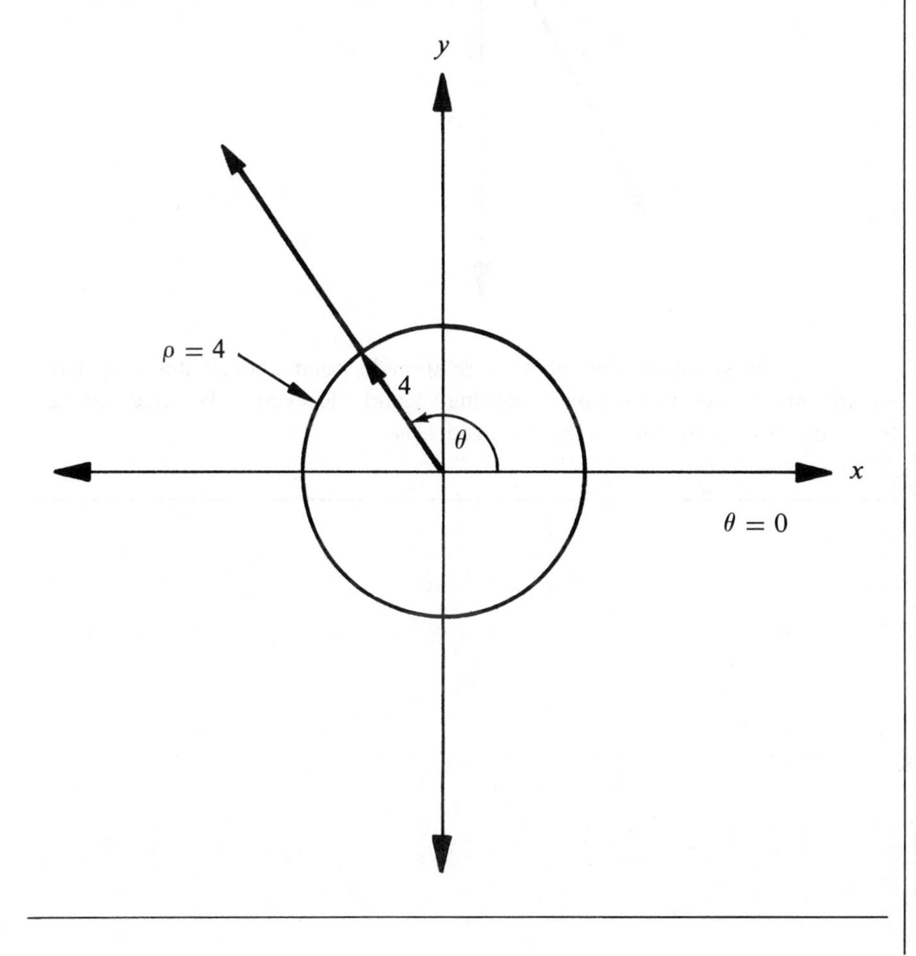

ANSWERS TO PAGE 342

$\sqrt{x^2 + y^2}$ $\quad \dfrac{y}{x}$

$x > 0 \qquad x < 0$

$\dfrac{\pi}{2}$

$\dfrac{3\pi}{2}$

(a) $\left(\sqrt{2}, \dfrac{-\pi}{4}\right)$ (b) $\left(2, \dfrac{\pi}{6}\right)$

(c) $\left(6, \dfrac{4\pi}{3}\right)$ (d) $\left(4, \dfrac{3\pi}{4}\right)$

no

Consider the graph of the relation defined by $\theta = \dfrac{\pi}{3}$. Here we have no restriction placed on ρ, but θ is constant. Thus the points of the graph lie on a

____

____.

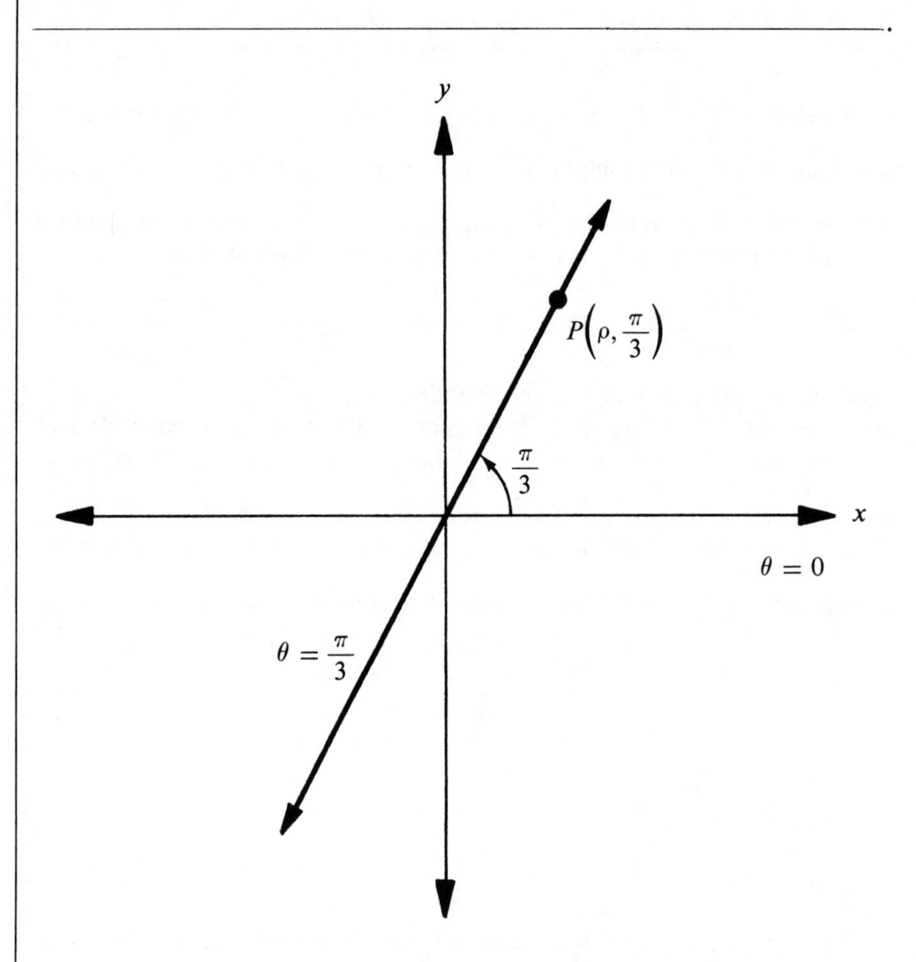

In a given situation, describing a relation in polar coordinates may have an advantage over rectangular coordinates and vice versa. We may change from one system to another as the need arises.

The diagram below illustrates the relation between the polar coordinates (ρ,θ) and rectangular coordinates (x,y) of a point P. An application of trigonometric functions results in $\sin\theta =$ ______ and $\cos\theta =$ ______. Hence,

$x =$ ____________________,

and

$y =$ ____________________.

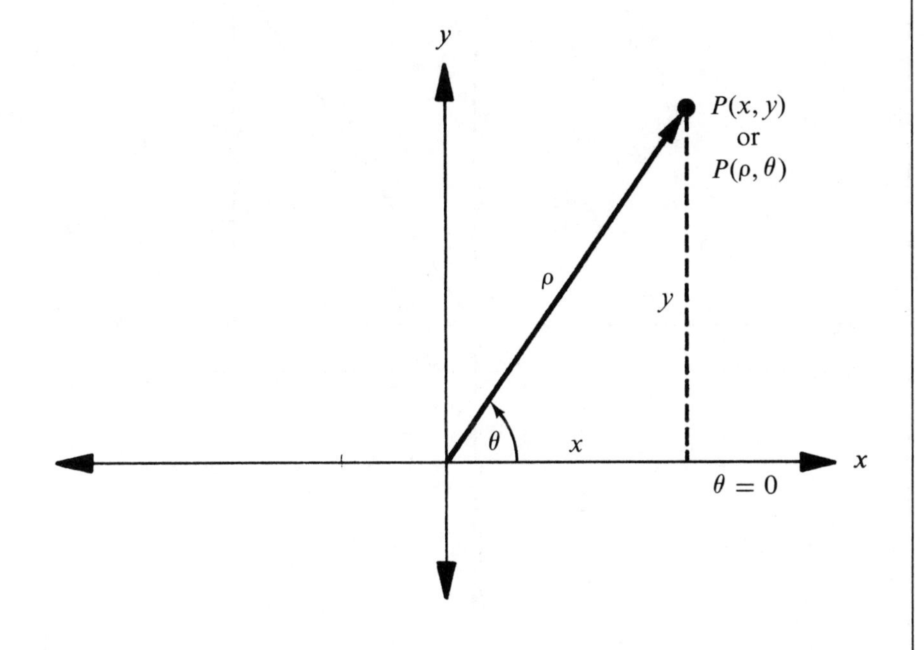

vertical line

circle

Examples:

Find the rectangular coordinates for the points whose polar coordinates are as follows:

(a) $\left(4, \frac{3\pi}{4}\right)$: (____________) (b) $\left(5, \frac{\pi}{6}\right)$: (____________)

$\left(x = 4\cos\frac{3\pi}{4}; y = 4\sin\frac{3\pi}{4}\right)$

(c) $\left(4, \frac{11\pi}{4}\right)$: (____________) (d) $\left(-8, \frac{11\pi}{6}\right)$: (____________)

(e) $\left(-4, \frac{7\pi}{4}\right)$: (____________) (f) $\left(4, \frac{5\pi}{3}\right)$: (____________)

4

a circle with radius 4

$\cos(-\theta) = \cos\theta$

6

π 0

0

$\frac{2\pi}{3}$	$\frac{3\pi}{4}$	$\frac{5\pi}{6}$	π
4.5	5.1	5.6	6

Given the rectangular coordinates of a point $P(x,y)$, we may also find a pair of polar coordinates for P. Complete the following relations for polar coordinates in terms of rectangular coordinates:

$\rho =$ __________ and $\tan\theta =$ ______.

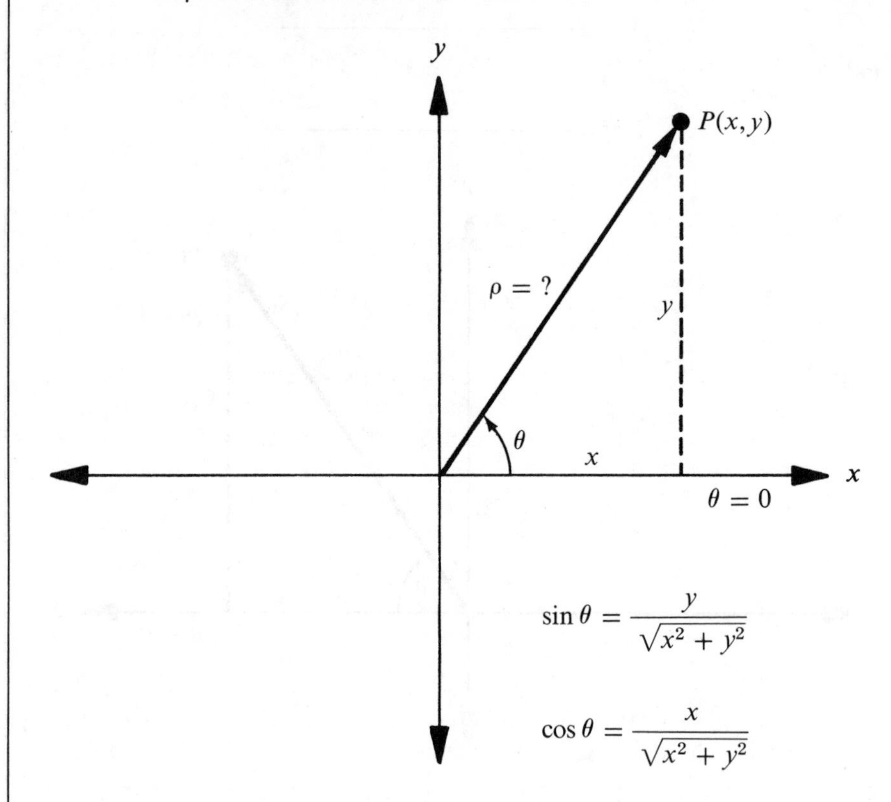

$$\sin\theta = \frac{y}{\sqrt{x^2 + y^2}}$$

$$\cos\theta = \frac{x}{\sqrt{x^2 + y^2}}$$

To find θ we must consider the quadrant in which the point $P(x,y)$ lies. Thus

$\theta = \text{Arctan}\ \frac{y}{x}$ when ______ and $\theta = \pi + \text{Arctan}\ \frac{y}{x}$ when ______.

If $x = 0$ and $y > 0$ for $P(x,y)$, then $\theta =$ ______. If $x = 0$ and $y < 0$, then

$\theta =$ __________.

Examples:

Find a set of polar coordinates for the points whose rectangular coordinates are as follows.

(a) $(1,-1)$ __________ (b) $(\sqrt{3},1)$ __________

(c) $(-3,-3\sqrt{3})$ __________ (d) $(-2\sqrt{2},2\sqrt{2})$ __________

Are the polar coordinates for each of these points unique? __________

Example:

Transform the polar equation

$$\rho - 4 \sin \theta = 0$$

into an equation involving rectangular coordinates and describe the corresponding graph.

Solution:

$\rho = \sqrt{x^2 + y^2}$, and $\sin \theta =$ ____________________. Substituting in

$\rho - 4 \sin \theta = 0$ results in ______________________________.

Multiplying both members by $\sqrt{x^2 + y^2} \neq 0$ results in _______________.

The corresponding graph has the form of ______________________________

____.

Sketching a graph in polar coordinates is facilitated by the use of Polar Graph Paper. Reasonably descriptive sketches may be made, however, by estimating the measures of special angles and the corresponding radial coordinates.

MOVE TO NEXT FRAME

ANSWERS TO PAGE 341

$\dfrac{y}{\rho}$ $\dfrac{x}{\rho}$

$x = \rho \cos \theta$

$y = \rho \sin \theta$

(a) $(-2\sqrt{2}, 2\sqrt{2})$ (b) $\left(\dfrac{5\sqrt{3}}{2}, \dfrac{5}{2}\right)$

(c) $(-2\sqrt{2}, 2\sqrt{2})$ (d) $(-4\sqrt{3}, 4)$

(e) $(-2\sqrt{2}, 2\sqrt{2})$ (f) $(2, -2\sqrt{3})$

the pole

Example:

Sketch the graph defined by $\rho = 3(1 - \cos\theta)$.

Solution:

The equation remains unchanged when θ is replaced by $-\theta$, since ______________________________. Hence the graph is symmetric about the x axis. (See the illustration.) Thus we only need to find values of ρ for $\theta \leq \pi$ and $\theta \geq 0$ and then reflect the graph about the x axis.

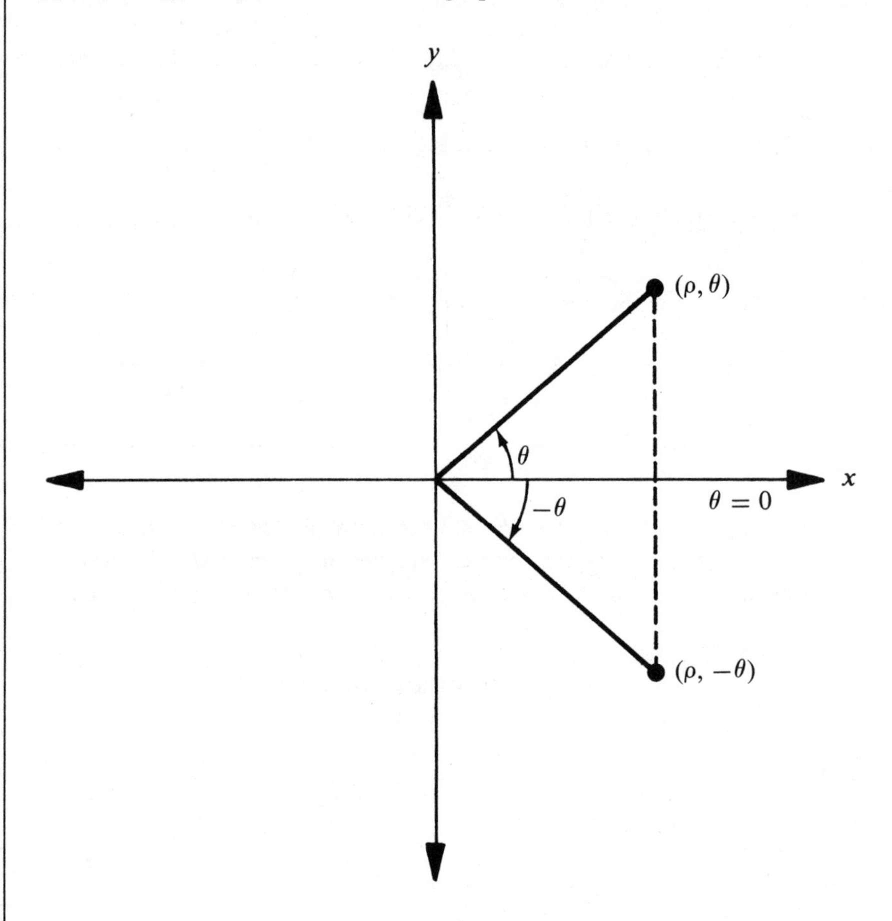

Since $-1 \leq \cos\theta \leq 1$, the maximum value of ρ is ______, which occurs when $\theta =$ ______, and the minimum value of ρ is ______ when $\theta =$ ______. Now complete the tables with approximate values of ρ for measures of special angles with $\pi < \theta \leq 0$.

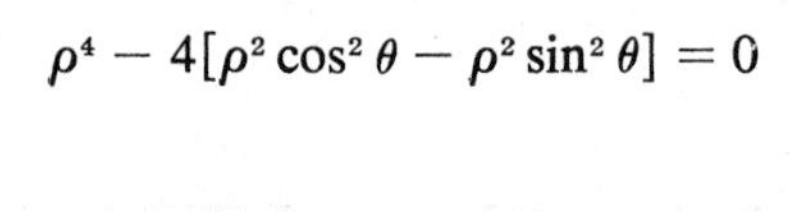

$\rho^4 - 4[\rho^2\cos^2\theta - \rho^2\sin^2\theta] = 0$

$\rho - 4(\cos^2\theta - \sin^2\theta)$

θ	0	$\frac{\pi}{6}$	$\frac{\pi}{4}$	$\frac{\pi}{3}$	$\frac{\pi}{2}$	$\frac{2\pi}{3}$	$\frac{3\pi}{4}$	$\frac{5\pi}{6}$	π
ρ	0	0.4	0.9	1.5	3.0				

Plot the points corresponding to these polar coordinates and sketch a smooth curve. Reflect it in the x axis for the complete graph. (This graph is called a **cardioid** because of its heart-shaped appearance.)

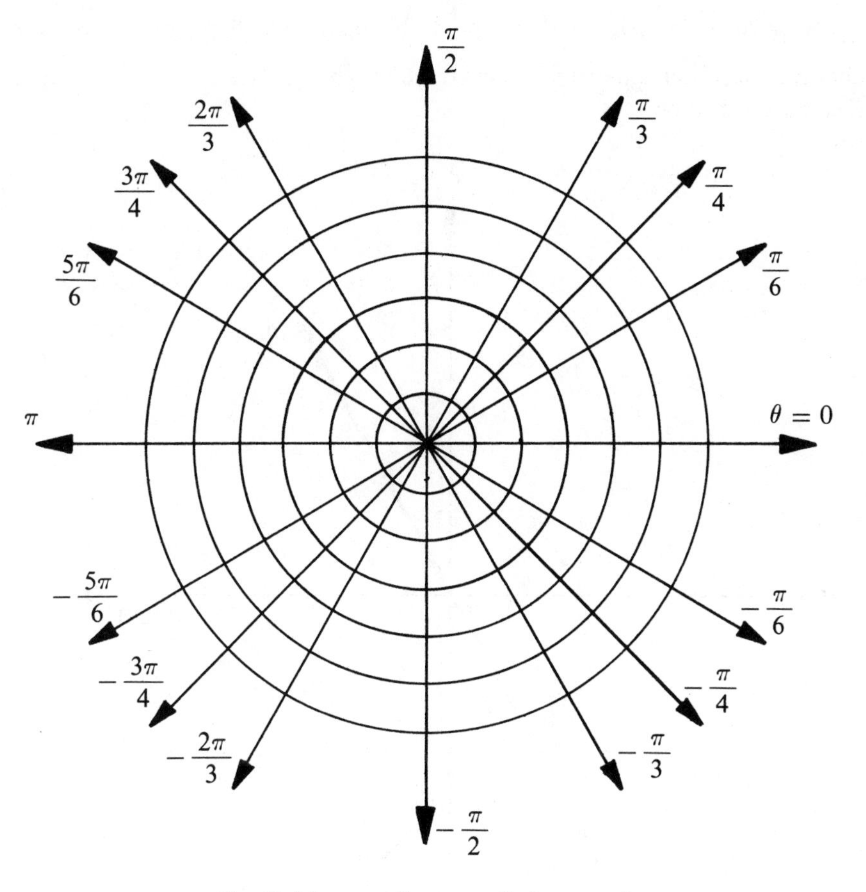

Cardioid $\rho = a(1 - \cos\theta)$ for $a = 3$

Symmetry about the x axis of the graph of an equation in polar coordinates is indicated when replacing ______ with ______ in the equation does not change its value.

Suppose θ is replaced by $\pi - \theta$, and the equation remains unchanged. This would indicate symmetry about ____________________.

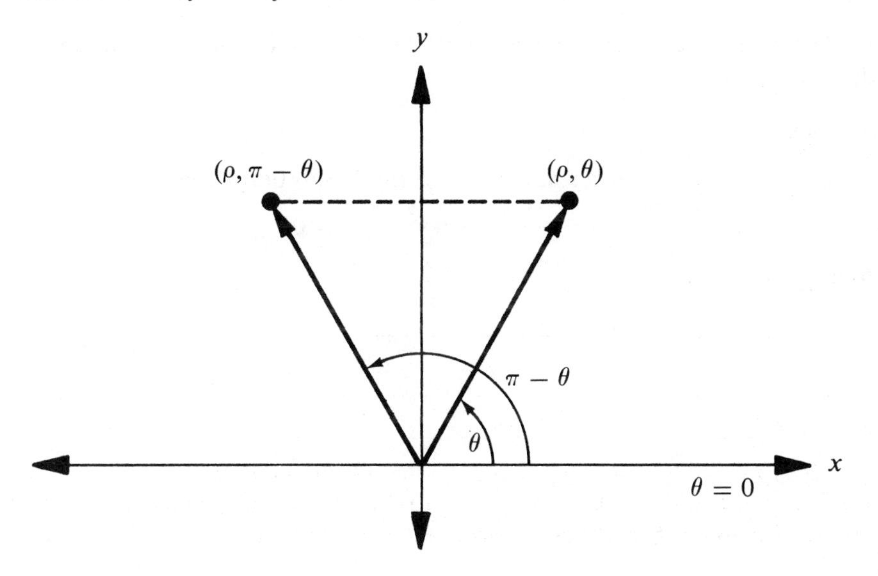

$$\frac{y}{\sqrt{x^2 + y^2}}$$

$$\sqrt{x^2 + y^2} - 4\left(\frac{y}{\sqrt{x^2 + y^2}}\right) = 0$$

$x^2 + y^2 - 4y = 0$ or
$x^2 + (y - 2)^2 = 4$

a circle with center (0,2) and radius of 2.

ANSWERS TO PAGE 348

$4^2 + \rho^2 - 2\rho(4)\cos\left(\theta - \frac{\pi}{6}\right)$

Suppose ρ is replaced by $-\rho$ in the polar equation, and there is no change. This would indicate symmetry through ____________________. (See the illustration.)

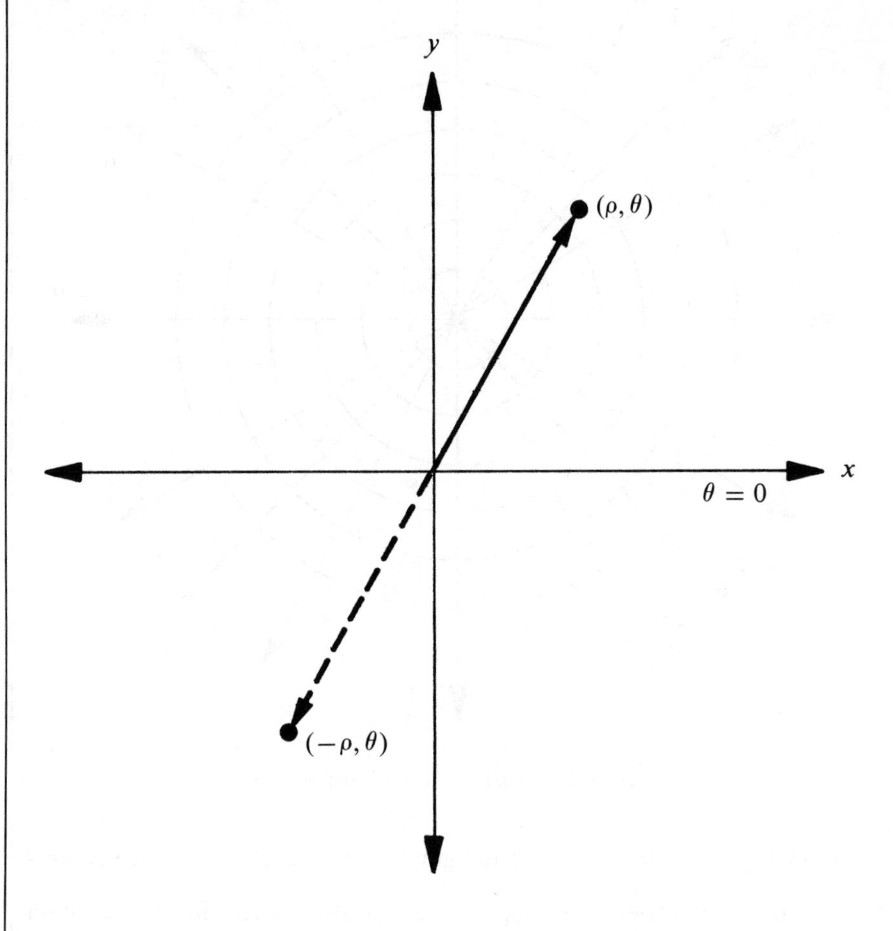

Example:

Determine the polar equation for $(x^2 + y^2)^2 - 4(x^2 - y^2) = 0$ and sketch the corresponding graph.

Solution:

$\rho^2 = x^2 + y^2$, $x = \rho \cos \theta$, and $y = \rho \sin \theta$. Substituting in

$$(x^2 + y^2)^2 - 4(x^2 - y^2) = 0$$

results in

____

or

$\rho^2($ ____________________________________ $) = 0.$

Thus,

$$\rho^2 = 0, \quad \text{or} \quad \rho = 4(\cos^2 \theta = \sin^2 \theta).$$

The equation $\rho^2 = 0$ may be ignored, since it does not contribute any points to the graph not also found from the other equation.

Substituting cos 2θ for ______________________ results in

$$\rho^2 - 4 \cos 2\theta = 0.$$

Since replacing ρ by $-\rho$ leaves the equation unchanged, it is symmetric about ______________. Is it symmetric through the x axis? ______ Is it symmetric about the y axis? ______ Sketch the graph on the coordinate system provided.

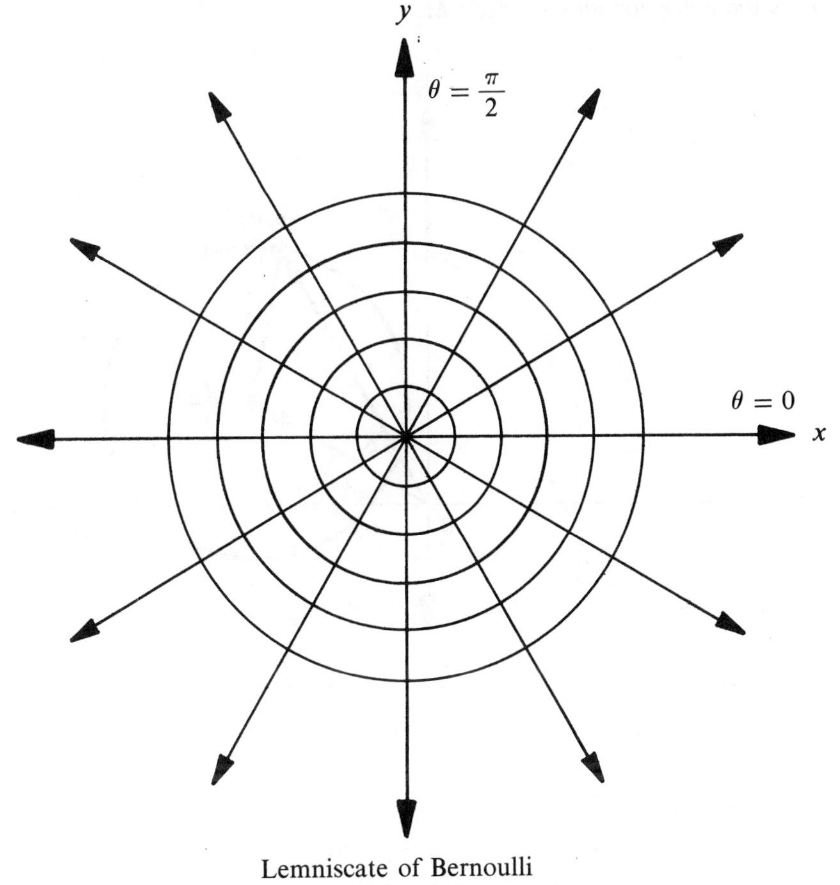

Lemniscate of Bernoulli
$\rho^2 - a^2 \cos 2\theta = 0$ for $a = 2$

We may find a polar equation for a relation by transforming an equation in rectangular coordinates, as has been seen. We may also find a polar equation directly from specified geometric properties.

MOVE TO NEXT FRAME

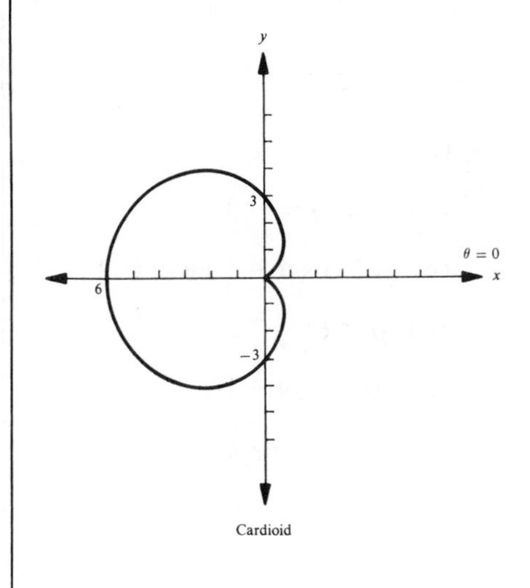

Cardioid

θ $\quad -\theta$

the y axis

ANSWERS TO PAGE 350

(c) $\left(8, \frac{\pi}{2}\right)$ (d) $\left(3, \frac{11\pi}{6}\right)$

(e) $(5,\pi)$ (f) $\left(\sqrt{13}, \text{Arctan}\,\frac{3}{2}\right)$

or $\left(\sqrt{13}, 0.9832\right)$

(4) (a) $\rho \cos \theta = 2$

(b) $\rho \sin \theta = -3$

(c) $\rho(3 \cos \theta + 4 \sin \theta) = 8$

(d) $\rho = 6$

(e) $\rho^2 \cos 2\theta = 16$

(f) $\rho = -6 \sin \theta$

(5) (a) $x^2 + y^2 = 25$

(b) $x = 4$

(c) $(x - 4)^2 + y^2 = 16$

(d) $y^2 = 2x + 1$

(e) $x^4 + x^2y^2 - 4y^2 = 0$

(6) (a) symmetry through the pole

(b) symmetry about the x axis

(c) symmetry about the y axis

(d) symmetry about the y axis

(e) symmetry through the pole

(7) See Appendix.

Example:

The polar coordinates of the center M of a circle are $\left(4, \frac{\pi}{6}\right)$. The radius of the circle is 3. Find the polar equation of the circle.

Let $P(\rho,\theta)$ be a point on circle M, and apply the Law of Cosines to $\triangle OMP$. (See the illustration.)

$3^2 =$ ______________________________,

or

$$0 = 7 + \rho^2 + 8\rho \cos\left(\theta - \frac{\pi}{6}\right).$$

This is the polar equation of circle M.

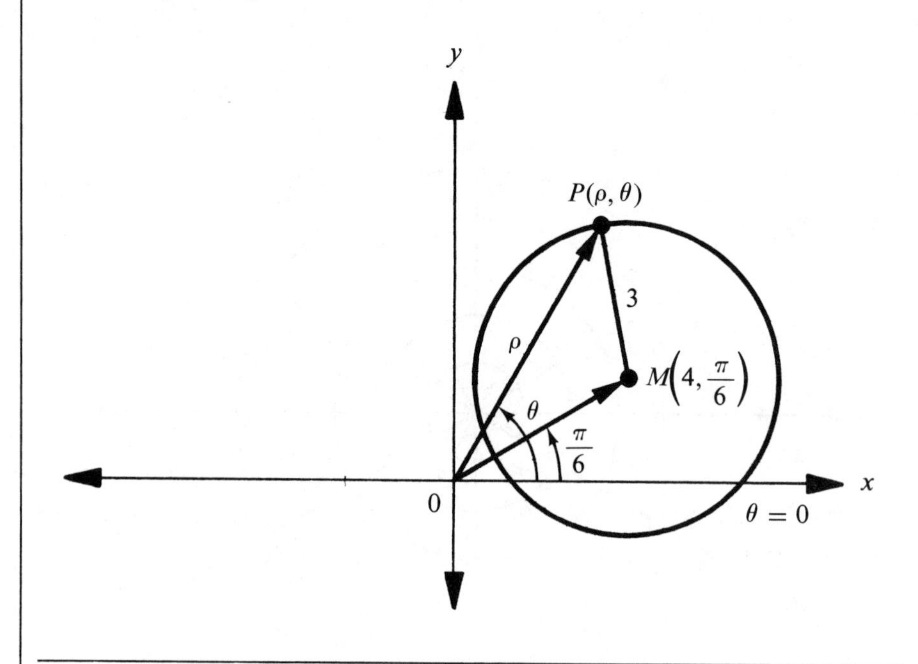

EXERCISES. 6.3

1. Give the complete set of polar coordinates for each of the points having the following polar coordinates.

   (a) $\left(3, \frac{\pi}{6}\right)$ ____________

   (b) $\left(3, \frac{-\pi}{6}\right)$ ____________

   (c) $\left(-3, \frac{\pi}{6}\right)$ ____________

   (d) $\left(-3, \frac{-\pi}{6}\right)$ ____________

2. Find rectangular coordinates corresponding to each of the following pairs of polar coordinates.

   (a) $\left(4, \frac{\pi}{3}\right)$ ____________

   (b) $\left(5, \frac{-\pi}{6}\right)$ ____________

   (c) $\left(6, \frac{3\pi}{4}\right)$ ____________

   (d) $\left(-6, \frac{\pi}{4}\right)$ ____________

   (e) $\left(-7, \frac{-2\pi}{3}\right)$ ____________

   (f) $\left(8, \frac{11\pi}{6}\right)$ ____________

3. Find a set of polar coordinates with polar angle θ such that $0 \leq \theta < 2\pi$ for each of the following points with rectangular coordinates.

   (a) $(3, -3\sqrt{3})$ ____________ (b) $(-2\sqrt{2}, 2\sqrt{2})$ ____________

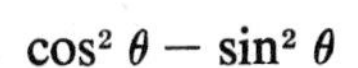

the pole yes

yes

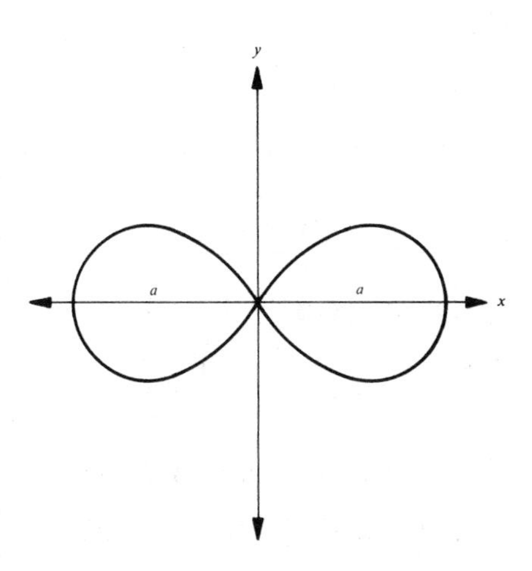

Lemniscate of Bernoulli

$\rho^2 - a^2 \cos \theta = 0, \quad \text{for } a = 2$

ANSWERS TO PAGE 352

∅

ordered pairs

$a = c$

$b = d$

$(a + c, b + d)$

(a) (1,9)

(b) 3   2

(c) (0,0)

(c) (0,8) ______ (d) $\left(\frac{3\sqrt{3}}{2}, \frac{-3}{2}\right)$ ______

(e) (−5,0) ______ (f) (2,3) ______

4. Find a polar equation corresponding to each of the following equations in rectangular coordinates.

(a) $x = 2$ ______

(b) $y = -3$ ______

(c) $3x + 4y = 8$ ______

(d) $x^2 + y^2 = 36$ ______

(e) $x^2 - y^2 = 16$ ______

(f) $x^2 + (y + 3)^2 = 9$ ______

5. Find equations in rectangular coordinates for each of the following polar equations.

(a) $\rho = 5$ ______

(b) $\rho \cos \theta = 4$ ______

(c) $\rho = 8 \cos \theta$ ______

(d) $\rho = \frac{1}{1 - \cos \theta}$ ______

(e) $\rho = 2 \tan \theta$ ______

6. What kind of symmetry occurs on the graph corresponding to a polar equation if the equation remains unchanged when

(a) ρ is replaced by $-\rho$? ______

(b) θ is replaced by $-\theta$? ______

(c) θ is replaced by $\pi - \theta$? ______

(d) ρ and θ are replaced by $-\rho$ and $-\theta$ respectively? ______

______

(e) θ is replaced by $\theta + \pi$? ______

7. Without actually sketching the graphs, describe the symmetries of the graphs corresponding to the following polar equations.

(a) $\rho \cos^2 \frac{\theta}{2} = 2$

(b) $\rho^2 = 9 \sin 2\theta$

(c) $\rho - \rho \cos \theta = 8$

(d) $\rho = \cos^2 2\theta$

8. Sketch the graphs corresponding to the following polar equations. (Use supplementary paper.)

(a) $\rho = \theta$ (Spiral of Archimedes)

(b) $\rho = 2 + 4 \cos \theta$ (Limacon)

(c) $\rho = 4 \sin 3\,\theta$ (Three-Leaved Rose)

(d) $\rho = 4 \cos 2\,\theta$ (Four-Leaved Rose)

(e) $\rho = \dfrac{4}{\theta}$ (Hyperbolic Spiral)

ANSWERS TO PAGE 349

(1)(a) $\left\{\left(3, \frac{\pi}{6}+2k\pi\right)\right.$ or $\left.\left(-3, \frac{7\pi}{6}+2k\pi\right)\right\}$, for some $k \epsilon J$

(b) $\left\{\left(3, \frac{-\pi}{6}+2k\pi\right)\right.$ or $\left(-3, \frac{5\pi}{6}+2k\pi\right)$ for some $\left.k \epsilon J\right\}$

(c) $\left\{\left(-3, \frac{\pi}{6}+2k\pi\right)\right.$ or $\left(3, \frac{7\pi}{6}+2k\pi\right)$ for some $\left.k \epsilon J\right\}$

(d) $\left\{\left(-3, \frac{-\pi}{6}+2k\pi\right)\right.$ or $\left(3, \frac{5\pi}{6}+2k\pi\right)$ for some $\left.k \epsilon J\right\}$

(2)(a) $(2, 2\sqrt{3})$

(b) $\left(\frac{5\sqrt{3}}{2}, \frac{-5}{2}\right)$

(c) $(-3\sqrt{2}, 3\sqrt{2})$

(d) $(-3\sqrt{2}, -3\sqrt{2})$

(e) $\left(\frac{7}{2}, \frac{7\sqrt{3}}{2}\right)$

(f) $(4\sqrt{3}, -4)$

(3)(a) $\left(6, \frac{5\pi}{3}\right)$ (b) $\left(4, \frac{3\pi}{4}\right)$

6.4. COMPLEX NUMBERS

If $x \in \mathcal{R}$, then the solution set for the equation $x^2 + 9 = 0$ is ________.

Complex numbers are constructed from the set of real numbers in order that equations such as $x^2 + 9 = 0$ may have solutions.

Vectors are elements of the set $\mathcal{R} \times \mathcal{R}$, i.e., vectors are ________ of real numbers.

Ordered pairs of real numbers, with multiplication defined in a special manner and with equality, addition, and scalar multiplication defined as for vectors (see section 2.2), are called **complex numbers.**

(a) (9,5)

(b) (−6,−5)

(c) (1,−2)

DEFINITION:

A **complex number** is an ordered pair of real numbers, with equality, addition, and scalar multiplication defined as for vectors and with multiplication of two complex numbers defined as follows:

$$(a,b)(c,d) = (ac - bd,\ ad + bc).$$

MOVE TO NEXT FRAME

(a) $(xr - ys, xs + yr)$

(b) (−23,−2)

(c) (16,12)

(d) (−17,−17)

From the definition of equality for ordered pairs of real numbers, the complex numbers (a,b) and (c,d) are equal if and only if ________ and ________.

Since complex numbers are added as vectors are added, the sum of two complex numbers (a,b) and (c,d) would be

$(a,b) + (c,d) =$ ________________

$(b_1c_1 - b_2c_2, b_1c_2 + b_2c_1)$

Examples:

(a) $(3,4) + (-2,5) =$ ________.

(b) Find x and y so that $(x,-6) + (-2,8) + (4 - x,y)$.

$x =$ ________; $y =$ ________.

(c) $(4,-5) + (-4,5) =$ ________.

From the properties of vector addition, we have the following properties of **addition of complex numbers.**

Let (a,b), (c,d), and (e,f) be elements of the set C of complex numbers. Then

(1) **Closure:**

$$(a,b) + (c,d) \in C.$$

(2) **Associative:**

$$(a,b) + [(c,d) + (e,f)] = [(a,b) + (c,d)] + (e,f).$$

(3) **Identity:** There exists exactly one complex number, namely $(0,0)$, in C such that

$$(a,b) + (0,0) = (0,0) + (a,b) = (a,b).$$

(4) **Inverse:** For $(a,b) \in C$ there exists exactly one complex number, denoted $-(a,b)$, in C such that

$$(a,b) + [-(a,b)] = -(a,b) + (a,b) = (0,0).$$

(5) **Commutative:**

$$(a,b) + (c,d) = (c,d) + (a,b).$$

MOVE TO NEXT FRAME

Is the set C of complex numbers a commutative group under addition?

____________________ (See section 2.2.)

What are the properties of a commutative (Abelian) group? (See section 2.2.) ____________________

Since $(a,b) + (-a,-b) =$ ________ by the definition of addition of complex numbers and $(a,b) + -(a,b) =$ ________ by the additive inverse property, $-(a,b) = (-a,-b)$. Thus, for example,

$$-(-4,3) = \_\_\_\_\_\_\_\_.$$

---

(8) See Appendix.

ANSWERS TO PAGE 356

definition of multiplication

---

equality of two ordered pairs

$\frac{x}{x^2 + y^2}, \frac{-y}{x^2 + y^2}$

$$(x,y)\left(\frac{x}{x^2 + y^2}, \frac{-y}{x^2 + y^2}\right)$$
$$= \left(x\left(\frac{x}{x^2 + y^2}\right) - y\left(\frac{-y}{x^2 + y^2}\right), x\left(\frac{-y}{x^2 + y^2}\right) + y\left(\frac{x}{x^2 + y^2}\right)\right)$$
$$= \left(\frac{x^2 + y^2}{x^2 + y^2}, \frac{-xy + xy}{x^2 + y^2}\right) = (1,0)$$

The definition of subtraction of complex numbers is also the same as that for vectors.

DEFINITIONS:

If $(a,b) \epsilon C$ and $(c,d) \epsilon C$, then

$$(a,b) - (c,d) = (a,b) + [-(c,d)].$$

MOVE TO NEXT FRAME

Examples:

Subtract the following as indicated.

(a) $(3,7) - (-6,2) = (3,7) + [-(-6,2)] = (3,7) + (6,-2) =$ ________.

(b) $(-4,-8) - (2,-3) =$ ________.

(c) $(2,-6) - (1,-4) =$ ________.

Use the definition of multiplication of complex numbers to find the following products.

(a) $(x,y)(r,s) =$ ________.

(b) $(2,3)(-4,5) =$ ________.

(c) $(-1,3)(2,-6) =$ ________.

(d) $(5,3)(-4,-1) =$ ________.

It can be shown that the nonzero complex numbers are a commutative group under multiplication. It can further be shown that multiplication of complex numbers distributes over addition. The associative property of multiplication will be proved in the next frame. Proofs of the commutative and distributive properties are similar and will be left as exercises.

MOVE TO NEXT FRAME

Example:

Prove that multiplication of complex numbers is associative.

Proof:

Let $a = (a_1,a_2)$, $b = (b_1,b_2)$, and $c = (c_1,c_2)$ be complex numbers. Then,

$$a(bc) = (a_1,a_2)\,[(b_1,b_2)(c_1,c_2)]$$
$$= (a_1,a_2)\,(\_\_\_\_\_\_\_\_),$$

by the definition of multiplication of complex numbers.

$$(a_1,a_2)(b_1c_1 - b_2c_2, b_1c_2 + b_2c_1) = [a_1(b_1c_1 - b_2c_2) - a_2(b_1c_2 + b_2c_1),$$
$$a_1(b_1c_2 + b_2c_1) + a_2(b_1c_1 - b_2c_2)],$$

also by the definition of multiplication of complex numbers.

$$a_1(b_1c_1 - b_2c_2) - a_2(b_1c_2 + b_2c_1), a_1(b_1c_2 + b_2c_1) + a_2(b_1c_1 - b_2c_2)$$
$$= (a_1b_1c_1 - a_1b_2c_2 - a_2b_1c_2 - a_2b_2c_1, a_1b_1c_2 + a_1b_2c_1 + a_2b_1c_1 - a_2b_2c_2)$$

by the usual ____________________ property in $\mathcal{R}$.

$$(a_1b_1c_1 - a_1b_2c_2 - a_2b_1c_2 - a_2b_2c_1, a_1b_1c_2 + a_1b_2c_1 + a_2b_1c_1 - a_2b_2c_2)$$
$$= [(a_1b_1 - a_2b_2)c_1 - (a_1b_2 + a_2b_1)c_2, (a_1b_2 + a_2b_1)c_1 + (a_1b_1 - a_2b_2)c_2]$$

by the usual associative, commutative, and distributive properties in $\mathcal{R}$.

$$[(a_1b_1 - a_2b_2)c_1 - (a_1b_2 + a_2b_1)c_2, (a_1b_2 + a_2b_1)c_1 + (a_1b_1 - a_2b_2)c_2]$$
$$= (a_1b_1 - a_2b_2, a_1b_2 + a_2b_1)(c_1,c_2)$$

by the definition of ____.

$$(a_1b_1 - a_2b_2, a_1b_2 + a_2b_1)(c_1,c_2) = [(a_1,a_2)(b_1,b_2)](c_1,c_2)$$

for the same reason as the previous step.

$$[(a_1,a_2)(b_1,b_2)](c_1,c_2) = (ab)c.$$

Thus, multiplication of complex numbers is associative.

The product of two complex numbers is a complex number. Thus we say C is ____________________ under multiplication.

Yes, since addition of complex numbers is the same as that for vectors.

For all $(x,y) \epsilon C$, $(x,y)(1,0) =$ ______. Thus, $(1,0)$ is the ____________________ element for C.

A commutative group is a set of elements which is closed, associative, and commutative, and which has an identity element and inverses for all elements for a defined operation.

We shall show in the next frame that for all $(x,y) \epsilon C$, $(x,y) \neq (0,0)$, there exists $(a,b) \epsilon C$ such that $(x,y)(a,b) - (1,0)$. In other words, every nonzero complex number has a ____________________ in C.

The multiplicative inverse or reciprocal of a complex number $(x,y) \neq (0,0)$, written $\frac{1}{(x,y)}$ or $(x,y)^{-1}$, can be found as follows:

Let

$$(x,y)^{-1} = (a,b),$$

then

$$(x,y)(a,b) = (1,0).$$

(0,0)

(0,0)

(4,−3)

(a,b)

$\dfrac{-b}{a^2 + b^2}$

$(c,d)\,(a,b)$

$(a,b)\,(c,d) + (a,b)\,(e,f)$

$(x + y,0)$

$(xy,0)$

This equation is equivalent to

$$(xa - yb, xb + ya) = (1,0).$$

(For what reason?) ________________________________

____

By the definition of ______________________, $xa - yb = 1$ and $xb + ya = 0$. Solving for a and b in these two equations,

$$(x,y)^{-1} = (a,b) = (\text{\_\_\_\_\_\_\_\_\_\_\_\_\_\_\_\_}).$$

Note that $x^2 + y^2 \neq 0$ since $(x,y) \neq (0,0)$.

Verify, by using the definition of multiplication, that

$$(x,y)\left(\frac{x}{x^2 + y^2}, \frac{-y}{x^2 + y^2}\right) = (1,0).$$

____

____

____

Division of complex numbers is defined in a manner analogous to division of real numbers. Recall that if a and b are real numbers with $b = 0$,

$$\frac{a}{b} = ab^{-1}.$$

DEFINITION:

If $(a,b) \epsilon\, C$ and $(c,d) \epsilon\, C$, and $(c,d) \neq (0,0)$, then the quotient $\dfrac{(a,b)}{(c,d)}$ is equal to the product of (a,b) and the multiplicative inverse of (c,d). Thus, $\dfrac{(a,b)}{(c,d)} = (a,b)\,(c,d)^{-1}$.

MOVE TO NEXT FRAME

Examples:

Perform the following divisions of complex numbers:

(a) $\dfrac{(4,7)}{(2,3)} = (4,7)\,(2,3)^{-1} = (4,7)\left(\dfrac{2}{13}, \underline{\qquad}\right)$

$= \underline{\qquad\qquad}$

(b) $(-2,5) \div (3,-4) = \underline{\qquad\qquad}$

The complex numbers form a commutative group under addition, and the nonzero complex numbers form a commutative group under multiplication. Furthermore, multiplication of complex numbers is distributive over addition. Thus the set C of complex numbers satisfies the same properties as those of the real number system. (See the Appendix for these properties.)

MOVE TO NEXT FRAME

These properties are called the **field properties.**

A **field** is defined to be a set of elements that forms a commutative group under each of two distinct operations (addition and multiplication) and in which one of these operations is distributive over the other (multiplication over addition).

Thus, we note that the set $\mathcal{R}$ of real numbers forms a field, and the set C of complex numbers forms a ________________.

Which of the following subsets of the set of real numbers form fields under the usual operations of addition and multiplication? __________

(a) N (b) W (c) J (d) Q (f) I (g) $\mathcal{R}$

Properties of multiplication of complex numbers:

Let (a,b), (c,d), and (e,f) be complex numbers. Then,

(1) **Closure:** The product of two complex numbers $(a,b)\,(c,d)$ is also a ________________.

(2) **Associative:**

$[(a,b)\,(c,d)]\,(e,f) = \underline{\qquad\qquad}$.

ANSWERS TO PAGE 355

distributive

multiplication of complex numbers

---

closed

(x,y)

multiplicative identity

---

multiplicative inverse

---

(3) **Identity:** There exists exactly one complex number, namely $(1,0)$, such that

$$(a,b)(1,0) = \underline{\hspace{4cm}}.$$

(4) **Inverses:** For every complex number $(a,b) \neq (0,0)$ there exists exactly one complex number, denoted by $\frac{1}{(a,b)}$ or $(a,b)^{-1}$, such that

$$(a,b)(a,b)^{-1} = (1,0).$$

Furthermore,

$$\frac{1}{(a,b)} = \left(\frac{a}{a^2 + b^2}, \underline{\hspace{4cm}}\right).$$

(5) **Commutative:**

$$(a,b)(c,d) = \underline{\hspace{4cm}}$$

(a) i (b) -1 (c) -1

(d) 1 (c) i (f) -1

(g) -1 (h) -1

Distributive Property of Complex Numbers:

If (a,b), (c,d), and (e,f) are complex numbers, then

$$(a,b)[(c,d) + (e,f)] = \underline{\hspace{4cm}}.$$

Since complex numbers form a field under the defined operations, the theorems of the algebra of real numbers whose proofs depend only upon the field properties are also theorems for the complex number system. (See the Appendix for a selection of these theorems.)

MOVE TO NEXT FRAME

(a) $4i$ (b) $2i\sqrt{3}$

(c) $i\sqrt{7}$ (d) $5i\sqrt{3}$

$\sqrt{ab}$ $\sqrt{\frac{a}{b}}$

(a) $\sqrt{-6} = i\sqrt{6}$

(b) $\sqrt{-5} = i\sqrt{5}$

Consider the set of all complex numbers whose second element is 0.

The sum

$$(x,0) + (y,0) = \underline{\hspace{4cm}},$$

and the product

$$(x,0)(y,0) = \underline{\hspace{4cm}}.$$

There is a one-to-one correspondence between the set of all $(x,0) \epsilon C$ and the set of real numbers, namely, the correspondence $(x,0) \leftrightarrow x$ in which the image of the complex number $(x,0)$ is the real number x. Furthermore, this correspondence preserves multiplication and addition, that is, the image of $(x,0)(y,0) = (xy,0)$ is xy which is the image of $(x,0)$ times the image of $(y,0)$; also, the image of $(x,0 + (y,0)$ is the image of $(x,0)$ plus the image of $(y,0)$. Thus the set of complex numbers of the form $(x,0)$ behaves just like the set of images, i.e., real numbers, as far as addition and multiplication properties are concerned; only the labeling is different. Thus it is customary to identify the complex numbers $(x,0)$ with the real numbers x and write $(x,0) = x$.

Because of this, it is customary to say that the set of real numbers $\mathcal{R}$ is a ____________ of the set of complex numbers C.

Perform the following multiplication.

$$(0,1)^2 = (0,1)(0,1) = \text{\_\_\_\_\_\_\_\_\_\_\_\_}.$$

The complex number $(0,1)$ is denoted by i. Thus, $(0,1)^2$ is written i^2. Hence $i^2 = (-1,0)$ or $i^2 = -1$ because of the relationship which has been established between the complex and real numbers.

Observe that

$$\begin{aligned}(x,y) &= (x,0) + (0,y)\\ &= (x,0) + (y,0)(0,1)\\ &= \text{\_\_\_\_\_\_\_\_\_\_\_\_}.\end{aligned}$$

Since $(x,0) =$ ______, $(y,0) =$ ______, and $(0,1) =$ ______, it follows by substitution that

$$(x,y) = x + yi.$$

From now on we will write the complex number (x,y) in the form $x + yi$ for convenience.

The **standard form of a complex number** is the form $x + yi$ where x and y are ________ numbers and i is a number such that $i^2 =$ ______.

Thus $i =$ ______. i is called the **imaginary unit.** The term "real" and "imaginary" were contributed by René Descartes (1637). Of course, i is no more "imaginary" than any other number, but the use of the term is historical and reflects the elusive nature of $\sqrt{-1}$ for early mathematicians. The **real part** of a complex number $x + yi$ is ____ and the **imaginary part** is ____.

If $x = 0$ and $y \neq 0$, then $x + yi = 0 + yi = yi$, and it is called a **pure imaginary number.** If $y = 0$ and $x \neq 0$, then $x + yi = x + 0(i) = x$, a real number. Thus, as was shown before, the set of real numbers is a ____________ of the set C of complex numbers. If $x = 0$ and $y = 0$, then $x + yi = 0$.

ANSWERS TO PAGE 357

(a) $\frac{-3}{13}$

$\left(\frac{29}{13}, \frac{2}{13}\right)$

(b) $\left(\frac{-26}{25}, \frac{7}{25}\right)$

field

d,g

complex number

$(a,b)[(c,d)(e,f)]$

ANSWERS TO PAGE 362

Integral powers of complex numbers are defined in a manner analogous to the definitions of powers of real numbers, that is, if $n \epsilon N$,

$$(x + yi)^n = (x + yi)(x + yi) \cdots (x + yi), \quad n \text{ factors,}$$

and

$$(x + yi)^{-n} = \frac{1}{(x + yi)^n}.$$

Also $(x + yi)^0 = 1$.

With these definitions, the usual rules for integral exponents are valid. Note that

$$i^{(n+4)} = i^n i^4 = i^n (i^2)^2 = i^n.$$

MOVE TO NEXT FRAME

(a) $a = c$ and $b = d$

(b) $(a + c) + i(b + d)$

(c) $(ac - bd) + (bc + ad)i$

(d) $(a + bi) + [-(c + di)]$

$(-c - di)$

Examples:

(a) $i^1 =$ ______ (b) $i^2 =$ ______ (c) $i^3 =$ ______

(d) $i^4 =$ ______ (e) $i^5 =$ ______ (f) $i^6 =$ ______

(g) $i^{30} =$ ______ (h) $i^{(4n+2)} =$ ______, $n \epsilon N$.

$\left(\frac{c}{c^2 + d^2} = i \frac{d}{c^2 + d^2}\right)$

DEFINITION:

If $a \epsilon \mathcal{R}$ and $a > 0$, then $\sqrt{-a} = i\sqrt{a}$.

MOVE TO NEXT FRAME

Examples:

(a) $\sqrt{-16} =$ ______ (b) $\sqrt{-12} =$ ______

(c) $\sqrt{-7} =$ ______ (d) $\sqrt{-75} =$ ______

(a) $-3 + 7i$

(b) -4

(c) $5 - 6i$

For $a > 0$ and $b > 0$, the Laws of Radicals for real numbers state that $\sqrt{a}\sqrt{b} =$ ______ and $\frac{\sqrt{a}}{\sqrt{b}} =$ ______. These laws remain valid if either a or b is negative.

Examples:

(a) $\sqrt{-2}\sqrt{3} =$ ______.

(b) $\frac{\sqrt{-20}}{\sqrt{4}} =$ ______.

a, b, c

b

$$\frac{\sqrt{a}}{\sqrt{b}} = \sqrt{\frac{a}{b}} \text{ is still valid when } a < 0 \text{ and } b < 0.$$

Example: $\dfrac{\sqrt{-32}}{\sqrt{-8}} = \sqrt{\dfrac{-32}{-8}} = \sqrt{4} = 2.$

MOVE TO NEXT FRAME

However, if both a and b are negative,

$$\sqrt{a} \cdot \sqrt{b} \neq \sqrt{ab}.$$

Examples:

(a) $\sqrt{-5}\sqrt{-12} = (i\sqrt{5})(2i\sqrt{3}) = 2i^2\sqrt{15}$

$= \_\_\_\_\_\_\_\_\_\_\_\_$, whereas

$\sqrt{(-5)(-12)} = \sqrt{60} = 2\sqrt{15}.$

(b) $\sqrt{-8}\sqrt{-2} = \_\_\_\_\_\_\_\_ \neq 4 = \sqrt{(-8)(-2)}.$

Furthermore, reçall that

(a) $(\sqrt{-3})^2 = \sqrt{-3}\sqrt{-3} = \_\_\_\_$, whereas

(b) $\sqrt{(-3)^2} = \_\_\_\_$. Thus

$$(\sqrt{-3})^2 \neq \sqrt{(-3)^2}.$$

Operations with radicals having negative radicands proceed quite easily if the radicals are first written in their corresponding "i form."

Example:

$$(\sqrt{-6})(-3\sqrt{2})\left(\frac{1}{4}\sqrt{-3}\right) = (i\sqrt{6})(-3\sqrt{2})\left(\frac{1}{4}i\sqrt{3}\right)$$

$$= \frac{-3}{4} i^2(\sqrt{6})(\sqrt{2})(\sqrt{3})$$

$$= \frac{-3}{4}(-1)(6)$$

$$= \_\_\_\_$$

ANSWERS TO PAGE 359

subset

$(-1,0)$

(x,y)

x y i

real -1

$\sqrt{-1}$

x yi

subset

(a) $3 + 4i$

(b) $-6 - 2i$

(c) $x^2 + y^2$

$\frac{1-2i}{1-2i}$ $1 - 2i$

Complete the following definitions for complex numbers written in standard form. They correspond to the definition for complex numbers written as ordered pairs.

DEFINITIONS:

(a) **Equality:**

$a + bi = c + di$ if and only if

______________________.

(b) **Addition:** $(a + bi) + (c + di) =$ ______________________.

(c) **Multiplication:** $(a + bi)(c + di) =$ ______________________.

(d) **Subtraction:** $(a + bi) - (c + di) =$ ______________________.

where $-(c + di) =$ ______________________.

(e) **Division:** $\left(\frac{a + bi}{c + di}\right) = (a + bi)(c + di)^{-1}$

$= (a + bi)\left(\frac{1}{c + di}\right)$

$= (a + bi)$ (______________________).

Use the definition of addition of complex numbers in standard form to add the following complex numbers.

(a) $(3 + 5i) + (-6 + 2i) =$ ____________

(b) $(-6 + 3i) + (2 - 3i) =$ ____________

(c) $(8 - 5i) + (-3 - i) =$ ____________

Which of the results in the frame above are complex numbers? ______

Which are real numbers? ______

Multiplication of complex numbers may be accomplished by regarding them as binomials, multiplying term by term, and then substituting -1 for i^2 in the result as follows.

$$(3 - 5i)(2 + 4i) = 6 + 12i - 10i - 20i^2$$
$$= 6 + 2i - 20(-1) = 26 + 2i$$

The result obtained by using the definition of multiplication of complex numbers is

$$(3 - 5i)(2 + 4i) = (3 \cdot 2 - (-5) \cdot 4) + (\_\_\_\_\_\_\_\_\_\_)i$$
$$= (6 + 20) + (\_\_\_\_\_\_\_\_\_\_)i$$
$$= 26 + 2i$$

In general,

$$(a + bi)(c + di) = ac + adi + bci + bdi^2$$
$$= (ac + bdi^2) + (ad + bc)i$$
$$= (ac - bd) + (ad + bc)i$$

when performing the usual binomial multiplication and substituting -1 for i^2.

(a) $-2\sqrt{15}$

(b) -4

Multiply the following complex numbers.

(a) $(-2 + 5i)(1 + 3i) =$ __________

(b) $(2 - \sqrt{-1})(6 + \sqrt{-12}) =$ __________

(c) $(i^4)(i^3)(i^2) =$ __________

(d) $(3 + 4i)(3 - 4i) =$ __________

(a) -3

(b) 3

Which of the results in the preceding frame are real numbers? ______

Which are complex numbers? __________

Examples:

(a) Subtract $3 + 5i$ from $-6 + 2i$. __________

(b) Find the difference $(\sqrt{3} - 7i) - (3\sqrt{3} + 2i)$. __________

Example:

Let z represent a complex number $x + yi$ and solve the equation:

$$3 - 2i + z = 6 + 4i.$$

Solution: $z = (6 + 4i) - (3 - 2i) =$ __________ .

$\frac{9}{2}$

DEFINITION:

The **conjugate** of the complex number $a + bi$, denoted $\overline{a + bi}$, is the complex number $a - bi$. Thus $\overline{a + bi} = a - bi$.

MOVE TO NEXT FRAME

(a) 13

(b) $5\sqrt{2}$

(c) $\sqrt{31}$

Examples:

(a) The conjugate of $3 - 4i$ is ________.

(b) The conjugate of $-6 + 2i$ is = ________.

(c) The product of the complex number $x + yi$ and its conjugate is ________.

Division of complex numbers may be facilitated by multiplying both the dividend and the divisor by the conjugate of the divisor as in the following.

MOVE TO NEXT FRAME

Example:

Express the quotient $\dfrac{3 - 4i}{1 + 2i}$ in standard form.

Solution:

Multiply numerator and denominator of $\dfrac{3 - 4i}{1 + 2i}$ by the conjugate of the denominator.

Thus, $\dfrac{(3 - 4i)(\qquad)}{(1 + 2i)(\qquad)} = \dfrac{5 - 10i}{5} =$ ________.

$\cos \theta + i \sin \theta$

It is evident that there is a one-to-one correspondence, $x + yi \longleftrightarrow (x,y)$, between the set C of complex numbers in standard form and $\mathcal{R} \times \mathcal{R}$. Since there is a standard geometric vector corresponding to each ordered pair of real numbers, it follows that a standard geometric vector may be used to represent a complex number.

MOVE TO NEXT FRAME

Let the points on the horizontal axis correspond to the set of real numbers and the points on the vertical axis correspond to a set of pure imaginary numbers. (See the illustration.) The geometric vector corresponding to the complex number ______________ is illustrated in this figure.

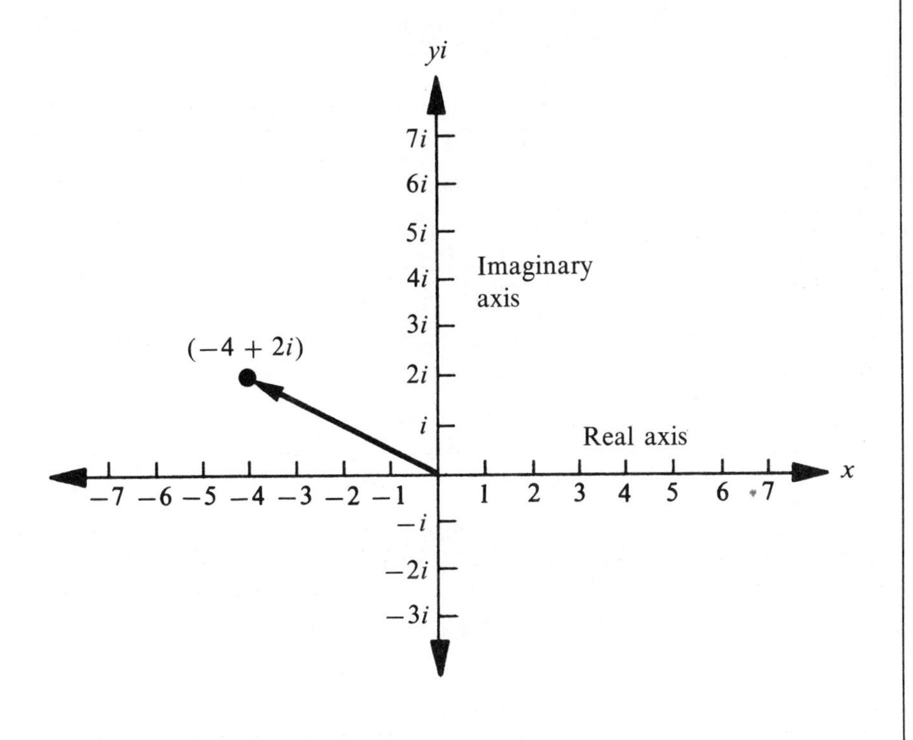

The sum of two complex numbers may be illustrated using the parallelogram law of vector addition. See the illustration for the geometric representation of the sum of $2 + i$ and $3 + 6i$, which is ______________.

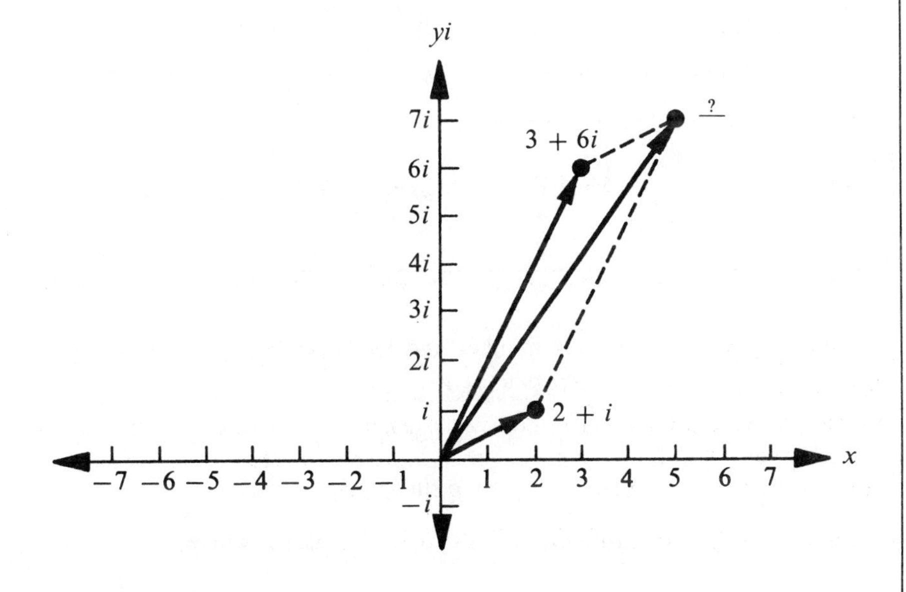

ANSWERS TO PAGE 363

$-5 \cdot 2 + 3 \cdot 4$

$-10 + 12$

(a) $-17 - i$

(b) $(12+2\sqrt{3})+i(-6+4\sqrt{3})$

(c) i

(d) 25

---

d

a, b, c, d

(a) $-9 - 3i$

(b) $-2\sqrt{3} - 9i$

$3 + 6i$

ANSWERS TO PAGE 368

$$2\left(\cos\frac{\pi}{6}+i\sin\frac{\pi}{6}\right)$$

or $$2\left[\cos\left(\frac{\pi}{6}+2k\pi\right)+i\sin\left(\frac{\pi}{6}+2k\pi\right)\right],\quad k\epsilon J$$

$$6\left(\cos\frac{3\pi}{4}+i\sin\frac{3\pi}{4}\right)$$

or $$6\left[\cos\left(\frac{3\pi}{4}+2k\pi\right)+i\sin\left(\frac{3\pi}{4}+2k\pi\right)\right],\quad k\epsilon J$$

$\{\theta + 2k\pi, k\epsilon J\}$

equal

2π

DEFINITION:

The **modulus** or **absolute value** of the complex number $x + yi$, denoted $|x + yi|$, is the nonnegative real number $\sqrt{x^2 + y^2}$.

MOVE TO NEXT FRAME

Examples:

(a) Find the modulus of $5 + 12i$. ________.

(b) The absolute value of $7 + i =$ ________.

(c) $|-5 - i\sqrt{6}| =$ ________.

The modulus of a complex number corresponds to the norm of a vector and has the following corresponding properties.

MOVE TO NEXT FRAME

THEOREM:

If $a + bi$ and $c + di$ are complex numbers, then

(a) $|a + bi| \geq 0$.

(b) $|a + bi| = 0$ if and only if $a + bi = 0 + 0i$.

(c) $|a + bi| + |c + di| \geq |(a + bi) + (c + di)|$.

Proof is left as an exercise.

MOVE TO NEXT FRAME

Let $x + yi$ be a complex number and let (ρ,θ) be the polar coordinates corresponding to the ordered pair (x,y). Then

$$x = \rho\cos\theta,$$

$$y = \rho\sin\theta,$$

and $x + yi$ becomes $\rho($________________$)$, where $\rho = |x + yi|$.

DEFINITION:

The **polar form** or **trigonometric form** of the complex number $x + yi$ is $\rho(\cos\theta + i\sin\theta)$ where $\rho = |x + yi|$, $x = \rho\cos\theta$, and $y = \rho\sin\theta$. An **amplitude** or **argument** of $\rho(\cos\theta + i\sin\theta)$ is a direction angle of the corresponding geometric vector, i.e., $\theta + 2k\pi$, where $k \epsilon J$. If $-\pi \leq \theta \leq \pi$, then θ is said to be the **principal argument** of $x + yi$.

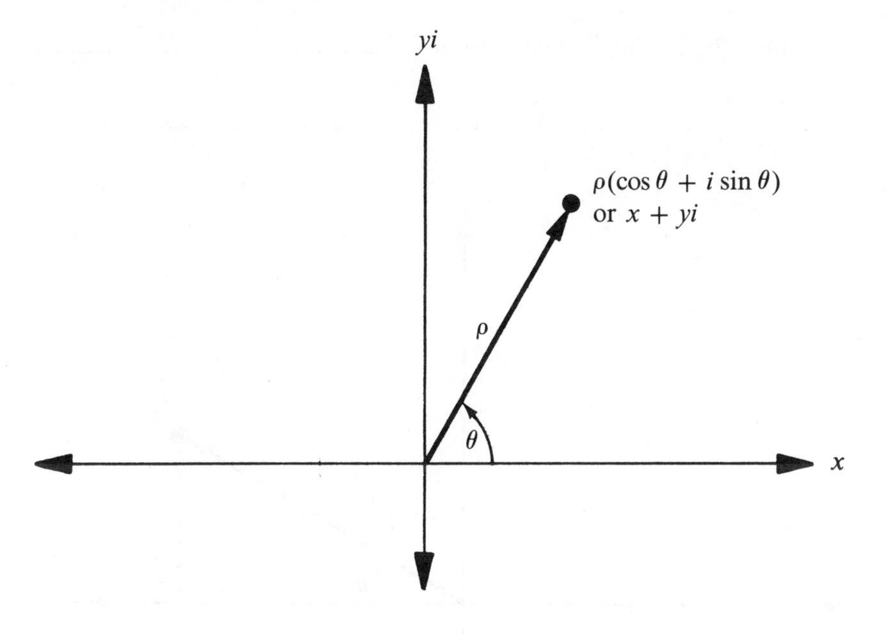

MOVE TO NEXT FRAME

$-4 + 2i$

Examples:

(a) Write $\sqrt{3} + i$ in polar form. (See the previous frame.)

$\rho =$ __________ and $\theta =$ __________.

$5 + 7i$

$\cos\theta_2 + i\sin\theta_2$

$i^2 \sin\theta_1 \sin\theta_2$

$\cos(\theta_1 + \theta_2) + i\sin(\theta_1 + \theta_2)$

Thus $\sqrt{3} + i =$ ____

____.

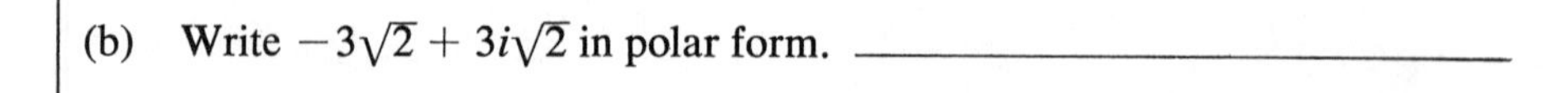

(b) Write $-3\sqrt{2} + 3i\sqrt{2}$ in polar form. ________________________

____

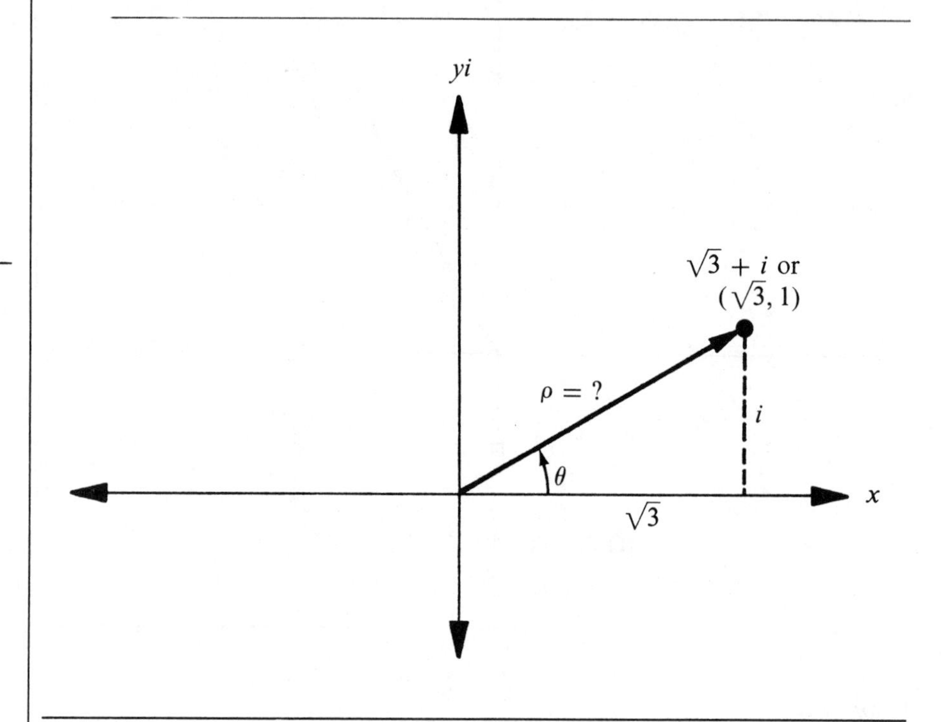

If θ is an amplitude of a complex number, then any element of the set ____ is also an amplitude of that complex number. Thus two complex numbers are equal if and only if their absolute values are __________________ and their amplitudes differ by an integral multiple of ________.

The principal amplitude θ of a complex number $x + yi$ is most easily found by sketching the geometric vector corresponding to the number in question. If (x,y) is in Quadrants I or IV, then $\theta =$ ______________.

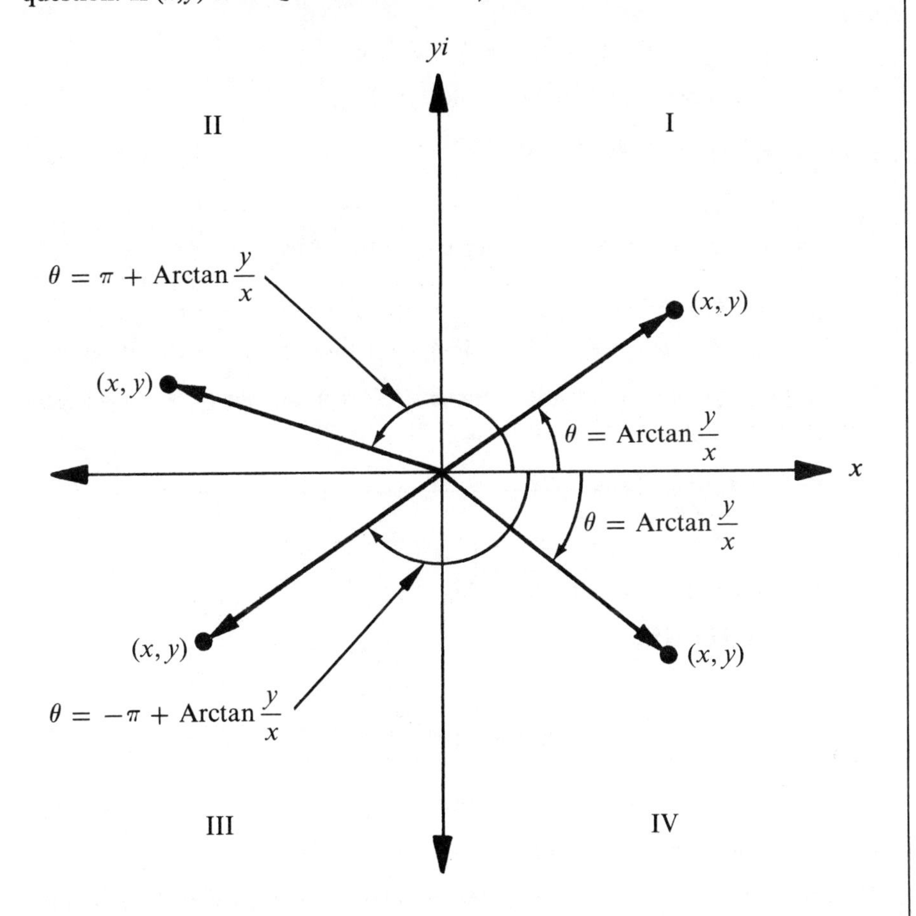

If (x,y) is in Quadrant II, then $\theta =$ ______________.

If (x,y) is in Quadrant III, then $\theta =$ ______________.

$\rho = |x + yi| \qquad \theta = \tan^{-1}\left(\frac{y}{x}\right)$

Consider the product of complex numbers when they are written in polar form. Let

$$z_1 = \rho_1(\cos\theta_1 + i\sin\theta_1)$$

and

$$z_2 = \rho_2(\cos\theta_2 + i\sin\theta_2)$$

be any two complex numbers, and calculate z_1z_2.

$$z_1z_2 = [\rho_1(\cos\theta_1 + i\sin\theta_1)]\,[\rho_2(\cos\theta_2 + i\sin\theta_2)]$$

$$= \rho_1\rho_2(\cos\theta_1 + i\sin\theta_1)(\underline{\qquad\qquad\qquad})$$

$$= \rho_1\rho_2(\cos\theta_1\cos\theta_2 + i\cos\theta_1\sin\theta_2 + i\sin\theta_1\cos\theta_2$$

$$+ \underline{\qquad\qquad\qquad}).$$

$$= \rho_1\rho_2[(\cos\theta_1\cos\theta_2 - \sin\theta_1\sin\theta_2) + i(\sin\theta_1\cos\theta_2) + (\cos\theta_1\sin\theta_2)]$$

Use of the trigonometric identities for $\cos(\theta_1 + \theta_2)$ and $\sin(\theta_1 + \theta_2)$ and substitution in the right member yields

$$z_1z_2 = \rho_1\rho_2[\underline{\qquad\qquad\qquad\qquad\qquad}].$$

$\frac{\pi}{3}$ $\frac{\pi}{3}$

The foregoing proves the following theorem.

THEOREM:

If

$$z_1 = \rho_1(\cos\theta_1 + i\sin\theta_1)$$

and

$$z_2 = \rho_2(\cos\theta_2 + i\sin\theta_2),$$

then $z_1z_2 = \rho_1\rho_2[\cos(\theta_1 + \theta_2) + i\sin(\theta_1 + \theta_2)]$.

Thus when two complex numbers are in polar form, they may be multiplied by adding their amplitudes and multiplying their moduli.

MOVE TO NEXT FRAME

$\rho^2(\cos 2\theta + i\sin 2\theta)$

$\rho^3(\cos 3\theta + i\sin 3\theta)$

Examples:

Multiply $z_1 = 3\left(\cos\frac{5\pi}{3} + i\sin\frac{5\pi}{3}\right)$

by

$$z_2 = 2\left(\cos\frac{\pi}{4} + i\sin\frac{\pi}{4}\right).$$

Solution:

$$z_1z_2 = 6\left[\cos\left(\frac{5\pi}{3} + \frac{\pi}{4}\right) + i\sin\left(\frac{5\pi}{3} + \frac{\pi}{4}\right)\right]$$

or

$$z_1z_2 = 6\left(\cos\frac{23\pi}{12} + i\sin\frac{23\pi}{12}\right).$$

MOVE TO NEXT FRAME

An amplitude θ of $z_1 z_2$ in the preceding example is any element of the set ______________________________. Write the product of $z_1 z_2$ when $0 \leq \theta \leq \frac{\pi}{2}$. ______________________________

(Recall that $\cos \theta = \cos(-\theta)$ and $\sin \theta = -\sin(-\theta)$.)

The conjugate of $z = x + yi$ is the number

$$\bar{z} = \overline{x + yi} = \underline{\hspace{3cm}}.$$

The conjugate of $z = \rho \cos \theta + \rho i \sin \theta$ is $\bar{z} =$ ______________.
Since $\cos \theta = \cos(-\theta)$ and $-\sin \theta = \sin(-\theta)$,

$$\bar{z} = \underline{\hspace{6cm}}.$$

Thus,

$$\bar{z} = \rho[\cos(-\theta) + i \sin(-\theta)].$$

THEOREM:

If

$$z_1 = \rho_1(\cos \theta_1 + i \sin \theta_1)$$

and

$$z_2 = \rho_2(\cos \theta_2 + i \sin \theta_2),\ z_2 \neq 0 + 0i,$$

then $$\frac{z_1}{z_2} = \frac{\rho_1}{\rho_2}[\cos(\theta_1 - \theta_2) + i \sin(\theta_1 - \theta_2)].$$

Proof is left as an exercise.

MOVE TO NEXT FRAME

Example:

Let

$$z_1 = 12(\cos 40° + i \sin 40°),$$

and

$$z_2 = 4(\cos 10° + i \sin 10°).$$

Find $\frac{z_1}{z_2}$. ______________________

Write $\frac{z_1}{z_2}$ in standard form. ______________________

ANSWERS TO PAGE 369

$\text{Arctan}\ \frac{y}{x}$

$\pi + \text{Arctan}\ \frac{y}{x}$

$-\pi + \text{Arctan}\ \frac{y}{x}$

$\frac{1}{z^n}$

conjugate

$\cos 0 + i \sin 0 = 1$

$-\sin x$

$\left(\cos \frac{5\pi}{4} + i \sin \frac{5\pi}{4}\right)$

Example:

$$\text{Let } z_1 = 8\left(\cos \frac{5\pi}{12} + i \sin \frac{5\pi}{12}\right)$$

and

$$z_2 = 5\left(\cos \frac{\pi}{12} + i \sin \frac{\pi}{12}\right)$$

and write $\frac{z_1}{z_2}$ in standard form.

Solution:

$$\frac{z_1}{z_2} = \frac{8\left(\cos \frac{5\pi}{12} + i \sin \frac{5\pi}{12}\right)}{5\left(\cos \frac{\pi}{12} + i \sin \frac{\pi}{12}\right)}$$

$$= \frac{8}{5}\,(\cos \underline{\qquad\qquad} + i \sin \underline{\qquad\qquad})$$

$$= \frac{8}{5}\left(\frac{1}{2} + i\frac{\sqrt{3}}{2}\right) = \frac{4}{5} + \frac{4i\sqrt{3}}{5}.$$

Let $z = \rho(\cos \theta + i \sin \theta)$,

then

$$z^2 = [\rho(\cos \theta + i \sin \theta)]\,[\rho(\cos \theta + i \sin \theta)]$$

$$= \underline{\qquad\qquad\qquad\qquad\qquad}$$

In the same fashion we find that $z^3 = \underline{\qquad\qquad\qquad\qquad\qquad}$.

This suggests the following theorem.

THEOREM:

If $\quad z = \rho(\cos \theta + i \sin \theta)$ and $n \epsilon N$,
then $\quad z^n = \rho^n(\cos n\theta + i \sin n\theta)$.

The proof, which utilizes the principle of mathematical induction, is not included.

MOVE TO NEXT FRAME

Example:

Find

z^3, if $z = \left(\frac{3}{2} - \frac{3\sqrt{3}}{2}i\right)$ and write in standard form.

Solution:

$$\rho = |z| = \left|\frac{3}{2} - \frac{3\sqrt{3}}{2}i\right| = \sqrt{\left(\frac{3}{2}\right)^2 + \left(\frac{3\sqrt{3}}{2}\right)^2} = \_\_.$$

$$\theta = \text{Arctan}\,\frac{y}{x} = \text{Arctan}\,\frac{\frac{-3\sqrt{3}}{2}}{\frac{3}{2}} = \text{Arctan}\,(-\sqrt{3}) = \_\_\_\_\_\_.$$

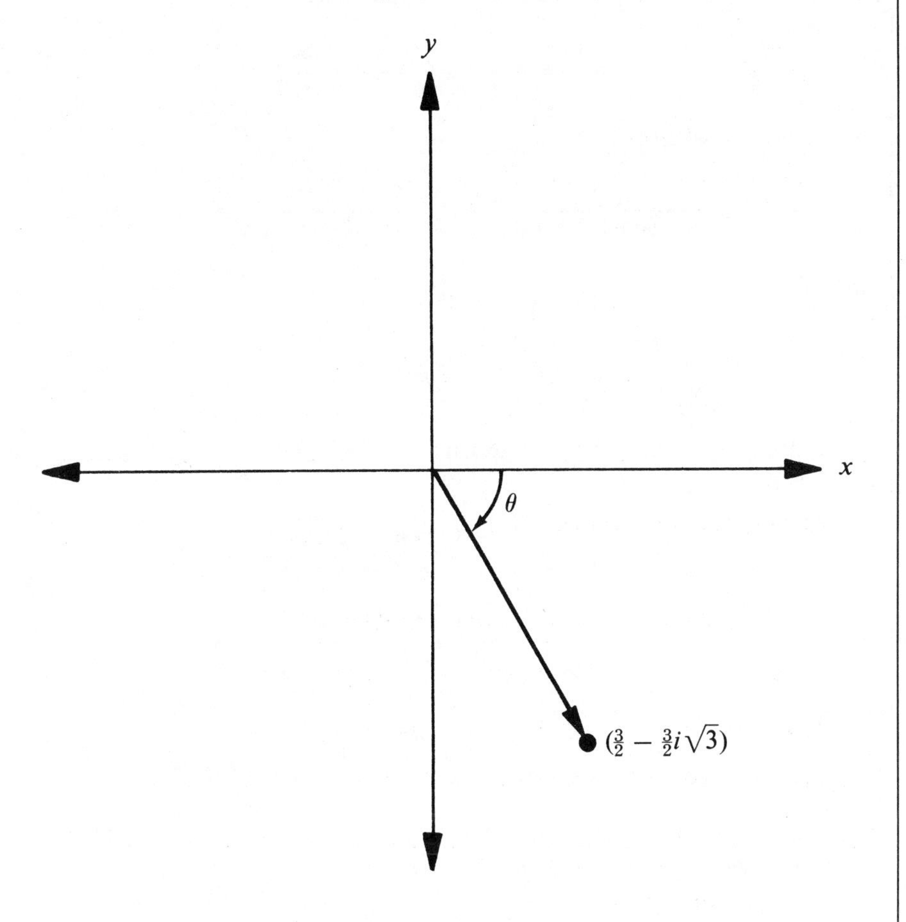

Thus in polar form,

$z = $ ______________________________________.

By the previous theorem,

$z^3 = 3^3(\cos$ ________ $+ i \sin$ ________ $).$

In standard form,

$z^3 = $ ___________________________.

$\left\{\frac{23\pi}{12} + 2k\pi, \text{ where } k \epsilon J\right\}$

$6\left(\cos\frac{\pi}{12} - i \sin\frac{\pi}{12}\right)$

$x - yi$

$\rho \cos\theta - \rho i \sin\theta$

$\rho \cos(-\theta) + \rho i \sin(-\theta)$

$3(\cos 30° + i \sin 30°)$

$\frac{3\sqrt{3}}{2} + \frac{3}{2}i$

$2\sqrt{2}\left(\cos\frac{\pi}{4} + i\sin\frac{\pi}{4}\right)$

2π

$2\sqrt{2}$ $2k\pi$ for some $k\epsilon J$

$\sqrt{2}$ $\frac{\pi}{4} + 2k\pi$

$\sqrt{2}\left(\cos\frac{17\pi}{12} + i\sin\frac{17\pi}{12}\right)$

$2\left(\cos\frac{25\pi}{12} + i\sin\frac{25\pi}{12}\right)$

THEOREM:

If $z = \rho(\cos\theta + i\sin\theta)$, $z \neq 0 + 0i$, and $n\epsilon N$,

then $z^{-n} = \rho^{-n}[\cos(-n\theta) + i\sin(-n\theta)]$.

Proof:

$z^{-n} =$ ______ by the definition of exponents.

$$\frac{1}{z^n} = \frac{1}{\rho^n(\cos n\theta + i\sin n\theta)}$$

by the previous theorem.

$$\frac{1}{\rho^n(\cos n\theta + i\sin n\theta)} = \frac{\rho^{-n}}{\cos n\theta + i\sin n\theta}$$

since

$$\frac{1}{\rho^n} = \rho^{-n}.$$

Multiplying numerator and denominator by the ____________ of the denominator,

$$\frac{\rho^{-n}}{\cos n\,\theta + i\sin\theta} = \frac{\rho^{-n}(\cos n\theta - i\sin n\theta)}{(\cos n\theta + i\sin n\theta)(\cos n\theta - i\sin n\theta)}$$

$$= \frac{\rho^{-n}(\cos n\theta - i\sin n\theta)}{\rule{6cm}{0.4pt}}.$$

But,

$$(\cos n\theta - i\sin n\theta) = \cos(-n\theta) + i\sin(-n\theta),$$

because $\cos(-x) = \cos x$ and $\sin(-x) =$ ____________. Therefore $z^{-n} = \rho^{-n}(\cos -n\theta) + i\sin(-n\theta)$ for $n\epsilon N$.

Example:

Write $(1 - i)^{-5}$ in standard form.

Solution:

$$1 - i = \sqrt{2}\left(\cos\frac{-\pi}{4} + i\sin\frac{-\pi}{4}\right).$$

Thus,

$$(1 - i)^{-5} = (\sqrt{2})^{-5}\ (\rule{6cm}{0.4pt})$$

by the previous theorem.

Therefore,

$$(1-i)^{-5} = \frac{\sqrt{2}}{8}\left(\frac{-\sqrt{2}}{2} - i\frac{\sqrt{2}}{2}\right)$$

$$= \underline{\hspace{6cm}}.$$

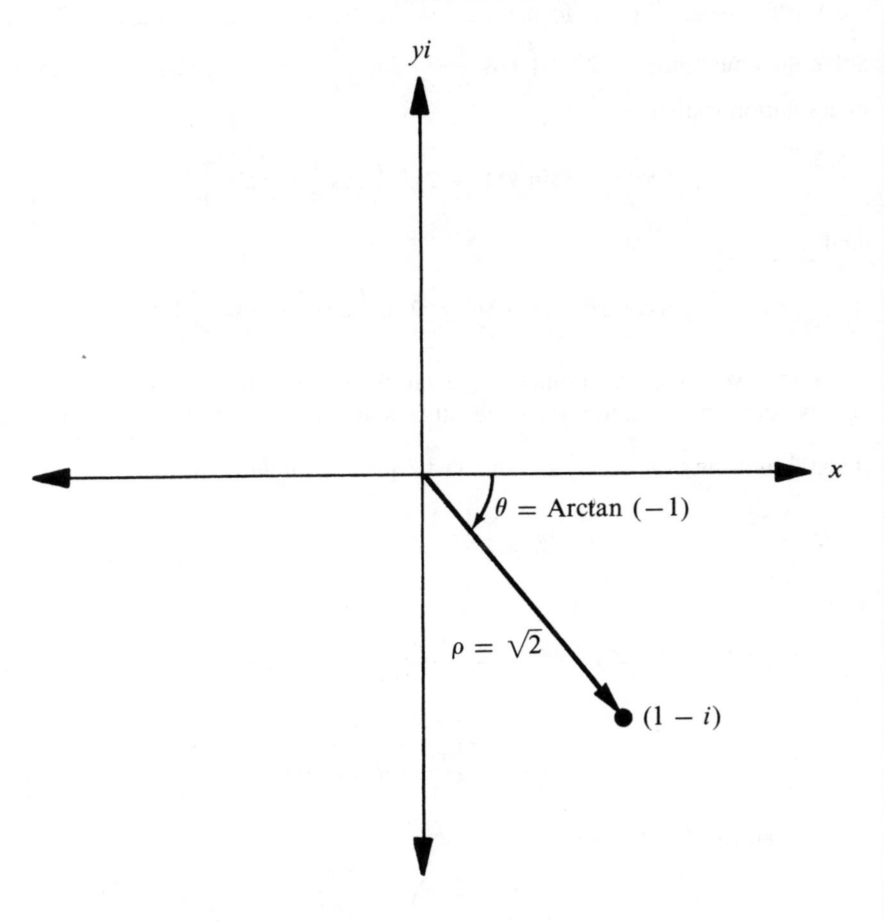

Finding the nth roots of a complex number $a + bi$ is equivalent to finding all complex numbers z such that

$$z^n = a + bi.$$

We will assume that such an equation has exactly n roots; they may be found with the procedure demonstrated in the following example.

MOVE TO NEXT FRAME

ANSWERS TO PAGE 373

3

$-\frac{\pi}{3}$

$\rho\left(\cos\frac{-\pi}{3} + i\sin\frac{-\pi}{3}\right)$

$3^3\left(\cos\frac{-3\pi}{3} + i\sin\frac{-3\pi}{3}\right)$

$-27 + 0i$ or -27

---

(1)(a) 3 7

(b) -4 -2

(c) -5 0

(d) 1 75

(e) -2 2

(f) $-\frac{1}{6}$ -4

(2)(a) $(-1,4)$

(b) $(-13,2)$

(c) $-5-8i$

(d) $(4,2)$

(e) $0+0i=0$

(f) $(a+c,b+d)$

(g) $(3,-4)$

(h) $\left(\frac{1}{12},0\right)$

(3)(a) $\{(5,-3)\}$

(b) $\{(-3,1)\}$

(c) $\left\{\left(2+\frac{i}{2}\right)\right\}$

(d) $\left\{-1+-\frac{3}{2}i\right\}$

(4)(a) $(-28,46)$

(b) $(-7,19)$

(c) $-16-12i$

(d) $-16-30i$

(e) $(45,0)$

(f) $(a^2-b^2)+2abi$

Example:

Find the three cube roots of $2+2i$.

Solution:

Write $2+2i$ in polar form. ______

Solve the equation $z^3 = 2\sqrt{2}\left(\cos\frac{\pi}{4} + i\sin\frac{\pi}{4}\right)$. Let $z = \rho(\cos\theta + i\sin\theta)$ be a solution so that

$$[\rho(\cos\theta + i\sin\theta)]^3 = 2\sqrt{2}\left(\cos\frac{\pi}{4} + i\sin\frac{\pi}{4}\right).$$

Thus,

$$\rho^3(\cos 3\theta + i\sin 3\theta) = 2\sqrt{2}\left(\cos\frac{\pi}{4} + i\sin\frac{\pi}{4}\right).$$

Since two complex numbers in polar form are equal if the modulus of one is equal to the modulus of the other and their amplitudes differ only in integral multiples of ______, this last equation implies

$$\rho^3 = \text{\_\_\_\_}, \qquad \text{and} \quad 3\theta - \frac{\pi}{4} = \text{\_\_\_\_\_\_}.$$

Thus,

$$\rho = \text{\_\_\_\_}, \quad 3\theta = \text{\_\_\_\_\_\_},$$

and

$$\theta = \frac{\pi}{12} + \frac{2k\pi}{3} \quad \text{for some } k\epsilon J.$$

Therefore, if $k\epsilon J$, then

$$z = \sqrt{2}\left[\cos\left(\frac{\pi}{12} + \frac{2k\pi}{3}\right) + i\sin\left(\frac{\pi}{12} + \frac{2k\pi}{3}\right)\right]$$

is a cube root of $2+2i$.

If $k=0$, $\quad z_0 = \sqrt{2}\left(\cos\frac{\pi}{12} + i\sin\frac{\pi}{12}\right).$

If $k=1$, $\quad z_1 = \sqrt{2}\left(\cos\frac{3\pi}{4} + i\sin\frac{3\pi}{4}\right).$

If $k=2$, $\quad z_2 =$ ______.

If $k=3$, $\quad z_3 =$ ______.

$$= \sqrt{2}\left(\cos\frac{\pi}{12} + i\sin\frac{\pi}{12}\right).$$

Note that if $k=3$, then $z_3 = z_0$, and the values of z repeat themselves for other values of k. Thus we have 3 different roots for $z^3 = 2+2i$, namely, z_0, z_1, and z_2.

In general, we have the following theorem:

THEOREM:

If $\rho(\cos \theta + i \sin \theta)$ is a nonzero complex number in polar form, where $\theta \epsilon \mathcal{R}$, $\rho \epsilon \mathcal{R}$, and $\rho > 0$, then the n roots of the equation

$$z^n = \rho(\cos \theta + i \sin \theta), n \epsilon N,$$

are

$$\rho^{\frac{1}{n}}\left[\cos\left(\frac{\theta}{n}+\frac{2k\pi}{n}\right) + i \sin\left(\frac{\theta}{n}+\frac{2k\pi}{n}\right), k = 0,1,2,\ldots, n-1.\right]$$

The proof is not included.

MOVE TO NEXT FRAME

ANSWERS TO PAGE 375

$$-\frac{1}{8}-\frac{i}{8}$$

(8) (a) 16

(b) 6

(c) 16

(d) $3i\sqrt{2}$

(e) 11

(f) $-7-24i$

(g) 163

(h) $\sqrt{2}$

(i) $i\sqrt{7}$

(j) $-7\sqrt{2}$

(k) $4i\sqrt{2}$

(9) (a) $2\left(\cos\frac{\pi}{6}+i\sin\frac{\pi}{6}\right)$

(b) $4\sqrt{2}\left[\cos\left(\frac{-\pi}{4}\right)+i\sin\left(\frac{-\pi}{4}\right)\right]$

(c) $2\left[\cos\left(\frac{-2\pi}{3}\right)+i\sin\left(\frac{-2\pi}{3}\right)\right]$

(d) $2\left(\cos\frac{\pi}{4}+i\sin\frac{\pi}{4}\right)$

(e) $\frac{4}{3}\left(\cos\frac{5\pi}{6}+i\sin\frac{5\pi}{6}\right)$

(10) (a) $\sqrt{29}\,(\cos 112° + i\sin 112°)$

(b) $4\sqrt{5}\,(\cos 153° + i\sin 153°)$

(c) $5[\cos(-127°) + i\sin(127°)]$

(d) $13[\cos(-67°) + i\sin(-67°)]$

(11) (a) $6\left(\cos\frac{13\pi}{12}+i\sin\frac{13\pi}{12}\right)$

EXERCISES. 6.4

1. Use the definition of equality of complex numbers to find x and y in each of the following.

   (a) $(x,7)=(3,y)$; $x=$ ______ $y=$ ______.

   (b) $-x+2i=4-yi$; $x=$ ______ $y=$ ______.

   (c) $x+yi=-5$; $x=$ ______ $y=$ ______.

   (d) $(3x,15)=\left(3,\frac{y}{5}\right)$; $x=$ ______ $y=$ ______.

   (e) $(4-2x,y+3)=(8,5)$; $x=$ ______ $y=$ ______.

   (f) $3xy+4i=2-yi$; $x=$ ______ $y=$ ______.

2. Perform the following additions or subtractions of complex numbers.

   (a) $(2,3)+(-3,1)=$ ______________.

   (b) $(-7,-2)-(6,-4)=$ ______________.

   (c) $(3-2i)+(-8-6i)=$ ______________.

   (d) $(4,2)-(0,0)=$ ______________.

   (e) $(7-3i)+(-7+3i)=$ ______________.

   (f) $(a,b)+(c,d)=$ ______________.

   (g) $(0,0)-(-3,4)=$ ______________.

   (h) $\left(\frac{1}{3},0\right)-\left(\frac{1}{4},0\right)=$ ______________.

3. Solve each of the following equations for the complex variable z.

   (a) $(3,4)+z=(8,1)$. ______________

   (b) $(4,1)+z=(2,6)-(1,4)$. ______________

   (c) $z-(4+7i)=-z-6i$. ______________

   (d) $3z+6-3i=z+4$. ______________

4. Perform each of the following multiplications of complex numbers.

   (a) $(2,5)(6,8)=$ ______________.

   (b) $(-3,1)(4,-5)=$ ______________.

   (c) $(6+2i)(-3-i)=$ ______________.

   (d) $(3-5i)^2=$ ______________.

   (e) $(3,6)(3,-6)=$ ______________.

   (f) $(a+bi)^2=$ ______________.

(g) $(6+i)(\overline{6+i}) =$ ________.

(h) $(0,1)(0,1) =$ ________.

(i) $(1,0)(1,0) =$ ________.

(j) $(-3,0)(0,-3) =$ ________.

(k) $(x+yi)\left(\frac{x}{x^2+y^2} - i\frac{y}{x^2+y^2}\right)$ ________.

5. (a) Complete the following.

If $a+bi$ is a square root of $-5-12i$, then $(a+b)^2 =$ ________.

Expand the left member, so that

(1) ________ $= -5-12i.$

From the definition of equality of complex numbers and (1),

(2) $a^2 - b^2 =$ ________, and

(3) $2ab =$ ________.

Therefore, $a+bi =$ ________ or

$a+bi =$ ________, by solving simultaneously and (3) above.

(b) Using the method of problem number 5(a) find the two square roots of $-19+20i$. ________

6. Perform the following divisions of complex numbers.

(a) $\frac{(6,1)}{(2,3)} =$ ________.

(b) $(3,4) \div (2,-2) =$ ________.

(c) $\frac{4-8i}{-3-5i} =$ ________.

(d) $\frac{3}{4+6i} =$ ________.

(e) $\frac{1}{(-3,1)} =$ ________.

(f) $\frac{1}{2-9i} =$ ________.

(g) $(4,-6) \div (0,0) =$ ________.

(h) $\frac{i}{1-i} =$ ________.

7. Compute each of the following and write it in it simplest form.

(a) $i^{10} =$ ________ (b) $i^{14} =$ ________

(c) $i^{30} =$ ________ (d) $i^{4n} =$ ________, $n \epsilon N$

(e) $i^{(4n+1)} =$ ________, $n \epsilon N$ (f) $i^{(4n+1)} =$ ________, $n \epsilon N$

ANSWERS TO PAGE 382

(1)(a) $(9,-6)$ (b) $(-8,2)$

(c) $(-1,4)$ (d) $\sqrt{117}$

(e) $\sqrt{68}$ (f) $\sqrt{17}$

(g) 0

(2)(a) $-\vec{t}$ $\vec{r}$

(b) $\vec{t}$ $-\vec{s}$

(c) $\overrightarrow{TR}$ $\overrightarrow{TS}$

(d) 0

(3) complementary

0.59

cofunction

(4)(a) B

(b) $\frac{\sqrt{5}}{5}$ (c) $\frac{2\sqrt{5}}{5}$

(d) $\frac{2\sqrt{5}}{5}$ (e) $\frac{\sqrt{5}}{5}$

8. Write each of the following in standard form and perform the indicated operation.

(a) $(2-\sqrt{-12})(2+\sqrt{-12}) =$ ________________.

(b) $(\sqrt{-3})(\sqrt{-6})(\sqrt{-2})(\sqrt{-1}) =$ ________________.

(c) $(-\sqrt{-32})(\sqrt{-8}) =$ ________________.

(d) $\sqrt{-32} + \sqrt{-8} - \sqrt{-18} =$ ________________.

(e) $(2+\sqrt{-7})(2-\sqrt{-7}) =$ ________________.

(f) $(-3+\sqrt{-16})^2 =$ ________________.

(g) $(-4+\sqrt{-147})(\overline{-4+\sqrt{-147}}) =$ ________________.

(h) $\frac{\sqrt{-32}}{\sqrt{-16}} =$ ________________.

(i) $\frac{\sqrt{-98}}{\sqrt{+14}} =$ ________________.

(j) $\sqrt{-7}\,\sqrt{-14} =$ ________________.

(k) $\sqrt{-4}\,\sqrt{8} =$ ________________.

9. Write each of the following complex numbers in polar form.

(a) $\sqrt{3} + i$ ________________.

(b) $4 - 4i$ ________________.

(c) $-1 - i\sqrt{3}$ ________________.

(d) $\sqrt{2} + i\sqrt{2}$ ________________.

(e) $\frac{-2\sqrt{3}}{3} + \frac{2}{3}i$ ________________.

10. Use Table I to find the amplitude to the nearest degree for the following complex numbers, then write in polar form.

(a) $-2 + 5i$ ________________

(b) $-8 + 4i$ ________________

(c) $-3 - 4i$ ________________

(d) $5 - 12i$ ________________

11. Find the products of the following complex numbers and write in polar form.

(a) $\left[3\left(\cos\frac{\pi}{4} + i\sin\frac{\pi}{4}\right)\right]\left[2\left(\cos\frac{5\pi}{6} + i\sin\frac{5\pi}{6}\right)\right]$

____

(b) $[5(\cos 150° + i \sin 150°)]\,[\cos(-90°) + i(\sin -90°)]$

______

12. Find the quotients of the following complex numbers and write in polar form.

(a) $\dfrac{5\left(\cos\dfrac{5\pi}{6} + i \sin\dfrac{5\pi}{6}\right)}{2\left(\cos\dfrac{6}{\pi} + i \sin\dfrac{\pi}{6}\right)} =$ ______

(b) $\dfrac{6(\cos 90° + i \sin 90°)}{12[\cos(-90°) + i \sin(-90°)]} =$ ______

13. Find each of the following by first writing in polar form and then by using the appropriate theorem. Write the result in standard form.

(a) $(\sqrt{3} - i)^3 =$ ______ .

(b) $(2\sqrt{2} + 2i\sqrt{2})^5 =$ ______ .

(c) $(-1 + i)^3 =$ ______ .

(d) $(-\sqrt{3} + i)^{-3} =$ ______ .

14. Find each of the following and write in polar form. (*Hint:* First write 1 in polar form $\cos(0 + 2k\pi) + i \sin(0 + 2k\pi)$.)

(a) The two square roots of 1. ______

______

(b) The three cube roots of 1. ______

______

______

(c) The four 4th roots of 1. ______

______

______

______

(d) An expression for the n nth roots of 1.

______

(e) The two square roots of $1 + i\sqrt{3}$.

______

______

ANSWERS TO PAGE 379

(g) 37

(h) $(-1,0)$

(i) $(1,0)$

(j) $(0,+9)$

(k) 1

(5) (a) $-5-12i$

$(a^2-b^2) + 2abi$

-5

-12

$2-3i$

$-2+3i$

(b) $2+5i$ or $-2-5i$

(6) (a) $\left(\dfrac{15}{13}, \dfrac{-16}{13}\right)$

(b) $\left(\dfrac{7}{4}, \dfrac{1}{4}\right)$

(c) $\dfrac{14}{17} + \dfrac{2}{17}i$

(d) $\dfrac{3}{13} - \dfrac{9}{26}i$

(e) $\left(\dfrac{-3}{10}, \dfrac{-1}{10}\right)$

(f) $\dfrac{2}{85} + \dfrac{9}{85}i$

(g) undefined

(h) $-\dfrac{1}{2} + \dfrac{1}{2}i$

(7) (a) -1 (b) -1

(c) -1 (d) 1

(e) i (f) $-i$

(14) (a) $(1, -\sqrt{3})$

(b) $(3\sqrt{3}, -3)$

(c) $(-2, -2\sqrt{3})$

(15) $\rho^2(5 \sin^2 \theta + 4) = 36$

(16) $y = 5$

(17) $y^2 - 8x - 16 = 0$

(18) (Lemniscate)

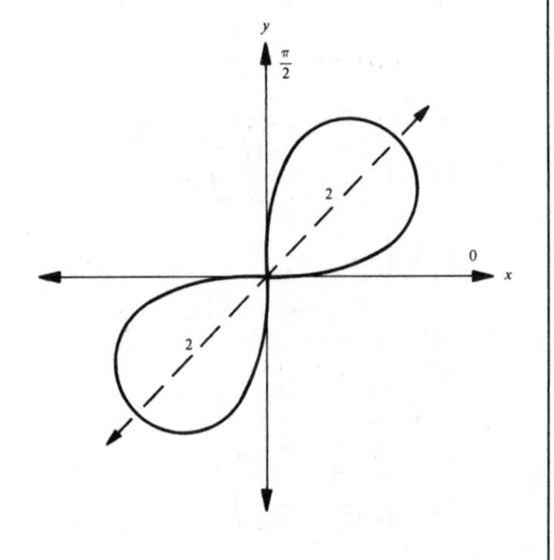

CHAPTER 6 REVIEW EXERCISES

1. $A(3,2)$, $B(4,-2)$, and $C(-5,4)$ are the vertices of $\triangle ABC$. Find each of the following. (6.1)

(a) $\vec{a} =$ ________________ (b) $\vec{b} =$ ________________

(c) $\vec{c} =$ ________________ (d) $a =$ ________________

(e) $b =$ ________________ (f) $c =$ ________________

(g) $\vec{a} + \vec{b} + \vec{c} =$ ____________.

2. In $\triangle RST$ illustrated, $\angle R$, $\angle S$, and $\angle T$ are the angles of the triangle. (6.1)

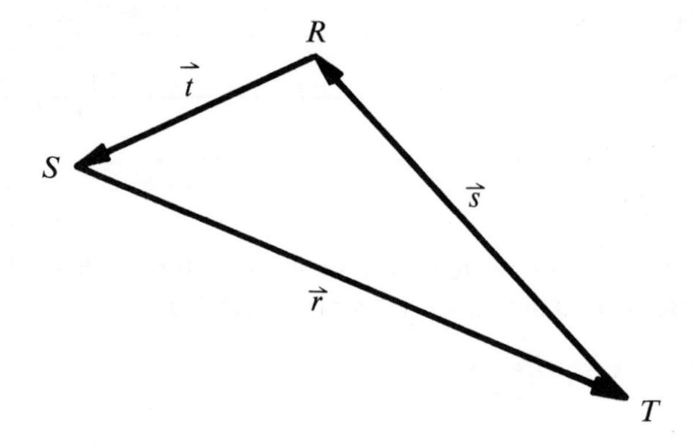

(a) The direction vectors for the sides of $\angle S$ are ______ and ______.

(b) The direction vectors for the sides of $\angle R$ are ______ and ______.

(c) $\angle T$ is measured from ray ______ to ray ______.

(d) If $\angle R$ is a right angle, then $\vec{s} \cdot \vec{t} =$ ______.

3. If $\triangle ABC$ is a right triangle with $m^\circ \angle C = 90^\circ$, then $\angle A$ and $\angle B$ are said to be ____________________. Furthermore, if $\sin A = 59$, then $\cos B =$ ________. Because the sine of an angle is equal to the cosine of the angle's complement, the sin and cos functions are called ____________________. (6.1)

4. Right $\triangle ABC$ has vertices $A(-3,0)$, $B(5,-2)$, and $C(6.2)$. Complete each of the following. (6.1)

(a) Angle ______ is the right angle.

(b) $\sin A =$ ________________ (c) $\cos A =$ ________________

(d) $\sin C =$ ________________ (e) $\cos C =$ ________________

5. In $\triangle RST$, $\angle R$ is a right angle, $m^\circ \angle S = 34$, and $t = 20$. Find each of the following. (6.1)

(a) $m^\circ \angle T =$ ________; (b) $s =$ ________;

(c) $r =$ ________.

6. Two forces of 560 pounds and 800 pounds act on a point at right angles to each other. Find the resultant force and the angle it determines with the 800-pound force. (6.1) Force = ________

Angle = ________

7. A 2000-pound weight is resting on a plane inclined at an angle of 12° with the horizontal. Find the magnitude of the force parallel to the plane that is necessary to prevent the weight from moving. (6.1)

____

8. Solve $\triangle ABC$ given that $m^\circ \angle C = 25°30'$, $m^\circ \angle B = 48°20'$, and $a = 32$. (6.2)

$m^\circ \angle A =$ ________ $b =$ ________

$c =$ ________

9. Solve $\triangle RST$ for which $m^\circ \angle T = 32°40'$, $t = 138$ feet, and $r = 208$ feet. (6.2)

$m^\circ \angle R =$ ________

$m^\circ \angle S =$ ________

$s =$ ________

10. Solve $\triangle PQR$ given that $m^\circ \angle Q = 27°10'$, $p = 28$, and $r = 32$. (6.2)

$q =$ ________, $m^\circ \angle R =$ ________,

$m^\circ \angle P =$ ________

11. Solve $\triangle ABC$ given that $a = 40$, $b = 80$, and $c = 100$. (6.2).

$m^\circ \angle A =$ ________, $m^\circ \angle B =$ ________, $m^\circ \angle C =$

________.

12. Use the Law of Tangents to find $m^\circ \angle S$ and $m^\circ \angle T$ in $\triangle RST$, given that $m^\circ \angle R = 42°30'$, $s = 84$, and $t = 68$.

$m^\circ \angle S =$ ________, $m^\circ \angle T =$ ________. (See Exercises 6 and 7, Section 6.2)

13. Give the complete set of polar coordinates for the point that has polar coordinates $\left(-5, \frac{\pi}{3}\right)$. (6.3)

____

____

ANSWERS TO PAGE 381

(b) $5(\cos 60° + i \sin 60°)$

(12) (a) $\frac{5}{2}\left(\cos \frac{2\pi}{3} + i \sin \frac{2\pi}{3}\right)$

(b) $\frac{1}{2}(\cos 180° + i \sin 180°)$

(13) (a) $8i$

(b) $-512\sqrt{2} - 512i\sqrt{2}$

(c) $2 + 2i$

(d) $-\frac{1}{8}i$

(14) (a) $\cos 0 + i \sin 0$

$\cos \pi + i \sin \pi$

(b) $\cos 0 + i \sin 0$

$\cos \frac{2\pi}{3} + i \sin \frac{2\pi}{3}$

$\cos \frac{4\pi}{3} + i \sin \frac{4\pi}{3}$

(c) $\cos 0 + i \sin 0$

$\cos \frac{\pi}{2} + i \sin \frac{\pi}{2}$

$\cos \pi + i \sin \pi$

$\cos \frac{3\pi}{2} + i \sin \frac{3\pi}{2}$

(d) $\cos \frac{2k\pi}{n} + i \sin \frac{2k\pi}{n}$
$n = 0,1,2,\cdots,n-1$

(e) $\sqrt{2}\left(\cos \frac{\pi}{6} + i \sin \frac{\pi}{6}\right)$

$\sqrt{2}\left(\cos \frac{7\pi}{6} + i \sin \frac{7\pi}{6}\right)$

ANSWERS TO PAGE 386

(27) (a) $\frac{3}{2}\left(\cos\frac{\pi}{3} + i\sin\frac{\pi}{3}\right)$

(b) $2(\cos 60° - i\sin 60°)$

(28) $-128 + 128i$

14. Find rectangular coordinates for each of the following points with polar coordinates. (6.3) (a) $\left(2, \frac{-\pi}{3}\right)$ ________________

(b) $\left(-6, \frac{5\pi}{6}\right)$ ________________

(c) $\left(4, \frac{22\pi}{3}\right)$ ________________

15. Find a polar equation for the rectangular equation $4x^2 + 9y^2 = 36$. (6.3)

____

16. Find an equation in rectangular coordinates for the equation $\rho \sin\theta = 5$. (6.3) ________________

17. Find an equation in rectangular coordinates for the equation $\rho - \rho\cos\theta = 4$. (6.3) ________________

18. Sketch the graph corresponding to the equation $\rho^2 = 4\sin 2\theta$. (6.)

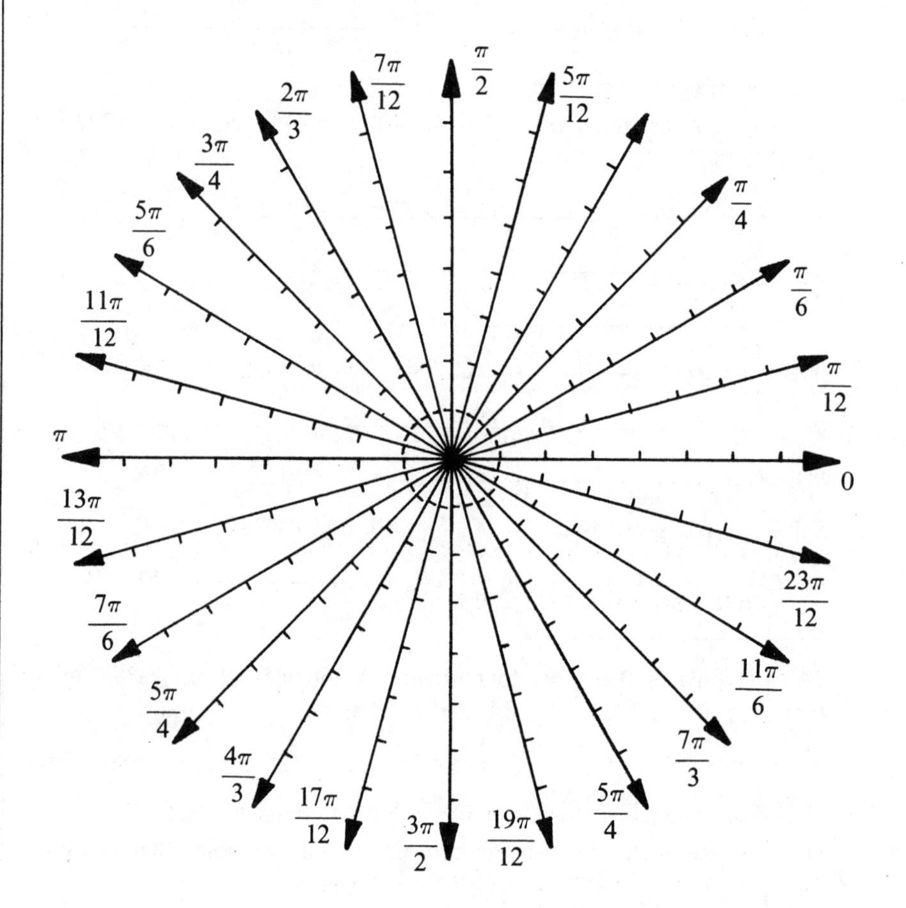

19. Find x and y for the following equations of complex numbers. (6.4)

(a) $(3x - 2, y) = (4x + 7, 2y - 3)$; $x =$ ______, $y =$ ______

(b) $2x + 3i = 4 - 2yi$; $x =$ ______, $y =$ ______

20. Solve each of the following equations for the complex variable z. (6.4)

(a) $(2, -5) + z = (-3, 4)$; $z =$ ______

(b) $z - (2 - 3i) = 3z - 7i$; $z =$ ______

21. Perform each of the following multiplications of complex numbers. (6.4)

(a) $(2, -5)(4, 3) =$ ______

(b) $(5 + 2i)(-3 - 7i) =$ ______

(c) $(7 + i)^2 =$ ______

(d) $(6 + 2i)(6 - 2i) =$ ______

(e) $(1 - 4i)(1 + 4i) =$ ______

22. Find the two squares of $8 - 6i$. (6.4)

______

23. Perform the following divisions of complex numbers. (6.4)

(a) $\frac{(3, -5)}{(2, 1)} =$ ______

(b) $\frac{6 - 5i}{2 + 3i} =$ ______

24. Compute each of the following and write in the simplest form. (6.4)

(a) $i^{13} =$ ______ (b) $i^{44} =$ ______

25. Write each of the following complex numbers in polar form with an amplitude θ such that $\theta \in \mathcal{R}$ and $0 \leq \theta < \frac{\pi}{2}$. (6.4)

(a) $3 - 3i$ ______

(b) $-2\sqrt{3} + 2i$ ______

26. Write the product for each of the following in polar form. (6.4)

(a) $\left[4\left(\cos \frac{7\pi}{3} + i \sin \frac{7\pi}{3}\right)\right] [3(\cos \pi + i \sin \pi)]$

______

(b) $[2(\cos 240° + i \sin 240°)]\ [3(\cos 30° + i \sin 30°)]$

______

ANSWERS TO PAGE 383

(5) (a) 56° (b) 13.49

(c) 24.12

(6) 976.5 pounds

35°00′

(7) 415.8 pounds

(8) 106°10′ 24.9

14.3

(9) This is an ambiguous case.

54°30′ or 125°30′

92°50′ or 21°50′

255 or 95

(10) 14.3 89°13′

63°37′

(11) 22°20′ 49°27′

108°13′

(12) 66°00′ 71°30′

(13) $\left\{\left(-5, \frac{\pi}{3} + 2k\pi\right)\right.$ or $\left.\left(5, \frac{4\pi}{3} + 2k\pi\right) \text{ for some } k \in J\right\}$

27. Find the quotient for each of the following and write in polar form. (6.4)

(a) $$\frac{6\left(\cos \frac{7\pi}{6} + i \sin \frac{7\pi}{6}\right)}{4\left(\cos \frac{5\pi}{6} + i \sin \frac{5\pi}{6}\right)} = \underline{\qquad\qquad}$$

(b) $$\frac{10(\cos 150° + i \sin 150°)}{5(\cos 210° + i \sin 210°)} = \underline{\qquad\qquad}$$

28. Evaluate $(2 - 2i)^5$ and write in standard form. (6.4) ______________

Appendix

SUPPLEMENTARY ANSWERS TO EXERCISES

Answers Exercises 1.2

14. Prove that for $x \epsilon \mathcal{R}$ and $y \epsilon \mathcal{R}$ $|x + y| \leq |x| + |y|$.

Proof: Since for any real number a, $|a| = \sqrt{a^2}$, the inequality

$$|x + y| \leq |x| + |y|$$

is equivalent to

$$\sqrt{(x + y)^2} \leq \sqrt{x^2} + \sqrt{y^2}.$$

Since both members are nonnegative, the inequality obtained by squaring both members will also be true, namely,

$$(x + y)^2 \leq x^2 + 2\sqrt{x^2} \cdot \sqrt{y^2} + y^2,$$

or

$$x^2 + 2xy + y^2 \leq x^2 + 2\sqrt{x^2} \cdot \sqrt{y^2} + y^2,$$

which in turn is equivalent to $xy \leq \sqrt{x^2}\sqrt{y^2}$.

Hence, the desired result may be established by showing

$$xy \leq \sqrt{x^2 \cdot y^2}.$$

To do this, note that

$$\sqrt{x^2y^2} = \sqrt{(xy)^2} = |xy|.$$

If x and y differ in sign,

$$xy < 0 \quad \text{and} \quad xy \leq \sqrt{x^2 \cdot y^2},$$

since the right member is always positive. If x and y have the same sign,

$$xy = \sqrt{x^2 \cdot y^2},$$

because if x and y are positive, the right member is $x \cdot y$, and if x and y are both negative, the right member is

$$(-x) \cdot (-y) = xy.$$

Therefore, $xy \leq \sqrt{x^2 \cdot y^2}$, for any x or any y, and

$$|x + y| \leq |x| + |y|.$$

Answers Exercises 1.3

7. Let f, g, and h be three linear functions where $f(x) = m_1x + b_1$, $g(x) = m_2x + b_2$, and $h(x) = m_3x + b_3$. We want to show that

$$f \circ (g \circ h) = (f \circ g) \circ h.$$

(19) (a) -9 $\quad 3$

(b) 2 $\quad \frac{-3}{2}$

(20) (a) $\{(-5,9)\}$

(b) $\{-1 + 5i\}$

(21) (a) $(23, -14)$

(b) $(-1 - 41i)$

(c) $48 + 14i$

(d) 40

(e) 17

(22) $3 - i$ or $-3 + i$

(23) (a) $\left(\frac{1}{5}, -\frac{13}{5}\right)$

(b) $\frac{-3}{13} - \frac{28}{13}i$

(24) (a) i (b) 1

(25) (a) $3\sqrt{2}\left(\cos\frac{\pi}{4} - i\sin\frac{\pi}{4}\right)$

(b) $4\left(-\cos\frac{\pi}{6} + i\sin\frac{\pi}{6}\right)$

(26) (a) $-12\left(\cos\frac{\pi}{3} + i\sin\frac{\pi}{3}\right)$

(b) $-6(\cos 90° + i\sin 90°)$

Proof:

$$g \circ h = \{(x,y): y = m_2(m_3x + b_3) + b_2\}$$
$$= \{(x,y): y = m_2m_3x + m_2b_3 + b_2\}$$
$$f \circ (g \circ h) = \{(x,y): y = m_1(m_2m_3x + m_2b_3 + b_2) + b_1\}$$
$$= \{(x,y): y = m_1m_2m_3x + m_1m_2b_3 + m_1b_2 + b_1\}$$
$$f \circ g = \{(x,y): y = m_1(m_2x + b_2) + b_1\}$$
$$= \{(x,y): y = m_1m_2x + m_1b_2 + b_1\}$$
$$(f \circ g) \circ h = \{(x,y): y = m_1m_2(m_3x + b_3) + m_1b_2 + b_1\}$$
$$= \{(x,y): y = m_1m_2m_3x + m_1m_2b_3 + m_1b_2 + b_1\}$$

$\therefore f \circ (g \circ h) = (f \circ g) \circ h$ whenever f, g, and h are linear functions.

9.

	Domain	Range
f	$\mathcal{R}$	$\{y: y \geq 0\}$
g	$\{x: \lvert x \rvert \leq 4\}$	$\{y: 0 \leq y \leq 4\}$
$f \circ g$	$\{x: \lvert x \rvert \leq 4\}$	$\{y: 0 \leq y \leq 16\}$
$g \circ f$	$\{x: \lvert x \rvert \leq 2\}$	$\{y: 0 \leq y \leq 4\}$

To find the domain of $f \circ g$ consider the intersection of the range of g and the domain of f. The domain of $f \circ g$ is the set of all x in the domain of g for which $g(x)$ is in the stated intersection. Find the domain of $g \circ f$ in a similar fashion.

Answers Exercises 2.1

8. Prove that if $\vec{v} \in \mathcal{R} \times \mathcal{R}$, then $\|\vec{v}\| = 0$ if and only if $\vec{v} = (0,0)$.

Proof:

Part 1. If $\vec{v} = (0,0)$,

$$\|\vec{v}\| = \sqrt{0^2 + 0^2} = \sqrt{0} = 0.$$

Part 2. If $\|\vec{v}\| = 0$,

$$\sqrt{x^2 + y^2} = 0$$

by definition of $\|\vec{v}\|$.

$\sqrt{x^2 + y^2} = 0$ implies that $x^2 + y^2 = 0$.

Suppose $x \neq 0$ or $y \neq 0$, then $x^2 > 0$, or $y^2 > 0$, and $x^2 + y^2 > 0$. This contradicts $x^2 + y^2 = 0$.

$\therefore x = y = 0$ and $v = (0.0)$.

Answers Exercises 2.2

4. Prove that vector addition is commutative, i.e., prove that

$$\vec{a} + \vec{b} = \vec{b} + \vec{a}.$$

Proof: Let $\vec{a} = (a_1,a_2)$, and $\vec{b} = (b_1,b_2)$.

$$\begin{aligned}\vec{a} + \vec{b} &= (a_1,a_2) + (b_1,b_2) \\ &= (a_1 + b_1, a_2 + b_2) \\ &= (b_1 + a_1, b_2 + a_2) \\ &= (b_1,b_2) + (a_1,a_2)\end{aligned}$$

$$\therefore \vec{a} + \vec{b} = \vec{b} + \vec{a}.$$

8. Prove the parallelogram law for vectors. *Proof:* Let points A, B, C, and O correspond to (x_1,y_1), (x_2,y_2), $(x_1 + x_2, y_1 + y_2)$, and $(0,0)$, respectively, where $(x_1,y_1) \neq k(y_2,y_2)$. (See illustration.)

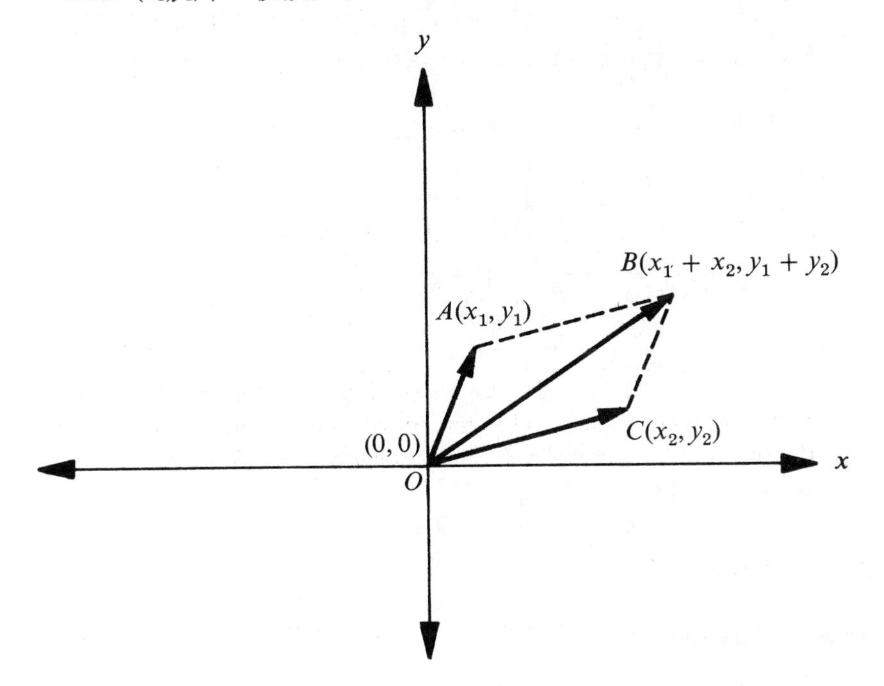

(a) If $x_1 \neq 0$, the slope of $\overline{OA}$ is $\frac{y_1}{x_1}$ and the slope of $\overline{CB}$ is

$$\frac{y_1 + y_2 - y_2}{x_1 + x_2 - x_2} = \frac{y_1}{x_1}.$$

If $x_1 = 0$, $\overline{CB}$ and $\overline{OA}$ are both vertical. In either case $\overline{OA} \| \overline{CB}$.

(b) If $x_2 \neq 0$, then the slope of $\overline{AB}$ is $\frac{y_1 + y_2 - y_1}{x_1 + x_2 - x_1} = \frac{y_2}{x_2}$, and the slope of $\overline{OC}$ is $\frac{y_2}{x_2}$. If $x_2 = 0$, then $\overline{AB}$ and $\overline{OC}$ are both vertical. In either case $\overline{OA} \| \overline{CB}$.

(c) Since $\overline{OA} \| \overline{CB}$ and $\overline{AB} \| \overline{OC}$, $\square OABC$ is a parallelogram with a diagonal $\overline{OB}$. Since the coordinates of B are $(x_1 + x_2, y_1 + y_2)$, which is the resultant of (x_1,y_1) and (x_2,y_2), the diagonal is the standard geometric vector representing the resultant.

Answers Exercises 2.3

5. Prove that for any scalar $k \epsilon \mathcal{R}$ and any vector $\vec{r}$,

$$||k\vec{r}|| = |k| \cdot ||\vec{r}||.$$

Proof: Let $\vec{r} = (r_1,r_2)$.

Then

$$\begin{aligned} ||k\vec{r}|| &= ||(kr_1,kr_2)|| = \sqrt{(kr_1)^2 + (kr_2)^2} \\ &= \sqrt{k^2r_1^2 + k^2r_2^2} = \sqrt{k^2(r_1^2 + r_2^2)} \\ &= |k|\sqrt{r_1^2 + r_2^2} = |k| \cdot ||\vec{r}||. \end{aligned}$$

8. Prove that $\left\| \dfrac{\vec{a}}{||\vec{a}||} \right\| = 1$, if $\vec{a} = (x,y)$.

1st Proof:

$$\begin{aligned} \left\| \frac{\vec{a}}{||\vec{a}||} \right\| &= \left\| \frac{(x,y)}{\sqrt{x^2 + y^2}} \right\| = \left\| \frac{x}{\sqrt{x^2 + y^2}}, \frac{y}{\sqrt{x^2 + y^2}} \right\| \\ &= \sqrt{\left(\frac{x}{\sqrt{x^2 + y^2}}\right)^2 + \left(\frac{y}{\sqrt{x^2 + y^2}}\right)^2} \\ &= \sqrt{\frac{x^2}{x^2 + y^2} + \frac{y^2}{x^2 + y^2}} = \sqrt{\frac{x^2 + y^2}{x^2 + y^2}} = \sqrt{1} = 1. \end{aligned}$$

2nd Proof: Using Exercise 5, with $k = \left\| \dfrac{1}{||\vec{a}||} \right\|$,

$$\left\| \frac{\vec{a}}{||\vec{a}||} \right\| = \left\| \frac{1}{||\vec{a}||} \cdot \vec{a} \right\| = \frac{1}{||\vec{a}||} \cdot ||\vec{a}|| = 1.$$

Answers Exercises 2.4

4. Prove IP2, i.e., prove that if $\vec{x}$ and $\vec{y}$ are vectors and k is a scalar, then $k(\vec{x} \cdot \vec{y}) = (k\vec{x}) \cdot \vec{y}$.

Proof:

Let

$$\vec{x} = (x_1,x_2) \quad \text{and} \quad \vec{y} = (y_1,y_2).$$

Then,

$$\begin{aligned} k(\vec{x} \cdot \vec{y}) &= k[(x_1,x_2) \cdot (y_1,y_2)] \\ &= k(x_1,y_1 + x_2,y_2) \\ &= k(x_1,y_1) + k(x_2,y_2) \\ &= (kx_1)y_1 + (kx_2)y_2 \\ &= (kx_1,kx_2) \cdot (y_1,y_2) \\ &= [k(x_1,x_2)] \cdot (y_1,y_2) \\ &= (k\vec{x}) \cdot \vec{y}. \end{aligned}$$

5. Prove that $(\vec{r}+\vec{s})\cdot(\vec{r}+\vec{s}) = ||\vec{r}||^2 + 2\vec{r}\cdot\vec{s} + ||\vec{s}||^2$.

Proof:

$$(\vec{r}+\vec{s})\cdot(\vec{r}+\vec{s}) = (\vec{r}+\vec{s})\cdot\vec{r} + (\vec{r}+\vec{s})\cdot\vec{s}$$

by the distributive property of inner product.

$$\begin{aligned}(\vec{r}+\vec{s})\cdot\vec{r} + (\vec{r}+\vec{s})\cdot\vec{s} &= \vec{r}(\vec{r}+\vec{s}) + \vec{s}\cdot(\vec{r}+\vec{s}) \\ &= \vec{r}\cdot\vec{r} + \vec{r}\cdot\vec{s} + \vec{s}\cdot\vec{r} + \vec{s}\cdot\vec{s} \\ &= ||\vec{r}||^2 + \vec{r}\cdot\vec{s} + \vec{s}\cdot\vec{r} + ||\vec{s}||^2 \\ &= ||\vec{r}||^2 + 2\vec{r}\cdot\vec{s} + ||\vec{s}||^2.\end{aligned}$$

Therefore,

$$(\vec{r}+\vec{s})\cdot(\vec{r}+\vec{s}) = ||\vec{r}||^2 + 2\vec{r}\cdot\vec{s} + ||\vec{s}||^2.$$

6. To show that "$\vec{a}\cdot\vec{c} = \vec{b}\cdot\vec{c}$ implies that $\vec{a} = \vec{b}$" is an invalid statement, it is sufficient to provide a counterexample. For example, let $\vec{a} = (3,2)$, $\vec{b} = \left(2, \frac{14}{5}\right)$ and $\vec{c} = (4,5)$.

Thus,

$$\vec{a}\cdot\vec{c} = (3,2)\cdot(4,5) = 12 + 10 = 22,$$

and

$$\vec{b}\cdot\vec{c} = \left(2, \frac{14}{5}\right)\cdot(4,5) = 8 + 14 = 22,$$

but

$$\vec{a} \neq \vec{b}.$$

7. Prove that the diagonals of a rhombus are perpendicular to each other.

Proof: The diagonals of the rhombus correspond to $\vec{r}+\vec{s}$ and $\vec{r}-\vec{s}$. It has been shown in this section that

$$(\vec{r}+\vec{s})\cdot(\vec{r}-\vec{s}) = ||\vec{r}||^2 - ||\vec{s}||^2.$$

Since a rhombus has sides of equal length,

$$||\vec{r}|| = ||\vec{s}||.$$

Thus,

$$(\vec{r}+\vec{s})\cdot(\vec{r}-\vec{s}) = 0,$$

and the diagonals are perpendicular.

8. Prove that if $\vec{x}$ is perpendicular to $\vec{y}$, then $\vec{x}$ is perpendicular to $-\vec{y}$.

Proof: If $\vec{x}\perp\vec{y}$, then $\vec{x}\cdot\vec{y} = \vec{0}$.

Thus,

$$(-\vec{y})\cdot\vec{x} = [-1(\vec{y})]\cdot\vec{x} = -1(\vec{y}\cdot\vec{x}) = -1(0) = 0.$$

Therefore $\vec{x}$ is perpendicular to $-\vec{y}$.

9. Prove IP4, i.e., if $\vec{v}$ is a vector, then $\vec{v} \cdot \vec{v} = ||\vec{v}||^2$.

Proof:

Let $\vec{v} = (v_1, v_2)$, then

$$\vec{v} \cdot \vec{v} = (v_1,v_2) \cdot (v_1,v_2) = v_1^2 + v_2^2$$
$$= (\sqrt{v_1^2 + v_2^2})^2 = ||\vec{v}||^2.$$

Answers Exercises 3.4

3. From the definition of cos x and sin x,

$$\cos^2 x + \sin^2 x = 1.$$

Thus if $\sin^2 x \neq 0$,

$$\frac{\cos^2 x}{\sin^2 x} + \frac{\sin^2 x}{\sin^2 x} = \frac{1}{\sin^2 x}.$$

By substitution from the definition of cot x and csc x this becomes

$$\cot^2 x + 1 = \csc^2 x.$$

This statement is true for all x such that $\sin x \neq 0$, that is, for

$$x \epsilon \{x : x \neq k\pi \text{ for all } k \epsilon J\}.$$

4. Multiply numerator and denominator of right member by $\tan x - \sin x$.

Thus,

$$\frac{\tan x \sin x (\tan x - \sin x)}{(\tan x + \sin x)(\tan x - \sin x)} = \frac{\tan x \sin x (\tan x - \sin x)}{\tan^2 x - \sin^2 x}$$

$$= \frac{\tan x \sin x (\tan x - \sin x)}{\dfrac{\sin^2 x}{\cos^2 x} - \sin^2 x}$$

$$= \frac{\tan x \sin x (\tan x - \sin x)}{\dfrac{\sin^2 x}{\cos^2 x} - \dfrac{\sin^2 x \cos^2 x}{\cos^2 x}} = \frac{\tan x \sin x (\tan x - \sin x)}{\dfrac{\sin^2 x}{\cos^2 x}(1 - \cos^2 x)}$$

$$= \frac{\tan x \sin x (\tan x - \sin x)}{\tan^2 x \sin^2 x} = \frac{\tan x - \sin x}{\tan x \sin x}.$$

Not defined for $x \epsilon \left\{x : x = \frac{k\pi}{2} \text{ for some } k \epsilon J\right\}$.

7. Transforming the left member we have

$$\sin x \cot x + \cos^2 x \sec x = \sin x \left(\frac{\cos x}{\sin x}\right) + \cos^2 x \left(\frac{1}{\cos x}\right)$$
$$= \cos x + \cos x; \ (\sin x \neq 0, \cos x \neq 0)$$
$$= 2 \cos x.$$

$\therefore \sin x \cot x + \cos^2 x \sec x = 2 \cos x; \ x \neq k\frac{\pi}{2}$ for all $k \epsilon J$.

8. Transforming the left member by performing the indicated addition,

$$\frac{\cos x}{1+\sin x}+\frac{\cos x}{1-\sin x}=\frac{\cos x\,(1-\sin x)+\cos x\,(1+\sin x)}{1-\sin^2 x}$$

$$=\frac{\cos x-\cos x\sin x+\cos x+\cos x\sin x}{1-\sin^2 x}$$

$$=\frac{\cos x+\cos x}{1-\sin^2 x}=\frac{2\cos x}{\cos^2 x}=\frac{2}{\cos x}=2\sec x.$$

$$\therefore \frac{\cos x}{1+\sin x}+\frac{\cos x}{1-\sin x}=2\sec x;\quad x\neq(2k+1)\frac{\pi}{2} \text{ for all } k\epsilon J.$$

9. $$\frac{\cos x}{1+\sin x}+\frac{1+\sin x}{\cos x}=\frac{\cos^2 x+(1+\sin x)^2}{\cos x\,(1+\sin x)}=$$

$$=\frac{\cos^2 x+1+2\sin x+\sin^2 x}{\cos x\,(1+\sin x)}$$

$$=\frac{2+2\sin x}{\cos x\,(1+\sin x)}$$

since $\cos^2 x+\sin^2 x=1$.

$$\frac{2+2\sin x}{\cos x\,(1+\sin x)}=\frac{2(1+\sin x)}{\cos x\,(1+\sin x)}=\frac{2}{\cos x}=2\sec x.$$

$$\therefore \frac{\cos x}{1+\sin x}+\frac{1+\sin x}{\cos x}=2\sec x;\quad x\neq(2k+1)\frac{\pi}{2} \text{ for all } k\epsilon J.$$

10. Dividing numerator and denominator of the left member by $\cos x\neq 0$ we have

$$\frac{\cos x}{\cos x-\sin x}=\frac{\frac{\cos x}{\cos x}}{\frac{\cos x}{\cos x}-\frac{\sin x}{\cos x}}=\frac{1}{1-\tan x}$$

Therefore,

$$\frac{\cos x}{\cos x-\sin x}=\frac{1}{1-\tan x};\ x\neq\frac{\pi}{4}+k\pi \text{ and } x\neq(2k+1)\frac{\pi}{2} \text{ for all } k\epsilon J.$$

11. Substituting $(1-\sin^2 x)^2$ for $\cos^4 x$ in the left member

$$\sin^4 x-\cos^4 x=\sin^4 x-(1-\sin^2 x)^2$$

$$=\sin^4 x-(1-2\sin^2 x+\sin^4 x)$$

$$=\sin^4 x-1+2\sin^2 x-\sin^4 x$$

$$=-1+2\sin^2 x.$$

$$\therefore \sin^4 x-\cos^4 x=2\sin^2 x-1 \quad \text{for all } x\epsilon\mathcal{R}.$$

12. Write the numerator of the left member as the difference of two fractions as follows.

$$\frac{1 - 2\cos^2 x}{\sin x \cos x} = \frac{1 - \cos^2 x - \cos^2 x}{\sin x \cos x} = \frac{1 - \cos^2 x}{\sin x \cos x} - \frac{\cos^2 x}{\sin x \cos x}$$

$$= \frac{\sin^2 x}{\sin x \cos x} - \frac{\cos^2 x}{\sin x}$$

$$= \frac{\sin x}{\cos x} - \frac{\cos x}{\sin x} = \tan x - \cot x.$$

$$\therefore \frac{1 - 2\cos^2 x}{\sin x \cos x} = \tan x - \cot x; \ x \neq \frac{k\pi}{2} \text{ for all } k \epsilon J.$$

13. Substituting $\frac{1}{\cos x}$ for $\sec x$ and $\frac{\sin x}{\cos x}$ for $\tan x$ in the left member,

$$\sec x - \tan x = \frac{1}{\cos x} - \frac{\sin x}{\cos x}$$

$$= \frac{1 - \sin x}{\cos x}.$$

Multiplying numerator and denominator by $1 + \sin x$,

$\left(x \neq (2k + 1)\frac{\pi}{2}\right)$,

$$\frac{1 - \sin x}{\cos x} = \frac{1 - \sin^2 x}{\cos x\,(1 + \sin x)} = \frac{\cos^2 x}{\cos x\,(1 + \sin x)} = \frac{\cos x}{1 + \sin x}.$$

$$\therefore \sec x - \tan x = \frac{\cos x}{1 + \sin x}; \ x \neq (2k + 1)\frac{\pi}{2} \text{ for all } k \epsilon J.$$

14. Multiply numerator and denominator of the fraction in the left member under the radical by $1 - \cos x$, and then take the square root remembering that $\sqrt{a^2} = |a|$.

$$\sqrt{\frac{1 - \cos x}{1 + \cos x}} = \sqrt{\frac{(1 - \cos x)^2}{1 - \cos^2 x}} = \frac{\sqrt{1 - \cos x)^2}}{\sqrt{\sin^2 x}}$$

$$= \left|\frac{1 - \cos x}{\sin x}\right| = \left|\frac{1}{\sin x} - \frac{\cos x}{\sin x}\right|$$

$$= |\csc x - \cot x|.$$

$$\therefore \sqrt{\frac{1 - \cos x}{1 + \cos x}} = |\csc x - \cot x|; \ x \neq \pi k \text{ for all } k \epsilon J.$$

15. Beginning with the right member, substitute $\frac{\cos x}{\sin x}$ for $\cot x$ and $\frac{\sin x}{\cos x}$ for $\tan x$.

$$\frac{\sin x}{1-\dfrac{\cos x}{\sin x}}+\frac{\cos x}{1-\dfrac{\sin x}{\cos x}}=\frac{\sin x}{\dfrac{\sin x-\cos x}{\sin x}}+\frac{\cos x}{\dfrac{\cos x-\sin x}{\cos x}}$$

$$=\frac{\sin^2 x}{\sin x-\cos x}+\frac{\cos^2 x}{\cos x-\sin x}$$

$$=\frac{\sin^2 x-\cos^2 x}{\sin x-\cos x}.$$

Factoring the numerator and cancelling,

$$\frac{(\sin x-\cos x)(\sin x+\cos x)}{(\sin x-\cos\ x)}=\sin x+\cos x.$$

$$\therefore\ \frac{\sin x}{1-\cos x}+\frac{\cos x}{1-\tan x}=\sin x+\cos x;\quad x\neq k\frac{\pi}{2}\text{ for all }k\epsilon J.$$

16. Beginning with the left member and multiplying numerator and denominator by $1-\sin x$, $\sin x\neq 1$.

$$\frac{1-\sin x}{1+\sin x}=\frac{(1-\sin x)(1-\sin x)}{(1+\sin x)(1-\sin x)}=\frac{(1-\sin x)^2}{1-\sin^2 x}$$

$$=\frac{1-2\sin x+\sin^2 x}{1-\sin^2 x}=\frac{1-2\sin x+\sin^2 x}{\cos^2 x}$$

$$=\frac{1}{\cos^2 x}-\frac{2\sin x}{\cos^2 x}+\frac{\sin^2 x}{\cos^2 x}.$$

Then by substituting $\sec x$ for $\dfrac{1}{\cos x}$, and $\tan x$ for $\dfrac{\sin x}{\cos x}$,

$$\sec^2 x-2\sec x\tan x+\tan^2 x=(\sec x-\tan x)^2$$

$$\therefore\ \frac{1-\sin x}{1+\sin x}=(\sec x-\tan x)^2;\quad x\neq(2k+1)\frac{\pi}{2}\text{ for all }k\epsilon J.$$

Answers Chapter 3 Review Exercises

32.

$$\sec x+\tan x=\frac{1}{\cos x}+\frac{\sin x}{\cos x}$$

$$=\frac{1+\sin x}{\cos x}$$

$$=\frac{1-\sin^2 x}{\cos x(1-\sin x)}$$

$$=\frac{\cos^2 x}{\cos x(1-\sin x)}$$

$$=\frac{\cos x}{1-\sin x},$$

$$x\epsilon\left\{x:x\epsilon\mathcal{R}\text{ and }x\neq(2k+1)\frac{\pi}{2}\text{for all }k\epsilon J\right\}$$

33. $\left\{x : x \in \mathcal{R} \text{ and } x \neq \frac{k\pi}{2} \text{ for all } k \in J\right\}$. From the left member, we have

$$(\csc x - 1)(1 + \csc x) = -(1 - \csc^2 x) = \csc^2 x - 1 = \cot^2 x.$$

From the right member we have

$$\frac{\csc x \cos x}{\sec x \sin x} = \frac{\dfrac{1}{\sin x} \cdot \cos x}{\dfrac{1}{\cos x} \sin x} = \frac{\left\|\dfrac{\cos x}{\sin x}\right\|}{\left\|\dfrac{\sin x}{\cos x}\right\|} = \frac{\cos^2 x}{\sin^2 x} = \cot^2 x.$$

The left member is equal to the right member, and the statement is proved.

Answers Exercises 4.1

1. (a) $\cos\left(\frac{\pi}{2} - x\right) = \cos\frac{\pi}{2}\cos x + \sin\frac{\pi}{2}\sin x$
$= 0(\cos x) + (1)\sin x$
$= \sin x.$

(b) $\sin\left(\frac{\pi}{2} - x\right) = \sin\frac{\pi}{2}\cos x - \cos\frac{\pi}{2}\sin x$
$= (1)\cos x - (0)\sin x$
$= \cos x.$

(c) $\cos\left(x + \frac{\pi}{2}\right) = \cos x \cos\frac{\pi}{2} - \sin x \sin\frac{\pi}{2}$
$= (\cos x)0 - (\sin x)1.$
$= -\sin x.$

(d) $\sin\left(x + \frac{\pi}{2}\right) = \sin x \cos\frac{\pi}{2} + \cos x \sin\frac{\pi}{2}$
$= (\sin x)(0) + (\cos x)(1)$
$= \cos x.$

(e) $\cos(\pi - x) = \cos\pi\cos x + \sin\pi\sin x$
$= -1(\cos x) + 0(\sin x)$
$= -\cos x.$

(f) $\sin(\pi - x) = \sin\pi\cos x - \cos\pi\sin x$
$= 0(\cos x) - (-1)\sin x$
$= \sin x.$

(g) $\cos\left(\frac{3\pi}{2} + x\right) = \cos\frac{3\pi}{2}\cos x - \sin\frac{3\pi}{2}\sin x$
$= 0(\cos x) - (-1)\sin x$
$= \sin x.$

(h) $\sin\left(\frac{3\pi}{2}+x\right)=\sin\frac{3\pi}{2}\cos x+\cos\frac{3\pi}{2}\sin x$

$$= -1(\cos x) + (0)\sin x$$

$$= -\cos x.$$

(i) (1) $\sin\left(\frac{\pi}{4}+x\right)=\sin\frac{\pi}{4}\cos x+\cos\frac{\pi}{4}\sin x$

$$=\frac{\sqrt{2}}{2}\cos x+\frac{\sqrt{2}}{2}\sin x.$$

(2) $\cos\left(\frac{\pi}{4}-x\right)=\cos\frac{\pi}{4}\cos x+\sin\frac{\pi}{4}\sin x$

$$=\frac{\sqrt{2}}{2}\cos x+\frac{\sqrt{2}}{2}\sin x.$$

Since the results in (1) and (2) are the same

$$\sin\left(\frac{\pi}{4}+x\right)=\cos\left(\frac{\pi}{4}-x\right).$$

(j) $-\tan(\pi-x)=-\dfrac{\tan\pi-\tan x}{1+\tan\pi\tan x}$

$$=-\frac{0-\tan x}{1+0(\tan x)}$$

$$=-\frac{-\tan x}{1}=\tan x$$

$$\tan(\pi+x)=\frac{\tan\pi+\tan x}{1-\tan\pi\tan x}=\frac{0+\tan x}{1-(0)\tan x}=\tan x.$$

$\therefore -\tan(\pi-x)=\tan(\pi+x).$

2. $\sin(x_1-x_2)=\sin(x_1+(-x_2))$

$$=\sin x_1\cos(-x_2)+\cos x_1\sin(-x_2)$$

$$=\sin x_1\cos x_2-\cos x_1\sin x_2,$$

by substituting $\cos x_2$ for $\cos(-x_2)$ and $-\sin(x_2)$ for $\sin(-x_2)$.

$$\therefore \sin(x_1-x_2)=\sin x_1\cos x_2-\cos x_1\sin x_2.$$

4. $\tan(x_1-x_2)=\tan(x_1+(-x_2))$

$$=\frac{\tan x_1+\tan(-x_2)}{1-\tan x_1\tan(-x_2)}$$

$$=\frac{\tan x_1-\tan x_2}{1+\tan x_1\tan x_2},\quad \text{because}\quad \tan(-x_2)=-\tan x_2.$$

5. $$\cot(x_1 + x_2) = \frac{\cos(x_1 + x_2)}{\sin(x_1 + x_2)}$$

$$= \frac{\cos x_1 \cos x_2 - \sin x_1 \sin x_2}{\sin x_1 \cos x_2 + \cos x_1 \sin x_2}$$

$$= \frac{\dfrac{\cos x_1 \cos x_2}{\sin x_1 \sin x_2} - \dfrac{\cancel{\sin x_1}\,\cancel{\sin x_2}}{\cancel{\sin x_1}\,\cancel{\sin x_2}}}{\dfrac{\cancel{\sin x_1} \cos x_2}{\cancel{\sin x_1} \sin x_2} + \dfrac{\cos x_1 \cancel{\sin x_2}}{\sin x_1 \cancel{\sin x_2}}} = \frac{\cot x_1 \cot x_2 - 1}{\cot x_2 + \cot x_1}.$$

6. $$\sin(x_1 + x_2) = \sin x_1 \cos x_2 + \cos x_1 \sin x_2.$$

Let $x_1 = x_2$ and substitute.

$$\sin(x_1 + x_1) = \sin x_1 \cos x_1 + \cos x_1 \sin x_1.$$

$$\therefore \sin 2x_1 = 2 \sin x_1 \cos x_1 \text{ or } \sin 2x = 2 \sin x \cos x.$$

7. Add the left and right members of the identities $\cos^2 y + \sin^2 y = 1$ and $\cos 2y = \cos^2 y - \sin^2 y$ as follows.

$$\begin{aligned} \cos^2 y + \sin^2 y &= 1 \\ \cos^2 y - \sin^2 y &= \cos 2y \\ \hline 2\cos^2 y \qquad &= 1 + \cos 2y \end{aligned}$$

Now let $y = \frac{1}{2}x$ so that $2y = x$, and substitute. Therefore

$2\cos^2 \frac{1}{2}x = 1 + \cos x$, $\cos^2 \frac{1}{2}x = \frac{1 + \cos x}{2}$, and

$$\left|\cos \frac{1}{2}x\right| = \sqrt{\frac{1 + \cos x}{2}}.$$

8. Subtract the members of the following identities.

$$\begin{aligned} \sin(y_1 + y_2) &= \sin y_1 \cos y_2 + \cos y_1 \sin y_2 \\ \sin(y_1 - y_2) &= \sin y_1 \cos y_2 - \cos y_1 \sin y_2 \\ \hline \sin(y_1 + y_2) - \sin(y_1 - y_2) &= 2 \cos y_1 \sin y_2 \end{aligned}$$

Let $y_1 + y_2 = x_1$ and $y_1 - y_2 = x_2$ so that by adding, $2y_1 = x_1 + x_2$

or $y_1 = \frac{1}{2}(x_1 + x_2)$ and by subtracting, $2y_2 = x_1 - x_2$ or

$y_2 = \frac{1}{2}(x_1 - x_2)$. Now by substitution

$$\sin x_1 - \sin x_2 = 2 \cos \frac{1}{2}(x_1 + x_2) \sin \frac{1}{2}(x_1 - x_2).$$

9. Similar to the method in 8 above, we subtract the members of the identities for $\cos(y_1 + y_2)$ and $\cos(y_1 - y_2)$ as follows.

$$\begin{array}{r}
\cos(y_1 + y_2) = \cos y_1 \cos y_2 - \sin y_1 \sin y_2 \\
\cos(y_1 - y_2) = \cos y_1 \cos y_2 + \sin y_1 \sin y_2 \\
\hline
\cos(y_1 + y_2) - \cos(y_1 - y_2) = -2 \sin y_1 \sin y_2
\end{array}$$

Now use the same substitution as in 8, i.e., $x_1 = y_1 + y_2$ and $x_2 = y_1 - y_2$.

Therefore,

$$\cos x_1 - \cos x_2 = -2 \sin \frac{1}{2}(x_1 + x_2) \sin \frac{1}{2}(x_1 - x_2).$$

10.
$$\begin{aligned}
\sin 3x &= \sin(2x + x) \\
&= \sin 2x \cos x + \cos 2x \sin x \\
&= 2 \sin x \cos x (\cos x) + (\cos^2 x - \sin^2 x) \sin x \\
&= 2 \sin x \cos^2 x + \cos^2 x \sin x - \sin^3 x \\
&= 2 \sin x (1 - \sin^2 x) + (1 - \sin^2 x) \sin x - \sin^3 x \\
&= 2 \sin x - 2 \sin^3 x + \sin x - \sin^3 x - \sin^3 x.
\end{aligned}$$

$\therefore \sin 3x = 3 \sin x - 4 \sin^3 x.$

11.
$$\left|\tan \frac{1}{2}x\right| = \left|\frac{\sin \frac{1}{2}x}{\cos \frac{1}{2}x}\right| = \left|\frac{\sin \frac{1}{2}x}{\cos \frac{1}{2}x}\right| = \frac{\sqrt{\frac{1 - \cos x}{2}}}{\sqrt{\frac{1 + \cos x}{2}}} = \sqrt{\frac{1 - \cos x}{1 + \cos x}}.$$

13. Let $\frac{\pi}{4} - x = \frac{1}{2}\left(\frac{\pi}{2} - 2x\right)$ so that

$$\begin{aligned}
\left|\sin\left(\frac{\pi}{4} - x\right)\right| = \left|\sin \frac{1}{2}\left(\frac{\pi}{2} - 2x\right)\right| &= \sqrt{\frac{1 - \cos\left(\frac{\pi}{2} - 2x\right)}{2}} \\
&= \sqrt{\frac{1 - \left(\cos \frac{\pi}{2} \cos 2x + \sin \frac{\pi}{2} \sin 2x\right)}{2}} \\
&= \sqrt{\frac{1 - \sin 2x}{2}},
\end{aligned}$$

because $\cos \frac{\pi}{2} = 0$

$$\begin{aligned}
&= \sqrt{\frac{1 - (2 \sin x \cos x)}{2} \; \frac{1 - \sin x}{2}} \\
&= \sqrt{\frac{\cos^2 x + \sin^2 x - 2 \sin x \cos x}{2}} \\
&= \sqrt{\frac{(\cos x - \sin x)^2}{2}} \\
&= \sqrt{\frac{\cos x - \sin x}{\sqrt{2}}}.
\end{aligned}$$

Answers Exercises 4.2

3. Let Arctan $x = y$ so that $\tan y = x$. The left member then becomes $\sin 2y$.

$\sin 2y = 2 \sin y \cos y$ and if $\tan y = x$, then $\sin y = \dfrac{x}{\sqrt{x^2+1}}$, and

$\cos y = \dfrac{1}{\sqrt{x^2+1}}$. Substituting for $\sin y$ and $\cos y$,

$$\sin 2y = 2\left(\frac{x}{\sqrt{x^2+1}}\right)\left(\frac{1}{\sqrt{x^2+1}}\right) = \frac{2x}{x^2+1}.$$

$\therefore \ \sin 2\,(\text{Arctan } x) = \dfrac{2x}{x^2+1}$.

Answers Chapter 4 Review Exercises

4. (a)

$$\begin{aligned}\cos\left(\frac{3\pi}{2} - x\right) &= \cos\frac{3\pi}{2}\cos x + \sin\frac{3\pi}{2}\sin x\\ &= (0)(\cos x) + (-1)\sin x\\ &= -\sin x.\end{aligned}$$

(b)

$$\begin{aligned}\sin(x - \pi) &= \sin x \cos \pi - \cos x \sin \pi\\ &= \sin x(-1) - \cos x(0)\\ &= -\sin x.\end{aligned}$$

(c)

$$\tan(\pi + x) = \frac{\tan \pi + \tan x}{1 - \tan \pi \tan x} = \frac{0 + \tan x}{1 - 0} = \tan x \left(x \neq \frac{k\pi}{2} \text{ for all } k \epsilon J\right).$$

(d)

$$\begin{aligned}\sin\left(x - \frac{3\pi}{2}\right) &= \sin x \cos\frac{3\pi}{2} - \cos x \sin\frac{3\pi}{2}\\ &= (\sin x)(0) - (\cos x)(-1)\\ &= \cos x.\end{aligned}$$

(e)

$$\begin{aligned}\cos\left(x - \frac{3\pi}{2}\right) &= \cos x \cos\frac{3\pi}{2} + \sin x \sin\frac{3\pi}{2}\\ &= \cos x(0) + \sin x(-1)\\ &= -\sin x.\end{aligned}$$

(f)

$$\cot\left(\frac{\pi}{4} + x\right) = \frac{\cot\frac{\pi}{4}\cot x - 1}{\cot\frac{\pi}{4} + \cot x} = \frac{1(\cot x) - 1}{1 + \cot x} = \frac{\cot x - 1}{1 + \cot x}$$

$$\left(x \neq \frac{3\pi}{4} + k\pi \text{ for all } k\epsilon J\right).$$

5. $$\tan\frac{x}{2} = \frac{\sin\frac{x}{2}}{\cos\frac{x}{2}} = \frac{\sin\frac{x}{2}\cos\frac{x}{2}}{\cos\frac{x}{2}\cos\frac{x}{2}} = \frac{2\sin\frac{x}{2}\cos\frac{x}{2}}{2\cos^2\frac{x}{2}} = \frac{\sin 2\left(\frac{x}{2}\right)}{1+\cos 2\left(\frac{x}{2}\right)}$$

$$= \frac{\sin x}{1+\cos x}. \qquad (x \neq k\pi, \text{ for all } k \epsilon J)$$

Multiplying numerator and denominator by $1 - \cos x$ results in

$$\frac{\sin x(1-\cos x)}{1-\cos^2 x} = \frac{\sin x(1-\cos x)}{\sin^2 x}$$

$$= \frac{1-\cos x}{\sin x}.$$

$$\therefore \tan\frac{x}{2} = \frac{\sin x}{1+\cos x} = \frac{1-\cos x}{\sin x}. \quad (x \neq k\pi, \text{ for all } k \epsilon J)$$

6. Write the right member in terms of $\sin x$ and $\cos x$ as follows.

$$\sec x - \tan x = \frac{1}{\cos x} - \frac{\sin x}{\cos x} = \frac{1-\sin x}{\cos x}.$$

Now multiply numerator and denominator by $1 + \sin x$.

$$\frac{(1-\sin x)(1+\sin x)}{\cos x(1+\sin x)} = \frac{1-\sin^2 x}{\cos x(1+\sin x)} = \frac{\cos^2 x}{\cos x(1+\sin x)} = \frac{\cos x}{1+\sin x}.$$

$$\therefore \frac{\cos x}{1+\sin x} = \sec x - \tan x. \left(x \neq \frac{\pi}{2} + k\pi \text{ for all } k\epsilon J\right)$$

8. Use $\cos^2\frac{x}{2} + \sin^2\frac{x}{2} = 1$

and

$$\cos^2\frac{x}{2} - \sin^2\frac{x}{2} = \cos x.$$

Adding these two equations yields

$$2\cos^2\frac{x}{2} = 1 + \cos x,$$

which was to be proved.

13. (a) Use

$$\sin(x_1 + x_2) = \sin x_1 \cos x_2 + \cos x_1 \sin x_2$$

and

$$\sin(x_1 - x_2) = \sin x_1 \cos x_2 - \cos x_1 \sin x_2.$$

Add the two equations.

$$\sin(x_1 + x_2) + \sin(x_1 - x_2) = 2\sin x_1 \cos x_2.$$

Divide by 2 for the desired result.

$$\frac{1}{2}[\sin(x_1 + x_2) + \sin(x_1 - x_2)] = \sin x_1 \cos x_2.$$

Answers Exercises 5.3

3. (a) Using $\tan(\alpha + \beta) = \dfrac{\tan\alpha + \tan\beta}{1 - \tan\alpha\tan\beta}$ and letting $\theta = \alpha = \beta$, the result after substitution is

$$\tan(\theta + \theta) = \frac{\tan\theta + \tan\theta}{1 - \tan\theta\tan\theta}$$

or

$$\tan 2\,\theta = \frac{2\tan\theta}{1 - \tan^2\theta}.$$

This is not defined when $\tan^2\theta = 1$, or $|\tan\theta| = 1$. Therefore the excluded values are

$$\theta\epsilon\{\theta : \theta = (2k + 1)45°, \text{ where } k\epsilon J\}$$

(b) Beginning with the left member, replace $\sec\dfrac{\alpha}{2}$ by $\dfrac{1}{\cos\dfrac{\alpha}{2}}$ and $\csc\dfrac{\alpha}{2}$ by $\dfrac{1}{\sin\dfrac{\alpha}{2}}$, and add.

(1)
$$\sec\frac{\alpha}{2} + \csc\frac{\alpha}{2} = \frac{1}{\cos\frac{\alpha}{2}} + \frac{1}{\sin\frac{\alpha}{2}} = \frac{\sin\frac{\alpha}{2} + \cos\frac{\alpha}{2}}{\cos\frac{\alpha}{2}\sin\frac{\alpha}{2}}.$$

Recall that $\sin 2\theta = 2\sin\theta\cos\theta$ and replace θ with $\dfrac{\alpha}{2}$.

$$\sin\alpha = 2\sin\frac{\alpha}{2}\cos\frac{\alpha}{2} \text{ or } \frac{\sin\alpha}{2} = \cos\frac{\alpha}{2}\sin\frac{\alpha}{2}.$$

Substitute this in (1).

$$\frac{\sin\frac{\alpha}{2} + \cos\frac{\alpha}{2}}{\cos\frac{\alpha}{2}\sin\frac{\alpha}{2}} = \frac{\sin\frac{\alpha}{2} + \cos\frac{\alpha}{2}}{\frac{\sin\alpha}{2}} = \frac{2\left(\sin\frac{\alpha}{2} + \cos\frac{\alpha}{2}\right)}{\sin\alpha}.$$

Thus,

$$\sec\frac{\alpha}{2} + \csc\frac{\alpha}{2} = \frac{2\left(\sin\frac{\alpha}{2} + \cos\frac{\alpha}{2}\right)}{\sin\alpha}.$$

The left member is not defined whenever $\sin\dfrac{\alpha}{2} = 0$ or $\cos\dfrac{\alpha}{2} = 0$. The right member is not defined whenever $\sin\alpha = 0$. Therefore, the set of excluded values are $\{\alpha : \alpha = k\pi, \text{ for some } k\epsilon J\}$, since no other excluded values were introduced in the proof.

(c) Find the product of the sum and difference formulas for sin.

$$\begin{array}{r}
\sin(\alpha+\beta) = \sin\alpha\cos\beta + \cos\alpha\sin\beta \\
\sin(\alpha-\beta) = \sin\alpha\cos\beta - \cos\alpha\sin\beta \\
\hline
\sin(\alpha+\beta)\sin(\alpha-\beta) = \sin^2\alpha\cos^2\beta - \cos^2\alpha\sin^2\beta
\end{array}$$

Substitute for $\cos^2\beta$ and $\cos^2\alpha$.

$$\sin(\alpha+\beta)\sin(\alpha-\beta) = \sin^2\alpha(1-\sin^2\beta) - (1-\sin^2\alpha)\sin^2\beta$$

$$= \sin^2\alpha - \sin^2\alpha\sin^2\beta - \sin^2\beta + \sin^2\alpha\sin^2\beta.$$

$$\therefore \sin(\alpha+\beta)\sin(\alpha-\beta) = \sin^2\alpha - \sin^2\beta,$$

which was to be proved.

(d) Begin with the right member and replace $\cos 2\theta$ with $\cos^2\theta - \sin^2\theta$ and replace 1 with $\cos^2\theta + \sin^2\theta$.

$$\frac{2}{1+\cos 2\theta} = \frac{2}{1+\cos^2\theta - \sin^2\theta}$$

$$= \frac{2}{\cos^2\theta + \sin^2\theta + \cos^2\theta - \sin^2\theta}$$

$$= \frac{2}{2\cos^2\theta} = \frac{1}{\cos^2\theta} = \sec^2\theta.$$

Therefore, by the transitive property,

$$\sec^2\theta = \frac{2}{1+\cos 2\theta}.$$

The excluded values occur when $\cos\theta = 0$. They are

$$\left\{\theta : \theta = (2k+1)\frac{\pi}{2}, \text{ for some } k \in J\right\}.$$

6. (a)
$$\sin(270° - \alpha) = \sin 270° \cos\alpha - \cos 270° \sin\alpha$$
$$= (-1)\cos\alpha - 0(\sin\alpha)$$
$$= -\cos\alpha.$$

(b)
$$\cos(270° + \alpha) = \cos 270° \cos\alpha - \sin 270° \sin\alpha$$
$$= 0(\cos\alpha) - (-1)\sin\alpha$$
$$= \sin\alpha.$$

(c)
$$\tan(180° + \alpha) = \frac{\tan 180° + \tan\alpha}{1 - \tan 180° \tan\alpha}$$
$$= \frac{0 + \tan\alpha}{1 - 0}$$
$$= \tan\alpha.$$

(d)

$$\tan(180° - \alpha) = \frac{\tan 180° - \tan\alpha}{1 - \tan 180° \tan\alpha} = \frac{0 - \tan\alpha}{1 - 0(\tan\alpha)} = -\tan\alpha.$$

(e) $$\cos(180° + \alpha) = \cos 180° \cos\alpha - \sin 180° \sin\alpha$$
$$= -1(\cos\alpha) = 0(\sin\alpha)$$
$$= -\cos\alpha.$$

(f) $$\sin(270° + \alpha) = \sin 270° \cos\alpha + \cos 270° \sin\alpha$$
$$= (-1)\cos\alpha + 0(\sin\alpha)$$
$$= -\cos\alpha.$$

Answers Chapter 5 Review Exercises

23. Begin with the left member and multiply numerator and denominator by the conjugate of the denominator as follows.

$$\frac{\sin\alpha + \cos\alpha}{\cos\alpha - \sin\alpha} = \frac{(\sin\alpha + \cos\alpha)(\cos\alpha + \sin\alpha)}{(\cos\alpha - \sin\alpha)(\cos\alpha + \sin\alpha)}$$
$$= \frac{\sin^2\alpha + 2\sin\alpha\cos\alpha + \cos^2\alpha}{\cos^2\alpha - \sin^2\alpha}$$
$$= \frac{1 + 2\sin\alpha\cos\alpha}{\cos^2\alpha - \sin^2\alpha} = \frac{1 + \sin 2\alpha}{\cos^2\alpha - \sin^2\alpha}$$
$$= \frac{1 + \sin 2\alpha}{\cos 2\alpha} = \frac{1}{\cos 2\alpha} + \frac{\sin 2\alpha}{\cos 2\alpha}$$
$$= \sec 2\alpha + \tan 2\alpha.$$
$$\therefore \frac{\sin\alpha + \cos\alpha}{\cos\alpha - \sin\alpha} = \tan 2\alpha + \sec 2\alpha.$$

24. Recognizing that the left member is one member of a double angle formula,

$$\cos^2(45° + \alpha) - \sin^2(45° + \alpha) = \cos 2(45° + \alpha) = \cos(90° + 2\alpha).$$

Apply the sum formula for cosine.

$$\cos(90° + 2\alpha) = \cos 90° \cos 2\alpha - \sin 90° \sin 2\alpha$$
$$= 0(\cos 2\alpha) - 1(\sin 2\alpha) = -\sin 2\alpha.$$
$$\therefore \cos^2(45° + \alpha) - \sin^2(45° + \alpha) = -\sin 2\alpha.$$

Answers Exercises 6.2

4. Show that $c = b\cos A + a\cos B$ in $\triangle ABC$. Let the vectors $\vec{a}$, $\vec{b}$, and $\vec{c}$ correspond to the sides of $\triangle ABC$ as illustrated.

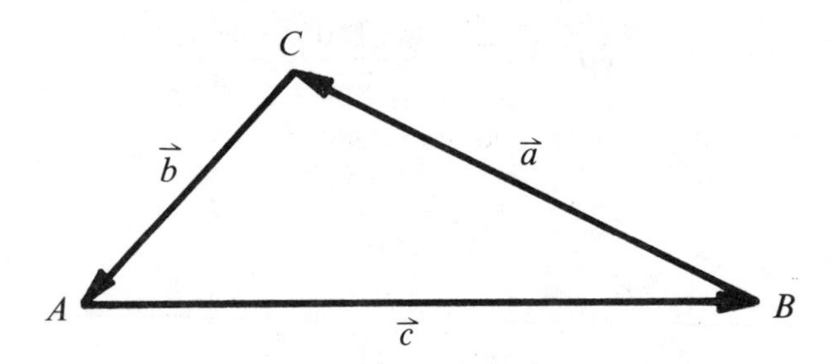

$$\vec{a} + \vec{b} + \vec{c} = \vec{0}.$$

Taking the inner product with $\vec{c}$ results in

$$\vec{c}(\vec{a} + \vec{b} + \vec{c}) = \vec{c} \cdot \vec{0}$$

or

$$\vec{c} \cdot \vec{a} + \vec{c} \cdot \vec{b} + \vec{c} \cdot \vec{c} = \vec{0}.$$

We know that

$$\vec{c} \cdot (-\vec{b}) = cb \cos A,$$

$$(-\vec{c}) \cdot \vec{a} = ca \cos B,$$

$$\text{and } \vec{c} \cdot \vec{c} = ||\vec{c}||^2 = c^2.$$

Substituting in (1),

$$-cb \cos A - ca \cos B + c^2 = 0.$$

Divide by c

$$b \cos A + a \cos B - c = 0,$$

or

$$c = b \cos A + a \cos B.$$

6. Show that $\dfrac{a - b}{a + b} = \dfrac{\sin A - \sin B}{\sin A + \sin B}$ follows from the Law of Sines. The

Law of Sines states

$$\frac{a}{\sin A} = \frac{b}{\sin B}.$$

By interchanging the means,

$$\frac{a}{b} = \frac{\sin A}{\sin B}.$$

Adding 1 to both members,

$$\frac{a}{b} + 1 = \frac{\sin A}{\sin B} + 1$$

or

(1) $$\frac{a + b}{b} = \frac{\sin A + \sin B}{\sin B}.$$

Now subtract 1 from both members of

$$\frac{a}{b} = \frac{\sin A}{\sin B},$$

(2) $$\frac{a - b}{b} = \frac{\sin A - \sin B}{\sin B}$$

Divide the equation in (2) by the equality in (1).

$$(3) \qquad \frac{a-b}{a+b} = \frac{\sin A - \sin B}{\sin A + \sin B}.$$

Substitute a product identity for the numerator and for the denominator of the right member of (3).

$$(4) \qquad \frac{a-b}{a+b} = \frac{2 \cos \frac{1}{2}(A+B) \sin \frac{1}{2}(A-B)}{2 \sin \frac{1}{2}(A+B) \cos \frac{1}{2}(A-B)}.$$

Divide numerator and denominator of the right member of (4) by

$\cos \frac{1}{2}(A+B) \cos \frac{1}{2}(A-B).$

$$\frac{a-b}{a+b} = \frac{\dfrac{\cos \frac{1}{2}(A+B) \sin \frac{1}{2}(A-B)}{\cos \frac{1}{2}(A+B) \cos \frac{1}{2}(A-B)}}{\dfrac{\sin \frac{1}{2}(A+B) \cos \frac{1}{2}(A-B)}{\cos \frac{1}{2}(A+B) \cos \frac{1}{2}(A-B)}}.$$

The result is

$$\frac{a-b}{a+b} = \frac{\tan \frac{1}{2}(A-B)}{\tan \frac{1}{2}(A+B)},$$

the Law of Tangents.

12. Let the vectors $\vec{a}$ and $\vec{b}$ correspond to consecutive sides of the parallelogram as illustrated. Let $\vec{c} = \vec{a} - \vec{b}$ correspond to the short diagonal and $\vec{d} = \vec{a} + \vec{b}$ correspond to the long diagonal. Finding the norm of each equation,

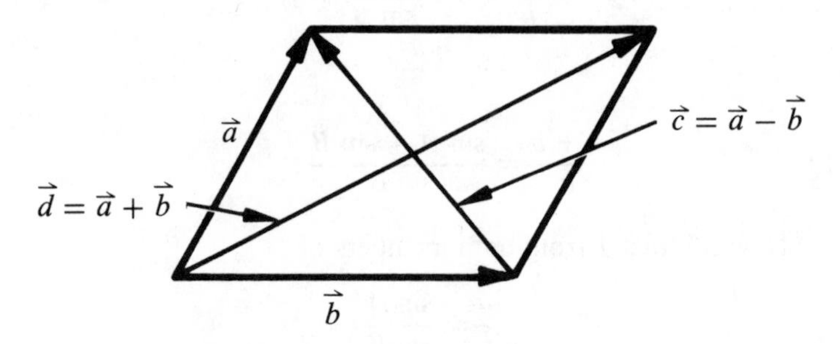

$$||\vec{c}|| = ||\vec{a} - \vec{b}|| \text{ and } ||\vec{d}|| = ||\vec{a} + \vec{b}||.$$

Square,

$$||\vec{c}||^2 = ||\vec{a} - \vec{b}||^2 \text{ and } ||\vec{d}||^2 = ||\vec{a} + \vec{b}||^2,$$

or $\|\vec{c}\|^2 = \|\vec{a}\|^2 - 2\vec{a} \cdot \vec{b} + \|\vec{b}\|^2$ and $\|\vec{d}\|^2 = \|\vec{a}\|^2 + 2\vec{a} \cdot \vec{b} + \|\vec{b}\|^2$.

Since $\|\vec{c}\|^2 = c^2$, $\|\vec{b}\|^2 = b^2$, $\|\vec{a}\|^2 = a^2$, and $\|\vec{d}\|^2 = d^2$, a substitution will yield

(1) $c^2 = a^2 - 2\vec{a} \cdot \vec{b} + b^2$ and

(2) $d^2 = a^2 + 2\vec{a} \cdot \vec{b} + b^2$. Add (1) and (2) to get

(3) $c^2 + d^2 = 2a^2 + 2b^2$ or $d = \sqrt{2a^2 + 2b^2 - c^2}$.

If $\vec{c}$ was selected to correspond to $\vec{a} + \vec{b}$ and $\vec{d}$ to correspond to $\vec{a} - \vec{b}$, the result would be the same.

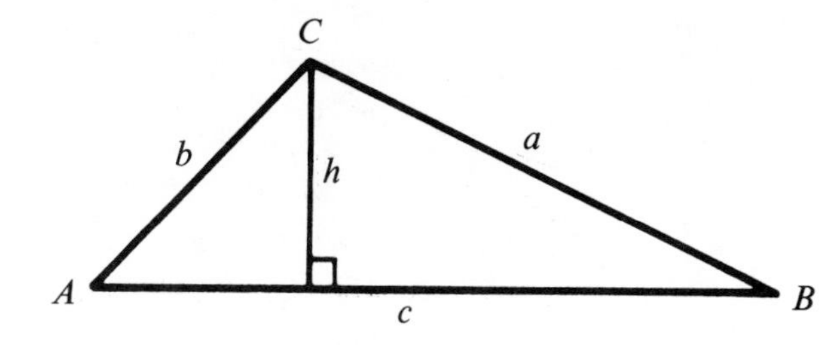

16. Use $\triangle ABC$ as illustrated. From the Law of Sines we have $\dfrac{a}{\sin A} = \dfrac{c}{\sin C}$.

Solve for a.

$$a = \frac{c \sin A}{\sin C}$$

The altitude h to side c forms a right triangle, from which we get

$\dfrac{h}{a} = \sin B$ or $h = a \sin B$. Substituting $\dfrac{c \sin A}{\sin C}$ for a,

$$h = \frac{c \sin A \sin B}{\sin C}$$

since $m^\circ \angle C = 180 - (m^\circ \angle A + m^\circ \angle B)$ and $\sin [180 - (A + B)] =$

$\sin (A + B)$ the formula for the altitude becomes

$$h = \frac{c \sin A \sin B}{\sin (A + B)}.$$

17. The area R of $\triangle ABC$ in Ex. 16 is $R = \dfrac{1}{2} ch$. Substituting

$$\frac{c \sin A \sin B}{\sin (A + B)}$$

for h

$$R = \frac{c^2 \sin A \sin B}{2 \sin (A + B)}.$$

Answers Exercises 6.3

7. (a) Since $\rho \cos^2 \frac{\theta}{2} = 2$ is equivalent to $\rho \cos^2\left(\frac{-\theta}{2}\right) = 2$, the graph is symmetric about the x axis.

   (b) Since $\rho^2 = 9\sin 2\theta$ is equivalent to $(-\rho)^2 = 9\sin 2\theta$, the graph is symmetric about the pole.

   (c) Since $\rho - \rho \cos \theta = 8$ is equivalent to $\rho - \rho \cos(-\theta)$, the graph is symmetric about the x axis.

   (d) Since $\rho = \cos^2 2\theta$ is equivalent to $\rho = \cos^2 2(-\theta)$, the graph is symmetric about the x axis.

8. (a)

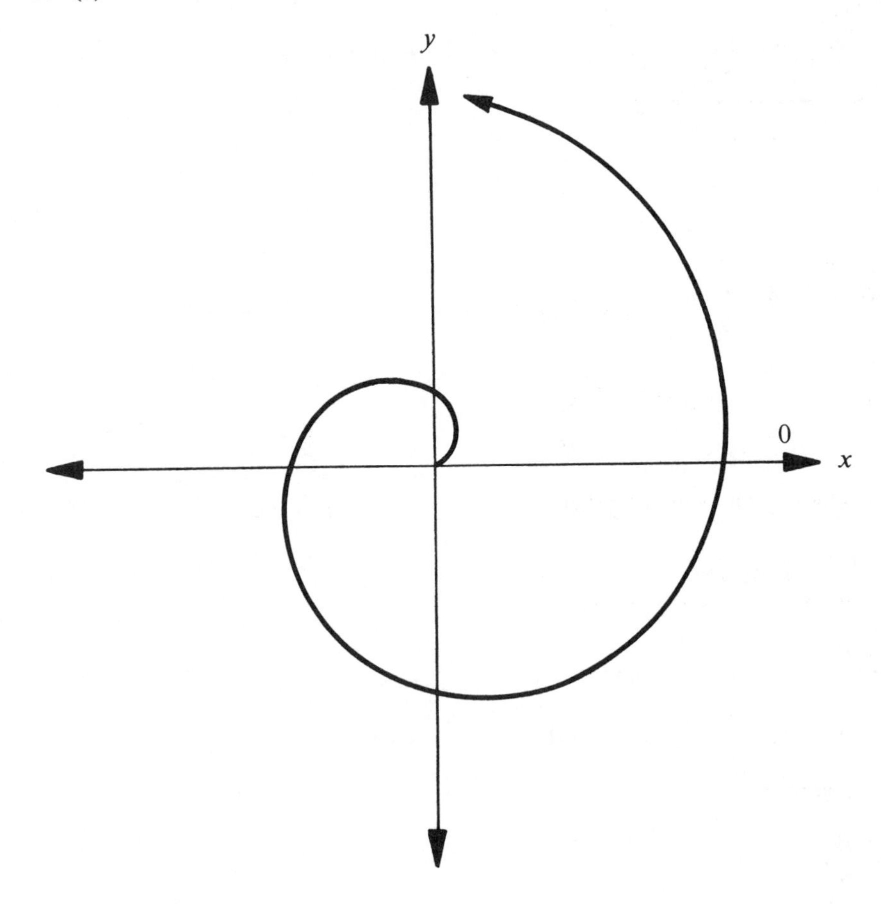

$\rho = \theta$

Spiral of Archimedes

(b)

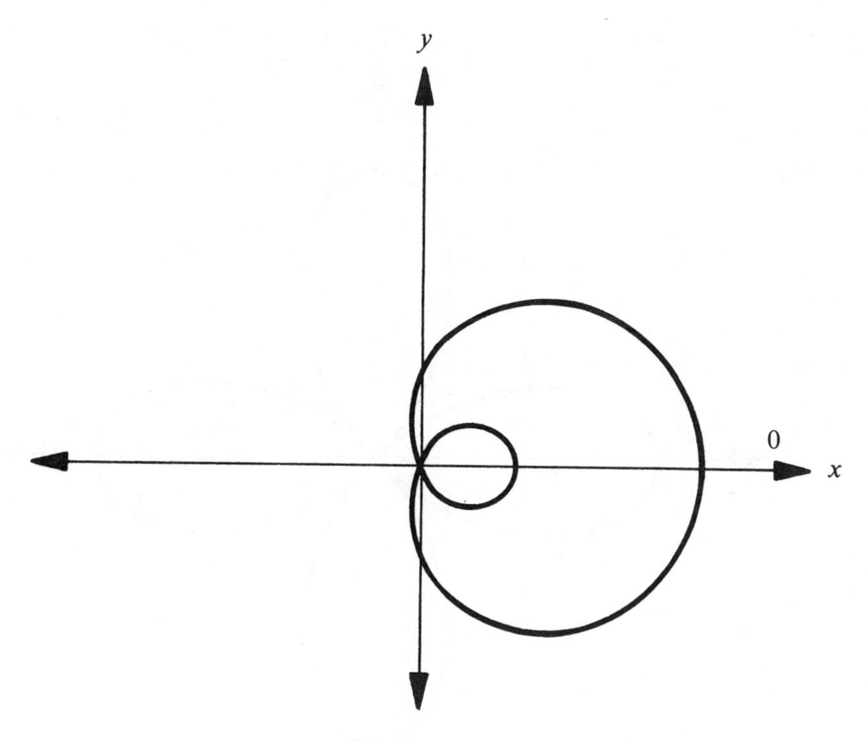

$\rho = 2 + 4 \cos \theta$
Limacon

(c)

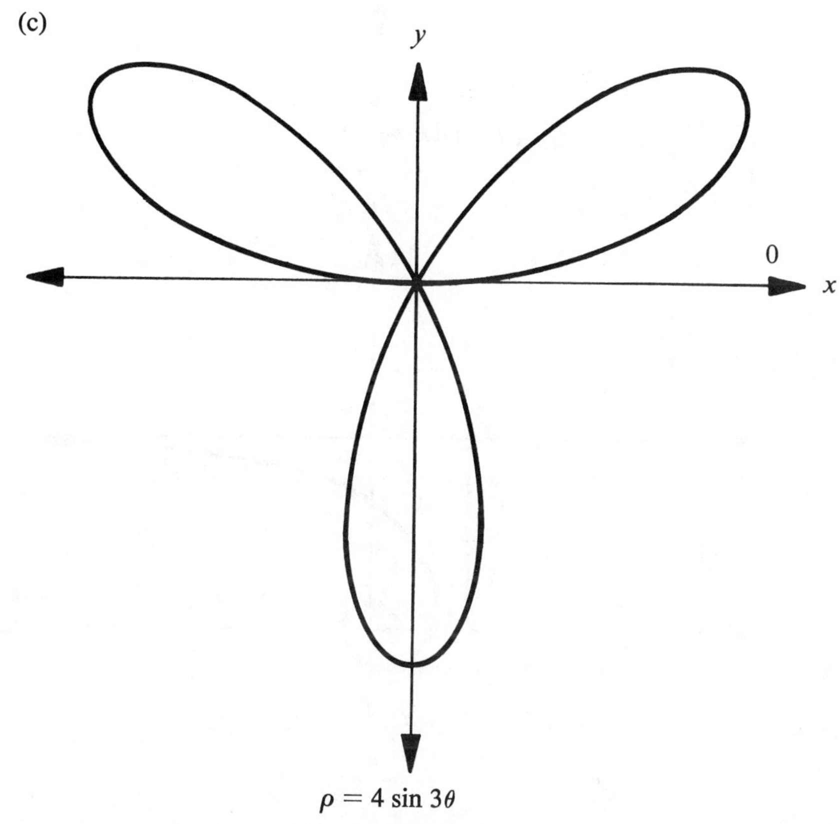

$\rho = 4 \sin 3\theta$
Three-Leaved Rose

(d)

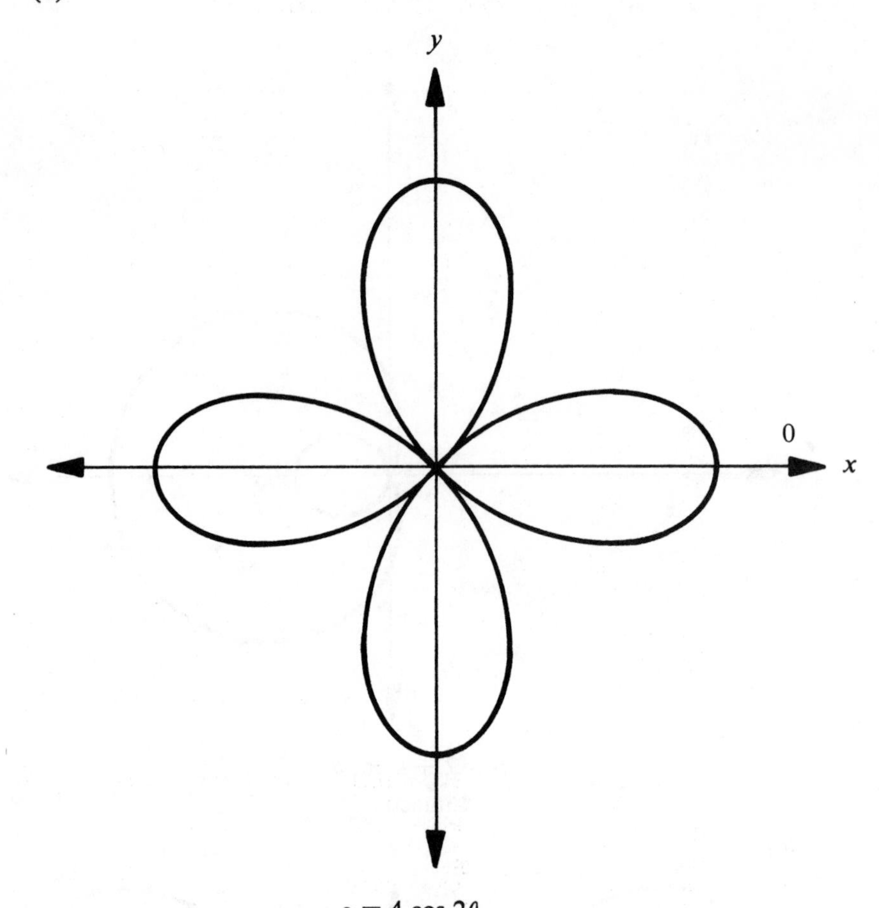

$\rho = 4 \cos 2\theta$

Four-Leaved Rose

(e)

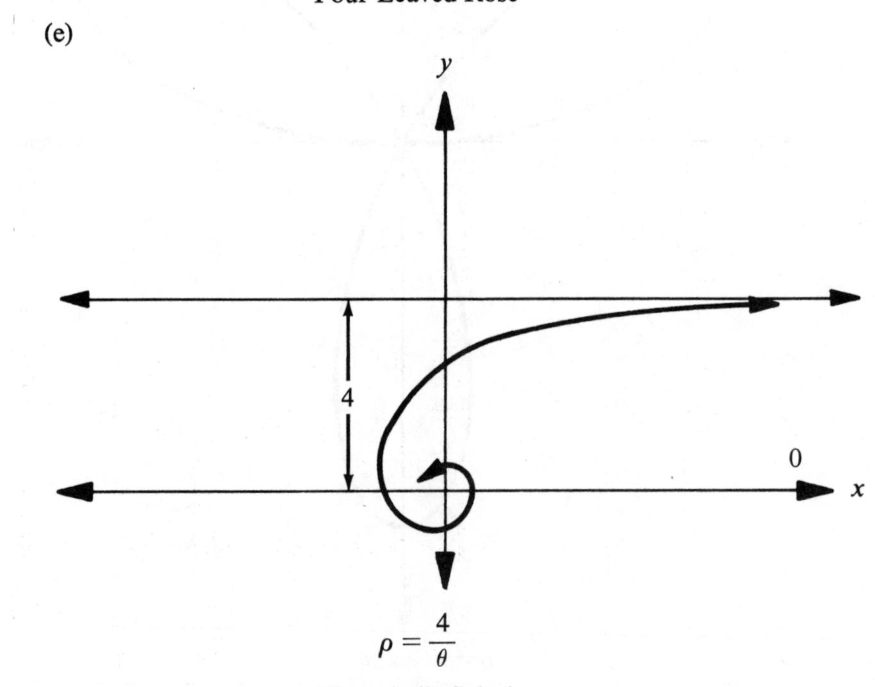

$\rho = \frac{4}{\theta}$

Hyperbolic Spiral

VALUES OF TRIGONOMETRIC
OR
CIRCULAR FUNCTIONS

$m^\circ \angle \theta$	$m^R \angle \theta$	Sin	Cos	Tan	Cot	Sec	Csc	$m^R \angle \theta$	$m^\circ \angle \theta$
0° 00′	.0000	.0000	1.0000	.0000	Undef.	1.000	Undef.	1.5708	**90° 00′**
10	029	029	1.0000	029	343.8	000	343.8	679	50
20	058	058	1.0000	058	171.9	000	171.9	650	40
30	.0087	.0087	1.0000	.0087	114.6	1.000	114.6	1.5621	30
40	.0116	116	.9999	116	85.94	000	85.95	592	20
50	.0145	145	.9999	145	68.75	000	68.76	563	10
1° 00′	.0175	.0175	.9998	.0175	57.29	1.000	57.30	1.5533	**89° 00′**
10	204	204	998	204	49.10	000	49.11	504	50
20	233	233	997	233	42.96	000	42.98	475	40
30	.0262	.0262	.9997	.0262	38.19	1.000	38.20	1.5446	30
40	291	291	996	291	34.37	000	34.38	417	20
50	320	320	995	320	31.24	001	31.26	388	10
2° 00′	.0349	.0349	.9994	.0349	28.64	1.001	28.65	1.5359	**88° 00′**
10	378	378	993	378	26.43	001	26.45	330	50
20	407	407	992	407	24.54	001	24.56	301	40
30	.0436	.0436	.9990	.0437	22.90	1.001	22.93	1.5272	30
40	465	465	989	466	21.47	001	21.49	243	20
50	495	494	988	495	20.21	001	20.23	213	10
3° 00′	.0524	.0523	.9986	.0524	19.08	1.001	19.11	1.5184	**87° 00′**
10	553	552	985	553	18.07	002	18.10	155	50
20	582	581	983	582	17.17	002	17.20	126	40
30	.0611	.0610	.9981	.0612	16.35	1.002	16.38	1.5097	30
40	640	640	980	641	15.60	002	15.64	068	20
50	669	669	978	670	14.92	002	14.96	039	10
4° 00′	.0698	.0698	.9976	.0699	14.30	1.002	14.34	1.5010	**86° 00′**
10	727	727	974	729	13.73	003	13.76	981	50
20	756	756	971	758	13.20	003	13.23	952	40
30	.0785	.0785	.9969	.0787	12.71	1.003	12.75	1.4923	30
40	814	814	967	816	12.25	003	12.29	893	20
50	844	843	964	846	11.83	004	11.87	864	10
5° 00′	.0873	.0872	.9962	.0875	11.43	1.004	11.47	1.4835	**85° 00′**
10	902	901	959	904	11.06	004	11.10	806	50
20	931	929	957	934	10.71	004	10.76	777	40
30	.0960	.0958	.9954	.0963	10.39	1.005	10.43	1.4748	30
40	989	987	951	992	10.08	005	10.13	719	20
50	.1018	.1016	948	.1022	9.788	005	9.839	690	10
6° 00′	.1047	.1045	.9945	.1051	9.514	1.006	9.567	1.4661	**84° 00′**
10	076	074	942	080	9.255	006	9.309	632	50
20	105	103	939	110	9.010	006	9.065	603	40
30	.1134	.1132	.9936	.1139	8.777	1.006	8.834	1.4573	30
40	164	161	932	169	8.556	007	9.614	544	20
50	193	190	929	198	8.345	007	8.405	515	10
7° 00′	.1222	.1219	.9925	.1228	8.144	1.008	8.206	1.4486	**83° 00′**
10	251	248	922	257	7.953	008	8.016	457	50
20	280	276	918	287	7.770	008	7.834	428	40
30	.1309	.1305	.9914	.1317	7.596	1.009	7.661	1.4399	30
40	338	334	911	346	7.429	009	7.496	370	20
50	367	363	907	376	7.269	009	7.337	341	10
8° 00′	.1396	.1392	.9903	.1405	7.115	1.010	7.185	1.4312	**82° 00′**
10	425	421	899	435	6.968	010	7.040	283	50
20	454	449	894	465	6.827	011	6.900	254	40
30	.1484	.1478	.9890	.1495	6.691	1.011	6.765	1.4224	30
40	513	507	886	524	6.561	012	6.636	195	20
50	542	536	881	554	6.435	012	6.512	166	10
9° 00′	.1571	.1564	.9877	.1584	6.314	1.012	6.392	1.4137	**81° 00′**
10	600	593	872	614	197	013	277	108	50
20	629	622	868	644	084	013	166	079	40
30	.1658	.1650	.9863	.1673	5.976	1.014	6.059	1.4050	30
40	687	679	858	703	871	014	5.955	1.4021	20
50	716	708	853	733	769	015	855	992	10
10° 00′	.1745	.1736	.9848	.1763	5.671	1.015	5.759	1.3963	**80° 00′**
10	774	765	843	793	576	016	665	934	50
20	804	794	838	823	485	016	575	904	40
30	.1833	.1822	.9833	.1853	5.396	1.017	5.487	1.3875	30
40	862	851	827	883	309	018	403	846	20
50	891	880	822	914	226	018	320	817	10
11° 00′	.1920	.1908	.9816	.1944	5.145	1.019	5.241	1.3788	**79° 00′**
10	949	937	811	974	066	019	164	759	50
20	978	965	805	.2004	4.989	020	089	730	40
$m^\circ \angle \theta$	$m^R \angle \theta$	Csc	Sec	Cot	Tan	Cos	Sin	$m^R \angle \theta$	$m^\circ \angle \theta$

VALUES OF TRIGONOMETRIC OR CIRCULAR FUNCTIONS

$m^\circ \angle \theta$	$m^R \angle \theta$	Sin	Cos	Tan	Cot	Sec	Csc	$m^R \angle \theta$	$m^\circ \angle \theta$
11° 00′	.1920	.1908	.9816	.1944	5.145	1.019	5.241	1.3788	**79° 00′**
30	.2007	.1994	.9799	.2035	4.915	1.020	5.016	1.3701	30
40	036	.2022	793	065	843	021	4.945	672	20
50	065	051	787	095	773	022	876	643	10
12° 00′	.2094	.2079	.9781	.2126	4.705	1.022	4.810	1.3614	**78° 00′**
10	123	108	775	156	638	023	745	584	50
20	153	136	769	186	574	024	682	555	40
30	.2182	.2164	.9763	.2217	4.511	1.024	4.620	1.3526	30
40	211	193	757	247	449	025	560	497	20
50	240	221	750	278	390	026	502	468	10
13° 00′	.2269	.2250	.9744	.2309	4.331	1.026	4.445	1.3439	**77° 00′**
10	298	278	737	339	275	027	390	410	50
20	327	306	730	370	219	028	336	381	40
30	.2356	.2334	9724	.2401	4.165	1.028	4.284	1.3352	30
40	385	363	717	432	113	029	232	323	20
50	414	391	710	462	061	030	182	294	10
14 °00′	.2443	.2419	.9703	.2493	4.011	1.031	4.134	1.3265	**76° 00′**
10	473	447	696	524	3.962	031	086	235	50
20	502	476	689	555	914	032	039	206	40
30	.2531	.2504	.9681	.2586	3.867	1.033	3.994	1.3177	30
40	560	532	674	617	821	034	950	148	20
50	589	560	667	648	776	034	906	119	10
15° 00′	.2618	.2588	.9659	.2679	3.732	1.035	3.864	1.3090	**75° 00′**
10	647	616	652	711	689	036	822	061	50
20	676	644	644	742	647	037	782	032	40
30	.2705	.2672	.9636	.2773	3.606	1.038	3.742	1.3003	30
40	734	700	628	805	566	039	703	974	20
50	763	728	621	836	526	039	665	945	10
16° 00′	.2793	.2756	.9613	.2867	3.487	1.040	3.628	1.2915	**74° 00′**
10	822	784	605	899	450	041	592	886	50
20	851	812	596	931	412	042	556	857	40
30	.2880	.2840	.9588	.2962	3.376	1.043	3.521	1.2828	30
40	909	868	580	994	340	044	487	799	20
50	938	896	572	.3026	305	045	453	770	10
17° 00′	.2967	.2924	.9563	.3057	3.271	1.046	3.420	1.2741	**73° 00′**
10	996	952	555	089	237	047	388	712	50
20	.3025	979	546	121	204	048	356	683	40
30	.3054	.3007	.9537	.3153	3.172	1.049	.3326	1.2654	30
40	083	035	528	185	140	049	295	625	20
50	113	062	520	217	108	050	265	595	10
18° 00′	.3142	.3090	.9511	.3249	3.078	1.051	3.236	1.2566	**72° 00′**
10	171	118	502	281	047	052	207	537	50
20	200	145	492	314	018	053	179	508	40
30	.3229	.3173	.9483	.3346	2.989	1.054	3.152	1.2479	30
40	258	201	474	378	960	056	124	450	20
50	287	228	465	411	932	057	098	421	10
19° 00′	.3316	.3256	.9455	.3443	2.904	1.058	3.072	1.2392	**71° 00′**
10	345	.3283	446	476	877	059	046	363	50
20	374	.3311	436	508	850	060	021	334	40
30	.3403	.3338	.9426	.3541	2.824	1.061	2.996	1.2305	30
40	432	365	417	574	798	062	971	275	20
50	462	393	407	607	773	063	947	246	10
20° 00′	.3491	.3420	.9397	.3640	2.747	1.064	2.924	1.2217	**70° 00′**
10	520	448	387	673	723	065	901	188	50
20	549	475	377	706	699	066	878	159	40
30	.3578	.3502	.9367	.3739	2.675	1.068	2.855	1.2130	30
40	607	529	356	772	651	069	833	101	20
50	636	557	346	805	628	070	812	072	10
21° 00′	.3665	.3584	.9336	.3839	2.605	1.071	2.790	1.2043	**69° 00′**
10	694	611	325	872	583	072	769	1.2014	50
20	723	638	315	906	560	074	749	985	40
30	.3752	.3665	.9304	.3939	2.539	1.075	2.729	1.1956	30
40	782	692	293	973	517	076	709	926	20
50	811	719	283	.4006	496	077	689	897	10
22° 00′	.3840	.3746	.9272	.4040	2.475	1.079	2.669	1.1868	**68° 00′**
10	869	773	261	074	455	080	650	839	50
20	898	800	250	108	434	081	632	810	40
30	.3927	.3827	.9239	.4142	2.414	1.082	2.613	1.1781	30
40	956	854	228	176	394	084	595	752	20
50	985	881	216	210	375	085	577	723	10
$m^\circ \angle \theta$	$m^R \angle \theta$	Csc	Sec	Cot	Tan	Cos	Sin	$m^R \angle \theta$	$m^\circ \angle \theta$

VALUES OF TRIGONOMETRIC OR CIRCULAR FUNCTIONS

$m° \angle\theta$	$m^R \angle\theta$	Sin	Cos	Tan	Cot	Sec	Csc	$m^R \angle\theta$	$m° \angle\theta$
23° 00′	.4014	.3907	.9205	.4245	2.356	1.086	2.559	1.1694	**67° 00′**
10	043	934	194	279	337	088	542	665	50
20	072	961	182	314	318	089	525	636	40
30	.4102	.3987	.9171	.4348	2.300	1.090	2.508	1.1606	30
40	131	.4014	159	383	282	092	491	577	20
50	160	041	147	417	264	093	475	548	10
24° 00′	.4189	.4067	.9135	.4452	2.246	1.095	2.459	1.1519	**66° 00′**
10	218	094	124	487	229	096	443	490	50
20	247	120	112	522	211	097	427	461	40
30	.4276	.4147	.9100	.4557	2.194	1.099	2.411	1.1432	30
40	305	173	088	592	177	100	396	403	20
50	334	200	075	628	161	102	381	374	10
25° 00′	.4363	.4226	.9063	.4663	2.145	1.103	2.366	1.1345	**65° 00′**
10	392	253	051	699	128	105	352	316	50
20	422	279	038	734	112	106	337	286	40
30	.4451	.4305	.9026	.4770	2.097	1.108	2.323	1.1257	30
40	480	331	013	806	081	109	309	228	20
50	509	358	001	841	066	111	295	199	10
26° 00′	.4538	.4384	.8988	.4877	2.050	1.113	2.281	1.1170	**64° 00′**
10	567	410	975	913	035	114	268	141	50
20	596	436	962	950	020	116	254	112	40
30	.4625	.4462	.8949	.4986	2.006	1.117	2.241	1.1083	30
40	654	488	936	.5022	1.991	119	228	054	20
50	683	514	923	059	977	121	215	1.1025	10
27° 00′	.4712	.4540	.8910	.5095	1.963	1.122	2.203	1.0996	**63° 00′**
10	741	566	897	132	949	124	190	966	50
20	771	592	884	169	935	126	178	937	40
30	.4800	.4617	.8870	.5206	1.921	1.127	2.166	1.0908	30
40	829	643	857	243	907	129	154	879	20
50	858	669	843	280	894	131	142	850	10
28° 00′	.4887	.4695	.8829	.5317	1.881	1.133	2.130	1.0821	**62° 00′**
10	916	720	816	354	868	134	118	792	50
20	945	746	802	392	855	136	107	763	40
30	.4974	.4772	.8788	.5430	1.842	1.138	2.096	1.0734	30
40	.5003	797	774	467	829	140	085	705	20
50	032	823	760	505	816	142	074	676	10
29° 00′	.5061	.4848	.8746	.5543	1.804	1.143	2.063	1.0647	**61° 00′**
10	091	874	732	581	792	145	052	617	50
20	120	899	718	619	780	147	041	588	40
30	.5149	.4924	.8704	.5658	1.767	1.149	2.031	1.0559	30
40	178	950	689	696	756	151	020	530	20
50	207	975	675	735	744	153	010	501	10
30° 00′	.5236	.5000	.8660	.5774	1.732	1.155	2.000	1.0472	**60° 00′**
10	265	025	646	812	720	157	1.990	443	50
20	294	050	631	851	709	159	980	414	40
30	.5323	.5075	.8616	.5890	1.698	1.161	1.970	1.0385	30
40	352	100	601	930	686	163	961	356	20
50	381	125	587	969	675	165	951	327	10
31° 00′	.5411	.5150	.8572	.6009	1.664	1.167	1.942	1.0297	**59° 00′**
10	440	175	557	048	653	169	932	268	50
20	469	200	542	088	643	171	923	239	40
30	.5498	.5225	.8526	.6128	1.632	1.173	1.914	1.0210	30
40	527	250	511	168	621	175	905	181	20
50	556	275	496	208	611	177	896	152	10
32° 00′	.5585	.5299	.8480	.6249	1.600	1.179	1.887	1.0123	**58° 000′**
10	614	324	465	289	590	181	878	094	50
20	643	348	450	330	580	184	870	065	4
30	.5672	.5373	.8434	.6371	1.570	1.186	1.861	1.0036	30
40	701	398	418	412	560	188	853	1.0007	20
50	730	422	403	453	550	190	844	977	10
33° 00′	.5760	.5446	.8387	.6494	1.540	1.192	1.836	.9948	**57° 00′**
10	789	471	371	536	530	195	828	919	50
20	818	495	355	577	520	197	820	890	40
30	.5847	.5519	.8339	.6619	1.511	1.199	1.812	.9861	30
40	876	544	323	661	501	202	804	832	20
50	905	568	307	703	1.492	204	796	803	10
34° 00′	.5934	.5592	.8290	.6745	1.483	1.206	1.788	.9774	**56° 00′**
10	963	616	274	787	473	209	781	745	50
20	992	640	258	830	464	211	773	716	40
30	.6021	.5664	.8241	.6873	1.455	1.213	1.766	.9687	30
$m° \angle\theta$	$m^R \angle\theta$	Csc	Sec	Cot	Tan	Cos	Sin	$m^R \angle\theta$	$m° \angle\theta$

VALUES OF TRIGONOMETRIC OR CIRCULAR FUNCTIONS

$m° \angle \theta$	$m^R \angle \theta$	Sin	Cos	Tan	Cot	Sec	Csc	$m^R \angle \theta$	$m° \angle \theta$
34° 00′	.5934	.5592	.8290	.6745	1.483	1.206	1.788	.9774	**56° 00′**
40	050	688	225	916	446	216	758	657	20
50	080	712	208	959	437	218	751	628	10
35° 00′	.6109	.5736	.8192	.7002	1.428	1.221	1.743	.9599	**55° 00′**
10	138	760	175	046	419	223	736	570	50
20	167	783	158	089	411	226	729	541	40
30	.6196	.5807	.8141	.7133	1.402	1.228	1.722	.9512	30
40	225	831	124	177	393	231	715	483	20
50	254	854	107	221	385	233	708	454	10
36° 00′	.6283	.5878	.8090	.7265	1.376	1.236	1.701	.9425	**54° 00′**
10	312	901	073	310	368	239	695	396	50
20	341	925	056	355	360	241	688	367	40
30	.6370	.5948	.8039	.7400	1.351	1.244	1.681	.9338	30
40	400	972	021	445	343	247	675	308	20
50	429	995	004	490	335	249	668	279	10
37° 00′	.6458	.6018	.7986	.7536	1.327	1.252	1.662	.9250	**53° 00′**
10	487	041	969	581	319	255	655	221	50
20	516	065	951	627	311	258	649	192	40
30	.6545	.6088	.7934	.7673	1.303	1.260	1.643	.9163	30
40	574	111	916	720	295	263	636	134	20
50	603	134	898	766	288	266	630	105	10
38° 00′	.6632	.6157	.7880	.7813	1.280	1.269	1.624	.9076	**52° 00′**
10	661	180	862	860	272	272	618	047	50
20	690	202	844	907	265	275	612	.9018	40
30	.6720	.6225	.7826	.7954	1.257	1.278	1.606	.8988	30
40	749	248	808	.8002	250	281	601	959	20
50	778	271	790	050	242	284	595	930	10
39° 00′	.6807	.6293	.7771	.8098	1.235	1.287	1.589	.8901	**51° 00′**
10	836	316	753	146	228	290	583	872	50
20	865	338	735	195	220	293	578	843	40
30	.6894	.6361	.7716	.8243	1.213	1.296	1.572	.8814	30
40	923	383	698	292	206	299	567	785	20
50	952	406	679	342	199	302	561	756	10
40° 00′	.6981	.6428	.7660	.8391	1.192	1.305	1.556	.8727	**50 °00′**
10	.7010	450	642	441	185	309	550	698	50
20	039	472	623	491	178	312	545	668	40
30	.7069	.6494	.7604	.8541	1.171	1.315	1.540	.8639	30
40	098	517	585	591	164	318	535	610	20
50	127	539	566	642	157	322	529	581	10
41° 00′	.7156	.6561	.7547	.8693	1.150	1.325	1.524	.8552	**49° 00′**
10	185	583	528	744	144	328	519	523	50
20	214	604	509	796	137	332	514	494	40
30	.7243	.6626	.7490	.8847	1.130	1.335	1.509	.8465	30
40	272	648	470	899	124	339	504	436	20
50	301	670	451	952	117	342	499	407	10
42° 00′	.7330	.6691	.7431	.9004	1.111	1.346	1.494	.8378	**48° 00′**
10	359	713	412	057	104	349	490	348	50
20	389	734	392	110	098	353	485	319	40
30	.7418	.6756	.7373	.9163	1.091	1.356	1.480	.8290	30
40	447	777	353	217	085	360	476	261	20
50	476	799	333	271	079	364	471	232	10
43° 00′	.7505	.6820	.7314	.9325	1.072	1.367	1.466	.8203	**47° 00′**
10	534	841	294	380	066	371	462	174	50
20	563	862	274	435	060	375	457	145	40
30	.7592	.6884	.7254	.9490	1.054	1.379	1.453	.8116	30
40	621	905	234	545	048	382	448	087	20
50	650	926	214	601	042	386	444	058	10
44° 00′	.7679	.6947	.7193	.9657	1.036	1.390	1.440	.8029	**46° 00′**
10	709	967	173	713	030	394	435	999	50
20	738	988	153	770	024	398	431	970	40
30	.7767	.7009	.7133	.9827	1.018	1.402	1.427	.7941	30
40	796	030	112	884	012	406	423	912	20
50	825	050	092	942	006	410	418	883	10
45° 00′	.7854	.7071	.7071	1.000	1.000	1.414	1.414	.7854	**45° 00′**
$m° \angle \theta$	$m^R \angle \theta$	Csc	Sec	Cot	Tan	Cos	Sin	$m^R \angle \theta$	$m° \angle \theta$

REVIEW OF SETS

A **set** is a well-defined collection of specified objects. The members of a set are specified by listing them in a **roster** or by stating a **rule**, or condition, an object must satisfy to be a member of the set.

Letters are usually used to denote sets. For the sake of convenience we will use the following letters to denote the corresponding sets of numbers:

$N = \{\text{natural numbers}\} = \{1,2,3, \ldots\}$

$W = \{\text{whole numbers}\} = \{0,1,2,3, \ldots\}$

$J = \{\text{integers}\} = \{\cdots -3,-2,-1,0,1,2,3, \ldots\}$

$Q = \{\text{rational numbers}\} = \left\{\frac{p}{q}, \text{ such that } p \epsilon J,\ q \epsilon J, \text{ and } q \neq 0\right\}$

$I = \{\text{irrational numbers}\} = \{\text{real numbers that are not rational}\}$

$\mathcal{R} = \{\text{real numbers}\}$

$C = \{\text{complex numbers}\} = \{(a + bi) \text{ such that } a \epsilon \mathcal{R},\ b \epsilon \mathcal{R}, \text{and } i = \sqrt{-1}\}$

The objects within a set are called **elements** or **members** of the set. The statement "-6 is an element of the set of integers" is denoted by "$-6 \epsilon J$."

The notation $\{x : x \geq 6\}$ is read "the set of all x such that x is greater than or equal to 6." It is called **set-builder notation.**

A vertical line | is sometimes used in lieu of the colon, and both are read "such that."

In expressions such as $\{x: |x| > 2\}$ it is understood that x is a **variable** representing a real number. If the variable is to represent an element in a set other than the real numbers, then that set will be noted. For example, $\{x : x \epsilon J$ and $-3 < x < 0\}$ specifies that x is an integer.

Set A is a **subset** of set B, denoted $A \subset B$, if and only if every element of A is also an element of B.

The set containing no elements, { }, is called the **null set** or the **empty set.** The symbol $\emptyset$ is also used for the empty set. By convention, $\emptyset \subset A$ for every A. That is, the null set is a subset of every set.

A set A is a subset of itself, but not a proper subset. Set B is a **proper subset** of C if and only if there is an element $x \epsilon C$ such that $x \epsilon B$.

Two sets, A and B, are said to be **equal** if and only if A is a subset of B and B is a subset of A, i.e., $A = B$ if and only if $A \subset B$ and $B \subset A$.

The **intersection** of set A and set B, denoted $A \cap B$, is the set of all elements x such that $x \epsilon A$ and $x \epsilon B$. The **union** of set A and set B, denoted $A \cup B$, is the set of all elements x such that $x \epsilon A$ or $x \epsilon B$.

Set A and set B are said to be **disjoint** sets if and only if $A \cap B = \emptyset$.

PROPERTIES OF THE REAL NUMBERS

The **group** and **field** properties, the **order** properties, and certain other fundamental properties of the set of **real numbers** $\mathcal{R}$ are summarized here.

(A) Addition in $\mathcal{R}$ satisfies the following properties.

(1) **Closure:** If $x \epsilon \mathcal{R}$ and $y \epsilon \mathcal{R}$, then $x + y$ is a unique element of $\mathcal{R}$.

(2) **Associative:** For all $x \epsilon \mathcal{R}$, $y \epsilon \mathcal{R}$, and $z \epsilon \mathcal{R}$,

$$(x + y) + z = x + (y + z).$$

(3) **Identity:** There exists a real number, denoted by 0, such that for every $x \epsilon \mathcal{R}$,

$$0 + x = x + 0 = x.$$

(4) **Inverses:** For every $x \epsilon \mathcal{R}$, there exists exactly one element of $\mathcal{R}$, denoted $-x$, such that $x + (-x) = 0$.

(5) **Commutative:** For all $x \epsilon \mathcal{R}$ and $y \epsilon \mathcal{R}$, $x + y = y + x$.

(B) Multiplication in $\mathcal{R}$ satisfies the following properties.

(6). **Closure:** If $x \epsilon \mathcal{R}$ and $y \epsilon \mathcal{R}$, then xy is a unique element in $\mathcal{R}$.

(7) **Associative:** For all $x \epsilon \mathcal{R}$, $y \epsilon \mathcal{R}$, and $z \epsilon \mathcal{R}$,

$$(xy)z = x(yz).$$

(8) **Identity:** There exists a nonzero real number, denoted by 1, such that for every $x \epsilon \mathcal{R}$,

$$1 \cdot x = x \cdot 1 = x.$$

(9) **Inverses:** For every $x \epsilon \mathcal{R}$, $x \neq 0$, there exists a real number, denoted by x^{-1}, such that $x \cdot x^{-1} = 1$.

(10) **Commutative:** For all $x \epsilon \mathcal{R}$ and $y \epsilon \mathcal{R}$,

$$xy = yx.$$

(C) The operation of multiplication is distributive over addition in $\mathcal{R}$.

(11) **Distributive:** For all $x \epsilon \mathcal{R}$, $y \epsilon \mathcal{R}$, and $z \epsilon \mathcal{R}$,

$$x(y + z) = (y + z)x = xy + xz.$$

The above eleven properties constitute the **field properties** and thus the set of real numbers form a field. Because of the properties 1-5, $\mathcal{R}$ is a **commutative group** under addition and because of properties 6-10, the nonzero real numbers are a commutative group under multiplication.

(D) The operations **subtraction** and **division** in $\mathcal{R}$ are **defined** in terms of the fundamental operations addition and multiplication.

(13) **Subtraction:** To subtract y from x, $x \epsilon \mathcal{R}$ and $y \epsilon \mathcal{R}$, add $-y$ to x.

Thus,

$$x - y = x + (-y).$$

(14) **Division:** To divide x by y when $y \neq 0$, $x \in \mathcal{R}$ and $y \in \mathcal{R}$, we multiply x by y^{-1}. Thus,

$$\frac{x}{y} = x(y^{-1}).$$

Division by 0 is not defined.

(E) The field of real numbers $\mathcal{R}$ is an ordered field, that is, there is an order relation in $\mathcal{R}$, denoted by $>$, (read "greater than") with the following properties.

(15) **Trichotomy** (sometimes called the **axiom of comparison**): For all $x \in \mathcal{R}$ and $y \in \mathcal{R}$, x and y satisfy exactly one of the following.

$$x > y, \quad x = y, \quad \text{or} \quad x < y.$$

(16) **Transitive:** For all x, y, and z in $\mathcal{R}$, if $x > y$ and $y > z$, then $x > z$.

(17) **Addition:** For all x, y, and z in $\mathcal{R}$, if $x > y$, then

$$x + z > y + z.$$

(18) **Multiplication:** For all x, y, and $z \in \mathcal{R}$, if $x > y$, and $z > 0$, then $xz > yz$. If $x > y$ and $z < 0$, then $xz < yz$.

(F) The following additional properties may be deducted from the field or order properties previously listed. w, x, y, and z are elements of $\mathcal{R}$. This list does not constitute all the properties of $\mathcal{R}$.

(19) **Cancellation for addition:** If $x + y = x + z$, then $y = z$.

(20) $-(-x) = x$.

(21) $x(y - z) = xy - xz$.

(22) $0 \cdot x = x \cdot 0 = 0$.

(23) **Cancellation for multiplication:** If $xy = xz$ and $z \neq 0$, then $y = z$.

(24) If $x \neq 0$, then$(x^{-1})^{-1} = x$.

(25) If $xy = 0$, then $x = 0$ or $y = 0$.

(26) $(-x)y = -(xy)$.

(27) $(-x)(-y) = xy$.

(28) $\left(\frac{x}{y}\right)\left(\frac{w}{z}\right) = \frac{xw}{yz}$, $y \neq 0$ and $z \neq 0$.

(29) $\dfrac{\left(\frac{x}{y}\right)}{\left(\frac{w}{z}\right)} = \frac{xz}{yw}$, $y \neq 0$, $w \neq 0$, and $z \neq 0$.

(30) $\left(\frac{x}{y}\right) + \left(\frac{w}{z}\right) = \frac{xz + yw}{yz}$, $y \neq 0$, and $z \neq 0$.

(31) If $x > 0$, then $-x < 0$, and if $x < 0$, then $-x > 0$.

(32) If $x > y$ and $w > z$, then $x + w > y + z$.

(33) If $x > 0$, $y > 0$, and $x > y$, then $x^2 > y^2$. If $x < 0$, $y < 0$, and $x < y$, then $x^2 > y^2$.

(34) If $xy > 0$, then either both $x > 0$ and $y > 0$ or both $x < 0$ and $y < 0$.

(35) If $x > 0$, then $\frac{1}{x} > 0$, and if $x < 0$, then $\frac{1}{x} < 0$.

LIST OF SYMBOLS

SYMBOL	DEFINITION	EXAMPLE
$=$	is equal to	$5+1=6$
$\approx$	is approximately equal to	$\sqrt{5}\approx 2.236$
$\neq$	is not equal to	$7-4\neq 2$
$>$	is greater than	$5>3$
$\geq$	is greater than or equal to	$5+2\geq 7$
$\ngtr$	is not greater than	$3\ngtr 4$
$<$	is less than	$2<5$
$\nless$	is not less than	$5\nless 3$
$\leq$	is less than or equal to	$3\leq 5$
$\{x:\cdots\}$ or $\{x\mid\cdots\}$	the set of all x such that	$\{x:x>5\}$. The set of all x such that x is greater than 5.
$\|x\|$	the absolute value of x	$\|2\|=2$ or $\|-2\|=2$
$+$	plus	$2+1=3$
$-$	minus	$7-4=3$
$\pm$	plus or minus	if $x\pm 3$, then $x=3$ or $x=-3$
$a\cdot b$ or $(a)(b)$	a multiplied by b or a times b (See also $\vec{v}\cdot\vec{u}$)	$5\cdot 6=30$
$a\div b$ or $\frac{a}{b}$	a divided by b	$\frac{12}{3}=4$
$\{\ \}$	set	$\{2,3\}$ is the set containing 2 and 3
$\cap$	intersection	if $A=\{1,2,3\}$ and $B=\{2,3,4\}$ then $A\cap B=\{2,3\}$
$\cup$	union	if $A=\{1,2,3\}$ and $B=\{2,3,4\}$ then $A\cup B=\{1,2,3,4\}$
$\subset$	is a subset of	if $A=\{1,2,3\}$ and $D=\{1,2,3,4,5\}$, then $A\subset D$
$\not\subset$	is not a subset of	if $A=\{1,2,3\}$ and $B=\{2,3,4\}$, then $A\not\subset B$
ϵ	is an element of	if $A=\{1,2,3\}$, then $3\epsilon A$

ϵ	is not an element of	if $A = \{1,2,3\}$, then $4 \epsilon A$
$\emptyset$	empty set or null set	if $A = \{1,2,3\}$ and $F = \{5,6\}$, then $A \cap F = \emptyset$
π	pi (approximately 3.14159); π is the ratio of the circumference to the diameter of a circle, i.e., $\pi = \frac{C}{D}$	if the diameter of a circle is 2, then $C = 2\pi$
$\cdots$	and so on in the same fashion	$\{1,2,3,\cdots\}$
N	The set of natural numbers	$4 \epsilon N$
W	The set of whole numbers	$0 \epsilon W$
J	The set of integers	$-6 \epsilon J$
Q	The set of rational numbers	$\frac{2}{3} \epsilon Q$
I	The set of irrational numbers	$\sqrt{3} \epsilon I$
$\mathcal{R}$	The set of real numbers	$x \epsilon \mathcal{R}$
C	The set of complex numbers	$z \epsilon C$
$\times$	Cartesian product	If $T = \{1,2\}$ and $S = \{a,b\}$ then $T \times S = \{(1,a),(1,b),(2,a),(2,b)\}$
(x,y)	an ordered pair	$(2,3)$
i	the complex number $(0,1)$ or $i = \sqrt{-1}$	$4 + 5i$
e	the natural base; $e \approx 2.7183$; e is the limit of the sequence of numbers formed by $\left(1 + \frac{1}{x}\right)^x$ as x approaches infinity	$e^{1.2} \approx 3.3201$
$\widehat{AB}$	the arc whose endpoints are A and B	A B
$\widehat{AXB}$	The arc containing point X whose endpoints are A and B	A X B

$m\widehat{AB}$	The length of arc $\widehat{AB}$	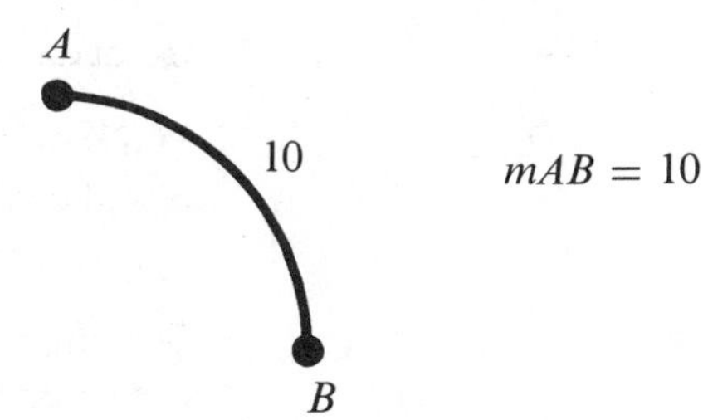 $mAB = 10$
$\angle ACB$, $\angle C$, $\angle BCA$, or $\angle\gamma$	The angle with vertex C formed by $\overrightarrow{CA}$ and $\overrightarrow{CB}$	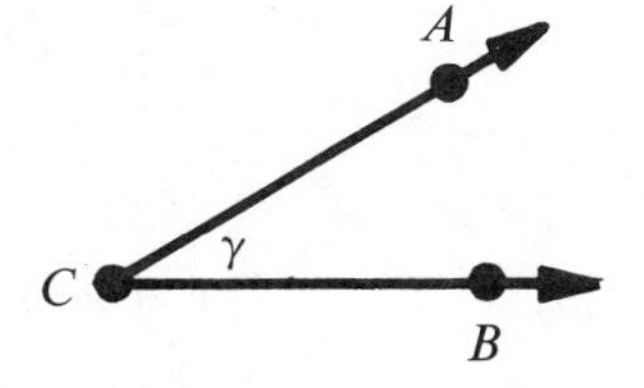
$m^\circ \angle ACB$	The measure in degrees of $\angle ACB$	$m^\circ \angle ACB = 39°15'20''$ or 39 degrees, 15 minutes, 20 seconds.
$m^R \angle ACB$ or $m^R \angle\alpha$	The measure in radians of $\angle ACB$ or $\angle\alpha$	$m^R \angle ACB = \frac{\pi}{2}$ or $m^R \angle ACB = \frac{\pi}{2}^R$
sector $\widehat{AB}$	The circular sector having boundary arc $\widehat{AB}$	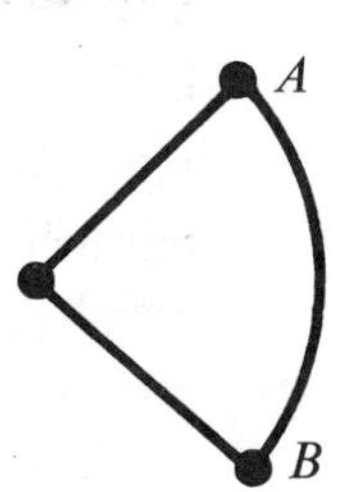
$\sqrt[n]{x}$	The nth root of x	$\sqrt[3]{8} = 2$
f	function	$f = \{(x,y): y = 3x - 5\}$
$f(x)$	The value of the function f at x	If $f(x) = x^2$, then $f(2) = 4$
$f \circ g$	The composite of two functions	If $f = \{(x,y): y = x^2\}$ and $g = \{(x,y): y = 2x + 1\}$ then $f \circ g = \{(x,y): y = (2x + 1)^2\}$
f^{-1}	The function which is the inverse of f	If $f = \{(x,y): y = 3x\}$ then $f^{-1} = \left\{(x,y): y = \frac{1}{3}x\right\}$
$\overrightarrow{AB}$	The displacement from point A to point B or the geometric vector from point A to point B	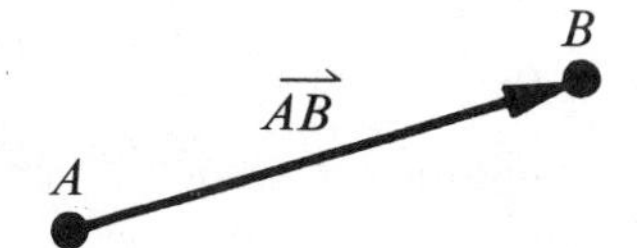

$\vec{v}$	vector	Let $\vec{v}$ be the vector (2,3)
$\overrightarrow{AB}$	The ray which has endpoint A and contains B	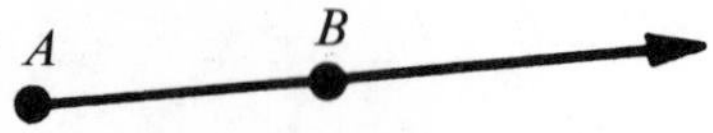 A B
$\vec{v} \cdot \vec{u}$	The inner product of vector $\vec{v}$ and vector $\vec{u}$	If $\vec{v} = (2,3)$ and $\vec{u} = (1,4)$, then $\vec{v} \cdot \vec{u} = (2,3) \cdot (1,4) = (2)(1) + (3)(4) = 14$
$\|\overrightarrow{AB}\|$	The length of the geometric vector $\overrightarrow{AB}$	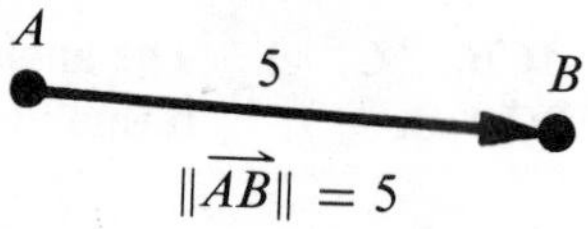 A 5 B $\|\overrightarrow{AB}\| = 5$
$\|\vec{v}\|$	The norm of the vector $\vec{v}$	If $\vec{v} = (3,4)$, then $\|\vec{v}\| = \sqrt{3^2 + 4^2} = 5$
$\vec{v}_p$	A vector perpendicular to $\vec{v}$	If $\vec{v} = (2,3)$, then $\vec{v}_p = (-3,2)$
$\overleftrightarrow{AB}$	The line containing points A and B	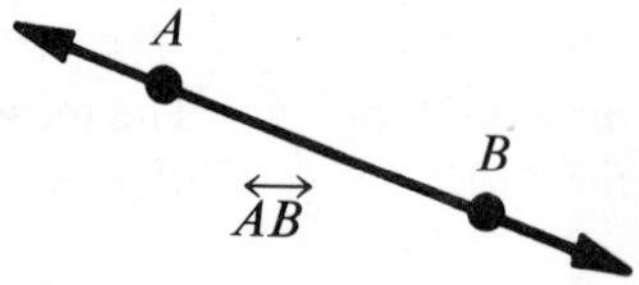 A B $\overleftrightarrow{AB}$
$\overline{AB}$	The segments whose endpoints are A and B	 A B
(ρ,θ)	Polar coordinates of a point having a radius vector of length ρ and an angle of θ	$\left(2, \frac{\pi}{6}\right)$ are the polar coordinates of the point whose rectangular coordinates are $(\sqrt{3},1)$
$\overline{a + bi}$	The conjugate of the complex number $a + bi$	$3 + 4i = 3 - 4i$
$\triangle ABC$	The triangle whose vertices are points A, B, and C	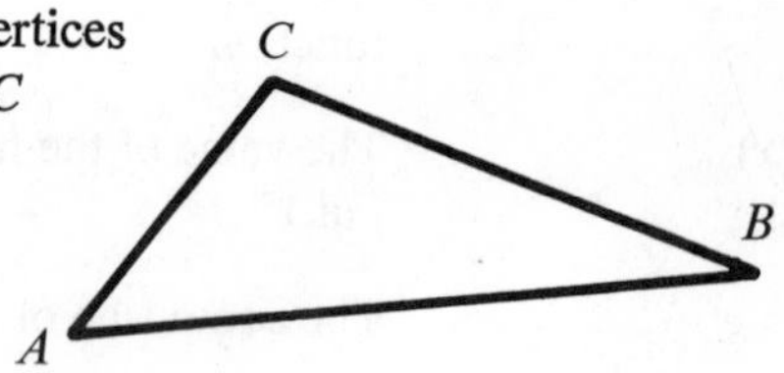 C B A

Greek Alphabet

α	alpha	η	eta	ν	nu	τ	tau
β	beta	θ	theta	ξ	xi	υ	upsilon
γ	gamma	ι	iota	o	omicron	ϕ	phi
δ	delta	κ	kappa	π	pi	χ	chi
ϵ	epsilon	λ	lambda	ρ	rho	ψ	psi
ζ	zeta	μ	mu	σ	sigma	ω	omega